HARALD CRAMÉR

MATHEMATICAL METHODS OF STATISTICS

PRINCETON MATHEMATICAL SERIES

Editors: MARSTON MORSE, H. P. ROBERTSON, A. W. TUCKER

---

1. The Classical Groups, Their Invariants and Representations. By HERMANN WEYL.
2. Topological Groups. By L. PONTRJAGIN. Translated by EMMA LEHMER.
3. An Introduction to Differential Geometry, with Use of the Tensor Calculus. By LUTHER PFAHLER EISENHART.
4. Dimension Theory. By WITOLD HUREWICZ and HENRY WALLMAN.
5. The Analytical Foundations of Celestial Mechanics. By AUREL WINTNER.
6. The Laplace Transform. By DAVID VERNON WIDDER.
7. Integration. By EDWARD JAMES McSHANE.
8. Theory of Lie Groups: I. By CLAUDE CHEVALLEY.
9. Mathematical Methods of Statistics. By HARALD CRAMÉR.
10. Several Complex Variables. By SALOMON BOCHNER and WILLIAM TED MARTIN.
11. Introduction to Topology. By SOLOMON LEFSCHETZ.
12. Topology of Surfaces and Their Transformations. By JAKOB NIELSEN and WERNER FENCHEL.
13. Algebraic Curves. By ROBERT J. WALKER.
14. The Topology of Fibre Bundles. By NORMAN STEENROD.

MATHEMATICAL METHODS OF STATISTICS

By

HARALD CRAMÉR

PROFESSOR IN THE UNIVERSITY
OF STOCKHOLM

PRINCETON
PRINCETON UNIVERSITY PRESS
1951

A 1951 reprinting of the offset edition first published
in the United States in 1946

First Published in Sweden, Uppsala 1945, by
Almqvist & Wiksells

To MARTA

PREFACE.

During the last 25 years, statistical science has made great progress, thanks to the brilliant schools of British and American statisticians, among whom the name of Professor R. A. Fisher should be mentioned in the foremost place. During the same time, largely owing to the work of French and Russian mathematicians, the classical calculus of probability has developed into a purely mathematical theory satisfying modern standards with respect to rigour.

The purpose of the present work is to join these two lines of development in an exposition of the mathematical theory of modern statistical methods, in so far as these are based on the concept of probability. A full understanding of the theory of these methods requires a fairly advanced knowledge of pure mathematics. In this respect, I have tried to make the book self-contained from the point of view of a reader possessing a good working knowledge of the elements of the differential and integral calculus, algebra, and analytic geometry.

In the first part of the book, which serves as a mathematical introduction, the requisite mathematics not assumed to be previously known to the reader are developed. Particular stress has been laid on the fundamental concepts of a distribution, and of the integration with respect to a distribution. As a preliminary to the introduction of these concepts, the theory of Lebesgue measure and integration has been briefly developed in Chapters 4—5, and the fundamental concepts are then introduced by straightforward generalization in Chapters 6—7.

The second part of the book contains the general theory of random variables and probability distributions, while the third part is devoted to the theory of sampling distributions, statistical estimation, and tests of significance. The selection of the questions treated in the last part is necessarily somewhat arbitrary, but I have tried to concentrate in the first hand on points of general importance. When these are fully mastered, the reader will be able to work out applications to particular problems for himself. In order to keep the volume of the book within reasonable limits, it has been necessary to exclude certain topics of great interest, which I had originally intended to treat, such as the theory of random processes, statistical time series and periodograms.

The theory of the statistical tests is illustrated by numerical examples borrowed from various fields of application. Owing to considerations of space, it has been necessary to reduce the number of these examples rather severely. It has also been necessary to restrain from every discussion of questions concerning the practical arrangement of numerical calculations.

It is not necessary to go through the first part completely before studying the rest of the book. A reader who is anxious to find himself *in medias res* may content himself with making some slight acquaintance with the fundamental concepts referred to above. For this purpose, it will be advisable to read Chapters 1—3, and the paragraphs 4.1—4.2, 5.1—5.3, 6.1—6.2, 6.4—6.6, 7.1—7.2, 7.4—7.5 and 8.1—8.4. The reader may then proceed to Chapter 13, and look up the references to the first part as they occur.

The book is founded on my University lectures since about 1930, and has been written mainly during the years 1942—1944. Owing to war conditions, foreign scientific literature was during these years only very incompletely and with considerable delay available in Sweden, and this must serve as an excuse for the possible absence of quotations which would otherwise have been appropriate.

The printing of the Scandinavian edition of the book has been made possible by grants from the Royal Swedish Academy of Science, and from Stiftelsen Lars Hiertas Minne. I express my gratitude towards these institutions.

My thanks are also due to the Editors of the Princeton Mathematical Series for their kind offer to include the book in the Series, and for their permission to print a separate Scandinavian edition.

I am further indebted to Professor R. A. Fisher and to Messrs Oliver and Boyd for permission to reprint tables of the t- and χ^2-distributions from »Statistical methods for research workers».

A number of friends have rendered valuable help during the preparation of the book. Professors Harald Bohr and Ernst Jacobsthal, taking refuge in Sweden from the hardships of the times, have read parts of the work in manuscript and in proof, and have given stimulating criticism and advice. Professor Herman Wold has made a very careful scrutiny of the whole work in proof, and I have greatly profited from his valuable remarks. Gösta Almqvist, Jan Jung, Sven G. Lindblom and Bertil Matérn have assisted in the numerical calculations, the revision of the manuscript, and the reading of the proofs. To all these I wish to express my sincere thanks.

Department of Mathematical Statistics
University of Stockholm
May 1945
H. C.

Table of Contents.

First Part.

MATHEMATICAL INTRODUCTION.

Chapters 1—3. Sets of Points.

Chapters 4—7. Theory of Measure and Integration in $\boldsymbol{R}_1$.

Second Part.

RANDOM VARIABLES AND PROBABILITY DISTRIBUTIONS.

CHAPTERS 13—14. FOUNDATIONS.

CHAPTERS 15—20. VARIABLES AND DISTRIBUTIONS IN R_1.

CHAPTERS 21—24. VARIABLES AND DISTRIBUTIONS IN R_n.

Third Part.

STATISTICAL INFERENCE.

CHAPTERS 25—26. GENERALITIES.

Chapters 27—29. Sampling Distributions.

Chapters 30—31. Tests of Significance, I.

Chapters 32—34. Theory of Estimation.

FIRST PART

MATHEMATICAL INTRODUCTION

Chapters 1–3. Sets of Points.

CHAPTER 1.

General Properties of Sets.

1.1. Sets. — In pure and applied mathematics, situations often occur where we have to consider the collection of all possible objects having certain specified properties. Any collection of objects defined in this way will be called a *set*, and each object belonging to such a set will be called an *element of the set.*

The elements of a set may be objects of any kind: points, numbers, functions, things, persons etc. Thus we may consider e. g. 1) the set of all positive integral numbers, 2) the set of all points on a given straight line, 3) the set of all rational functions of two variables, 4) the set of all persons born in a given country and alive at the end of the year 1940. In the first part of this book we shall mainly deal with cases where the elements are points or numbers, but in this introductory chapter we shall give some considerations which apply to the general case when the elements may be of any kind.

In the example 4) given above, our set contains a finite, though possibly unknown, number of elements, whereas in the three first examples we obviously have to do with sets where the number of elements is not finite. We thus have to distinguish between *finite* and *infinite* sets.

An infinite set is called *enumerable* if its elements may be arranged in a *sequence:* $x_1, x_2, \ldots, x_n, \ldots$, such that a) every x_n is an element of the set, and b) every element of the set appears at a definite place in the sequence. By such an arrangement we establish a *one-to-one correspondence* between the elements of the given set and those of the set containing all positive integral numbers $1, 2, \ldots, n, \ldots$, which forms the simplest example of an enumerable set.

We shall see later that there exist also infinite sets which are *non-enumerable.* If, from such a set, we choose any sequence of elements $x_1, x_2, \ldots$, there will always be elements left in the set which do not appear in the sequence, so that a non-enumerable set may be said to represent a higher order of infinity than an enumerable set. It will be shown later (cf 4. 3) that the set of all points on a given straight line affords an example of a non-enumerable set.

1.2. Subsets, space. — If two sets S and S_1 are such that every element of S_1 also belongs to S, we shall call S_1 a *subset* of S, and write

$$S_1 < S \quad \text{or} \quad S > S_1.$$

We shall sometimes express this also by saying that S_1 is *contained in* S or *belongs to* S. — When S_1 consists of one single element x, we use the same notation $x < S$ to express that x *belongs to* S.

In the particular case when both the relations $S_1 < S$ and $S < S_1$ hold, the sets are called *equal*, and we write

$$S = S_1.$$

It is sometimes convenient to consider a set S which does not contain any element at all. This we call the *empty set*, and write $S = 0$. The empty set is a subset of any set. If we regard the empty set as a particular case of a finite set, it is seen that *every subset of a finite set is itself finite, while every subset of an enumerable set is finite or enumerable.* Thus the set of all integers between 20 and 30 is a finite subset of the set 1, 2, 3, . . ., while the set of all odd integers 1, 3, 5, . . . is an enumerable subset of the same set.

In many investigations we shall be concerned with the properties and the mutual relations of various subsets of a given set $\boldsymbol{S}$. The set $\boldsymbol{S}$, which thus contains the totality of all elements that may appear in the investigation, will then be called the *space* of the investigation. If, e.g., we consider various sets of points on a given straight line, we may choose as our space the set $\boldsymbol{S}$ of all points on the line. Any subset S of the space $\boldsymbol{S}$ will be called briefly a *set in* $\boldsymbol{S}$.

1.3. Operations on sets. — Suppose now that a space $\boldsymbol{S}$ is given, and let us consider various sets in $\boldsymbol{S}$. We shall first define the operations of *addition*, *multiplication* and *subtraction* for sets.

The *sum* of two sets S_1 and S_2,

$$S' = S_1 + S_2,$$

is the set S' of all elements *belonging to at least one* of the sets S_1 and S_2. — The *product*

$$S'' = S_1 S_2$$

is the *common part* of the sets, or the set S'' of all elements *belonging to both* S_1 and S_2. — Finally, the *difference*

$$S''' = S_1 - S_2$$

will be defined only in the case when S_2 is a subset of S_1, and is then the set S''' of all elements *belonging to* S_1 *but not to* S_2.

Thus if S_1 and S_2 consist of all points inside the curves C_1 and C_2 respectively (cf Fig. 1), $S_1 + S_2$ will be the set of all points inside at least one of the two curves, while $S_1 S_2$ will be the set of all points common to both domains.

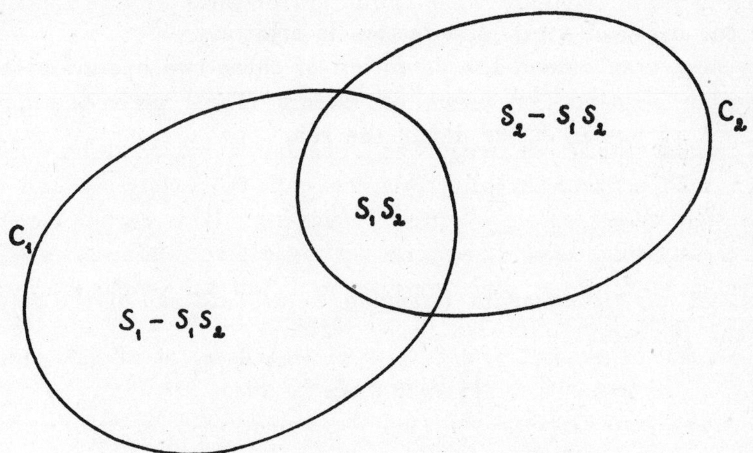

Fig. 1. Simple operations on sets.

The product $S_1 S_2$ is evidently a subset of both S_1 and S_2. The difference $S_n - S_1 S_2$, where n may denote 1 or 2, is the set of all points of S_n which do not belong to $S_1 S_2$.

In the particular case when S_1 and S_2 have no common elements, the *product* is empty, so that we have $S_1 S_2 = 0$. On the other hand, if $S_1 = S_2$ the *difference* is empty, and we have $S_1 - S_2 = 0$.

In the particular case when S_2 is a subset of S_1 we have $S_1 + S_2 = S_1$ and $S_1 S_2 = S_2$.

It follows from the symmetrical character of our definitions of the sum and the product that the operations of addition and multiplication are *commutative*, i. e. that we have

$$S_1 + S_2 = S_2 + S_1 \quad \text{and} \quad S_1 S_2 = S_2 S_1.$$

Further, a moment's reflection will show that these operations are also *associative* and *distributive*, like the corresponding arithmetic operations. We thus have

$$(S_1 + S_2) + S_3 = S_1 + (S_2 + S_3),$$
$$(S_1 S_2) S_3 = S_1 (S_2 S_3),$$
$$S_1 (S_2 + S_3) = S_1 S_2 + S_1 S_3.$$

It follows that we may without ambiguity talk of the sum or product of any finite number of sets:

$$S_1 + S_2 + \cdots + S_n \quad \text{and} \quad S_1 S_2 \cdots S_n,$$

where the order of terms and factors is arbitrary.

We may even extend the definition of these two operations to an enumerable sequence of terms or factors. Thus, given a sequence $S_1, S_2, \ldots$ of sets in $\mathbf{S}$, we define the sum

$$\sum_1^\infty S_\nu = S_1 + S_2 + \cdots$$

as the set of all elements *belonging to at least one* of the sets S_ν, while the product

$$\prod_1^\infty S_\nu = S_1 S_2 \cdots$$

is the set of all elements *belonging to all* S_ν. — We then have, e.g., $S(S_1 + S_2 + \cdots) = SS_1 + SS_2 + \cdots$.

Thus if S_ν denotes the set of all real numbers x such that $\frac{1}{\nu + 1} \leqq x \leqq \frac{1}{\nu}$, we find that $\sum_1^\infty S_\nu$ will be the set of all x such that $0 < x \leqq 1$, while the product set will be empty, $\prod_1^\infty S_\nu = 0$. — On the other hand, if S_ν denotes the set of all x such that $0 \leqq x \leqq \frac{1}{\nu}$, the sum $\sum_1^\infty S_\nu$ will coincide with S_1, while the product $\prod_1^\infty S_\nu$ will be a set containing one single element, viz. the number $x = 0$.

For the operation of subtraction, an important particular case arises when S_1 coincides with the whole space $\mathbf{S}$. The difference

$$S^* = \mathbf{S} - S$$

is the set of all elements of our space which do not belong to S, and will be called the *complementary set* or simply the *complement* of S. We obviously have $S + S^* = \mathbf{S}$, $SS^* = 0$, and $(S^*)^* = S$.

It is important to observe that the complement of a given set S is relative to the space $\mathbf{S}$ in which S is considered. If our space is the set of all points on a given straight line L, and if S is the set of all points situated on the positive side of an origin O on this line, the complement S^* will consist of O itself and all points on the negative side of O. If, on the other hand, our space consists of all points in a certain plane P containing L, the complement S^* of the same set S will also include all points of P not belonging to L. — In all cases where there might be a risk of a mistake, we shall use the expression: S^* is the complement of S *with respect to* $\mathbf{S}$.

The operations of addition and multiplication may be brought into relation with one another by means of the concept of complementary sets. We have, in fact, for any finite or enumerable sequence $S_1, S_2, \ldots$ the relations

$$(1.3.1)\qquad \begin{aligned} (S_1 + S_2 + \cdots)^* &= S_1^* S_2^* \cdots, \\ (S_1 S_2 \cdots)^* &= S_1^* + S_2^* + \cdots. \end{aligned}$$

The first relation expresses that *the complementary set of a sum is the product of the complements of the terms.* This is a direct consequence of the definitions. As a matter of fact, the complement $(S_1 + \cdots)^*$ is the set of all elements x of the space, of which it is not true that they occur in at least one S_ν. This is, however, the same thing as the set of all elements x which are absent from every S_ν, or the set of all x which belong to every complement S_ν^*, i. e. the product $S_1^* S_2^* \cdots$. The second relation is obtained from the first by substituting S_ν^* for S_ν. — For the operation of subtraction, we obtain by a similar argument the relation

$$(1.3.2)\qquad S_1 - S_2 = S_1 S_2^*.$$

The reader will find that the understanding of relations such as (1.3.1) and (1.3.2) is materially simplified by the use of figures of the same type as Fig. 1.

1.4. Sequences of sets. — When we use the word *sequence* without further specification, it will be understood that we mean a *finite or* *enumerable* sequence. A sequence $S_1, S_2, \ldots, S_n, \ldots$ will often be briefly called the sequence $\{S_n\}$.

When we are concerned with the sum of a sequence of sets

$$S = S_1 + S_2 + \cdots,$$

it is sometimes useful to be able to represent S as the sum of a sequence of sets such that *no two have a common element.*

This may be effected by the following transformation. Let us put

$$\begin{aligned} Z_1 &= S_1, \\ Z_2 &= S_1^* S_2, \\ &\cdot\ \cdot\ \cdot\ \cdot\ \cdot \\ Z_\nu &= S_1^* S_2^* \cdots S_{\nu-1}^* S_\nu, \\ &\cdot\ \cdot\ \cdot\ \cdot\ \cdot\ \cdot\ \cdot\ \cdot\ \cdot \end{aligned}$$

Thus Z_ν is the set of all elements of S_ν not contained in any of the preceding sets $S_1, \ldots, S_{\nu-1}$. It is then easily seen that Z_μ and Z_ν have no common element, as soon as $\mu \neq \nu$. Suppose e.g. $\mu < \nu$; then Z_μ is a subset of S_μ, while Z_ν is a subset of S_μ^*, so that $Z_\mu Z_\nu = 0$.

Let us now put $S' = Z_1 + Z_2 + \cdots$. Since $Z_\nu < S_\nu$ for all ν, we have $S' < S$. On the other hand, let x denote any element of S. By definition, x belongs to at least one of the S_ν. Let S_n be the *first* set of the sequence $S_1, S_2, \ldots$ that contains x as an element. Then the definition of Z_n shows that x belongs to Z_n and consequently also to S'. Thus we have both $S < S'$ and $S' < S$, so that $S' = S$ and

$$S = Z_1 + Z_2 + \cdots.$$

We shall use this transformation to show that *the sum of a sequence of enumerable sets is itself enumerable.* If S_ν is enumerable, then Z_ν as a subset of S_ν must be finite or enumerable. Let the elements of Z_ν be $x_{\nu 1}, x_{\nu 2}, \ldots$. Then the elements of $S = \Sigma S_\nu = \Sigma Z_\nu$ form the double sequence

$$\begin{matrix} x_{11} & x_{12} & x_{13} & \cdots \\ x_{21} & x_{22} & x_{23} & \cdots \\ x_{31} & x_{32} & x_{33} & \cdots \\ \cdot & \cdot & \cdot & \cdot\ \cdot\ \cdot \end{matrix}$$

and these may be arranged in a simple sequence e. g. by reading along diagonals: $x_{11}, x_{12}, x_{21}, x_{13}, x_{22}, x_{31}, \ldots$. It is readily seen that every element of S appears at a definite place in the sequence, and thus S is enumerable.

1.5. Monotone sequences. — A sequence $S_1, S_2, \ldots$ is *never decreasing*, if we have $S_n < S_{n+1}$ for all n. If, on the contrary, we have $S_n > S_{n+1}$ for all n, the sequence is *never increasing*. With a common name, both types of sequences are called *monotone*.

For a never decreasing infinite sequence, we have

$$S_n = \sum_1^n S_\nu,$$

and this makes it natural to define the *limit* of such a sequence by writing

$$\lim_{n \to \infty} S_n = \sum_1^\infty S_\nu.$$

Similarly, we have for a never increasing sequence

$$S_n = \prod_1^n S_\nu,$$

and accordingly we define in this case

$$\lim_{n \to \infty} S_n = \prod_1^\infty S_\nu.$$

Thus if S_n denotes the set of all points (x, y, z) inside the sphere $x^2 + y^2 + z^2 = 1 - \frac{1}{n}$, the sequence $S_1, S_2, \ldots$ will be never decreasing, and $\lim S_n$ will be the set of all points inside the sphere $x^2 + y^2 + z^2 = 1$. On the other hand, if S_n denotes the set of all points inside the sphere $x^2 + y^2 + z^2 = 1 + \frac{1}{n}$, the sequence will be never increasing, and $\lim S_n$ will consist of all points belonging to the inside *or the surface* of the sphere $x^2 + y^2 + z^2 = 1$.

It is possible to extend the definition of a limit also to certain types of sequences that are not monotone. We shall, however, have no occasion to use such an extension in this book.

1.6. Additive classes of sets. — Given a space $\boldsymbol{S}$, we may consider various *classes of sets* in $\boldsymbol{S}$. We shall make an important use of the concept of an *additive class of sets* in $\boldsymbol{S}$. A class $\mathfrak{C}$ of sets in $\boldsymbol{S}$ will be called additive[1]), if it satisfies the following three conditions:

a) The whole space $\boldsymbol{S}$ belongs to $\mathfrak{C}$.

b) If every set of the sequence $S_1, S_2, \ldots$ belongs to $\mathfrak{C}$, then the sum $S_1 + S_2 + \cdots$ and the product $S_1 S_2 \ldots$ both belong to $\mathfrak{C}$.

c) If S_1 and S_2 belong to $\mathfrak{C}$, and $S_2 < S_1$, then the difference $S_1 - S_2$ belongs to $\mathfrak{C}$.

If $\mathfrak{C}$ is an additive class, we can thus perform the operations of addition, multiplication and subtraction any finite or enumerable number of times on members of $\mathfrak{C}$ without ever encountering a set that is not a member of $\mathfrak{C}$.

It may be remarked that the three above conditions are evidently not independent of one another. As a matter of fact, the relations (1.3.1) and (1.3.2) show that the following is an entirely equivalent form of the conditions:

a$_1$) The whole space $\boldsymbol{S}$ belongs to $\mathfrak{C}$.

b$_1$) If every set of the sequence $S_1, S_2, \ldots$ belongs to $\mathfrak{C}$, then the sum $S_1 + S_2 + \cdots$ belongs to $\mathfrak{C}$.

c$_1$) If S belongs to $\mathfrak{C}$, then the complementary set S^* belongs to $\mathfrak{C}$.

The name »additive class» is due to the important place which, in this form of the conditions, is occupied by the additivity condition b$_1$).

The class of all possible subsets of $\boldsymbol{S}$ is an obvious example of an additive class. In the following chapter we shall, however, meet with a more interesting case.

CHAPTER 2.

Linear Point Sets.

2.1. Intervals. — Let our space be the set $\boldsymbol{R}_1$ of all points on a given straight line. Any set in $\boldsymbol{R}_1$ will be called a *linear point set*.

---

[1]) In this book, we shall always use the word »additive» in the same sense as in this paragraph, i. e. with reference to a *finite or enumerable* sequence of terms. It may be remarked that some authors use in this sense the expression »completely additive», while »additive» or »simply additive» is used to denote a property essentially restricted to a *finite* number of terms.

If we choose on our line an origin O, a unit of measurement and a positive direction, it is well known that we can establish a one-to-one correspondence between all real numbers and all points on the line. Thus we may talk without distinction of a point x on the line or the real number x that corresponds to the point. We consider only points corresponding to *finite* numbers; thus infinity does not count as a point.

A simple case of a linear point set is an *interval.* If a and b are any points such that $a \leqq b$, we shall use the following expressions to denote the set of all x such that:

$a \leqq x \leqq b$, . . . *the closed interval* (a, b);

$a < x < b$, . . . *the open interval* (a, b);

$a < x \leqq b$, . . . *the half-open interval* (a, b), *closed on the right*;

$a \leqq x < b$, . . . *the half-open interval* (a, b), *closed on the left.*

When we talk simply of an interval (a, b) without further specification in the context, it will be understood that anything that we say shall be true for all four kinds of intervals.

In the limiting case when $a = b$, we shall say that the interval is *degenerate.* In this case, the closed interval reduces to a set containing the single point $x = a$, while each of the other three intervals is empty.

If, in the above inequalities, we allow b to tend to $+\infty$, we obtain the inequalities defining the *closed* and the *open infinite interval* $(a, +\infty)$ respectively:

$$x \geqq a \quad \text{and} \quad x > a.$$

Similarly when a tends to $-\infty$ we obtain

$$x \leqq b \quad \text{and} \quad x < b$$

for the *closed* and the *open infinite interval* $(-\infty, b)$. — Finally, the whole space $\boldsymbol{R}_1$ may be considered as the infinite interval $(-\infty, \infty)$.

It will be shown below (*cf* 4.3) *that any non-degenerate interval is a non-enumerable set.*

The product of a finite or enumerable sequence of intervals is always an interval, but the sum of two intervals is generally not an interval. In order to give an example of a case when a sum of intervals is another interval, we consider $n+1$ points $a < x_1 < \cdots < x_{n-1} < b$. If all intervals appearing in the following relation are half-open and closed on the same side, we obviously have

$$(a, b) = (a, x_1) + (x_1, x_2) + \cdots + (x_{n-1}, b),$$

and no two terms in the second member have a common point. The same relation holds if all intervals are closed, but in this case any two consecutive terms have precisely one common point. If all intervals are open, on the other hand, the relation is not true.

2.2. Various properties of sets in R_1. — Consider a non-empty set S. When a point α exists such that, for any $\varepsilon > 0$, there is at least one point of S in the closed interval $(\alpha, \alpha + \varepsilon)$, while there is none in the open interval $(-\infty, \alpha)$, we shall call α the *lower bound of* S. When no finite α with this property exists, we shall say that the lower bound of S is $-\infty$. In a similar way we define the *upper bound* β of S. A set is *bounded*, when its lower and upper bounds are both finite. A bounded set S is a subset of the closed interval (α, β). The points α and β themselves may or may not belong to S.

If ε is any positive number, the open interval $(x - \varepsilon,\ x + \varepsilon)$ will be called a *neighbourhood* of the point x or, more precisely, the *ε-neighbourhood* of x.

A point z is called a *limiting point* of the set S if every neighbourhood of z contains at least one point of S different from z. If this condition is satisfied, it is readily seen that every neighbourhood of z even contains an infinity of points of S. The point z itself may or may not belong to S. The *Bolzano-Weierstrass theorem* asserts that *every bounded infinite set has at least one limiting point.* We assume this to be already known. — If z is a limiting point, the set S always contains a sequence of points $x_1, x_2, \ldots$ such that $x_n \to z$ as $n \to \infty$.

A point x of S is called an *inner point* of S if we can find ε such that the whole ε-neighbourhood of x is contained in S. Obviously an inner point is always a limiting point.

We shall now give some examples of the concepts introduced above. — In the first place, let S be a finite non-degenerate interval (a, b). Then a is the lower bound and b is the upper bound of S. Every point belonging to the *closed* interval (a, b) is a limiting point of S, while every point belonging to the *open* interval (a, b) is an inner point of S.

Consider now the set R of all rational points $x = p/q$ belonging to the half-open interval $0 < x \leqq 1$. If we write the sequence

$$\begin{array}{llll} \frac{1}{1}, & & & \\ \frac{1}{2}, & \frac{2}{2}, & & \\ \frac{1}{3}, & \frac{2}{3}, & \frac{3}{3}, & \\ \frac{1}{4}, & \frac{2}{4}, & \frac{3}{4}, & \frac{4}{4}, \\ \cdots & \cdots & \cdots & \end{array}$$

and then discard all numbers p/q such that p and q have a common factor, every point of R will occur at precisely one place in the sequence, and hence R is enumerable. There are no inner points of R. Every point of the closed interval $(0, 1)$ is a limiting point. — The complement R^* of R with respect to the half-open interval $0 < x \leqq 1$ is the set of all irrational points contained in that interval. R^* is not an enumerable set, as in that case the interval $(0, 1)$ would be the sum of two enumerable sets and thus itself enumerable. Like R itself, R^* has no inner points, and every point of the closed interval $(0, 1)$ is a limiting point.

Since R is enumerable, it immediately follows that the set R_n of all rational points x belonging to the half-open interval $n < x \leqq n + 1$ is, for every positive or negative integer n, an enumerable set. From a proposition proved in 1.4 it then follows that *the set of all positive and negative rational numbers is enumerable.* The latter set is, in fact, the sum of the sequence $\{R_n\}$, where n assumes all positive and negative integral values, and is thus by 1.4 an enumerable set.

2.3. Borel sets. — Consider the class of all intervals in $\boldsymbol{R}_1$ — closed, open and half-open, degenerate and non-degenerate, finite and infinite, including in particular the whole space $\boldsymbol{R}_1$ itself. Obviously this is *not* an additive class of sets as defined in 1.6, since the sum of two intervals is generally not an interval. *Let us try to build up an additive class by associating further sets to the intervals.*

As a first generalization we consider the class $\mathfrak{J}$ of *all point sets I such that I is the sum of a finite or enumerable sequence of intervals.* If $I_1, I_2, \ldots$ are sets belonging to the class $\mathfrak{J}$, the sum $I_1 + I_2 + \cdots$ is, by 1.4, also the sum of a finite or enumerable sequence of intervals, and thus belongs to $\mathfrak{J}$. The same thing holds for any *finite* product $I_1 I_2 \ldots I_n$, on account of the extension of the distributive property indicated in 1.3. We shall, however, show by examples that neither the *infinite* product $I_1 I_2 \ldots$ nor the difference $I_1 - I_2$ necessarily belongs to $\mathfrak{J}$. In fact, the set R considered in the preceding paragraph belongs to $\mathfrak{J}$, since it is the sum of an enumerable sequence of degenerate intervals, each containing one single point p/q. The difference $(0, 1) - R$, on the other hand, does not contain any non-degenerate interval, and if we try to represent it as a sum of degenerate intervals, a non-enumerable set of such intervals will be required. Thus the difference does not belong to the class $\mathfrak{J}$. Further, this difference set may also be represented as a product $I_1 I_2 \ldots$, where I_n denotes the difference between the interval $(0, 1)$ and the set containing only the n:th point of the set R. Thus this product of sets in $\mathfrak{J}$ does not itself belong to the class $\mathfrak{J}$.

Though we shall make in Ch. 4 an important use of the class $\mathfrak{J}$, it is thus clear that for our present purpose this class is not sufficient. In order to build up an additive class, we must associate with $\mathfrak{J}$ further sets of a more general character.

If we associate with $\mathfrak{J}$ all sums and products of sequences of sets in $\mathfrak{J}$, and all differences between two sets in $\mathfrak{J}$ such that the difference is defined — some of which sets are, of course, already included in $\mathfrak{J}$ — we obtain an extended class of sets. It can, however, be shown that not even this extended class will satisfy all the conditions for an additive class. We thus have to repeat the same process of association over and over again, without ever coming to an end. Any particular set reached during this process has the property that it can be defined by starting from intervals and performing the operations of addition, multiplication and subtraction a finite or enumerable number of times. *The totality of all sets ever reached in this way is called the class* $\mathfrak{B}_1$ *of Borel sets in* $\boldsymbol{R}_1$, *and this is an additive class.* As a matter of fact, every given Borel set can be formed as described by at most an enumerable number of steps, and any sum, product or difference formed with such sets will still be contained in the class of all sets obtainable in this way.

Thus any sum, product or difference of Borel sets is itself a Borel set. In particular, the limit of a monotone sequence (cf 1.5) of Borel sets is always a Borel set.

On the other hand, let $\mathfrak{C}$ be any additive class of sets in $\boldsymbol{R}_1$ containing all intervals. It then follows directly from the definition of an additive class that $\mathfrak{C}$ must contain every set that can be obtained from intervals by any finite or enumerable repetition of the operations of addition, multiplication and subtraction. Thus $\mathfrak{C}$ must contain the whole class $\mathfrak{B}_1$ of Borel sets, and we may say that *the class* $\mathfrak{B}_1$ *is the smallest additive class of sets in* $\boldsymbol{R}_1$ *that includes all intervals.*

CHAPTER 3.

Point Sets in n Dimensions.

3.1. Intervals. — Just as we may establish a one-to-one correspondence between all real numbers x and all points on a straight line, it is well known that a similar correspondence may be established between all pairs of real numbers (x_1, x_2) and all points in a plane, or between all triplets of real numbers (x_1, x_2, x_3) and all points in a three-dimensional space.

Generalizing, we may regard any system of n real numbers $(x_1, x_2, \ldots, x_n)$ as representing a *point* or *vector* $\boldsymbol{x}$ in an *euclidean space* $\boldsymbol{R}_n$ *of n dimensions.* The numbers $x_1, \ldots, x_n$ are called the *coordinates* of $\boldsymbol{x}$. As in the one-dimensional case, we consider only points corresponding to finite values of the coordinates. — The *distance* between two points

$$\boldsymbol{x} = (x_1, \ldots, x_n) \quad \text{and} \quad \boldsymbol{y} = (y_1, \ldots, y_n)$$

is the non-negative quantity

$$|\boldsymbol{x} - \boldsymbol{y}| = \sqrt{(x_1 - y_1)^2 + \cdots + (x_n - y_n)^2}.$$

The distance satisfies the *triangular inequality:*

$$|\boldsymbol{x} - \boldsymbol{y}| \leqq |\boldsymbol{x} - \boldsymbol{z}| + |\boldsymbol{y} - \boldsymbol{z}|.$$

Let $2n$ numbers $a_1, \ldots, a_n$ and $b_1, \ldots, b_n$ be given, such that $a_\nu \leqq b_\nu$ for $\nu = 1, \ldots, n$. The set of all points $\boldsymbol{x}$ defined by $a_\nu \leqq x_\nu \leqq b_\nu$ for $\nu = 1, \ldots, n$ is called a *closed n-dimensional interval.* If all the signs $\leqq$ are replaced by $<$, we obtain an *open* interval, and if both kinds of signs occur in the defining inequalities, we have a *half-open* interval. In the limiting case when $a_\nu = b_\nu$ for at least one value of ν, the interval is *degenerate.* When one or more of the a_ν tend to $-\infty$, or one or more of the b_ν to $+\infty$, we obtain an *infinite* interval. As in 2.1, the whole space $\boldsymbol{R}_n$ may be considered as an extreme case of an infinite interval.

It will be shown below (cf 4.3) that any non-degenerate interval is a non-enumerable set. The product of a finite or enumerable sequence of intervals is always an interval, but the sum of two intervals is generally not an interval.

3.2. Various properties of sets in $\boldsymbol{R}_n$. — A set S in $\boldsymbol{R}_n$ is *bounded*, if all points of S are contained in a finite interval.

If $\boldsymbol{a} = (a_1, \ldots, a_n)$ is a given point, and ε is a positive number, the set of all points $\boldsymbol{x}$ such that $|\boldsymbol{x} - \boldsymbol{a}| < \varepsilon$ is called a *neighbourhood* of $\boldsymbol{a}$ or, more precisely, the *ε-neighbourhood* of $\boldsymbol{a}$.

The definitions of the concepts of *limiting point* and *inner point*, and the remarks made in 2.2 in connection with these concepts for the case $n = 1$, apply without modification to the general case here considered.

We have seen in 2.2 that the set of all rational points in $\boldsymbol{R}_1$ is enumerable. By means of 1.4 it then follows that the set of all points with rational coordinates in a plane is enumerable, and further by induction that *the set of all points in $\boldsymbol{R}_n$ with rational coordinates is enumerable.*

3.3. Borel sets. — The class of all intervals in $\boldsymbol{R}_n$ is, like the corresponding class in $\boldsymbol{R}_1$, not an additive class of sets. In order to extend this class so as to form an additive class we proceed in the same way as in the case of intervals in $\boldsymbol{R}_1$.

Thus we consider first the class $\mathfrak{I}_n$ of all sets I that are sums of finite or enumerable sequences of intervals in $\boldsymbol{R}_n$. If $I_1, I_2, \ldots$ are sets belonging to this class, the sum $I_1 + I_2 + \cdots$ and the finite product $I_1 I_2 \ldots I_n$ also belong to $\mathfrak{I}_n$. As in the case $n = 1$, the infinite product $I_1 I_2 \ldots$ and the difference $I_1 - I_2$ do not, however, always belong to $\mathfrak{I}_n$.

We thus extend the class $\mathfrak{I}_n$ by associating all sums, products and differences formed by means of sets in $\mathfrak{I}_n$. Repeating the same association process over and over again, we find that any particular set reached in this way has the property that it can be defined by starting from intervals and performing the operations of addition, multiplication and subtraction a finite or enumerable number of times. *The totality of all sets ever reached in this way is called the class $\mathfrak{B}_n$ of Borel sets in $\boldsymbol{R}_n$, and this is an additive class.*

In the same way as in the case $n = 1$, we find that *the class $\mathfrak{B}_n$ is the smallest additive class of sets in $\boldsymbol{R}_n$ that includes all intervals.*

3.4. Linear sets. — When $n > 3$, the set of all points in $\boldsymbol{R}_n$ which satisfy a single equation $F(x_1, \ldots, x_n) = 0$ will be called a *hypersurface*. When F is a linear function, the hypersurface becomes a *hyperplane*. The equation of a hyperplane may always be written in the form

$$a_1(x_1 - m_1) + \cdots + a_n(x_n - m_n) = 0,$$

where $\boldsymbol{m} = (m_1, \ldots, m_n)$ is an arbitrary point of the hyperplane. — Let

(3.4.1) $$H_i = a_{i1}(x_1 - m_1) + \cdots + a_{in}(x_n - m_n) = 0,$$

where $i = 1, 2, \ldots, p$, be the equations of p hyperplanes passing through the same point $\boldsymbol{m}$. The equations (3.4.1) will be called *linearly independent*, if there is no linear combination $k_1 H_1 + \cdots + k_p H_p$ with constant k_i not all $= 0$, which reduces identically to zero. The corresponding hyperplanes are then also said to be linearly independent.

Suppose $p < n$, and consider the set L of all points in $\boldsymbol{R}_n$ common to the p linearly independent hyperplanes (3.4.1). If (3.4.1) is considered as a system of linear equations with the unknowns $x_1, \ldots, x_n$, the general solution (cf 11.8) is

$$x_i = m_i + c_{i1} t_1 + \cdots + c_{i,\,n-p}\, t_{n-p},$$

where the c_{ik} are constants depending on the coefficients a_{ik}, while $t_1, \ldots, t_{n-p}$ are arbitrary parameters.

The coordinates of a point of the set L may thus be expressed as linear functions of $n - p$ arbitrary parameters. Accordingly the set L will be called a *linear set of $n - p$ dimensions*, and will usually be denoted by L_{n-p}. For $p = 1$, this is a hyperplane, while for $p = n - 2$ L forms an ordinary plane, and for $p = n - 1$ a straight line. — Conversely, if L_{n-p} is a linear set of $n - p$ dimensions, and if $\boldsymbol{m} = (m_1, \ldots, m_n)$ is an arbitrary point of L_{n-p}, then L_{n-p} may be represented as the common part (i. e. the product set) of p linearly independent hyperplanes passing through $\boldsymbol{m}$.

3.5. Subspace, product space. — Consider the space $\boldsymbol{R}_n$ of all points $\boldsymbol{x} = (x_1, \ldots, x_n)$. Let us select a group of $k < n$ coordinates, say $x_1, \ldots, x_k$, and put all the remaining $n - k$ coordinates equal to zero: $x_{k+1} = \cdots = x_n = 0$. We thus obtain a system of $n - k$ linearly independent relations, which define a linear set L_k of k dimensions. This will be called the k-dimensional *subspace* corresponding to the coordinates $x_1, \ldots, x_k$. The subspace corresponding to any other group of k coordinates is, of course, defined in a similar way. Thus in the case $n = 3$, $k = 2$, the two-dimensional subspace corresponding to x_1 and x_2 is simply the (x_1, x_2)-plane.

Let S denote a set in the k-dimensional subspace of $x_1, \ldots, x_k$. The set of all points $\boldsymbol{x}$ in $\boldsymbol{R}_n$ such that $(x_1, \ldots, x_k, 0, \ldots, 0) < S$ will be called a *cylinder set* with the *base* S. — In the case $n = 3$, $k = 2$, this is an ordinary three-dimensional cylinder in the (x_1, x_2, x_3)-space, having the set S in the (x_1, x_2)-plane as its base.

Further, if S_1 and S_2 are sets in the subspaces of $x_1, \ldots, x_k$ and $x_{k+1}, \ldots, x_n$ respectively, the set of all points $\boldsymbol{x}$ in $\boldsymbol{R}_n$ such that $(x_1, \ldots, x_k, 0, \ldots, 0) < S_1$ and $(0, \ldots, 0, x_{k+1}, \ldots, x_n) < S_2$ will be called a *rectangle set* with the *sides* S_1 and S_2. — In the case when $n = 2$, while S_1 and S_2 are one-dimensional intervals, this is an ordinary rectangle in the (x_1, x_2)-plane.

Finally, let $\boldsymbol{R}_m$ and $\boldsymbol{R}_n$ be spaces of m and n dimensions respectively. Consider the set of all pairs of points $(\boldsymbol{x}, \boldsymbol{y})$ where $\boldsymbol{x} = (x_1, \ldots, x_m)$ is a point in $\boldsymbol{R}_m$, while $\boldsymbol{y} = (y_1, \ldots, y_n)$ is a point in $\boldsymbol{R}_n$. This set will be called the *product space* of $\boldsymbol{R}_m$ and $\boldsymbol{R}_n$. It is a space of $m + n$ dimensions, with all points $(x_1, \ldots, x_m, y_1, \ldots, y_n)$ as its elements. — Thus for $m = n = 1$, we find that the (x_1, x_2)-plane may be regarded as the product of the one-dimensional x_1- and x_2-spaces. For $m = 2$ and $n = 1$, we obtain the (x_1, x_2, x_3)-space as the product of the (x_1, x_2)-plane and the one-dimensional x_3-space, etc. The extension of the above definition to product spaces of more than two spaces is obvious. (Note that the *product space* introduced here is something quite different from the *product set* defined in 1.3.)

References to chapters 1—3. — The theory of sets of points was founded by G. Cantor about 1880. It is of a fundamental importance for many branches of mathematics, such as the modern theory of integration and the theory of functions. Most treatises on these subjects contain chapters on sets of points. The reader may be referred e.g. to the books by Borel (Ref. 6) and de la Vallée Poussin (Ref. 40).

CHAPTERS 4–7.

THEORY OF MEASURE AND INTEGRATION IN R_1.

CHAPTER 4.

THE LEBESGUE MEASURE OF A LINEAR POINT SET.

4.1. Length of an interval. — The *length* of a finite interval (a, b) in R_1 is the non-negative quantity $b - a$. Thus the length has the same value for a closed, an open and a half-open interval with the same end-points. For a degenerate interval, the length is zero. The length of an infinite interval we define as $+\infty$.

Thus with every interval $i = (a, b)$ we associate a definite non-negative length, which may be finite or infinite. We may express this by saying that the length $L(i)$ is a *non-negative function of the interval* i, and writing

$$L(i) = b - a, \quad \text{or} \quad L(i) = +\infty,$$

according as the interval i is finite or infinite.

If an interval i is the sum (cf 2.1) of a finite number of intervals, no two of which have a common point:

$$i = i_1 + i_2 + \cdots + i_n \qquad (i_\mu i_\nu = 0 \text{ for } \mu \neq \nu),$$

the length of the total interval i is obviously equal to the sum of the lengths of the parts:

$$L(i) = L(i_1) + L(i_2) + \cdots + L(i_n).$$

We now propose to show that this relation may be extended to an enumerable sequence of parts. To a reader who studies the subject for the first time, this will no doubt seem trivial. A careful study of the following proof may perhaps convince him that it is not. — In order to give a rigorous proof of our statement, we shall require the following important proposition known as *Borel's lemma*:

We are given a finite closed interval (a, b) *and a set* Z *of intervals such that every point of* (a, b) *is an inner point of at least one interval belonging to Z. Then there is a subset Z′ of Z containing only a finite number of intervals, such that every point of* (a, b) *is an inner point of at least one interval belonging to Z′.*

Divide the interval (a, b) into n parts of equal length. The lemma will be proved, if we can show that it is possible so to choose n that each of the n parts — considered as a closed interval — is entirely contained in an interval belonging to Z.

Suppose, in fact, that this is not possible, and denote by i_n the first of the n parts, starting from the end-point a, which is not entirely contained in an interval belonging to Z. The length of i_n obviously tends to zero as n tends to infinity. Let the middle point of i_n be denoted by x_n, and consider the sequence $x_1, x_2, \ldots$. Since this is a bounded infinite sequence, it has by the Bolzano-Weierstrass theorem (cf 2.2) certainly a limiting point x. Every neighbourhood of the point x then contains an interval i_n, which is not entirely contained in any interval belonging to Z. On the other hand, x is a point of (a, b) and is thus, by hypothesis, itself an inner point of some interval belonging to Z. This evidently implies a contradiction, and so the lemma is proved.

It is evident that both the lemma and the above proof may be directly generalized to any number of dimensions.

Let us now consider a sequence of intervals $i_\nu = (a_\nu, b_\nu)$ such that the sum of all i_ν is a *finite* interval $i = (a, b)$, while no two of the i_ν have a common point:

$$i = \sum_1^\infty i_\nu \qquad (i_\mu\, i_\nu = 0 \text{ for } \mu \neq \nu).$$

We want to prove that the corresponding relation holds for the lengths:

$$L(i) = \sum_1^\infty L(i_\nu). \tag{4.1.1}$$

In the first place, the n intervals $i_1, \ldots, i_n$ are a finite number of intervals contained in i, so that we have $\sum_1^n L(i_\nu) \leqq L(i)$ and hence, allowing n to tend to infinity,

$$\sum_1^\infty L(i_\nu) \leqq L(i).$$

It remains to prove the opposite inequality. This is the non-trivial part of the proof.

Consider the set Z which consists of the following intervals: 1) the intervals i_ν, 2) the open intervals $(a-\varepsilon, a+\varepsilon)$ and $(b-\varepsilon, b+\varepsilon)$, 3) the open intervals $\left(a_\nu - \frac{\varepsilon}{2^\nu}, a_\nu + \frac{\varepsilon}{2^\nu}\right)$ and $\left(b_\nu - \frac{\varepsilon}{2^\nu}, b_\nu + \frac{\varepsilon}{2^\nu}\right)$, where $\nu = 1, 2, \ldots$, while ε is positive and arbitrarily small. It is then evident that every point of the closed interval (a, b) is an inner point of at least one interval belonging to Z. According to Borel's lemma we may thus entirely cover i by means of a *finite* number of intervals belonging to Z, and the sum of the lengths of these intervals will then certainly be greater than $L(i) = b - a$. The sum of *all* intervals belonging to Z will a fortiori be greater than $L(i)$, so that we have

$$\sum_1^\infty L(i_\nu) + 4\varepsilon + 4\sum_1^\infty \frac{\varepsilon}{2^\nu} = \sum_1^\infty L(i_\nu) + 8\varepsilon > L(i).$$

Since ε is arbitrary, it follows that

$$\sum_1^\infty L(i_\nu) \geqq L(i),$$

and (4.1.1) is proved.

It is further easily proved that (4.1.1) holds also in the case when i is an *infinite* interval. In this case, we have $L(i) = +\infty$, and if i_0 is any finite interval contained in i, it follows from the latter part of the above proof that we have

$$\sum_1^\infty L(i_\nu) \geqq L(i_0).$$

Since i is infinite we may, however, choose i_0 such that $L(i_0)$ is greater than any given quantity, and thus (4.1.1) holds in the sense that both members are infinite.

We have thus proved that, if an interval is divided into a finite or enumerable number of intervals without common points, the length of the total interval is equal to the sum of the lengths of the parts. This property will be expressed by saying that the length $L(i)$ is an additive function of the interval i.

4.2. Generalization. — The length of an interval is a *measure* of the extension of the interval. We have seen in the preceding paragraph that this measure has the fundamental properties of being *non-negative* and *additive*. The length of an interval i is a *non-negative* *and additive interval function* $L(i)$. The value of this function may be finite or infinite.

We now ask if it is possible to define a measure with the same fundamental properties also for more complicated sets than intervals. With any set S belonging to some more or less general class, we thus want to associate a finite or infinite[1] number $L(S)$, the *measure* of S, in such a way that the following three conditions are satisfied:

a) $L(S) \geqq 0$.

b) If $S = S_1 + S_2 + \cdots$, where $S_\mu S_\nu = 0$ for $\mu \neq \nu$, then we have $L(S) = L(S_1) + L(S_2) + \cdots$.

c) In the particular case when S is an interval, $L(S)$ is equal to the length of the interval.

Thus we want to *extend the definition* of the interval function $L(i)$, so that we obtain a *non-negative and additive set function* $L(S)$ which, in the particular case when S is an interval i, coincides with $L(i)$.

It might well be asked why this extension should be restricted to »some more or less general class of sets», and why we should not at once try to define $L(S)$ for *every* set S. It can, however, be shown that this is not possible. We shall accordingly content ourselves to show that *a set function $L(S)$ with the required properties can be defined for a class of sets that includes the whole class $\mathfrak{B}_1$ of Borel sets. This set function $L(S)$ is known as the Lebesgue measure of the set S. We shall further show that the extension is unique or, more precisely, that $L(S)$ is the only set function which is defined for all Borel sets and satisfies the conditions* a) — c).

4.3. The measure of a sum of intervals. — We shall first define a measure $L(I)$ for the sets I belonging to the class $\mathfrak{I}$ considered in 2.3. Every set in $\mathfrak{I}$ is the sum of a finite or enumerable sequence of intervals and, by the transformation used in 1.4, we can always take these intervals such that no two of them have a common point. (In fact, if the sets S_ν considered in 1.4 are intervals, every Z_ν will be the sum of a finite number of intervals without common points.)

Any set in $\mathfrak{I}$ may thus be represented in the form

$$I = i_1 + i_2 + \cdots, \tag{4.3.1}$$

[1]) For the set function $L(S)$, and the more general set functions considered in Ch. 6, we shall admit the existence of *infinite values*. For sets of points and for ordinary functions, on the other hand, we shall only deal with infinity in the sense of a limit, but not as an independent point or value (cf 2.1 and 3.1).

where the i_ν are intervals such that $i_\mu i_\nu = 0$ for $\mu \neq \nu$. By the conditions b) and c) of 4.2, we must then define the measure $L(I)$ by writing

(4.3.2) $$L(I) = L(i_1) + L(i_2) + \cdots,$$

where as before $L(i_\nu)$ denotes the length of the interval i_ν.

The representation of I in the form (4.3.1) is, however, obviously not unique. Let

(4.3.3) $$I = j_1 + j_2 + \cdots$$

be another representation of the same set I, the j_ν being intervals such that $j_\mu j_\nu = 0$ for $\mu \neq \nu$. We must then show that (4.3.1) and (4.3.3) yield the same value of $L(I)$, i. e. that

(4.3.4) $$\sum_{\mu=1}^{\infty} L(i_\mu) = \sum_{\nu=1}^{\infty} L(j_\nu).$$

This may be proved in the following way. For any interval i_μ we have, since $i_\mu < I$,

$$i_\mu = i_\mu I = i_\mu \sum_\nu j_\nu = \sum_\nu i_\mu j_\nu$$

and thus, by the additive property of the length of an interval,

$$L(i_\mu) = \sum_\nu L(i_\mu j_\nu),$$

(4.3.5) $$\sum_\mu L(i_\mu) = \sum_\mu \sum_\nu L(i_\mu j_\nu).$$

In the same way we obtain

(4.3.6) $$\sum_\nu L(j_\nu) = \sum_\nu \sum_\mu L(i_\mu j_\nu).$$

Now the following three cases may occur: 1) The intervals $i_\mu j_\nu$ are all finite, and the double series with non-negative terms $\sum_{\mu,\nu} L(i_\mu j_\nu)$ is convergent. 2) All the $i_\mu j_\nu$ are finite, and the double series is divergent. 3) At least one of the $i_\mu j_\nu$ is an infinite interval.

In case 1), the expressions in the second members of (4.3.5) and (4.3.6) are finite and equal, and thus (4.3.4) holds. In cases 2) and 3) the same expressions are both infinite. Thus in any case (4.3.4) is proved, and it follows that the definition (4.3.2) yields a uniquely determined — finite or infinite — value of $L(I)$.

It is obvious that the measure $L(I)$ thus defined satisfies the conditions a) and c) of 4.2. It remains to show that condition b) is also satisfied.

Let $I_1, I_2, \ldots$ be a sequence of sets in $\mathfrak{J}$, such that $I_\mu I_\nu = 0$ for $\mu \neq \nu$, and let

$$I_\mu = \sum_\nu i_{\mu\nu}$$

be a representation of I_μ in the form used above. Then

$$I = \sum_\mu I_\mu = \sum_\mu \sum_\nu i_{\mu\nu}$$

is also a set in $\mathfrak{J}$, and no two of the $i_{\mu\nu}$ have a common point. If $i', i'', \ldots$ is an arrangement of the double series $\sum_{\mu,\nu} i_{\mu\nu}$ in a simple sequence (e. g. by diagonals as in 1.4), we have

$$I = i' + i'' + \cdots,$$

$$L(I) = L(i') + L(i'') + \cdots.$$

A discussion of possible cases similar to the one given above then shows that we always have

$$L(I) = \sum_\mu \sum_\nu L(i_{\mu\nu}) = \sum_\mu L(I_\mu).$$

We have thus proved that (4.3.2) *defines for all sets I belonging to the class $\mathfrak{J}$ a unique measure $L(I)$ satisfying the conditions* a) — c) *of* 4.2.

We shall now deduce some properties of the measure $L(I)$. In the first place, we consider a sequence $I_1, I_2, \ldots$ of sets in $\mathfrak{J}$, *without* assuming that I_μ and I_ν have no common points. For the sum $I = I_1 + I_2 + \cdots$, we obtain as above the representation $I = i' + i'' + \cdots$, but the intervals $i', i'', \ldots$ may now have common points. By the transformation used in 1.4 it is then easily seen that we always have

$$L(I) \leqq L(i') + L(i'') + \cdots,$$

which gives

(4.3.7) $$L(I_1 + I_2 + \cdots) \leqq L(I_1) + L(I_2) + \cdots.$$

(In the particular case when $I_\mu I_\nu = 0$ for $\mu \neq \nu$, we have already seen that the sign of equality holds in this relation.)

We further observe that any enumerable set of points $x_1, x_2, \ldots$ is a set in $\mathfrak{J}$, since each x_n may be regarded as a degenerate interval, the length of which reduces to zero. It then follows from the definition (4.3.2) that *the measure of an enumerable set is always equal to zero.* — Hence we obtain a simple proof of a property mentioned above (1.1 and 2.1) without proof: *the set of all points belonging to a non-degenerate interval is a non-enumerable set.* In fact, the measure of this set is equal to the length of the interval, which is a positive quantity, while any enumerable set is of measure zero. A fortiori, the same property holds for a non-degenerate interval in $\boldsymbol{R}_n$ with $n > 1$ (cf 3.1).

Finally, we shall prove the following theorem that will be required in the sequel for the extension of the definition of measure to more general classes of sets: *If I and J are sets in $\mathfrak{J}$ that are both of finite measure, we have*

$$L(I+J) = L(I) + L(J) - L(IJ). \tag{4.3.8}$$

Consider first the case when I and J both are sums of a *finite* number of intervals. From the relations

$$I + J = I + (J - IJ),$$
$$J = IJ + (J - IJ)$$

we obtain, since all sets belong to $\mathfrak{J}$, and the two terms in each second member have no common point,

$$L(I+J) = L(I) + L(J - IJ),$$
$$L(J) = L(IJ) + L(J - IJ),$$

and then by subtraction we obtain (4.3.8).

In the general case, when I and J are sums of finite *or enumerable* sequences of intervals, we cannot argue in this simple way, as we are not sure that $J - IJ$ is a set in $\mathfrak{J}$ (cf 2.3) and, if this is not the case, the measure $L(J - IJ)$ has not yet been defined. Let

$$I = \sum_{\mu=1}^{\infty} i_\mu, \quad J = \sum_{\nu=1}^{\infty} j_\nu$$

be representations of I and J of the form (4.3.1), and put

$$I_n = \sum_{\mu=1}^{n} i_\mu, \quad J_n = \sum_{\nu=1}^{n} j_\nu.$$

According to the above, we then have

$$L(I_n + J_n) = L(I_n) + L(J_n) - L(I_n J_n).$$

Allowing now n to tend to infinity, each term of the last relation tends to the corresponding term of (4.3.8), and thus this relation is proved.

4.4. Outer and inner measure of a bounded set. — In the preceding paragraph, we have defined a measure $L(I)$ for all sets I belonging to the class $\mathfrak{J}$. In order to extend the definition to a more general class of sets, we shall now introduce two auxiliary functions, the *inner* and *outer measure*, that will be defined for every *bounded* set in $\boldsymbol{R}_1$.

Throughout this paragraph, we shall only consider *bounded* sets. We choose a fixed finite interval (a, b) as our space and consider only points and sets belonging to (a, b). When speaking about the complement S^* of a set S, we shall accordingly always mean the complement *with respect to* (a, b). (Cf 1.3.)

In order to define the new functions, we consider a set I belonging to the class $\mathfrak{J}$, such that $S < I < (a, b)$. Thus we *enclose* the set S in a sum I of intervals, which in its turn is a subset of (a, b). This can always be done, since we may e. g. choose $I = (a, b)$. The enclosing set I has a measure $L(I)$ defined in the preceding paragraph. Consider the set formed by the numbers $L(I)$ corresponding to *all possible enclosing sets* I. Obviously this set has a finite lower bound, since we have $L(I) \geqq 0$.

The outer measure $\overline{L}(S)$ *of the set* S *will be defined as the lower bound of the set of all these numbers* $L(I)$. *The inner measure* $\underline{L}(S)$ *of* S *will be defined by the relation* $\underline{L}(S) = b - a - \overline{L}(S^*)$.

Since every set S considered here is a subset of the interval (a, b), which is itself a set in $\mathfrak{J}$, we obviously have

$$0 \leqq \overline{L}(S) \leqq b-a, \quad 0 \leqq \underline{L}(S) \leqq b-a.$$

Directly from the definitions we further find that $\overline{L}(S)$ and $\underline{L}(S)$ are both *monotone* functions of S, i. e. that we have

$$\overline{L}(S_1) \leqq \overline{L}(S_2), \quad \underline{L}(S_1) \leqq \underline{L}(S_2), \tag{4.4.1}$$

as soon as $S_1 < S_2$. In fact, for any I such that $S_2 < I$, we then also have $S_1 < I$, and hence the first inequality follows immediately. The second inequality is obtained from the first by considering the complementary sets.

Further, if $S < I_1$ and $S^* < I_2$, every point of (a, b) belongs to at least one of the sets I_1 and I_2. Since I_1 and I_2 are both contained in (a, b), we then have $I_1 + I_2 = (a, b)$ and thus by (4.3.7)

$$L(I_1) + L(I_2) \geqq b-a.$$

Choosing the enclosing sets I_1 and I_2 in all possible ways, we find that the corresponding inequality must hold for the lower bounds of $L(I_1)$ and $L(I_2)$, so that we may write

$$\bar{L}(S) + \bar{L}(S^*) \geqq b-a$$

or

$$\underline{L}(S) \leqq \bar{L}(S). \tag{4.4.2}$$

Let $S_1, S_2, \ldots$ be a given sequence of sets *with or without common points.* According to the definition of outer measure, we can for every n find I_n such that $S_n < I_n$ and

$$L(I_n) < \bar{L}(S_n) + \frac{\varepsilon}{2^n},$$

where ε is arbitrarily small. We then have $S_1 + S_2 + \cdots < I_1 + I_2 + \cdots$, and from (4.3.7) we obtain

$$\begin{aligned} \bar{L}(S_1 + S_2 + \cdots) &\leqq L(I_1 + I_2 + \cdots) \\ &\leqq L(I_1) + L(I_2) + \cdots \\ &< \bar{L}(S_1) + \bar{L}(S_2) + \cdots + \varepsilon(\tfrac{1}{2} + \tfrac{1}{4} + \cdots). \end{aligned}$$

Since ε is arbitrary, it follows that

$$\bar{L}(S_1 + S_2 + \cdots) \leqq \bar{L}(S_1) + \bar{L}(S_2) + \cdots. \tag{4.4.3}$$

In order to deduce a corresponding inequality for the inner measure $\underline{L}(S)$, we consider two sets S_1 and S_2 *without common points.* Let the complementary sets S_1^* and S_2^* be enclosed in I_1 and I_2 respectively. Abbreviating the words »lower bound of» by »l. b.», we then have

$$\begin{aligned} b-a - \underline{L}(S_1) &= \bar{L}(S_1^*) = \text{l. b. } L(I_1), \\ b-a - \underline{L}(S_2) &= \bar{L}(S_2^*) = \text{l. b. } L(I_2), \end{aligned} \tag{4.4.4}$$

where the enclosing sets I_1 and I_2 have to be chosen in all possible ways. Further, we have by (1.3.1)

$$(S_1 + S_2)^* = S_1^* S_2^* < I_1 I_2,$$

but here we can only infer that

$$b-a-\underline{L}(S_1 + S_2) = \overline{L}[(S_1 + S_2)^*] \leqq \text{l. b. } L(I_1 I_2), \tag{4.4.5}$$

since there may be other enclosing I-sets for $(S_1 + S_2)^*$ besides those of the form $I_1 I_2$. From (4.4.4) and (4.4.5) we deduce, using (4.3.8),

$$\begin{aligned}\underline{L}(S_1 + S_2) - \underline{L}(S_1) - \underline{L}(S_2) &\geqq \text{l. b. } [L(I_1) + L(I_2)] - \text{l. b. } L(I_1 I_2) - (b-a)\\ &\geqq \text{l. b. } [L(I_1) + L(I_2) - L(I_1 I_2)] - (b-a)\\ &= \text{l. b. } L(I_1 + I_2) - (b-a).\end{aligned}$$

Since S_1 and S_2 have no common point we have, however, $S_1 S_2 = 0$ and $I_1 + I_2 > S_1^* + S_2^* = (S_1 S_2)^* = (a, b)$. On the other hand, I_1 and I_2 are both contained in (a, b), so that $I_1 + I_2 < (a, b)$. Thus $I_1 + I_2 = (a, b)$, and

$$\underline{L}(S_1 + S_2) \geqq \underline{L}(S_1) + \underline{L}(S_2).$$

Let now $S_1, S_2, \ldots$ be a sequence of sets, *no two of which have a common point.* By a repeated use of the last inequality, we then obtain

$$\underline{L}(S_1 + S_2 + \cdots) \geqq \underline{L}(S_1) + \underline{L}(S_2) + \cdots. \tag{4.4.6}$$

In the particular case when S is an interval, it is easily seen from the definitions that $\overline{L}(S)$ and $\underline{L}(S)$ are both equal to the length of the interval. If $I = \Sigma i_\nu$ is a set in $\mathfrak{I}$, where the i_ν are intervals without common points, we then obtain from (4.4.3) and (4.4.6)

$$\overline{L}(I) \leqq \Sigma L(i_\nu), \quad \underline{L}(I) \geqq \Sigma L(i_\nu),$$

and thus by (4.4.2) and (4.3.2)

$$\overline{L}(I) = \underline{L}(I) = L(I). \tag{4.4.7}$$

Finally, we observe that the outer and inner measures are *independent of the interval* (a, b) in which we have assumed all our sets to be contained. By 2.2, a bounded set S is always contained in the closed interval (α, β), where α and β are the lower and upper bounds of S. If (a, b) is any other interval containing S, we must have $a \leqq \alpha$ and $b \geqq \beta$. A simple consideration will then show that the two intervals (a, b) and (α, β) will yield the same values of the outer and inner measures of S. Thus the quantities $\overline{L}(S)$ and $\underline{L}(S)$ depend only on the set S itself, and not on the interval (a, b).

4.5. Measurable sets and Lebesgue measure. — A *bounded* set S will be called *measurable*, if its outer and inner measures are equal. Their common value will then be denoted by $L(S)$ and called the *Lebesgue measure* or simply the *measure* of S:

$$\overline{L}(S) = \underline{L}(S) = L(S).$$

An *unbounded* set S will be called measurable if the product $i_x S$, where i_x denotes the closed interval $(-x, x)$, is measurable for every $x > 0$. The measure $L(S)$ will then be defined by the relation

$$L(S) = \lim_{x \to \infty} L(i_x S).$$

By (4.4.1), $L(i_x S)$ is a never decreasing function of x. Thus the limit. which may be finite or infinite, always exists.

In the particular case when S is a set in $\mathfrak{J}$, the new definition of measure is consistent with the previous definition (4.3.2). For a bounded set I, this follows immediately from (4.4.7). For an unbounded set I, we obtain the same result by considering the bounded set $i_x I$ and allowing x to tend to infinity.

According to (4.4.1), $\overline{L}(S)$ and $\underline{L}(S)$ are both monotone functions of the set S. It then follows from the above definition that the same holds for $L(S)$. For any two measurable sets S_1 and S_2 such that $S_1 < S_2$ we thus have

$$L(S_1) \leqq L(S_2). \tag{4.5.1}$$

We shall now show that the measure $L(S)$ satisfies the conditions a)–c) of 4.2. — With respect to the conditions a) and c), this follows directly from the above, so that it only remains to prove that the condition b) is satisfied. This is the content of the following theorem.

If $S_1, S_2, \ldots$ are measurable sets, no two of which have a common point, then the sum $S_1 + S_2 + \cdots$ is also measurable, and we have

$$L(S_1 + S_2 + \cdots) = L(S_1) + L(S_2) + \cdots. \tag{4.5.2}$$

Consider first the case when $S_1, S_2, \ldots$ are all contained in a finite interval (a, b). The relations (4.4.3) and (4.4.6) then give, since all the S_n are measurable,

$$\overline{L}(S_1 + S_2 + \cdots) \leqq \overline{L}(S_1) + \overline{L}(S_2) + \cdots = L(S_1) + L(S_2) + \cdots,$$

$$\underline{L}(S_1 + S_2 + \cdots) \geqq \underline{L}(S_1) + \underline{L}(S_2) + \cdots = L(S_1) + L(S_2) + \cdots.$$

By (4.4.2) we have, however, $\underline{L}(S_1 + S_2 + \cdots) \leqq \overline{L}(S_1 + S_2 + \cdots)$, and thus

$$\overline{L}(S_1 + S_2 + \cdots) = \underline{L}(S_1 + S_2 + \cdots) = L(S_1) + L(S_2) + \cdots,$$

so that in this case our assertion is true.

In the general case, we consider the products $i_x S_1, i_x S_2, \ldots$, all of which are contained in the finite interval i_x. The above argument then shows that the product $i_x(S_1 + S_2 + \cdots)$ is measurable for any x, and that

$$L[i_x(S_1 + S_2 + \cdots)] = L(i_x S_1) + L(i_x S_2) + \cdots.$$

Then, by definition, $S_1 + S_2 + \cdots$ is measurable and we have, since every term of the last series is a never decreasing function of x,

$$\begin{aligned} L(S_1 + S_2 + \cdots) &= \lim_{x \to \infty} [L(i_x S_1) + L(i_x S_2) + \cdots] \\ &= L(S_1) + L(S_2) + \cdots. \end{aligned}$$

Thus (4.5.2) is proved, and the Lebesgue measure $L(S)$ satisfies all three conditions of 4.2.

A set S such that $L(S) = 0$ is called a *set of measure zero.* If the outer measure $\overline{L}(S) = 0$, it follows from the definition of measure that S is of measure zero. We have seen in 4.3 that, in particular, any enumerable set has this property. — The following two propositions are easily found from the above. *Any subset of a set of measure zero is itself of measure zero. The sum of a sequence of sets of measure zero is itself of measure zero.* — These propositions are in fact direct consequences of the relations (4.4.1) and (4.4.3) for the outer measure.

4.6. The class of measurable sets. — Let us consider the class $\mathfrak{L}$ of all measurable sets in $\boldsymbol{R}_1$. We are going to show that $\mathfrak{L}$ *is an additive class of sets* (cf 1.6). Since we have seen in the preceding paragraph that $\mathfrak{L}$ contains all intervals, it then follows from 2.3 that $\mathfrak{L}$ contains the whole class $\mathfrak{B}_1$ of all Borel sets, so that *all Borel sets are measurable.*

We shall, in fact, prove that the class $\mathfrak{L}$ satisfies the conditions a_1), b_1) and c_1) of 1.6. With respect to a_1), this is obvious, so that we need only consider b_1) and c_1).

Let us first take c_1). It is required to show that *the complement S^* of a measurable set S is itself measurable.* Consider first the case of a bounded set S and its complement S^* with respect to some finite interval (a, b) containing S. By the definition of inner measure (4.4) we then have, since S is measurable,

$$\underline{L}(S^*) = b - a - \overline{L}(S) = b - a - \underline{L}(S) = \overline{L}(S^*),$$

so that S^* is measurable, and has the measure $b-a-L(S)$. — In the general case when S is measurable but not necessarily bounded, the same argument shows that the product $i_x S^*$, where S^* is now the complement with respect to the whole space $\boldsymbol{R}_1$, is measurable for any $x > 0$. Then, by definition, S^* is measurable.

Consider now the condition b_1). We have to show that *the sum* $S_1 + S_2 + \cdots$ *of any measurable sets* $S_1, S_2, \ldots$ *is itself measurable.* — In the particular case when $S_\mu S_\nu = 0$ for $\mu \neq \nu$, this has already been proved in connection with (4.5.2), but it still remains to prove the general case.

It is sufficient to consider the case when all S_n are contained in a finite interval (a, b). In fact, if our assertion has been proved for this case, we consider the sets $i_x S_1, i_x S_2, \ldots$, and find that their sum $i_x(S_1 + S_2 + \cdots)$ is measurable for any $x > 0$. Then, by definition, $S_1 + S_2 + \cdots$ is measurable.

We thus have to prove that, if the measurable sets $S_1, S_2, \ldots$ are all contained in (a, b), the sum $S_1 + S_2 + \cdots$ is measurable.

We shall first prove this for the particular case of only two sets S_1 and S_2. Let n denote any of the indices 1 and 2, and let the complementary sets be taken with respect to (a, b). Since S_n and S_n^* are both measurable, we can find two sets I_n and J_n in $\mathfrak{J}$ such that

$$S_n < I_n < (a, b), \qquad S_n^* < J_n < (a, b), \tag{4.6.1}$$

while the differences $L(I_n) - L(S_n)$ and $L(J_n) - L(S_n^*)$ are both smaller than any given $\varepsilon > 0$. Now by (4.6.1) any point of (a, b) must belong to at least one of the sets I_n and J_n, so that we have $I_n + J_n = (a, b)$, and thus by (4.3.8)

$$\begin{aligned} L(I_n J_n) &= L(I_n) + L(J_n) - (b-a) \\ &= L(I_n) + L(J_n) - L(S_n) - L(S_n^*) < 2\varepsilon. \end{aligned} \tag{4.6.2}$$

It further follows from (4.6.1) that

$$S_1 + S_2 < I_1 + I_2,$$

$$(S_1 + S_2)^* = S_1^* S_2^* < J_1 J_2,$$

and hence

$$\begin{aligned} \overline{L}(S_1 + S_2) &\leqq L(I_1 + I_2), \\ \underline{L}(S_1 + S_2) &\geqq b-a - L(J_1 J_2). \end{aligned} \tag{4.6.3}$$

By the same argument as before, we find that $I_1 + I_2 + J_1 J_2 = (a, b)$. The relations (4.6.3) then give, using once more (4.3.8),

$$\overline{L}(S_1 + S_2) - \underline{L}(S_1 + S_2) \leqq L[(I_1 + I_2) J_1 J_2].$$

Now

$$(I_1 + I_2) J_1 J_2 = I_1 J_1 J_2 + I_2 J_1 J_2 < I_1 J_1 + I_2 J_2,$$

so that we obtain by means of (4.5.1), (4.3.7) and (4.6.2)

$$\overline{L}(S_1 + S_2) - \underline{L}(S_1 + S_2) \leqq L(I_1 J_1) + L(I_2 J_2) < 4\,\varepsilon.$$

Since ε is arbitrary, and since the outer measure is always at least equal to the inner measure, it then follows that $\overline{L}(S_1 + S_2) = \underline{L}(S_1 + S_2)$, so that $S_1 + S_2$ is measurable.

It immediately follows that any sum $S_1 + \cdots + S_n$ of a *finite* number of measurable sets, all contained in (a, b), is measurable. The relation $S_1 S_2 \ldots S_n = (S_1^* + \cdots + S_n^*)^*$ then shows that the same property holds for a product.

Consider finally the case of an *infinite* sum. By the transformation used in 1.4, we have $S = S_1 + S_2 + \cdots = Z_1 + Z_2 + \cdots$, where $Z_\nu = S_1^* \ldots S_{\nu-1}^* S_\nu$, and $Z_\mu Z_\nu = 0$ for $\mu \neq \nu$. Since $S_1^*, \ldots, S_{\nu-1}^*$ and S_ν are all measurable, the finite product Z_ν is measurable. Finally, by (4.5.2), the sum $Z_1 + Z_2 + \cdots$ is measurable.

We have thus completed the proof that the measurable sets form an additive class $\mathfrak{L}$. It follows that any sum, product or difference of a finite or enumerable number of measurable sets is itself measurable. In particular, all Borel sets are measurable.

4.7. Measurable sets and Borel sets. — The class $\mathfrak{L}$ of measurable sets is, in fact, more general than the class $\mathfrak{B}_1$ of Borel sets. As an illustration of the difference in generality between the two classes, we mention without proof the following proposition: *Any measurable set is the sum of a Borel set and a set of measure zero.* All sets occurring in ordinary applications of mathematical analysis are, however, Borel sets, and we shall accordingly in general restrict ourselves to the consideration of the class $\mathfrak{B}_1$, and the corresponding class $\mathfrak{B}_n$ in spaces of n dimensions.

We shall now prove the statement made in 4.2 that *the Lebesgue measure is the only set function defined for all Borel sets and satisfying the conditions* a)–c) *of* 4.2.

Let, in fact, $\Lambda(S)$ be any set function satisfying all the conditions just stated. For any set I in $\mathfrak{I}$, we must obviously have $\Lambda(I) = L(I)$, since our definition (4.3.2) of $L(I)$ was directly imposed by the conditions b) and c) of 4.2. Let now S be a bounded Borel set, and enclose S in a sum I of intervals. From the conditions a) and b) it then follows that we have $\Lambda(S) \leqq \Lambda(I) = L(I)$. The lower bound of $L(I)$ for all enclosing I is equal to $L(S)$, and so we have $\Lambda(S) \leqq L(S)$. Replacing S by its complement S^* with respect to some finite interval, we have $\Lambda(S^*) \leqq L(S^*)$, and hence $\Lambda(S) \geqq L(S)$. Thus $\Lambda(S)$ and $L(S)$ are identical for all bounded Borel sets. This identity holds even for unbounded sets, since any unbounded Borel set may obviously be represented as the sum of a sequence of bounded Borel sets.

We shall finally prove a theorem concerning the measure of the limit (cf 1.5) of a monotone sequence of Borel sets. By 2.3, we know that any such limit is always a Borel set.

For a non-decreasing sequence $S_1, S_2, \ldots$ of Borel sets we have

$$\lim L(S_n) = L(\lim S_n). \tag{4.7.1}$$

For a non-increasing sequence, the same relation holds provided that $L(S_1)$ is finite.

For a non-decreasing sequence we may in fact write

$$\lim S_n = S_1 + (S_2 - S_1) + (S_3 - S_2) + \cdots,$$

and then obtain by (4.5.2)

$$\begin{aligned} L(\lim S_n) &= L(S_1) + L(S_2 - S_1) + \cdots \\ &= \lim\,[L(S_1) + L(S_2 - S_1) + \cdots + L(S_n - S_{n-1})] \\ &= \lim L(S_n). \end{aligned}$$

For a non-increasing sequence such that $L(S_1)$ is finite, the same relation is proved by considering the complementary sets S_n^* with respect to S_1. — The example $S_n = (n, +\infty)$ shows that the condition that $L(S_1)$ should be finite cannot be omitted.

CHAPTER 5.

The Lebesgue Integral for Functions of One Variable.

5.1. The integral of a bounded function over a set of finite measure. — *All point sets considered in the rest of this book are Borel sets, unless expressly stated otherwise.*[1]) *Generally this will not be explicitly mentioned, and should then always be tacitly understood.*

[1]) In order to give a full account of the theory of the Lebesgue integral, it would be necessary to consider *measurable* sets, and not only Borel sets. As stated in 4.7 the restriction to Borel sets is, however, amply sufficient for our purposes.

Let S be a given set of *finite* measure $L(S)$, and $g(x)$ a function of the real variable x defined for all values of x belonging to S. We shall suppose that $g(x)$ is *bounded* in S, i. e. that the lower and upper bounds of $g(x)$ in S are finite. We denote these bounds by m and M respectively, and thus have $m \leqq g(x) \leqq M$ for all x belonging to S. Let us divide S into a finite number of parts $S_1, S_2, \ldots, S_n$, no two of which have a common point, so that we have

$$S = S_1 + S_2 + \cdots + S_n, \quad (S_\mu S_\nu = 0 \text{ for } \mu \neq \nu).$$

In the set S_ν, the function $g(x)$ has a lower bound m_ν and an upper bound M_ν, such that $m \leqq m_\nu \leqq M_\nu \leqq M$.

We now define the *lower* and *upper Darboux sums* associated with this division of S by the relations

$$(5.1.1) \qquad z = \sum_1^n m_\nu L(S_\nu), \quad Z = \sum_1^n M_\nu L(S_\nu).$$

It is then obvious that we have

$$m L(S) \leqq z \leqq Z \leqq M L(S).$$

It is also directly seen that any division of S *superposed* on the above division, i. e. any division obtained by subdivision of some of the parts S_ν, will give a lower sum at least equal to the lower sum of the original division, and an upper sum at most equal to the upper sum of the original division.

Any division of S in an arbitrary finite number of parts without common points yields, according to (5.1.1), a lower sum z and an upper sum Z. Consider the set of all possible lower sums z, and the set of all possible upper sums Z. We shall call these briefly the z-set and the Z-set. Both sets are bounded, since all z and Z are situated between the points $m L(S)$ and $M L(S)$. *We shall now show that the upper bound of the z-set is at most equal to the lower bound of the Z-set.* Thus the two sets have at most one common point, and apart from this point, the entire z-set is situated to the left of the entire Z-set.

In order to prove this statement, let z' be an arbitrary lower sum, corresponding to the division $S = S_1' + \cdots + S_{n'}'$, while Z'' is an arbitrary upper sum, corresponding to the division $S = S_1'' + \cdots + S_{n''}''$. It is then clearly sufficient to prove that we have $z' \leqq Z''$. This follows, however, immediately if we consider the division $S = \sum_{i=1}^{n'} \sum_{k=1}^{n''} S'_i S''_k$, which is superposed on both the previous divisions. If the corresponding Darboux sums are z_0 and Z_0, we have by the above remark $z' \leqq z_0 \leqq Z_0 \leqq Z''$, and thus our assertion is proved.

The upper bound of the z-set will be called the *lower integral* of $g(x)$ over S, while the lower bound of the Z-set will be called the *upper integral* of $g(x)$ over S. We write

$$(5.1.2) \qquad \begin{aligned} \underline{\int_S} g(x)\,dx &= \text{upper bound of } z\text{-set}, \\ \overline{\int_S} g(x)\,dx &= \text{lower bound of } Z\text{-set}. \end{aligned}$$

It then follows from the above that we have

$$(5.1.3) \qquad m\,L(S) \leqq \underline{\int_S} g(x)\,dx \leqq \overline{\int_S} g(x)\,dx \leqq M\,L(S).$$

If the lower and upper integrals are equal (i. e. if the upper bound of the z-set is equal to the lower bound of the Z-set), $g(x)$ is said to be *integrable in the Lebesgue sense over* S, or briefly *integrable over* S. The common value of the two integrals is then called *the Lebesgue integral of* $g(x)$ *over* S, and we write

$$\underline{\int_S} g(x)\,dx = \overline{\int_S} g(x)\,dx = \int_S g(x)\,dx.$$

A necessary and sufficient condition for the integrability of $g(x)$ over S is that, to every $\varepsilon > 0$, we can find a division of S such that the corresponding difference $Z - z$ is smaller than ε. In fact, if this condition is satisfied, it follows from our definitions of the lower and upper integrals that the difference between these is smaller than ε, and since ε is arbitrary, the two integrals must be equal. Conversely, if it is known that $g(x)$ is integrable, it immediately follows that there must be one lower sum z' and one upper sum Z'', such that $Z'' - z' < \varepsilon$. The division superposed on both the corresponding divisions in the manner considered above will then give a lower sum z_0 and an upper sum Z_0 such that $Z_0 - z_0 < \varepsilon$.

It will be seen that all this is perfectly analogous to the ordinary textbook definition of the Riemann integral. In that case, the set S is an interval which is divided into a finite number of sub-intervals S_ν, and the Darboux sums z and Z are then formed according to (5.1.1), where now $L(S_\nu)$ denotes the *length* of the ν:th sub-interval S_ν. The only difference is that, in the present case, we consider a more general class of sets than intervals, since S and the parts S_ν may be any Borel sets. At the same time, we have replaced the length of the interval S_ν by its natural generalization, the measure of the set S_ν.

In the particular case when S is a finite interval (a, b), any division of (a, b) in sub-intervals considered in the course of the definition of the Riemann integral is a special case of the divisions in Borel sets occurring in the definition of the Lebesgue integral. In the latter case, however, we consider also divisions of the interval (a, b) in parts which are Borel sets other than intervals. These more general divisions may possibly increase the value of the upper bound of the z-set, and reduce the value of the lower bound of the Z-set. Thus we see that the lower and upper integrals defined by (5.1.2) are situated between the corresponding Riemann integrals. If $g(x)$ is integrable in the Riemann sense, the latter are equal, and thus a fortiori the two integrals (5.1.2) are equal, so that $g(x)$ is also integrable in the Lebesgue sense, with the same value of the integral. *When we are concerned with functions integrable in the Riemann sense, and with integrals over an interval, it is thus not necessary to distinguish between the two kinds of integrals.*

The definition of the Lebesgue integral is, of course, somewhat more complicated than the definition of the Riemann integral. The introduction of this complication is justified by the fact that the properties of the Lebesgue integral are simpler than those of the Riemann integral. — In order to show by an example that the Lebesgue integral exists for a more general class of functions than the Riemann integral, we consider a function $g(x)$ equal to 0 when x is irrational, and to 1 when x is rational. In every non-degenerate interval this function has the lower bound 0 and the upper bound 1. The lower and upper Darboux sums occurring in the definition of the Riemann integral of $g(x)$ over the interval $(0, 1)$ are thus, for any division in subintervals, equal to 0 and 1 respectively, so that the Riemann integral does not exist. If, on the other hand, we divide the interval $(0, 1)$ into the two parts S_i and S_r, containing respectively the irrational and the rational numbers of the interval, $g(x)$ is equal to 0 everywhere in S_i, and to 1 everywhere in S_r. Further, S_i has the measure 1, and S_r the measure 0, so that both Darboux sums (5.1.1) corresponding to this division are equal to 0. Then the lower and upper integrals (5.1.2) are both equal to 0, and thus the Lebesgue integral of $g(x)$ over $(0, 1)$ exists and has the value 0.

The Lebesgue integral over an interval (a, b) is usually written in the same notation as a Riemann integral:

$$\int_a^b g(x)\,dx.$$

We shall see below (cf 5.3) that this integral has the same value whether we consider (a, b) as closed, open, or half-open. — In the particular case when $g(x)$ is continuous for $a \leqq x \leqq b$, the integral

$$G(x) = \int_a^x g(t)\,dt$$

exists as a Riemann integral, and thus a fortiori as a Lebesgue integral, and we have

(5.1.4) $$G'(x) = g(x)$$

for all x in (a, b).

5.2. B-measurable functions. — A function $g(x)$ defined for all x in a set S is said to be *measurable in the Borel sense* or *B-measurable* in the set S if the subset of all points x in S such that $g(x) \leqq k$ is a Borel set for every real value of k. We shall prove the following important theorem:

If $g(x)$ is bounded and B-measurable in a set S of finite measure, then $g(x)$ is integrable over S.

Suppose that we have $m < g(x) \leqq M$ for all x belonging to S. Let $\varepsilon > 0$ be given, and divide the interval (m, M) in sub-intervals by means of points y_ν such that

$$m = y_0 < y_1 < \cdots < y_{n-1} < y_n = M,$$

the length of each sub-interval being $< \varepsilon$. Obviously this can always be done by taking n sufficiently large. Now let S_ν denote the set of all points x belonging to S such that

$$y_{\nu-1} < g(x) \leqq y_\nu, \qquad (\nu = 1, 2, \ldots, n).$$

Then $S = S_1 + \cdots + S_n$, and $S_\mu S_\nu = 0$ for $\mu \neq \nu$. Further, S_ν is the difference between the two Borel sets defined by the inequalities $g(x) \leqq y_\nu$ and $g(x) \leqq y_{\nu-1}$ respectively, so that S_ν is a Borel set. The difference $M_\nu - m_\nu$ between the upper and lower bounds of $g(x)$ in S_ν is at most equal to $y_\nu - y_{\nu-1} < \varepsilon$. Hence we obtain for the Darboux sums corresponding to this division of S

$$Z - z = \sum_1^n (M_\nu - m_\nu)\, L(S_\nu) < \varepsilon \sum_1^n L(S_\nu) = \varepsilon\, L(S).$$

But ε is arbitrarily small, and thus by the preceding paragraph $g(x)$ is integrable over S.

The importance of the theorem thus proved follows from the fact that all functions occurring in ordinary applications of mathematical analysis are B-measurable. — Accordingly, we shall in the sequel only consider B-measurable functions. As in the case of the Borel sets, this will generally not be explicitly mentioned, and should then always be tacitly understood.

We shall here only indicate the main lines of the proof of the above statement, referring for further detail to special treatises, e. g. de la Vallée Poussin (Ref. 40). We first consider the case when the set S is a finite or infinite interval (a, b), and write simply »B-measurable» instead of »B-measurable in (a, b)». If g_1 and g_2 are B-measurable functions, the sum $g_1 + g_2$, the difference $g_1 - g_2$ and the product $g_1 g_2$ are also B-measurable. We shall give the proof for the case of the sum, the other cases being proved in a similar way. Let k be given, and let U denote the set of all x in (a, b) such that $g_1 + g_2 \leqq k$, while U'_r and U''_r denote the sets defined by the inequalities $g_1 \leqq r$ and $g_2 \leqq k - r$ respectively. Then by hypothesis U'_r and U''_r are Borel sets for any values of k and r, and it will be verified without difficulty that we have $U = \prod (U'_r + U''_r)$, where r runs through the enumerable sequence of all positive and negative rational numbers. Hence by 2.3 it follows that U is a Borel set for any value of k, and thus $g_1 + g_2$ is B-measurable. — The extension to the sum or product of a finite number of B-measurable functions is immediate.

Consider now an *infinite* sum $g = g_1 + g_2 + \cdots$ of B-measurable functions, assumed to be convergent for any x in (a, b). Let $\varepsilon_1, \varepsilon_2, \ldots$ be a decreasing sequence of positive numbers tending to zero, and let Q_{mn} denote the set of all x in (a, b) such that $g_1 + \cdots + g_m \leqq k + \varepsilon_n$. Then Q_{mn} is a Borel set, and if we put

$$R_{mn} = Q_{mn} Q_{m+1,n} \ldots, \quad U_n = R_{1n} + R_{2n} + \cdots, \quad U = U_1 U_2 \ldots,$$

some reflection will show that U is the set of all x in (a, b) such that $g(x) \leqq k$. Since only sums and products of Borel sets have been used, U is a Borel set, and $g(x)$ is B-measurable. — Further, if g is the limit of a convergent *sequence* $g_1, g_2, \ldots$ of B-measurable functions, we may write $g = g_1 + (g_2 - g_1) + (g_3 - g_2) + \cdots$, and thus g is B-measurable.

Now it is evident that the function $g(x) = c x^n$ is B-measurable for any constant c and any non-negative integer n. It follows that any polynomial is B-measurable. Any continuous function is the limit of a convergent sequence of polynomials, and is thus B-measurable. Similarly all functions obtained by limit processes from continuous functions are B-measurable.

By arguments of this type, our statement is proved for the case when S is an interval. If $g(x)$ is B-measurable in (a, b), and S is any Borel set in (a, b), the function $e(x)$ equal to 1 in S, and to 0 in S^*, is evidently B-measurable in (a, b). Then the product $e(x) g(x)$ is B-measurable in (a, b), and this implies that $g(x)$ is B-measurable in S. — If, in particular, S is the set of all x in (a, b) such that $g(x) \leqq 0$, we have $|g(x)| = g(x) - 2\, e(x) g(x)$. Thus the modulus of a B-measurable function is itself B-measurable.

When we are dealing with B-measurable functions, all the ordinary analytical operations and limit processes will thus lead to B-measurable functions. By the theorem proved above, any bounded function obtained in this way will be integrable in the Lebesgue sense over any set of finite measure. For the Riemann integral, the corresponding statement is *not* true,[1]) and this is one of the properties that renders the Lebesgue integral simpler than the Riemann integral.

We shall finally add a remark that will be used later (cf 14.5). Let $g(x)$ be B-measurable in a set S. The equation $y = g(x)$ defines a correspondence between the variables x and y. Denote by Y a given set on the y-axis, and by X the set of all x in S such that $y = g(x) < Y$. We shall then say that the set X *corresponds* to Y. It is obvious that, if Y is the sum, product or difference of certain sets $Y_1, Y_2, \ldots$, then X is the sum, product or difference of the corresponding sets $X_1, X_2, \ldots$ Further, when Y is a closed infinite interval $(-\infty, k)$, we know that X is a Borel set. Now any Borel set may be formed from such intervals by addition, multiplication and subtraction. *It follows that the set X corresponding to any Borel set Y is a Borel set.*

5.3. Properties of the integral. — *In this paragraph we consider only bounded functions and sets of finite measure.* — The following propositions (5.3.1)—(5.3.4) are perfectly analogous to the corresponding propositions for the Riemann integral and are proved in the same way as these, using the definitions given in 5.1:

$$\int_S (g_1(x) + g_2(x))\,dx = \int_S g_1(x)\,dx + \int_S g_2(x)\,dx, \tag{5.3.1}$$

$$\int_S c\,g(x)\,dx = c\int_S g(x)\,dx, \tag{5.3.2}$$

$$m\,L(S) \leqq \int_S g(x)\,dx \leqq M\,L(S), \tag{5.3.3}$$

$$\int_{S_1+S_2} g(x)\,dx = \int_{S_1} g(x)\,dx + \int_{S_2} g(x)\,dx, \tag{5.3.4}$$

---

[1]) Even if the limit $g(x)$ of a sequence of functions integrable in the Riemann sense is bounded in an interval (a, b), we cannot assert that the Riemann integral of $g(x)$ over (a, b) exists. Consider, e. g., the sequence $g_1, g_2, \ldots$, where g_n is equal to 1 for all rational numbers x with a denominator $< n$, and otherwise equal to 0. Obviously g_n is integrable in the Riemann sense over $(0, 1)$, but the limit of g_n when $n \to \infty$ is the function $g(x)$ equal to 1 or 0 according as x is rational or irrational, and we have seen in the preceding paragraph that the Riemann integral of this function over $(0, 1)$ does not exist.

where c is a constant, m and M denote the lower and upper bounds of $g(x)$ in S, while S_1 and S_2 are two sets without common points. (5.3.1) and (5.3.4) are immediately extended to an arbitrary finite number of terms. — If we consider the non-negative functions $|g(x)| \pm g(x)$, it follows from (5.3.3) that we have

$$\left|\int_S g(x)\,dx\right| \leqq \int_S |g(x)|\,dx. \tag{5.3.5}$$

In the particular case when $g(x)$ is identically equal to 1, (5.3.3) gives

$$\int_S dx = L(S).$$

It further follows from (5.3.3) that the integral of any bounded $g(x)$ over a set of measure zero is always equal to zero. By means of (5.3.4) we then infer that, if $g_1(x)$ and $g_2(x)$ are equal for all x in a set S, except for certain values of x forming a subset of measure zero, then

$$\int_S g_1(x)\,dx = \int_S g_2(x)\,dx.$$

Thus if the values of the function to be integrated are arbitrarily changed on a subset of measure zero, this has no influence on the value of the integral. We may even allow the function to be completely undetermined on a subset of measure zero. We also see that, if two sets S_1 and S_2 differ by a set of measure zero, the integrals of any bounded $g(x)$ over S_1 and S_2 are equal. Hence follows in particular the truth of a statement made in 5.1, that the value of an integral over an interval is the same whether the interval is closed, open or half-open.

It follows from the above that in the theory of the Lebesgue integral we may often neglect a set of measure zero. If a certain condition is satisfied for all x belonging to some set S under consideration, with the exception at most of certain values of x forming a subset of measure zero, we shall say that the condition is satisfied *almost everywhere in* S or *for almost all values of* x *belonging to* S.

We shall now prove an important theorem due to Lebesgue concerning the integral of the limit of a convergent sequence of functions. We shall say that a sequence $g_1(x)$, $g_2(x)$, ... is *uniformly bounded* in the set S, if there is a constant K such that $|g_\nu(x)| < K$ for all ν and for all x in S.

If the sequence $\{g_\nu(x)\}$ *is uniformly bounded in* S, *and if* $\lim_{\nu\to\infty} g_\nu(x) = g(x)$ *exists almost everywhere in* S, *we have*

$$\lim_{\nu\to\infty} \int_S g_\nu(x)\,dx = \int_S g(x)\,dx. \tag{5.3.6}$$

If $\lim g_\nu(x)$ does not exist for all x in S, we complete the definition of $g(x)$ by putting $g(x) = 0$ for all x such that the limit does not exist. We then have $|g(x)| \leqq K$ for all x in S, and it follows from the preceding paragraph that $g(x)$ is B-measurable in S and is thus integrable over S. Let now $\varepsilon > 0$ be given, and consider the set S_n of all x in S such that $|g_\nu(x) - g(x)| \leqq \varepsilon$ for $\nu = n, n+1, \ldots$. Then S_n is a Borel set, the sequence $S_1, S_2, \ldots$ is never decreasing, and the limiting set $\lim S_n$ (cf 1.5) contains every x in S such that $\lim g_\nu(x)$ exists. Thus by hypothesis $\lim S_n$ has the same measure as S, and we have by (4.7.1)

$$\lim L(S_n) = L(\lim S_n) = L(S).$$

We can thus choose n such that $L(S_n) > L(S) - \varepsilon$, or $L(S - S_n) < \varepsilon$, and then obtain for all $\nu \geqq n$

$$\int_S |g_\nu(x) - g(x)|\,dx = \int_{S_n} + \int_{S-S_n} < \varepsilon\,[L(S) + 2K].$$

Since ε is arbitrary, and since

$$\left|\int_S g_\nu(x)\,dx - \int_S g(x)\,dx\right| \leqq \int_S |g_\nu(x) - g(x)|\,dx,$$

this proves our theorem.

The theorem (5.3.6) can be stated in another form as a theorem on *term-by-term integration of a series:*

If the series $\sum_1^\infty f_\nu(x)$ *converges almost everywhere in* S, *and if the partial sums* $\sum_1^n f_\nu(x)$ *are uniformly bounded in* S, *then*

$$\int_S \left(\sum_1^\infty f_\nu(x)\right) dx = \sum_1^\infty \int_S f_\nu(x)\,dx. \tag{5.3.7}$$

Under this form, the theorem appears as a generalization of (5.3.1) to an infinite number of terms. We shall now show that a corresponding generalization of (5.3.4) may be deduced as a corollary from (5.3.7).

If $S = S_1 + S_2 + \cdots$, *where* $S_\mu S_\nu = 0$ *for* $\mu \neq \nu$, *then*

$$\int\limits_S g(x)\,dx = \sum_1^\infty \int\limits_{S_\nu} g(x)\,dx. \tag{5.3.8}$$

Let $e_\nu(x)$ denote a function equal to 1 for all x in S_ν and otherwise equal to zero. For any x belonging to S, we then have

$$g(x) = \sum_1^\infty e_\nu(x)\,g(x),$$

and it is obvious that the partial sums of this series are uniformly bounded in S. Then (5.3.7) gives

$$\int\limits_S g(x)\,dx = \sum_1^\infty \int\limits_S e_\nu(x)\,g(x)\,dx = \sum_1^\infty \int\limits_{S_\nu} g(x)\,dx.$$

In the particular case $g(x) = 1$, (5.3.8) reduces to the additivity relation (4.5.2) for Lebesgue measure.

5.4. The integral of an unbounded function over a set of finite measure. — In 5.1 and 5.2 we have seen that the Lebesgue integral

$$\int\limits_S g(x)\,dx$$

has a definite meaning under the two assumptions that 1) $g(x)$ is bounded in S, and 2) S is of finite measure. We shall now try to remove these restrictions. In this paragraph, we consider the case when S is still of finite measure, but $g(x)$ is not necessarily bounded in S.

Let a and b be any numbers such that $a < b$, and put

$$g_{a,b}(x) = \begin{cases} a & \text{if} \quad g(x) < a, \\ g(x) & \text{»} \quad a \leqq g(x) \leqq b, \\ b & \text{»} \quad g(x) > b. \end{cases}$$

Obviously $g_{a,b}(x)$ is bounded and B-measurable in S, and thus integrable over S. If the limit

$$\lim_{\substack{a\to-\infty\\ b\to+\infty}} \int_S g_{a,b}(x)\,dx = \int_S g(x)\,dx \tag{5.4.1}$$

exists and has a finite value, we shall say that $g(x)$ is *integrable over* S. This limit is then, by definition, the Lebesgue integral of $g(x)$ over S.

It follows directly from the definition that any function is integrable over a set of measure zero, and that the value of the integral is zero, as in the case of a bounded function.

In the definition (5.4.1), we may assume $a < 0$, $b > 0$, and then have

$$g_{a,b}(x) = g_{a,b} = g_{a,0} + g_{0,b},$$
$$|g(x)|_{a,b} = |g|_{a,b} = -g_{-b,0} + g_{0,b}.$$

For fixed x, $g_{a,0}(x)$ and $g_{0,b}(x)$ are never decreasing functions of a and b respectively. It follows that both $g(x)$ and $|g(x)|$ are integrable if, and only if, the limits

$$\lim_{a\to-\infty} \int_S g_{a,0}(x)\,dx \quad \text{and} \quad \lim_{b\to+\infty} \int_S g_{0,b}(x)\,dx \tag{5.4.2}$$

are both finite. Hence the integrability of $g(x)$ is equivalent with the integrability of $|g(x)|$. It further follows that, if $g(x)$ is integrable over S, it is also integrable over any subset of S.

If, for all x in S, we have $|g(x)| < G(x)$, where $G(x)$ is integrable over S, we have $|g|_{a,b} \leqq G_{a,b}$, so that $|g(x)|$ and thus also $g(x)$ are integrable over S.

We now immediately find that the properties (5.3.2)—(5.3.5) of the integral hold true for any integrable $g(x)$. With respect to (5.3.3) it should, of course, be observed that one of the bounds m and M, or both, may be infinite.

We proceed to the generalization of (5.3.1), which is a little more difficult. Suppose that $f(x)$ and $g(x)$ are both integrable over S. From

$$|f+g|_{a,0} = 0, \qquad |f+g|_{0,b} \leqq |f|_{0,b} + |g|_{0,b},$$

it follows that $f(x) + g(x)$ is also integrable. We have to show that the property (5.3.1) holds in the present case, i.e. that

$$\int_S (f+g)\,dx = \int_S f\,dx + \int_S g\,dx. \tag{5.4.3}$$

Suppose in the first place that f and g are both non-negative in S. Then

$$(f+g)_{a,0} = f_{a,0} = g_{a,0} = 0,$$
$$(f+g)_{0;b} \leqq f_{0,b} + g_{0,b} \leqq (f+g)_{0,2b},$$

and hence

$$\int_S (f+g)_{a,b}\,dx \leqq \int_S f_{a,b}\,dx + \int_S g_{a,b}\,dx \leqq \int_S (f+g)_{a,2b}\,dx.$$

Allowing a and b to tend to their respective limits, we obtain (5.4.3). — Now S may be divided into at most six subsets, no two of which have a common point, such that in each subset none of the three functions f, g and $f+g$ changes its sign. For each subset, (5.4.3) is proved by the above argument. Adding the results and using (5.3.4) we obtain (5.4.3) for the general case.

We have thus shown that all the properties (5.3.1)—(5.3.5) of the integral hold true in the present case. In order to generalize also the properties expressed by the relations (5.3.6)—(5.3.8), we shall first prove the following lemma:

If $g(x)$ is integrable over S_0, and if $\varepsilon > 0$ is given, we can always find $\delta > 0$ such that

(5.4.4) $$\left|\int_S g(x)\,dx\right| < \varepsilon$$

for every subset $S < S_0$ which satisfies the condition $L(S) < \delta$.

Since we have seen that (5.3.5) holds in the present case, it is sufficient to prove the lemma for a non-negative function $g(x)$. In that case

$$\int_{S_0} g\,dx = \lim_{b\to\infty} \int_{S_0} g_{0,b}\,dx,$$

and thus we can find b such that

$$0 \leqq \int_{S_0} (g - g_{0,b})\,dx < \tfrac{1}{2}\varepsilon.$$

Since the integrand is non-negative, it follows by means of (5.3.4) and (5.3.3) that we have for any subset $S < S_0$

$$\int_S (g - g_{0,b})\,dx < \tfrac{1}{2}\varepsilon$$

or

$$\int_S g\,dx < \int_S g_{0,b}\,dx + \tfrac{1}{2}\varepsilon \leqq b\,L(S) + \tfrac{1}{2}\varepsilon.$$

Choosing $\delta = \dfrac{\varepsilon}{2b}$, the truth of the lemma follows immediately.

A consequence of the lemma is that, if $g(x)$ is integrable over an interval (a, b), the integral $\int_a^x g(t)\,dt$ is a continuous function of x for $a < x < b$.

We can now proceed to the generalization of (5.3.6). Assuming that $\lim_{\nu \to \infty} g_\nu(x) = g(x)$ almost everywhere in S, we shall show that the relation

$$\lim_{\nu \to \infty} \int_S g_\nu(x)\,dx = \int_S g(x)\,dx \tag{5.4.5}$$

holds if the sequence $\{g_\nu(x)\}$ is *uniformly dominated by an integrable function*, i. e. if $|g_\nu(x)| < G(x)$ for all ν and for all x in S, where $G(x)$ is integrable over S. — In the particular case $G(x) = \text{const.}$, this reduces to (5.3.6).

The proof is quite similar to the proof of (5.3.6). We first observe that it follows from the hypothesis that $|g(x)| \leqq G(x)$ almost everywhere in S; thus $g_\nu(x)$ and $g(x)$ are integrable over S. Given $\varepsilon > 0$, we then denote by S_n the set of all x in S such that $|g_\nu(x) - g(x)| \leqq \varepsilon$ for all $\nu \geqq n$. Then $S_1, S_2, \ldots$ is a never decreasing sequence, and $L(S_n) \to L(S)$. Using lemma (5.4.4), we now determine δ such that $\int_{S'} G(x)\,dx < \varepsilon$ for every $S' < S$ with $L(S') < \delta$, and then choose n such that $L(S_n) > L(S) - \delta$, and consequently $L(S - S_n) < \delta$. We then obtain for all $\nu \geqq n$

$$\begin{aligned} \int_S |g_\nu(x) - g(x)|\,dx &= \int_{S_n} + \int_{S-S_n} \\ &< \varepsilon L(S) + 2\int_{S-S_n} G(x)\,dx < \varepsilon[L(S) + 2], \end{aligned}$$

and thus (5.4.5) is proved. — The corresponding generalization of (5.3.7) and (5.3.8) is immediate.

5.5. The integral over a set of infinite measure. — We shall now remove also the second restriction mentioned at the beginning of 5.4, and consider Lebesgue integrals over sets of infinite measure. Let S be a Borel set of infinite measure, and denote by $S_{a,b}$ the product (common part) of S with the closed interval (a, b), where a and b are finite. Then $S_{a,b}$ is, of course, of finite measure.

If $g(x)$ is integrable over $S_{a,b}$ for all a and b, and if the limit

$$\lim_{\substack{a \to -\infty \\ b \to +\infty}} \int_{S_{a,b}} |g(x)|\, dx = \int_S |g(x)|\, dx$$

exists and has a finite value, we shall say that $g(x)$ is *integrable over* S.[1]) It is easily seen that in this case the limit

$$\lim_{\substack{a \to -\infty \\ b \to +\infty}} \int_{S_{a,b}} g(x)\, dx = \int_S g(x)\, dx \tag{5.5.1}$$

also exists and has a finite value, and we shall accordingly say that the Lebesgue integral of $g(x)$ over the set S is *convergent*[1]). The limit (5.5.1) is then, by definition, the value of this integral. — If $g(x)$ is integrable over S, it is also integrable over any subset of S.

If $|g(x)| < G(x)$ for all x in S, where $G(x)$ is integrable over S, it is easily seen that $g(x)$ is integrable over S. Since $|g_1 + g_2| \leqq \leqq |g_1| + |g_2|$, it follows that the sum of two integrable functions is itself integrable.

It follows directly from the definition that the properties (5.3.1), (5.3.2) and (5.3.4) hold true in the case of functions integrable over a set of infinite measure. Instead of (5.3.3), we obtain here only the inequality

$$\int_S g(x)\, dx \geqq 0 \quad \text{if} \quad g(x) \geqq 0 \quad \text{for all } x \text{ in } S.$$

This is, however, sufficient for the deduction of (5.3.5) for any integrable $g(x)$.

We now proceed to the generalization of (5.4.5), which is itself a generalization of (5.3.6). If $\lim g_\nu(x) = g(x)$ almost everywhere in S, and if $|g_\nu| < G$, where G is integrable over S, it follows as in the preceding paragraph that $|g| \leqq G$ almost everywhere in S. Consequently $g(x)$ is integrable over S, and we can choose a and b such that for all ν

$$\int_{S-S_{a,b}} |g_\nu - g|\, dx < 2 \int_{S-S_{a,b}} G(x)\, dx < \tfrac{1}{2}\varepsilon.$$

Now $S_{a,b}$ is of finite measure, and it then follows from the proof of (5.4.5) that we can choose n such that for all $\nu \geqq n$

$$\int_{S_{a,b}} |g_\nu - g|\, dx < \tfrac{1}{2}\varepsilon.$$

---

[1]) Strictly speaking, we ought to say that $g(x)$ is *absolutely integrable over* S, and that the integral of $g(x)$ over S is *absolutely convergent*. As we shall only in exceptional cases use non-absolutely convergent integrals we may, however, without inconvenience use the simpler terminology adopted in the text.

We then have for $\nu \geqq n$

$$\int_S |g_\nu - g|\, dx = \int_{S_{a,b}} + \int_{S-S_{a,b}} < \varepsilon.$$

Since ε is arbitrary, we have thus proved the following theorem, which contains (5.3.6) and (5.4.5) as particular cases:

If $\lim_{\nu\to\infty} g_\nu(x) = g(x)$ *exists almost everywhere in the set* S *of finite or infinite measure, and if* $|g_\nu(x)| < G(x)$ *for all* ν *and for all* x *in* S, *where* $G(x)$ *is integrable over* S, *then* $g(x)$ *is integrable over* S, *and*

$$\lim_{\nu\to\infty} \int_S g_\nu(x)\, dx = \int_S g(x)\, dx. \tag{5.5.2}$$

The theorem (5.5.2) may, of course, also be stated as a theorem on term-by-term integration of series analogous to (5.3.7). — Finally, the argument used for the proof of (5.3.8) evidently applies in the present case and leads to the following generalized form of that theorem: *If* $g(x)$ *is integrable over* S, *and if* $S = S_1 + S_2 + \cdots$, *where* $S_\mu S_\nu = 0$ *for* $\mu \neq \nu$, *then*

$$\int_S g(x)\, dx = \sum_1^\infty \int_{S_\nu} g(x)\, dx. \tag{5.5.3}$$

5.6. The Lebesgue integral as an additive set function. — Let us consider a fixed *non-negative* function $f(x)$, integrable over any finite interval, and put for any Borel set S

$$P(S) = \begin{cases} \int_S f(x)\, dx, & \text{if } f(x) \text{ is integrable over } S, \\ +\infty & \text{otherwise.} \end{cases} \tag{5.6.1}$$

Then $P(S)$ is a non-negative function of the set S, uniquely defined for all Borel sets S. Let now $S = S_1 + S_2 + \cdots$, where $S_\mu S_\nu = 0$ for $\mu \neq \nu$. It then follows from (5.5.3) that the additivity relation

$$P(S) = P(S_1) + P(S_2) + \cdots$$

holds as soon as $P(S)$ is finite. The same relation holds, however, even if $P(S)$ is infinite. For if this were not true, it would be possible to choose the sets S and $S_1, S_2, \ldots$ such that $P(S) = +\infty$, while the sum $P(S_1) + P(S_2) + \cdots$ would be finite. This would, however, imply the relation

$$\int\limits_{S_{a,b}} f(x)\,dx = \sum_1^\infty \int\limits_{(S_\nu)_{a,b}} f(x)\,dx$$

$$\leqq \sum_1^\infty \int\limits_{S_\nu} f(x)\,dx = \sum_1^\infty P(S_\nu).$$

Allowing here a and b to tend to their respective limits, it follows that $f(x)$ would be integrable over S, against our hypothesis. *Thus $P(S)$ as defined by* (5.6.1) *is a non-negative and additive set function, defined for all Borel sets S in $\boldsymbol{R}_1$.*

In the particular case when $f(x) = 1$, we have $P(S) = L(S)$, so that $P(S)$ is identical with the Lebesgue measure of the set S. Another important particular case arises when $f(x)$ is integrable over the whole space $\boldsymbol{R}_1$. In this case, $P(S)$ is always finite, and we have for any Borel set S

$$P(S) \leqq \int\limits_{-\infty}^{\infty} f(x)\,dx.$$

CHAPTER 6.

Non-Negative Additive Set Functions in $\boldsymbol{R}_1$.

6.1. Generalization of the Lebesgue measure and the Lebesgue integral. — In Ch. 4 we have determined the Lebesgue measure $L(S)$ for any Borel set S. $L(S)$ is a number associated with S or, as we have expressed it, a *function of the set S.* We have seen that this set function satisfies the three conditions of 4.2, which require that $L(S)$ should be a) non-negative, b) additive, and c) for any interval equal to the length of the interval. We have finally seen that $L(S)$ is the only set function satisfying the three conditions.

On the other hand, if we omit the condition c), $L(S)$ will no longer be the only set function satisfying our conditions. Thus e. g. the function $P(S)$ defined by (5.6.1) satisfies the conditions a) and b), while c) is only satisfied in the particular case $f(x) = 1$, when $P(S) = L(S)$. — Another example is obtained in the following way. Let $x_1, x_2, \ldots$ be a sequence of points, and $p_1, p_2, \ldots$ a sequence of positive quantities. Then let us put for any Borel set S

$$P(S) = \sum_{x_\nu < S} p_\nu$$

the sum being extended to all x_ν belonging to S. It is readily seen that the set function $P(S)$ thus defined satisfies the conditions a) and b), but not c).

We are thus led to the general concept of a *non-negative and additive set function*, as a natural generalization of the Lebesgue measure $L(S)$. In the present chapter we shall first, in the paragraphs 6.2—6.4, investigate some general properties of functions of this type.

In the applications to probability theory and statistics, that will be made later in this book, a fundamental part is played by a particular class of non-negative and additive set functions. This class will be considered in the paragraphs 6.5—6.8.

In the following Chapter 7, we shall then proceed to show that the whole theory of the Lebesgue integral may be generalized by replacing, in the basic definition (5.1.1) of the Darboux sums, the Lebesgue measure $L(S)$ by a general non-negative and additive set function $P(S)$. The generalized integral obtained in this way, which is known as the *Lebesgue-Stieltjes integral*, will also be of a fundamental importance for the applications.

6.2. Set functions and point functions. — *We shall consider a set function $P(S)$ defined for all Borel sets S and satisfying the following three conditions:*

A) $P(S)$ *is non-negative*: $P(S) \geqq 0$.

B) $P(S)$ *is additive:*

$$P(S_1 + S_2 + \cdots) = P(S_1) + P(S_2) + \cdots \qquad (S_\mu S_\nu = 0 \text{ for } \mu \neq \nu).$$

C) $P(S)$ *is finite for any bounded set* S.

All set functions considered in the sequel will be assumed to satisfy these conditions.

From the conditions A) and B), which are the same as in the particular case of the Lebesgue measure $L(S)$, we directly obtain certain properties of $P(S)$, which are proved in the same way as the corresponding properties of $L(S)$. Thus if $S_1 < S_2$ we have

$$P(S_1) \leqq P(S_2). \tag{6.2.1}$$

For the empty set we have $P(0) = 0$. If $S_1, S_2, \ldots$ are sets which may or may not have common points, we have (cf 4.3.7, which obviously holds for any Borel sets)

$$(6.2.2) \qquad P(S_1 + S_2 + \cdots) \leqq P(S_1) + P(S_2) + \cdots.$$

For a *non-decreasing* sequence $S_1, S_2, \ldots$, we have (cf 4.7.1)

$$(6.2.3) \qquad \lim P(S_n) = P(\lim S_n).$$

For a *non-increasing* sequence, the same relation holds provided that $P(S_1)$ is finite.

When a set S consists of all points ξ that satisfy a certain relation, we shall often denote the value $P(S)$ simply by replacing the sign S within the brackets by the relation in question. Thus e. g. if S is the closed interval (a, b), we shall write

$$P(S) = P(a \leqq \xi \leqq b).$$

When S is the set consisting of the single point $\xi = a$, we shall write

$$P(S) = P(\xi = a),$$

and similarly in other cases.

We have called $P(S)$ a *set function*, since the argument of this function is a *set*. For an ordinary function $F(x_1, \ldots, x_n)$ of one or more variables, the argument may be considered as a *point* with the coordinates $x_1, \ldots, x_n$, and we shall accordingly often refer to such a function as a *point function*. — When a set function $P(S)$ and a constant k are given, we define a corresponding point function $F(x; k)$ by putting

$$(6.2.4) \qquad F(x; k) = \begin{cases} P(k < \xi \leqq x) & \text{for } x > k, \\ 0 & \text{»} \quad x = k, \\ -P(x < \xi \leqq k) & \text{»} \quad x < k. \end{cases}$$

Whatever the value of the constant parameter k, we then find for any finite interval (a, b)

$$F(b; k) - F(a; k) = P(a < \xi \leqq b) \geqq 0,$$

which shows that $F(x; k)$ is a non-decreasing function of x. If in the last relation we allow a to tend to $-\infty$, or b to tend to $+\infty$, or both, it follows from (6.2.3) that the same relation holds also for infinite intervals. — In the particular case when $P(S)$ is the Lebesgue measure $L(S)$, we have $F(x; k) = x - k$.

The functions $F(x; k)$ corresponding to two different values of the parameter k differ by a quantity independent of x. In fact, if $k_1 < k_2$ we obtain

$$F(x; k_1) - F(x; k_2) = P(k_1 < \xi \leqq k_2).$$

Thus if we choose an arbitrary value k_0 of k and denote the corresponding function $F(x; k_0)$ simply by $F(x)$, any other $F(x; k)$ will be of the form $F(x) + \text{const.}$

We may thus say that to any set function $P(S)$ satisfying the conditions A)—C), *there corresponds a non-decreasing point function $F(x)$ such that for any finite or infinite interval (a, b) we have*

$$F(b) - F(a) = P(a < \xi \leqq b). \tag{6.2.5}$$

$F(x)$ is uniquely determined except for an additive constant.

We now choose an arbitrary, but fixed value of the parameter k, and consider the corresponding function $F(x)$. Since $F(x)$ is non-decreasing, the two limits from above and from below

$$F(a + 0) = \lim_{x \to a+0} F(x), \qquad F(a - 0) = \lim_{x \to a-0} F(x)$$

exist for all values of a, and $F(a - 0) \leqq F(a + 0)$. According to (6.2.5) we have for $x > a$

$$F(x) - F(a) = P(a < \xi \leqq x).$$

Consider this relation for a decreasing sequence of values of x tending to the fixed value a. The corresponding half-open intervals $a < \xi \leqq x$ form a decreasing sequence of sets, the limiting set of which is empty. Thus by (6.2.3) we have $F(x) - F(a) \to 0$, i. e.

$$F(a + 0) = F(a).$$

On the other hand, for $x < a$

$$F(a) - F(x) = P(x < \xi \leqq a),$$

and a similar argument shows that

$$F(a - 0) = F(a) - P(\xi = a) \leqq F(a).$$

Thus the function $F(x)$ is always continuous to the right. For every value of x such that $P(\xi = x) > 0$, $F(x)$ has a discontinuity with the saltus $P(\xi = x)$. For every value of x such that $P(\xi = x) = 0$, $F(x)$ is continuous.

Any x such that $P(S)$ takes a positive value for the set S consisting of the single point x, is thus a discontinuity point of $F(x)$.

These points are called discontinuity points also for the set function $P(S)$, and any continuity point of $F(x)$ is also called a continuity point of $P(S)$.

The discontinuity points of $P(S)$ *and* $F(x)$ *form at most an enumerable set.* — Consider, in fact, the discontinuity points x belonging to the interval i_n defined by $n < x \leqq n+1$, and such that $P(\xi = x) > \frac{1}{c}$. Let S_ν be a set consisting of any ν of these points, say $x_1, \ldots, x_\nu$. Since S_ν is a subset of the interval i_n, we then obtain

$$P(i_n) \geqq P(S_\nu) = P(\xi = x_1) + \cdots + P(\xi = x_\nu) > \frac{\nu}{c},$$

or $\nu < c\,P(i_n)$. Thus there can at most be a finite number of points x, and if we allow c to assume the values $c = 1, 2, \ldots$, we find that the discontinuity points in i_n form at most an enumerable set. Summing over $n = 0, \pm 1, \pm 2 \ldots$, we obtain (cf 1.4) the proposition stated.

Let now $x_1, x_2, \ldots$ be all discontinuity points of $P(S)$ and $F(x)$, let X denote the set of all the points x_ν, and put $P(\xi = x_\nu) = p_\nu$. For any set S, the product set SX consists of all the points x_ν belonging to S, while the set $S - SX = SX^*$ contains all the remaining points of S. We now define two new set functions P_1 and P_2 by writing

$$P_1(S) = P(SX) = \sum_{x_\nu < S} p_\nu, \qquad P_2(S) = P(SX^*). \tag{6.2.6}$$

It is then immediately seen that P_1 and P_2 both satisfy our conditions A)—C). Further, we have $S = SX + SX^*$, and hence

$$P(S) = P_1(S) + P_2(S). \tag{6.2.7}$$

It follows from (6.2.6) that $P_1(S)$ is the sum of the saltuses p_ν for all discontinuities x_ν belonging to S. Thus $P_1(S) = 0$ for a set S which does not contain any x_ν. On the other hand, (6.2.6) shows that $P_2(S)$ is everywhere continuous, since all points belonging to X^* are continuity points of $P(S)$. Thus (6.2.7) gives a decomposition of the non-negative and additive set function $P(S)$ in a *discontinuous part* $P_1(S)$ and a *continuous part* $P_2(S)$.

If F, F_1 and F_2 are the non-decreasing point functions corresponding to P, P_1 and P_2, and if we choose the same value of the additive constant k in all three cases, we obtain from (6.2.4) and (6.2.7)

$$F(x) = F_1(x) + F_2(x). \tag{6.2.8}$$

Here, F_2 is everywhere continuous, while F_1 is a »step-function», which is constant over every interval free from the points x_ν, but has a »step» of the height p_ν in every x_ν. — It is easily seen that any non-decreasing function $F(x)$ may be represented in the form (6.2.8), as the sum of a step-function and an everywhere continuous function, both non-decreasing and uniquely determined.

6.3. Construction of a set function. — We shall now prove the following converse of theorem (6.2.5):

To any non-decreasing point function $F(x)$, that is finite for all finite x and is always continuous to the right, there corresponds a set function $P(S)$, uniquely determined for all Borel sets S and satisfying the conditions A)—C) *of* 6.2, *in such a way that the relation*

$$F(b) - F(a) = P(a < \xi \leqq b)$$

holds for any finite or infinite interval (a, b). — It is then evident that two functions $F_1(x)$ and $F_2(x)$ yield the same $P(S)$ if and only if the difference $F_1 - F_2$ is constant.

Comparing this with theorem (6.2.5) we find that, if two functions F_1 and F_2 differing by a constant are counted as identical, there is a one-to-one correspondence between the set functions $P(S)$ and the non-decreasing point functions $F(x)$.

In the first place, the non-decreasing point function $F(x)$ determines a *non-negative interval function* $P(i)$, which may be defined as *the increase of $F(x)$ over the interval i*. For any half-open interval defined by $a < x \leqq b$, $P(i)$ assumes the value $P(a < x \leqq b) = F(b) - F(a)$. For the three other types of intervals with the same end-points a and b we determine the value of $P(i)$ by a simple limit process and thus obtain

$$\begin{aligned} P(a \leqq x \leqq b) &= F(b) - F(a-0), \\ P(a < x < b) &= F(b-0) - F(a), \\ P(a < x \leqq b) &= F(b) - F(a), \\ P(a \leqq x < b) &= F(b-0) - F(a-0), \end{aligned} \tag{6.3.1}$$

so that $P(i)$ is completely determined for any interval i.

The theorem to be proved asserts that it is possible to find a non-negative and additive set function, defined for all Borel sets S, and equal to $P(i)$ in the particular case when S is an interval i.

This is, however, a straightforward generalization of the problem treated in Ch. 4. In that chapter, we have been concerned with the particular case $F(x) = x$, and with the corresponding interval function: the length $L(i)$ of an interval i. The whole theory of Lebesgue measure as developed in Ch. 4 consists in the construction of a non-negative and additive set function, defined for all Borel sets S and equal to $L(i)$ in the particular case when S is an interval i. It is now required to perform the analogous construction in the case when the length or »*L-measure*» of an interval, $L(i) = b - a$, has been replaced by the more general »*P-measure*» $P(i)$ defined by (6.3.1).

Now this may be done by exactly the same method as we have applied to the particular case treated in Ch. 4. With two minor exceptions to be discussed below, every word and every formula of Ch. 4 will hold good, if 1) the words *measure* and *measurable* are throughout replaced by *P-measure* and *P-measurable*, 2) the length $L(i) = b - a$ of an interval is replaced by the P-measure $P(i)$, and 3) the signs L and $\mathfrak{L}$ are everywhere replaced by P and $\mathfrak{P}$. In this way, strictly following the model set out in 4.1—4.5, we establish the existence of a non-negative and additive set function $P(S)$, uniquely defined for a certain class $\mathfrak{P}$ of sets that are called *P-measurable*, and equal to $P(i)$ when S is an interval i. Further, it is shown exactly as in 4.6 that the class $\mathfrak{P}$ of all P-measurable sets is an additive class and thus contains all Borel sets. Finally, we prove in the same way as in 4.7 that $P(S)$ is the only non-negative and additive set function defined for all Borel sets, which reduces to the interval function $P(i)$ when S is an interval.

In this way, our theorem is proved. Moreover, the proof explains why it will be advantageous to restrict ourselves throughout to the consideration of Borel sets. We find, in fact, that although the class of all P-measurable sets may depend on the particular function $F(x)$ which forms our starting point, it always contains the whole class $\mathfrak{B}_1$ of Borel sets. Thus any Borel set is always P-measurable, and the set function $P(S)$ corresponding to any given $F(x)$ can always be defined for all Borel sets.

It now only remains to consider the two exceptional points in Ch. 4 referred to above. The first point is very simple, and is not directly concerned with the proof of the above theorem. In 4.3 we have proved that the Lebesgue measure of an enumerable set is always equal to zero. This follows from the fact that an enumerable set may be considered as the sum of a sequence of degenerate intervals, each of which has the length zero. The corresponding proposition for P-

measure is obviously false, as soon as the function $F(x)$ has at least one discontinuity point. A degenerate interval consisting of the single point a may then well have a positive P-measure, since the first relation (6.3.1) gives

$$P(x = a) = F(a) - F(a - 0).$$

As soon as an enumerable set contains at least one discontinuity point of $F(x)$, it has thus a positive P-measure.

The second exceptional point arises in connection with the generalization of paragraph 4.1, where we have proved that the length is an additive interval function. In order to prove the same proposition for P-measure, we have to show that

$$P(i) = P(i_1) + P(i_2) + \cdots, \tag{6.3.2}$$

where i and $i_1, i_2, \ldots$ are intervals such that $i = i_1 + i_2 + \cdots$ and $i_\mu i_\nu = 0$ for $\mu \neq \nu$.

For a *continuous* $F(x)$, this is shown by Borel's lemma exactly in the same way as in the case of the corresponding relation (4.1.1), replacing throughout length by P-measure. Let us, however, note that in the course of the proof of (4.1.1) we have considered certain intervals, e.g. the interval $(a - \varepsilon,\ a + \varepsilon)$ which is chosen so as to make its *length* equal to $2\,\varepsilon$. When generalizing this proof to P-measure, we should replace this interval by $(a - h,\ a + h)$, choosing h such that the *P-measure* $F(a + h) - F(a - h)$ becomes equal to $2\,\varepsilon$.

On the other hand, if $F(x)$ is a *step-function* possessing in i the discontinuity points $x_1, x_2, \ldots$ with the respective steps $p_1, p_2, \ldots$, we have

$$P(i) = \sum_1^\infty p_\nu, \qquad P(i_n) = \sum_{x_\nu < i_n} p_\nu.$$

Since no two of the i_n have a common point, every x_ν belongs to exactly one i_n, and it then follows from the properties of convergent double series that (6.3.2) is satisfied.

Finally, by the remark made in connection with (6.2.8) any $F(x)$ is the sum of a step-function F_1 and a continuous component F_2, both non-decreasing. For both these functions, (6.3.2) holds, and thus the same relation also holds for their sum $F(x)$. — We have thus dealt with the two exceptional points arising in the course of the generalization of Ch. 4 to an arbitrary P-measure, and the proof of our theorem is hereby completed.

6.4. *P*-measure. — A set function $P(S)$ satisfying the conditions $A)$—$C)$ of 6.2 defines a *P-measure* of the set S, which constitutes a generalization of the Lebesgue measure $L(S)$. Like the latter, the P-measure is non-negative and additive.

By the preceding paragraph, the P-measure is uniquely determined for any Borel set S, if the corresponding non-decreasing point function $F(x)$ is known. Since, by 6.2, $F(x)$ is always continuous to the right, it is sufficient to know $F(x)$ in all its points of continuity.

If, for a set S, we have $P(S) = 0$, we shall say that S is a *set of P-measure zero*. By (6.2.1), any subset of S is then also of P-measure zero. The sum of a sequence of sets of P-measure zero is, by (6.2.2), itself of P-measure zero. If $F(a) = F(b)$, the half-open interval $a < x \leqq b$ is of P-measure zero.

When a certain condition is satisfied for all points belonging to some set S under consideration, except possibly certain points forming a subset of P-measure zero, we shall say (cf 5.3) that the condition is satisfied *almost everywhere* (P) or *for almost all* (P) *points* in the set S.

6.5. Bounded set functions. — For any Borel set S we have by (6.2.1) $P(S) \leqq P(\boldsymbol{R}_1)$. If $P(\boldsymbol{R}_1)$ is finite, we shall say that the set function $P(S)$ is *bounded*. When $P(S)$ is bounded, we shall always fix the additive constant in the corresponding non-decreasing point function $F(x)$ by taking $k = -\infty$ in (6.2.4), so that we have for all values of x

$$F(x) = P(\xi \leqq x). \tag{6.5.1}$$

When x tends to $-\infty$ in this relation, the set of all points $\xi \leqq x$ tends to a limit (cf 1.5), which is the empty set. Thus by (6.2.3) we have $F(-\infty) = 0$. On the other hand, when $x \to +\infty$, the set $\xi \leqq x$ tends to the whole space $\boldsymbol{R}_1$, and (6.2.3) now gives $F(+\infty) = P(\boldsymbol{R}_1)$. Since $F(x)$ is non-decreasing, we thus have for all x

$$0 \leqq F(x) \leqq P(\boldsymbol{R}_1). \tag{6.5.2}$$

6.6. Distributions. — Non-negative and additive set functions $P(S)$ such that $P(\boldsymbol{R}_1) = 1$ play a fundamental part in the applications to mathematical probability and statistics. A function $P(S)$ belonging to this class is obviously bounded, and the corresponding non-decreasing point function $F(x)$ is defined by (6.5.1), so that

$$F(x) = P(\xi \leqq x),$$

(6.6.1) $$0 \leqq F(x) \leqq 1,$$

$$F(-\infty) = 0, \qquad F(+\infty) = 1.$$

A pair of functions $P(S)$ and $F(x)$ of this type will often be concretely interpreted by means of a *distribution of mass over the one-dimensional space* $\boldsymbol{R}_1$. Let us imagine a unit of mass distributed over $\boldsymbol{R}_1$ in such a way that for every x the quantity of mass allotted to the infinite interval $\xi \leqq x$ is equal to $F(x)$. The construction of a set function $P(S)$ by means of a given point function $F(x)$, as explained in 6.3, may then be interpreted by saying that any Borel set S will carry a determined mass quantity $P(S)$. The total quantity of mass on the whole line is $P(\boldsymbol{R}_1) = 1$.

We are at liberty to define such a distribution either by the set function $P(S)$ or by the corresponding point function $F(x)$. Using a terminology adapted to the applications of these concepts that will be made in the sequel, we shall call $P(S)$ the *probability function* of the distribution, while $F(x)$ will be called the *distribution function.*

Thus a distribution function is a non-decreasing point function $F(x)$ which is everywhere continuous to the right and is such that $F(-\infty) = 0$ and $F(+\infty) = 1$. Conversely, it follows from 6.3 that any given $F(x)$ with these properties determines a unique distribution, having $F(x)$ for its distribution function.

If x_0 is a discontinuity point of $F(x)$, with a saltus equal to p_0, the mass p_0 will be concentrated in the point x_0, which is then called a *discrete mass point* of the distribution. On the other hand, if x_0 is a continuity point, the quantity of mass situated in the interval $(x - h, x + h)$ will tend to zero with h.

The ratio $\dfrac{F(x+h) - F(x-h)}{2h}$ is the mean density of the mass belonging to the interval $x - h < \xi \leqq x + h$. If the derivative $F'(x) = f(x)$ exists, the mean density tends to $f(x)$ as h tends to zero, and accordingly $f(x)$ represents the *density of mass at the point* x. In the applications to probability theory, $f(x)$ will be called the *probability density* or the *frequency function* of the distribution. Any frequency function $f(x)$ is non-negative and has the integral 1 over $(-\infty, \infty)$.

From (6.2.7) and (6.2.8) it follows that any distribution may be decomposed into a discontinuous and a continuous part by writing

$$P(S) = c_1 P_1(S) + c_2 P_2(S),$$
$$F(x) = c_1 F_1(x) + c_2 F_2(x). \tag{6.6.2}$$

Here c_1 and c_2 are non-negative constants such that $c_1 + c_2 = 1$. P_1 and F_1 denote the probability function and distribution function of a distribution, the total mass of which is concentrated in discrete mass points (thus F_1 is a step-function). P_2 and F_2, on the other hand, correspond to a distribution without any discrete mass points (thus F_2 is everywhere continuous). The constants c_1 and c_2, as well as the functions P_1, P_2, F_1 and F_2 are uniquely determined by the given distribution.

In the extreme case when $c_1 = 1$, $c_2 = 0$, the distribution function $F(x)$ is a step-function, and the whole mass of the distribution is concentrated in the discontinuity points of $F(x)$, each of which carries a mass quantity equal to the corresponding saltus. The opposite extreme is characterized by $c_1 = 0$, $c_2 = 1$, when $F(x)$ is everywhere continuous, and there is no single point carrying a positive quantity of mass.

In Ch. 15 we shall give a detailed treatment of the general theory of distributions in $\boldsymbol{R}_1$. In the subsequent Chs. 16—19, certain important special distributions will be discussed and illustrated by figures. At the present stage, the reader may find it instructive to consult Figs 4—5 (p. 169), which correspond to the case $c_1 = 1$, $c_2 = 0$, and Figs 6—7 (p. 170—171), which correspond to the case $c_1 = 0$, $c_2 = 1$.

6.7. Sequences of distributions. — An interval (a, b) will be called a *continuity interval* for a given non-negative and additive set function $P(S)$, and for the corresponding point function $F(x)$, when both extremes[1]) a and b are continuity points (cf 6.2) of $P(S)$ and $F(x)$. If two set functions agree for all intervals that are continuity intervals for both, it is easily seen that the corresponding point functions $F(x)$ differ by a constant, so that the set functions are identical.

Consider now a sequence of distributions, with the probability functions $P_1(S), P_2(S), \ldots$ and the distribution functions $F_1(x), F_2(x), \ldots$. We shall say that the sequence is *convergent*, if there is a non-negative and additive set function $P(S)$ such that $P_n(S) \to P(S)$ whenever S is a continuity interval for $P(S)$.

Since we always have $0 \leqq P_n(S) \leqq 1$, it follows that for a convergent sequence we have $0 \leqq P(S) \leqq 1$ for any continuity interval

[1]) Note that any *inner* point of the interval may be a discontinuity. The name of *continuity-bordered interval,* though longer, would perhaps be more adequate.

$S = (a, b)$. When $a \to -\infty$ and $b \to +\infty$, it then follows from (6.2.3) that $P(\boldsymbol{R}_1) \leqq 1$. — The case when $P(\boldsymbol{R}_1) = 1$ is of special interest. In this case $P(S)$ is the probability function of a certain distribution, and we shall accordingly say that our sequence *converges to a distribution*, viz. to the distribution corresponding to $P(S)$. — Usually it is only this mode of convergence that is interesting in the applications, and we shall often want a criterion that will enable us to decide whether a given sequence of distributions converges to a distribution or not. The important problem of finding such a criterion will be solved later (cf 10.4); for the present we shall only give the following preliminary proposition:

A sequence of distributions with the distribution functions $F_1(x)$, $F_2(x), \ldots$ *converges to a distribution when and only when there is a distribution function* $F(x)$ *such that* $F_n(x) \to F(x)$ *in every continuity point of* $F(x)$. — *When such a function* $F(x)$ *exists,* $F(x)$ *is the distribution function corresponding to the limiting distribution of the sequence, and we shall briefly say that the sequence* $\{F_n(x)\}$ *converges to the distribution function* $F(x)$.

We shall first show that the condition is necessary, and that the limit $F(x)$ is the distribution function of the limiting distribution. Denoting as usual by $P_n(S)$ the probability function corresponding to $F_n(x)$, we thus assume that $P_n(S)$ tends to a probability function $P(S)$ whenever S is a continuity interval (a, b) for $P(S)$. Denoting by $F(x)$ the distribution function corresponding to $P(S)$, we have to show that $F_n(x) \to F(x)$, where x is an arbitrary continuity point of $F(x)$. Since $P(\boldsymbol{R}_1) = 1$, we can choose a continuity interval $S = (a, b)$ including x such that $P(S) > 1 - \varepsilon$, where $\varepsilon > 0$ is arbitrarily small. Then $1 - \varepsilon < P(S) = F(b) - F(a) \leqq 1 - F(a)$, so that $0 \leqq F(a) < \varepsilon$. Further, we have by hypothesis $F_n(b) - F_n(a) \to F(b) - F(a) > 1 - \varepsilon$, so that for all sufficiently large n we have $F_n(b) - F_n(a) > 1 - 2\varepsilon$, or $0 \leqq F_n(a) < F_n(b) - 1 + 2\varepsilon \leqq 2\varepsilon$. Since (a, x) is a continuity interval for $P(S)$, we have by hypothesis $F_n(x) - F_n(a) \to F(x) - F(a)$. For all sufficiently large n we thus have $|F_n(x) - F(x) - F_n(a) + F(a)| < \varepsilon$, and hence according to the above $|F_n(x) - F(x)| < 3\varepsilon$. Since ε is arbitrary, it follows that $F_n(x) \to F(x)$.

Conversely, if we assume that $F_n(x)$ tends to a distribution function $F(x)$ in every continuity point of $F(x)$, and if we denote by $P(S)$ the probability function corresponding to $F(x)$, it immediately follows that $F_n(b) - F_n(a) \to F(b) - F(a)$, i. e. that $P_n(S) \to P(S)$, whenever S is a half-open continuity interval $a < x \leqq b$ for $P(S)$. Further, since $F(x)$

is never decreasing and continuous for $x=a$ and $x=b$, it follows that $F_n(a-0) \to F(a)$ and $F_n(b-0) \to F(b)$. Hence we obtain the same relation $P_n(S) \to P(S)$ whether the continuity interval $S=(a, b)$ is regarded as closed, open or half-open. Thus the proposition is proved.

In order to show by an example that a sequence of distributions may *converge* without *converging to a distribution*, we consider first the distribution which has the whole mass unit placed in the single point $x=0$. Denoting the corresponding distribution function by $\varepsilon(x)$, we have

$$\varepsilon(x)=\begin{cases} 0 & \text{for } x<0, \\ 1 & \text{for } x \geqq 0. \end{cases} \tag{6.7.1}$$

Then $\varepsilon(x-a)$ is the distribution function of a distribution which has the whole mass unit placed in the point $x=a$. Consider now the sequence of distributions defined by the distribution functions $F_n(x)=\varepsilon(x-n)$, where $n=1, 2, \ldots$. Obviously this sequence is convergent according to the above definition, since the mass contained in any finite interval tends to zero as $n \to \infty$. The limiting set function is, however, identically equal to zero, and is thus not a probability function. When $n \to \infty$, the mass in our distributions disappears, as it were, towards $+\infty$.

It might perhaps be asked why, in our convergence definition, we should not require that $P_n(S) \to P(S)$ *for every Borel set* S. It is, however, easily shown that this would be a too restrictive definition. Consider, in fact, the sequence of distributions defined by the distribution functions $\varepsilon(x-1/n)$, where $n=1, 2, \ldots$. The n:th distribution in this sequence has its whole mass unit placed in the point $x=1/n$. It is evident that any reasonable convergence definition must be such that this sequence converges to the distribution defined by (6.7.1), where the whole mass unit is placed in $x=0$. It is easily verified that the convergence definition given above satisfies this condition. If, on the other hand, we consider the set S containing the single point $x=0$, our sequence gives $P_n(S)=0$ for every n, while for the limiting distribution we have $P(S)=1$, so that $P_n(S)$ does certainly not tend to $P(S)$. Accordingly the distribution function $\varepsilon(x-1/n)$ tends to $\varepsilon(x)$ in every continuity point of $\varepsilon(x)$, i.e. for any $x \neq 0$, but not in the discontinuity point $x=0$.

6.8. A convergence theorem. — A sequence of distribution functions $F_1(x), F_2(x), \ldots$ is said to be *convergent*, if there is a non-decreasing function $F(x)$ such that $F_n(x) \to F(x)$ in every continuity point of $F(x)$. We then always have $0 \leqq F(x) \leqq 1$, but the example $F_n(x)=\varepsilon(x-n)$ considered in the preceding paragraph shows that $F(x)$ is not necessarily a distribution function. Thus a sequence $\{F_n(x)\}$ may be *convergent* without *converging to a distribution function*. — We shall now prove the following proposition that will be required in the sequel: *Every sequence* $\{F_n(x)\}$ *of distribution functions contains a convergent sub-sequence. The limit* $F(x)$ *can always be determined so as to be everywhere continuous to the right.*

Let $r_1, r_2, \ldots$ be the enumerable (cf 2.2) set of all positive and negative rational numbers, including zero, and consider the sequence $F_1(r_1), F_2(r_1), \ldots$. This is a bounded infinite sequence of real numbers, which by the Bolzano-Weierstrass theorem (2.2) has at least one limiting point. The sequence of numbers $\{F_n(r_1)\}$ thus always contains a convergent sub-sequence. The same thing may also be expressed by saying that the sequence of functions $\{F_n(x)\}$ always contains a sub-sequence Z_1 convergent for the particular value $x = r_1$. By the same argument, we find that Z_1 contains a sub-sequence Z_2 convergent for $x = r_1$ and for $x = r_2$. Repeating the same procedure, we obtain successively the sub-sequences $Z_1, Z_2, \ldots$, where Z_n is a sub-sequence of Z_{n-1}, and Z_n converges for the particular values $x = r_1, r_2, \ldots, r_n$. Forming finally the »diagonal» sequence Z consisting of the first member of Z_1, the second member of $Z_2, \ldots$, it is readily seen that Z converges for every rational value of x.

Let the members of Z be $F_{n_1}(x), F_{n_2}(x), \ldots$, and put

$$\lim_{\nu \to \infty} F_{n_\nu}(r_i) = c_i \qquad (i = 1, 2, \ldots).$$

Then $\{c_i\}$ is a bounded sequence, and since every F_{n_ν} is a non-decreasing function, it follows that we have $c_i \leqq c_k$ as soon as $r_i \leqq r_k$.

Now we define a function $F(x)$ by writing

$$F(x) = \text{lower bound of } c_i \text{ for all } r_i > x.$$

It then follows directly from the definition that $F(x)$ is a bounded non-decreasing function of x. It is also easily proved that $F(x)$ is everywhere continuous to the right. We shall now show that in every continuity point of $F(x)$ we have

$$\lim_{\nu \to \infty} F_{n_\nu}(x) = F(x), \tag{6.8.1}$$

so that the sub-sequence Z is convergent.

If x is a continuity point of $F(x)$ we can, in fact, choose $h > 0$ such that the difference $F(x + h) - F(x - h)$ is smaller than any given $\varepsilon > 0$. Let r_i and r_k be rational points situated in the open intervals $(x - h, x)$ and $(x, x + h)$ respectively, so that

$$F(x - h) \leqq c_i \leqq F(x) \leqq c_k \leqq F(x + h). \tag{6.8.2}$$

Further, for every ν we have

$$F_{n_\nu}(r_i) \leqq F_{n_\nu}(x) \leqq F_{n_\nu}(r_k). \tag{6.8.3}$$

As ν tends to infinity, $F_{n_\nu}(r_i)$ and $F_{n_\nu}(r_k)$ tend to the limits c_i and c_k respectively. The difference between these limits is, according to (6.8.2), smaller than ε, and the quantity $F(x)$ is included between c_i and c_k. Since ε is arbitrary, it follows that $F_{n_\nu}(x)$ tends to $F(x)$. Thus the sub-sequence Z is convergent, and our theorem is proved.

CHAPTER 7.

The Lebesgue-Stieltjes Integral for Functions of One Variable.

7.1. The integral of a bounded function over a set of finite *P*-measure. — In the preceding chapter, we have seen that the theory of Lebesgue measure given in Ch. 4 may be generalized by the introduction of the concept of a general non-negative and additive P-measure. We now proceed to show that an exactly analogous generalization may be applied to the theory of the Lebesgue integral developed in Ch. 5.

Let us assume that a fixed P-measure is given. This measure may be defined by a non-negative and additive set function $P(S)$, or by the corresponding non-decreasing point function $F(x)$. We have seen in the preceding chapter that these two functions are perfectly equivalent for the purpose of defining the P-measure.

Let further $g(x)$ be a given function of x, defined and bounded for all x belonging to a given set S of finite P-measure. In the same way as in 5.1, we divide S into an arbitrary finite number of parts $S_1, S_2, \ldots, S_n$, no two of which have a common point. In the basic definition (5.1.1) of the Darboux sums, we now replace L-measure by P-measure, and so obtain the generalized Darboux sums

$$(7.1.1) \qquad z = \sum_{1}^{n} m_\nu P(S_\nu), \qquad Z = \sum_{1}^{n} M_\nu P(S_\nu),$$

where, as in the previous case, m_ν and M_ν denote the lower and upper bounds of $g(x)$ in S_ν.

The further development is exactly analogous to 5.1. The upper bound of the set of all possible z-values is called the *lower integral* of $g(x)$ over S with respect to the given P-measure, while the lower bound of the set of all possible Z-values is the corresponding *upper integral.* As in 5.1 it is shown that the lower integral is at most equal to the upper integral.

If the lower and upper integrals are equal, $g(x)$ is said to be *integrable over S with respect to the given P-measure*, and the common value of the two integrals is called *the Lebesgue-Stieltjes integral of* $g(x)$ *over S with respect to the given P-measure*, and is denoted by any of the two expressions

$$\int_S g(x)\, dP(S) = \int_S g(x)\, dF(x).$$

When there is no risk of a misunderstanding, we shall write simply dP and dF instead of $dP(S)$ and $dF(x)$. Instead of integral or integrable *with respect to the given P-measure*, we shall usually say *with respect to* $P(S)$, or *with respect to* $F(x)$, according as we consider the P-measure to be defined by $P(S)$ or by $F(x)$. As long as we are dealing with functions of a single variable, we shall as a rule prefer to use $F(x)$.

In the particular case when $F(x) = x$, we have $P(S) = L(S)$, and it is evident that the above definition of the Lebesgue-Stieltjes integral reduces to the definition of the Lebesgue integral given in 5.1. Thus the Lebesgue-Stieltjes integral is obtained from the Lebesgue integral simply by replacing, in the definition of the integral, the Lebesgue measure by the more general P-measure.

All properties of the Lebesgue integral deduced in 5.2 and 5.3 are now easily generalized to the Lebesgue-Stieltjes integral, no other modification of the proofs being required than the substitution of P-measure for L-measure. Thus we find that, if $g(x)$ is bounded and B-measurable in a set S of finite P-measure, then $g(x)$ is integrable over S with respect to $P(S)$. For bounded functions and sets of finite P-measure, we further obtain the following generalizations of relations deduced in 5.3:

(7.1.2) $$\int_S (g_1(x) + g_2(x))\, dF = \int_S g_1(x)\, dF + \int_S g_2(x)\, dF,$$

(7.1.3) $$\int_S c\, g(x)\, dF = c \int_S g(x)\, dF,$$

(7.1.4) $$m\, P(S) \leqq \int_S g(x)\, dF \leqq M\, P(S),$$

(7.1.5) $$\int_{S_1+S_2} g(x)\, dF = \int_{S_1} g(x)\, dF + \int_{S_2} g(x)\, dF,$$

$$\left|\int_S g(x)\,dF\right| \leqq \int_S |g(x)|\,dF, \tag{7.1.6}$$

where c is a constant, m and M denote the lower and upper bounds of $g(x)$ in S, while S_1 and S_2 are two sets without common points. It follows from (7.1.4) that the integral of a bounded function over a set of P-measure zero is equal to zero. Thus the value of an integral is not affected if the values of the function $g(x)$ are arbitrarily changed over a set of P-measure zero.

We also have the following proposition generalizing (5.3.6): If the sequence $\{g_\nu(x)\}$ is uniformly bounded in S, and if $\lim\limits_{\nu\to\infty} g_\nu(x) = g(x)$ exists almost everywhere (P) in S, then

$$\lim_{\nu\to\infty} \int_S g_\nu(x)\,dF = \int_S g(x)\,dF. \tag{7.1.7}$$

The analogous generalizations of (5.3.7) and (5.3.8) are obtained in the same way as in 5.3.

If c_1 and c_2 are non-negative constants, we easily deduce the following relation, which has no analogue for the Lebesgue integral:

$$\int_S g(x)\,d(c_1 F_1 + c_2 F_2) = c_1 \int_S g(x)\,dF_1 + c_2 \int_S g(x)\,dF_2.$$

In the particular case when the set S consists of a single point x_0, we obtain directly from the definition

$$\int_{(x=x_0)} g(x)\,dF = g(x_0)\,P(x = x_0).$$

Consider now the case when $F(x)$ is a step-function (cf 6.2) with steps of the height p_ν in the points $x = x_\nu$, and denote the set of all points x_ν by X. Using the fact that the integral over a set of P-measure zero is equal to zero, and the generalization of (5.3.8) mentioned above, we then obtain

$$\int_S g(x)\,dF = \int_{SX} g(x)\,dF = \sum_{x_\nu \subset S} \int_{(x=x_\nu)} g(x)\,dF = \sum_{x_\nu \subset S} p_\nu\, g(x_\nu). \tag{7.1.8}$$

In the further particular case when $g(x) = 1$, we have

$$\int_S dF = \int_S dP = P(S).$$

We shall often have to consider integrals, where the function $g(x)$ is *complex-valued*, say $g(x) = a(x) + i\,b(x)$, where $a(x)$ and $b(x)$ are real and bounded in S. We then define the integral by writing

$$\int_S g(x)\,dF = \int_S a(x)\,dF + i\int_S b(x)\,dF.$$

All properties deduced above extend themselves easily to integrals of this type. For the relation (7.1.6), this extension is a little less obvious than in the other cases, and will be shown here. Put

$$\int_S g(x)\,dF = r\,e^{iv},$$

where r and v are real, and $r \geqq 0$. The real part of the quantity $|g(x)| - e^{-iv} g(x)$ is always $\geqq 0$. Consequently the real integral

$$\begin{aligned}\int_S (|g(x)| - e^{-iv} g(x))\,dF &= \int_S |g(x)|\,dF - r\\ &= \int_S |g(x)|\,dF - \left|\int_S g(x)\,dF\right|\end{aligned}$$

is $\geqq 0$, and this is equivalent to (7.1.6).

7.2. Unbounded functions and sets of infinite P-measure. — The extensions of the Lebesgue integral treated in 5.4 and 5.5 may be applied in a perfectly analogous way to the Lebesgue-Stieltjes integral. In fact, every word and every formula of 5.4 and 5.5 hold good, if Lebesgue measure is throughout replaced by P-measure, and Lebesgue integrals are replaced by Lebesgue-Stieltjes integrals with respect to $P(S)$ or $F(x)$.

Thus $g(x)$ is called *integrable with respect to* $P(S)$ — *or* $F(x)$ — over a set S of finite P-measure, if the limit (cf 5.4.1)

$$\lim_{\substack{a \to -\infty \\ b \to +\infty}} \int_S g_{a,b}(x)\,dP = \int_S g(x)\,dP = \int_S g(x)\,dF$$

exists and has a finite value. If this is the case, $|g(x)|$ is also integrable with respect to P over S.

Further, when S is of infinite P-measure[1]), $g(x)$ is called integrable with respect to P — or F — over S, if (cf 5.5) $g(x)$ is integrable

[1]) In the case of a *bounded* $P(S)$ (e.g. when $P(S)$ is a probability function, cf 6.6) there are, of course, no sets of infinite P-measure.

with respect to P — or F — over $S_{a,b}$ for all a and b, and if the limit

$$\lim_{\substack{a \to -\infty \\ b \to +\infty}} \int_{S_{a,b}} |g(x)|\, dP = \int_S |g(x)|\, dP = \int_S |g(x)|\, dF$$

exists and has a finite value. If this is the case, the limit (cf 5.5.1)

$$\lim_{\substack{a \to -\infty \\ b \to +\infty}} \int_{S_{a,b}} g(x)\, dP = \int_S g(x)\, dP = \int_S g(x)\, dF \tag{7.2.1}$$

also exists and is finite, and we shall accordingly say that the Lebesgue-Stieltjes integral of $g(x)$ with respect to P — or F — over the set S is *convergent*[1]). The limit (7.2.1) is then, by definition, the value of this integral. — If $|g(x)| < G(x)$, where $G(x)$ is integrable, then $g(x)$ is itself integrable.

The properties (7.1.2)—(7.1.6) of the Lebesgue-Stieltjes integral hold true for any functions integrable with respect to the given P-measure. In the case of a set S of infinite P-measure the relation (7.1.4) should, however, be replaced by

$$\int_S g(x)\, dF \geqq 0 \quad \text{if} \quad g(x) \geqq 0 \text{ for all } x \text{ in } S.$$

We finally have the following generalization of the proposition expressed by (7.1.7): *If* $\lim g_\nu(x) = g(x)$ *exists almost everywhere* (P) *in the set* S *of finite or infinite* P*-measure, and if* $|g_\nu(x)| < G(x)$ *for all* ν *and for all* x *in* S, *where* $G(x)$ *is integrable with respect to* F *over* S, *then* $g(x)$ *is integrable with respect to* F *over* S, *and*

$$\lim_{\nu \to \infty} \int_S g_\nu(x)\, dF = \int_S g(x)\, dF. \tag{7.2.2}$$

The generalization of the above considerations to the case of integrals with a complex-valued function $g(x)$ is obvious.

In the particular case when $F(x) = x$ all our theorems reduce, of course, to the corresponding theorems on ordinary Lebesgue integrals.

7.3. Lebesgue-Stieltjes integrals with a parameter. — We shall often be concerned with integrals of the type

$$u(t) = \int_S g(x, t)\, dF(x),$$

[1]) With respect to the terminology, the same remark should be made here as in the case of (5.5.1).

where t is a parameter, while S is a given set of finite or infinite P-measure. We shall require certain theorems concerning continuity, differentiation and integration of such integrals with respect to t. In the particular case when $F(x) = x$, these theorems reduce to theorems on Lebesgue integrals.

We assume that $g(x, t)$ is complex-valued and that, for every fixed t that will be considered, the real and imaginary parts are B-measurable functions of x which are integrable over S with respect to $F(x)$. By $G_1(x)$, $G_2(x)$, ..., we denote functions which are integrable over S with respect to $F(x)$.

I) *Continuity. — If, for almost all* (P) *values of* x *in* S, *the function* $g(x, t)$ *is continuous with respect to* t *in the point* $t = t_0$, *and if, for all* t *in some neighbourhood of* t_0, *we have* $|g(x, t)| < G_1(x)$, *then* $u(t)$ *is continuous for* $t = t_0$, *so that we have*[1])

$$\lim_{t \to t_0} \int_S g(x, t)\, dF(x) = \int_S g(x, t_0)\, dF(x). \tag{7.3.1}$$

This is a direct corollary of (7.2.2). For any sequence of values $t_1, t_2, \ldots$, belonging to the given neighbourhood and tending to t_0, the conditions of (7.2.2) are, in fact, satisfied if we take $g_\nu(x) = g(x, t_\nu)$ and $g(x) = g(x, t_0)$. Thus by (7.2.2) we have $u(t_\nu) \to u(t_0)$, and it follows that the same relation holds when t tends continuously to t_0. — When the conditions of 1) are satisfied for *all* t_0 in the open interval (a, b), it is seen that $u(t)$ is continuous in the whole interval.

II) *Differentiation. — If, for almost all* (P) *values of* x *in* S *and for a fixed value of* t, *the following conditions are satisfied:*

1) *The partial derivative* $\dfrac{\partial g(x, t)}{\partial t}$ *exists,*

2) *We have* $\left|\dfrac{g(x, t+h) - g(x, t)}{h}\right| < G_2(x)$ *for* $0 < |h| < h_0$, *where* h_0 *is independent of* x, *then*

$$u'(t) = \frac{d}{dt} \int_S g(x, t)\, dF(x) = \int_S \frac{\partial g(x, t)}{\partial t}\, dF(x). \tag{7.3.2}$$

Like the preceding proposition, this is a direct corollary of (7.2.2). For any sequence $h_1, h_2, \ldots$, where $|h_\nu| < h_0$ and h_ν tends to zero, the conditions of (7.2.2) are satisfied if we take

[1]) The theorem holds, with the same proof, even if t_0 is replaced by $+\infty$ or $-\infty$.

$$g_\nu(x) = \frac{g(x, t+h_\nu) - g(x, t)}{h_\nu} \quad \text{and} \quad g(x) = \frac{\partial g(x, t)}{\partial t}.$$

Thus

$$\frac{u(t+h) - u(t)}{h} = \int_S \frac{g(x, t+h) - g(x, t)}{h} \, dF(x) \to \int_S \frac{\partial g(x, t)}{\partial t} \, dF(x),$$

so that the derivative $u'(t)$ exists and has the value given by (7.3.2).

We remark that, if the partial derivative $\frac{\partial g}{\partial t}$ *exists and satisfies the condition* $\left|\frac{\partial g(x, t)}{\partial t}\right| < G_3(x)$ *for all* t *in the open interval* (a, b), *it follows from the relation*

$$g(x, t+h) - g(x, t) = h \left(\frac{\partial g}{\partial t}\right)_{t+\theta h}, \qquad (0 < \theta < 1),$$

that (7.3.2) *holds for all* t *in* (a, b).

Note that the condition 2) of II) is *not* satisfied e. g. if we take $F(x) = x$, $S = (-\infty, +\infty)$, and

$$g(x, t) = \begin{cases} e^{t-x} & \text{for } x \geqq t, \\ 0 & \text{for } x < t. \end{cases}$$

In this case we have

$$u(t) = \int_{-\infty}^{\infty} g(x, t) \, dx = \int_t^{\infty} e^{t-x} \, dx = 1,$$

and the application of (7.3.2) would give

$$u'(t) = \int_{-\infty}^{\infty} \frac{\partial g}{\partial t} \, dx = \int_t^{\infty} e^{t-x} \, dx = 1,$$

which is obviously false. The correct way of calculating $u'(t)$ is here, of course, to take account of the variable lower limit of the integral, thus obtaining

$$u'(t) = \int_t^{\infty} e^{t-x} \, dx - 1 = 0.$$

III) *Integration. — If, for almost all* (P) *values of* x *in* S, *the function* $g(x, t)$ *is continuous with respect to* t *in the finite open interval* (a, b) *and satisfies the condition* $|g(x, t)| < G_4(x)$ *for all* t *in* (a, b), *then*

$$\begin{aligned} \int_a^b u(t) \, dt &= \int_a^b \left[\int_S g(x, t) \, dF(x)\right] dt \\ &= \int_S \left[\int_a^b g(x, t) \, dt\right] dF(x). \end{aligned} \tag{7.3.3}$$

Further, if the above conditions are satisfied for every finite interval (a, b) *and if, in addition, we have* $\int_{-\infty}^{\infty} |g(x,t)|\,dt < G_5(x)$, *then*[1])

$$(7.3.4) \qquad \int_{-\infty}^{\infty} u(t)\,dt = \int_S \left[\int_{-\infty}^{\infty} g(x,t)\,dt\right] dF(x).$$

We consider first the case of a finite interval (a, b). For almost all (P) values of x in S, the integral

$$h(x,t) = \int_a^t g(x,\tau)\,d\tau$$

has, by (5.1.4), for all t in (a, b) the partial derivate $\frac{\partial h(x,t)}{\partial t} = g(x,t)$, so that we have $\left|\frac{\partial h(x,t)}{\partial t}\right| < G_4(x)$. Further $|h(x,t)| < (b-a)\,G_4(x)$, so that $h(x,t)$ is integrable over S with respect to $F(x)$. Writing

$$v(t) = \int_S h(x,t)\,dF(x),$$

we may now apply the remark to theorem II), and find

$$v'(t) = \int_S g(x,t)\,dF(x) = u(t).$$

By I), the function $u(t)$ is continuous in (a, b), so that the difference

$$\Delta(t) = \int_a^t u(\tau)\,d\tau - v(t)$$

has a derivative $\Delta'(t) = u(t) - v'(t) = 0$. For $t = a$, we have $h(x,a) = 0$, $v(a) = 0$, and thus $\Delta(a) = 0$. It follows that $\Delta(t) = 0$ for $a \leqq t \leqq b$, and thus in particular $\Delta(b) = 0$, which is identical with (7.3.3).

When the conditions of the second part of the theorem are satisfied, (7.3.3) holds for any finite (a, b), and we have

---

[1]) It is evident how the conditions should be modified when we want to integrate $u(t)$ over (a, ∞) or $(-\infty, b)$.

$$\int_a^b |u(t)|\,dt \leqq \int_a^b \left[\int_S |g(x,t)|\,dF(x)\right] dt = \int_S \left[\int_a^b |g(x,t)|\,dt\right] dF(x)$$
$$\leqq \int_S G_5(x)\,dF(x).$$

Thus the integral $\int_{-\infty}^{\infty} |u(t)|\,dt$ is convergent. If, in the relation (7.3.3), we allow a and b to tend to $-\infty$ and $+\infty$ respectively, it follows that the first member tends to the first member of (7.3.4). An application of (7.2.2) shows that, at the same time, the second member of (7.3.3) tends to the second member of (7.3.4). Thus (7.3.4) is proved.

The theorems proved in this paragraph show that, subject to certain conditions, analytical operations such as limit passages, differentiations and integrations with respect to a parameter may be performed *under a sign of integration.*

7.4. Lebesgue-Stieltjes integrals with respect to a distribution. — If $P(S)$ is the probability function of a distribution (cf 6.6), the integral

$$\int_{R_1} g(x)\,dP = \int_{-\infty}^{\infty} g(x)\,dP = \int_{-\infty}^{\infty} g(x)\,dF \tag{7.4.1}$$

may be concretely, though somewhat vaguely, interpreted as a weighted mean of the values of $g(x)$ for all values of x, the weights being furnished by the mass quantities dP or dF situated in the neighbourhood of each point x. The sum of all weights is unity, since we have

$$\int_{-\infty}^{\infty} dP = \int_{-\infty}^{\infty} dF = P(\mathbf{R}_1) = 1.$$

Every bounded and B-measurable $g(x)$ is integrable with respect to P (or F) over $(-\infty, \infty)$.

If the mass distribution is represented as the sum of two components according to (6.6.2), the integral (7.4.1) becomes

$$\int_{-\infty}^{\infty} g(x)\,dF = c_1 \int_{-\infty}^{\infty} g(x)\,dF_1 + c_2 \int_{-\infty}^{\infty} g(x)\,dF_2,$$

where the first term of the second member reduces to a sum over the discrete mass points of the distribution, as shown in (7.1.8).

If, for a positive integer ν, the function x^ν is integrable with respect to $F(x)$ over $(-\infty, \infty)$, the integral

$$\alpha_\nu = \int_{-\infty}^{\infty} x^\nu \, d\, F(x)$$

is called the *moment of order* ν, or simply the *ν:th moment*, of the distribution, and we say that the ν:th moment *exists*. It is then easily seen that any moment of order $\nu' < \nu$ also exists.

It is known from elementary mechanics that the first order moment α_1 is the abscissa of the *centre of gravity* of the mass in the distribution, while the second order moment α_2 represents the *moment of inertia* of the mass with respect to a perpendicular axis through the point $x = 0$. — The moments of a distribution will play an important part in the applications made later in this book.

If, for some $k > 0$, the distribution function $F(x)$ satisfies the conditions (with respect to the notations, cf 12.1)

$$F(x) = O(|x|^{-k}) \qquad \text{when } x \to -\infty,$$
$$1 - F(x) = O(x^{-k}) \qquad \text{when } x \to +\infty,$$

then any moment of order $\nu < k$ exists. In order to prove this, it is according to 7.2 sufficient to show that the integral of $|x|^\nu$ with respect to $F(x)$ over an interval (a, b) is less than a constant independent of a and b. Now we have by hypothesis

$$\int_{2^{r-1}}^{2^r} |x|^\nu \, d\, F(x) \leqq 2^{r\nu} (F(2^r) - F(2^{r-1}))$$
$$\leqq 2^{r\nu} (1 - F(2^{r-1})) < \frac{C}{2^{r(k-\nu)}},$$

where C is independent of r, and a similar relation for the integral over $(-2^r, -2^{r-1})$. Summing over $r = 1, 2, \ldots$ and adding the integral over $(-1, 1)$, which is $\leqq 1$, we find for any interval (a, b)

$$\int_a^b |x|^\nu \, d\, F(x) < 1 + \frac{2\,C}{2^{k-\nu} - 1},$$

and thus the ν:th moment exists.

7.5. The Riemann-Stieltjes integral. — Consider the Lebesgue-Stieltjes integral

$$\int_I g(x)\, d\, F(x) \tag{7.5.1}$$

in the particular case when I is a finite half-open interval

$$I = (a < x \leqq b),$$

while $g(x)$ is continuous in I and tends to a finite limit as $x \to a + 0$.

We divide I in n sub-intervals $i_\nu = (x_{\nu-1} < x \leqq x_\nu)$ by means of the points

$$a = x_0 < x_1 < \cdots < x_n = b$$

and consider the Darboux sums (7.1.1) which correspond to the division $I = i_1 + \cdots + i_n$. We then obtain

$$(7.5.2) \qquad \begin{aligned} Z &= \sum_1^n M_\nu [F(x_\nu) - F(x_{\nu-1})], \\ z &= \sum_1^n m_\nu [F(x_\nu) - F(x_{\nu-1})], \end{aligned}$$

m_ν and M_ν being the lower and upper bounds of $g(x)$ in i_ν. Now let $\varepsilon > 0$ be given. By hypothesis we can then find δ such that $M_\nu - m_\nu < \varepsilon$ as soon as $x_\nu - x_{\nu-1} < \delta$. Choosing n and the x_ν such that $x_\nu - x_{\nu-1} < \delta$ for all ν, we then have

$$Z - z < \varepsilon [F(b) - F(a)].$$

Thus when n tends to infinity, and at the same time the maximum length of the sub-intervals i_ν tends to zero, Z and z tend to a common limit which must be equal to the integral (7.5.1):

$$(7.5.3) \qquad \lim_{n\to\infty} Z = \lim_{n\to\infty} z = \int_a^b g(x)\, dF(x).$$

Thus in the particular case here considered the simple expression (7.5.2) of the Darboux sums is sufficient to determine the value of the Lebesgue-Stieljes integral. If we put $F(x) = x$, these expressions become identical with the Darboux sums considered in the theory of the ordinary Riemann integral. Accordingly, the integral defined by (7.5.3) is called a *Riemann-Stieltjes integral*. It follows from the above that, when this integral exists, it always has the same value as the corresponding Lebesgue-Stieltjes integral.

If, in every sub-interval i_ν, we take an arbitrary point ξ_ν, we obviously have

$$(7.5.4) \qquad \lim_{n\to\infty} \sum_1^n g(\xi_\nu) [F(x_\nu) - F(x_{\nu-1})] = \int_a^b g(x)\, dF(x),$$

since the sum in the first member is included between z and Z.

The Riemann-Stieltjes integral (7.5.3) exists even in the more general case when $g(x)$ is bounded in (a, b) and has at most a finite number of discontinuity points r_ν, *provided that* $F(x)$ *is continuous in every* r_ν. We can, in fact, then surround each r_ν by a sub-interval i_ν which gives an arbitrarily small contribution to the sums z and Z.

In the particular case when $F(x)$ is continuous everywhere in (a, b) and has a continuous derivative $F'(x)$, except at most in a finite number of points, we have for every i_ν not containing any of the exceptional points

$$F(x_\nu) - F(x_{\nu-1}) = (x_\nu - x_{\nu-1}) F'(\xi_\nu),$$

where ξ_ν is a point belonging to i_ν. By means of (7.5.4) it follows that in this case the integral (7.5.3) reduces to an ordinary Riemann integral:

$$\int_a^b g(x)\, d\, F(x) = \int_a^b g(x)\, F'(x)\, d\, x. \tag{7.5.5}$$

All these properties immediately extend themselves to the case of a complex-valued function $g(x)$, and also to infinite intervals (a, b) subject to the condition that $g(x)$ is integrable over (a, b) with respect to $F(x)$. If this condition is satisfied, we have e.g. the following generalization of (7.5.4):

$$\lim_{n \to \infty} \sum_1^n g(\xi_\nu)\,[F(x_\nu) - F(x_{\nu-1})] = \int_{-\infty}^{\infty} g(x)\, d\, F(x), \tag{7.5.6}$$

where as before the maximum length of the sub-intervals $(x_{\nu-1}, x_\nu)$ tends to zero as $n \to \infty$, while at the same time $x_0 \to -\infty$ and $x_n \to +\infty$.

Suppose now that two non-decreasing functions $F(x)$ and $G(x)$ are given, which are both continuous in the closed interval (a, b), except at most for a finite number of discontinuity points, which are all inner points of (a, b). We further suppose that no point in (a, b) is a discontinuity point for *both* functions F and G. Choosing the sub-intervals so that no x_ν is a discontinuity point, we then have

$$\begin{aligned} F(b)\, G(b) - F(a)\, G(a) &= \sum_1^n [F(x_\nu)\, G(x_\nu) - F(x_{\nu-1})\, G(x_{\nu-1})] \\ &= \sum_1^n F(x_\nu)\,[G(x_\nu) - G(x_{\nu-1})] + \sum_1^n G(x_{\nu-1})\,[F(x_\nu) - F(x_{\nu-1})]. \end{aligned}$$

The two terms in the last expression are included between the lower and upper Darboux sums corresponding to the integrals $\int F\,d\,G$ and $\int G\,d\,F$ respectively. Passing to the limit, we thus obtain the *formula of partial integration*:

$$\int_a^b d(F\,G) = \int_a^b F\,d\,G + \int_a^b G\,d\,F. \tag{7.5.7}$$

Finally, we consider a sequence of distribution functions (cf 6.7) $F_1(x), F_2(x), \ldots$, which converge to a non-decreasing function $F(x)$ in every continuity point of the latter. (By 6.7, the limit $F(x)$ is not necessarily a distribution function.) Let $g(x)$ be everywhere continuous. For any finite interval (a, b) such that a and b are continuity points of $F(x)$, an inspection of the Darboux sums that determine the integrals then shows that we have

$$\lim_{n\to\infty} \int_a^b g(x)\,d\,F_n(x) = \int_a^b g(x)\,d\,F(x). \tag{7.5.8}$$

Suppose further that, to any $\varepsilon > 0$, we can find A such that

$$\int_{-\infty}^{-A} |\,g(x)\,|\,d\,F_n(x) + \int_A^{\infty} |\,g(x)\,|\,d\,F_n(x) < \varepsilon$$

for $n = 1, 2, \ldots$ We may then always choose A such that $F(x)$ is continuous for $x = A$, and by means of (7.5.8) we find that

$$\int_A^B g(x)\,|\,d\,F_n(x) \to \int_A^B |\,g(x)\,|\,d\,F(x)$$

where $B > A$ is another continuity point of $F(x)$. Thus the last integral is $\leqq \varepsilon$ for any $B > A$, and for the integral over $(-B, -A)$ there is a corresponding relation. It follows that $g(x)$ is integrable over $(-\infty, \infty)$ with respect to $F(x)$. If, in (7.5.8), we take $a = -A$ and $b = +A$, each integral will differ by at most $2\,\varepsilon$ from the corresponding integral over $(-\infty, \infty)$. Since ε is arbitrary, we then have

$$\lim_{n\to\infty} \int_{-\infty}^{\infty} g(x)\,d\,F_n(x) = \int_{-\infty}^{\infty} g(x)\,d\,F(x). \tag{7.5.9}$$

This relation is immediately extended to complex-valued functions $g(x)$.

References to chapters 4—7. — The classical theory of integration received its final form in a famous paper by Riemann (1854). About 1900, the theory of the measure of sets of points was founded by Borel and Lebesgue, and the latter introduced the concept of integral which bears his name. The integral with respect to a non-decreasing function $F(x)$ had been considered already in 1894 by Stieltjes, and in 1913 Radon (Ref. 205) investigated the general properties of additive set functions, and the theory of integration with respect to such functions.

There are a great number of treatises on modern integration theory. The reader is particularly referred to the books of Lebesgue himself (Ref. 23), de la Vallée Poussin (Ref. 40) and Saks (Ref. 23). De la Vallée Poussin gives an excellent introduction to the theory of the Lebesgue integral, and contains also some chapters on additive set functions, while the two other books go deeper into the more difficult parts of the theory.

CHAPTER 8.

LEBESGUE MEASURE AND OTHER ADDITIVE SET FUNCTIONS IN R_n.

8.1. Lebesgue measure in R_n. — The elementary measure of extension of a one-dimensional interval is the *length* of the interval. The corresponding measure for a two-dimensional interval (cf 3.1) is the *area*, and for a three-dimensional interval the *volume* of the interval.

Generally, if i denotes the finite n-dimensional interval defined by the inequalities

$$a_\nu \leqq x_\nu \leqq b_\nu \qquad (\nu = 1, 2, \ldots, n),$$

we shall define the *n-dimensional volume of the interval i* as the non-negative quantity

$$L(i) = \prod_1^n (b_\nu - a_\nu).$$

For an open or half-open interval with the same extremes a_ν and b_ν, the volume will be the same as in the case of the closed interval. A degenerate interval has always the volume zero. For an infinite non-degenerate interval, we put $L(i) = +\infty$.

The Borel lemma (cf 4.1) is directly extended to n dimensions, and by an easy generalization of the proof of (4.1.1) we find that *$L(i)$ is an additive function of the interval.*

In the same way as in 4.2, we now ask if a measure with the same fundamental properties as $L(i)$ can be defined even for a more general class of sets than intervals. — We thus want to find a non-negative and additive set function $L(S)$, defined for all Borel sets S in R_n, and taking the value $L(i)$ as soon as S is an interval i. In 4.3—4.7, we have given a detailed treatment of this problem in the case $n=1$, and we have seen that there is a unique solution, viz. the Lebesgue measure in R_1. The case of a general n requires no modification whatever. Every word and every formula of 4.3—4.7

hold true, if linear sets are throughout replaced by n-dimensional ones, and the length of a linear interval is replaced by the n-dimensional volume.

It thus follows that there is a non-negative and additive set function $L(S)$, *uniquely defined for all Borel sets* S *in* $\boldsymbol{R}_n$ *and such that, in the particular case when* S *is an interval,* $L(S)$ *is equal to the* n*-dimensional volume of the interval.* $L(S)$ *is called the* n*-dimensional Lebesgue measure*[1]) *of* S.

8.2. Non-negative additive set functions in $\boldsymbol{R}_n$. — In the same way as in the one-dimensional case, we may also for $n > 1$ consider non-negative and additive set functions $P(S)$ of a more general kind than the n-dimensional Lebesgue measure $L(S)$.

We shall consider set functions $P(S)$ defined for all Borel sets S in $\boldsymbol{R}_n$ and satisfying the conditions A)—C) of 6.2. It is immediately seen that these conditions do not contain any reference to the number of dimensions. The relations (6.2.1)—(6.2.3) then obviously hold for any number of dimensions.

With any set function $P(S)$ of this type we may associate a point function $F(\boldsymbol{x}) = F(x_1, \ldots, x_n)$, in a similar way as shown by (6.2.4) for the one-dimensional case. The direct generalization of (6.2.4) is, however, somewhat cumbersome for a general n, and we shall content ourselves to develop the formulae for the particular case of a *bounded* $P(S)$, where the definition of the associated point function may be simplified in the way shown for the one-dimensional case by (6.5.1). This will be done in the following paragraph.

As in the case $n = 1$, any non-negative and additive set function $P(S)$ in $\boldsymbol{R}_n$ defines an n-dimensional *P-measure* of the set S, which constitutes a generalization of the n-dimensional Lebesgue measure $L(S)$. The remarks of 6.4 on sets of P-measure zero apply to sets in any number of dimensions.

---

[1]) In order to be quite precise, we ought to adopt a notation showing explicitly the number of dimensions, e. g. by writing $L_n(S)$ instead of $L(S)$. There should, however, be no risk of misunderstanding, if it is always borne in mind that the measure of a given point set is relative to the space in which it is considered. Thus if we consider e. g. the interval $(0, 1)$ on a straight line as a set of points in $\boldsymbol{R}_1$, its (one-dimensional) measure has the value 1. If, on the other hand, we take the line as x-axis in a plane, and consider the same interval as a set of points in $\boldsymbol{R}_2$, we are concerned with a degenerate interval, the (two-dimensional) measure of which is equal to zero.

8.3. Bounded set functions. — When $P(\mathbf{R}_n)$ is finite, we shall say (cf 6.5) that $P(S)$ is *bounded*. We have then always $P(S) \leqq P(\mathbf{R}_n)$. For a bounded $P(S)$ we define, in generalization of (6.5.1):

$$F(\boldsymbol{x}) = F(x_1, \ldots, x_n) = P(\xi_1 \leqq x_1, \ldots, \xi_n \leqq x_n). \tag{8.3.1}$$

Evidently $F(\boldsymbol{x})$ is, in each variable x_ν, a non-decreasing function which is everywhere continuous to the right, and we have for all $\boldsymbol{x}$ (cf 6.5.2)

$$0 \leqq F(\boldsymbol{x}) \leqq P(\mathbf{R}_n).$$

In the one-dimensional case, the value of $P(S)$ for a half-open interval i_1 defined by $a < x \leqq a + h$ is, by (6.2.5), given by a first order difference of $F(x)$:

$$P(i_1) = \Delta F(a) = F(a + h) - F(a).$$

This formula may be generalized to the case of an arbitrary n. Consider first a set function $P(S)$ in $\mathbf{R}_2$, and a two-dimensional interval i_2 defined by $a_1 < x_1 \leqq a_1 + h_1$, $a_2 < x_2 \leqq a_2 + h_2$. We then have

$$\begin{aligned} P(i_2) &= \Delta_2 F(a_1, a_2) \\ &= F(a_1 + h_1, a_2 + h_2) - F(a_1, a_2 + h_2) - F(a_1 + h_1, a_2) + F(a_1, a_2). \end{aligned} \tag{8.3.2}$$

This will be clear from Fig. 2. If $M_1, \ldots, M_4$ are the values assumed by $P(S)$ for each of the rectangular domains indicated in the figure, the additive property of $P(S)$ gives

$$M_4 = (M_1 + M_2 + M_3 + M_4) - (M_1 + M_2) - (M_1 + M_3) + M_1,$$

and according to the definition (8.3.1) of $F(\boldsymbol{x})$, this is identical with (8.3.2).

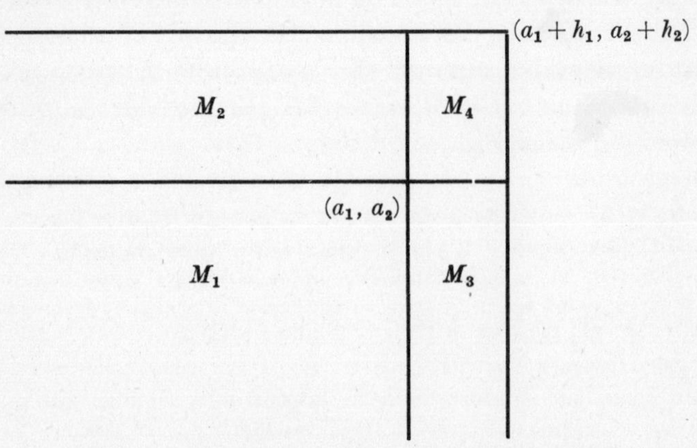

Fig. 2. Set functions and point functions in $\mathbf{R}_2$.

The generalization to an arbitrary n is immediate. If $P(S)$ is a set function $\boldsymbol{R}_n$, and if i_n is the half-open interval defined by $a_\nu < x_\nu \leqq a_\nu + h_\nu$ for $\nu = 1, 2, \ldots, n$, we have

$$
\begin{aligned}
P(i_n) &= \Delta_n F(a_1, \ldots, a_n) \\
&= F(a_1 + h_1, \ldots, a_n + h_n) \\
&\quad - F(a_1, a_2 + h_2, \ldots, a_n + h_n) \\
&\qquad\qquad - \cdots - F(a_1 + h_1, \ldots, a_{n-1} + h_{n-1}, a_n) \\
&\quad + \cdots\cdots\cdots\cdots\cdots\cdots\cdots\cdots \\
&\quad \cdots\cdots\cdots\cdots\cdots\cdots\cdots\cdots \\
&\quad + (-1)^n F(a_1, \ldots, a_n).
\end{aligned}
\tag{8.3.3}
$$

To any bounded $P(S)$ in $\boldsymbol{R}_n$, there thus corresponds a point function $F(x_1, \ldots, x_n)$ which, in each x_ν, is non-decreasing and continuous to the right, and is such that the n:th difference $\Delta_n F$ as defined by (8.3.3) is always non-negative. — Conversely, a generalization of the argument of 6.3 shows that any given F with these properties uniquely determines a set function $P(S)$ satisfying the conditions A)—C) of 6.2, which for any interval i_n assumes the value given by (8.3.3).

When one of the variables in F, say x_ν, tends to $-\infty$, while all the others remain fixed, it is shown as in 6.5 that F tends to zero. Similarly, when all the x_ν tend simultaneously to $+\infty$, F tends to $P(\boldsymbol{R}_n)$.

When all the variables in F except one, say x_ν, tend to $+\infty$, F will tend to a limit, which is a bounded non-decreasing function $F_\nu(x_\nu)$ of the remaining variable x_ν. By 6.2, the function $F_\nu(x_\nu)$ has at most an enumerable number of discontinuity points $z'_\nu, z''_\nu, \ldots$ Let us consider these as *excluded values* for the variable x_ν, which is thus only allowed to assume values different from $z'_\nu, z''_\nu, \ldots$ In the same way, each variable $x_1, \ldots, x_n$ has its own finite or enumerable set of excluded values. — *For any non-excluded point $\boldsymbol{x} = (x_1, \ldots, x_n)$, the function F is continuous.* This follows from the inequality

$$
\begin{aligned}
|F(\boldsymbol{x} + \boldsymbol{h}) - F(\boldsymbol{x})| &\leqq F(\boldsymbol{x} + |\boldsymbol{h}|) - F(\boldsymbol{x} - |\boldsymbol{h}|) \leqq \\
&\leqq \sum_1^n \left(F_\nu(x_\nu + |h_\nu|) - F_\nu(x_\nu - |h_\nu|)\right),
\end{aligned}
$$

where $\boldsymbol{h} = (h_1, \ldots, h_n)$ is an arbitrary point, while $|\boldsymbol{h}|$ denotes here the point $(|h_1|, \ldots, |h_n|)$, and the sums and differences $\boldsymbol{x} + \boldsymbol{h}$ etc. are formed according to the rules of vector addition (cf 11.1—11.2). An inspection of Fig. 2 will help to make this inequality clear.

An n-dimensional interval such that none of the extremes a_ν and b_ν is an excluded value for the corresponding variable x_ν is called a *continuity interval* of $P(S)$. The value assumed by $P(S)$ when S is a continuity interval will obviously change in a continuous way for small variations in the a_ν and b_ν. If two bounded set functions in $\boldsymbol{R}_n$ agree for all intervals that are continuity intervals for both, it follows (cf 6.7) that the set functions are identical.

8.4. Distributions. — Non-negative and additive set functions $P(S)$ such that $P(\boldsymbol{R}_n) = 1$ play, like the corresponding one-dimensional functions (cf 6.6), a fundamental part in the applications. By the preceding paragraph, the point function $F(\boldsymbol{x})$ associated with a set function $P(S)$ of this class satisfies the relations

$$
\begin{aligned}
&F(\boldsymbol{x}) = F(x_1, \ldots, x_n) = P(\xi_1 \leqq x_1, \ldots, \xi_n \leqq x_n),\\
&0 \leqq F(\boldsymbol{x}) \leqq 1, \qquad \Delta_n F \geqq 0,\\
&F(-\infty, x_2, \ldots, x_n) = \cdots = F(x_1, \ldots, x_{n-1}, -\infty) = 0,\\
&F(+\infty, \ldots, +\infty) = 1.
\end{aligned}
\tag{8.4.1}
$$

As in the one-dimensional case, the functions $P(S)$ and $F(\boldsymbol{x})$ will be interpreted by means of a *distribution of a unit of mass* over the space $\boldsymbol{R}_n$, such that every Borel set S carries the mass $P(S)$. As in 6.6, we are at liberty to define the distribution either by the set function $P(S)$ or by the corresponding point function $F(\boldsymbol{x})$, which represents the quantity of mass allotted to the infinite interval $\xi_1 \leqq x_1, \ldots, \xi_n \leqq x_n$. The difference between these two equivalent modes of definition is, of course, only formal, and it will be a matter of convenience to decide which of them should be used in a given case. — As in 6.6, $P(S)$ will be called the *probability function*, and $F(\boldsymbol{x})$ the *distribution function* of the distribution.

Thus a distribution function is a function $F(\boldsymbol{x}) = F(x_1, \ldots, x_n)$ which, in each x_ν, is non-decreasing and everywhere continuous to the right, and is such that the n:th difference as defined by (8.3.3) is always non-negative. Conversely, it follows from the preceding paragraph that any given F with these properties is the distribution function of a uniquely determined distribution in $\boldsymbol{R}_n$.

If the set which consists of the single point $x = a$ carries a positive quantity of mass, a is a *discrete mass point* of the distribution. The set of all discrete mass points of a distribution is enumerable, as we find by a direct generalization of the corresponding proof in 6.2. Obviously any discrete mass point a is a discontinuity point for the distribution function F. In the case $n = 1$ we have seen in 6.6 that, conversely, F is continuous in all points x except the discrete mass points. *This is generally not true when* $n > 1$. In fact, in a multi-dimensional space the mass may be distributed on lines, surfaces or hypersurfaces in such a way that there is no single point carrying a positive quantity of mass, while still F may be discontinuous in certain points. In the preceding paragraph we have, however, seen that it is possible to exclude certain values for each variable x_ν, so that the function F will be continuous in all »non-excluded» points.

Consider e. g. a distribution of a mass unit with uniform density over the interval $(0, 1)$ of the x_2-axis in the plane of the variables x_1, x_2. Obviously this distribution has no discrete mass points, and still the corresponding distribution function $F(x_1, x_2)$ is discontinuous in every point $(0, x_2)$ with $x_2 > 0$. Accordingly it will be seen that the function $F_1(x_1) = \lim_{x_2 \to +\infty} F(x_1, x_2)$ discussed in the preceding paragraph is here discontinuous for $x_1 = 0$, which is the only »excluded» value for x_1. For x_2 there are no excluded values, and accordingly $F(x_1, x_2)$ is continuous in any point (x_1, x_2) with $x_1 \neq 0$.

We further see that any distribution in $\boldsymbol{R}_n$ can be uniquely represented in the form (6.6.2), as the sum of two components, the first of which corresponds to a distribution with its whole mass concentrated in discrete mass points, while the second component corresponds to a distribution without discrete mass points. It follows from the above that, when $n > 1$, we cannot assert that the distribution function F_2 of the second component is everywhere continuous.

Let I denote the n-dimensional interval defined by

$$x_\nu - h_\nu < \xi_\nu \leqq x_\nu + h_\nu$$

for $\nu = 1, 2, \ldots, n$. The ratio

$$\frac{P(I)}{L(I)} = \frac{\Delta_n F}{2^n h_1 h_2 \cdots h_n},$$

where the difference $\Delta_n F$ is defined as in (8.3.3), represents the average density of the mass in the interval I. If the partial derivative

$$f(x_1, \ldots, x_n) = \frac{\partial^n F}{\partial x_1 \partial x_2 \cdots \partial x_n}$$

exists, the average density will tend to this value as all the h_ν tend to zero, and accordingly $f(x_1, \ldots, x_n)$ represents the *density of mass at the point* $\boldsymbol{x}$. As in the one-dimensional case, this function will be called the *probability density* or the *frequency function* of the distribution.

Let $F(x_1, \ldots, x_n)$ be the distribution function of a given distribution. When all the variables except x_ν tend to $+\infty$, F will (cf 8.3) tend to a limit $F_\nu(x_\nu)$ which is a distribution function in x_ν. We have, e. g., $F_1(x_1) = F(x_1, +\infty, \ldots, +\infty)$. The function $F_\nu(x_\nu)$ defines a one-dimensional distribution, which will be called the *marginal distribution* of x_ν. We may obtain a concrete representation of this marginal distribution by allowing every mass particle in the original n-dimensional distribution to move in a direction perpendicular to the axis of x_ν, until it arrives at a point of this axis. When, finally, the whole mass is in this way projected on the axis of x_ν, a one-dimensional distribution is generated on the axis, and this is the marginal distribution of x_ν. Each variable x_ν has, of course, its own marginal distribution, that may be different from the marginal distributions of the other variables.

Let us now take any group of $k < n$ variables, say $x_1, \ldots, x_k$, and allow the $n-k$ remaining variables to tend to $+\infty$. Then F will tend to a distribution function in $x_1, \ldots, x_k$, which defines the *k-dimensional marginal distribution* of this group of variables. The distribution may be concretely represented by a projection of the mass in the original n-dimensional distribution on the k-dimensional subspace (cf 3.5) of the variables $x_1, \ldots, x_k$. — Let P be the probability function of the n-dimensional distribution, while $P_{1, \ldots, k}$ is the probability function of the marginal distribution of $x_1, \ldots, x_k$. Let, further, S' denote any set in the k-dimensional subspace of $x_1, \ldots, x_k$, while S is the cylinder set (cf 3.5) of all points $\boldsymbol{x}$ in $\boldsymbol{R}_n$ that are projected on the subspace in a point belonging to S'. Obviously we then have

$$P_{1, \ldots, k}(S') = P(S), \tag{8.4.2}$$

which is the analytical expression of the projection of the mass in the original n-dimensional distribution on the k-dimensional subspace of the variables $x_1, \ldots, x_k$.

The theory of distributions in $\boldsymbol{R}_n$ will be further developed in Chs. 21—24.

8.5. Sequences of distributions. — As in the one-dimensional case (cf 6.7), we shall say that a sequence of distributions in $\boldsymbol{R}_n$ is *con-*

vergent, when the corresponding probability functions converge to a non-negative and additive set function $P(S)$, in every continuity interval of the latter. If, in addition, the limit $P(S)$ is a probability function, i. e. if $P(\boldsymbol{R}_n) = 1$, we shall say that the sequence *converges to a distribution*. From the point of view of the applications, it is generally only the latter mode of convergence that is important.

For a sequence which is convergent without converging to a distribution, we have $P(\boldsymbol{R}_n) < 1$, which may be interpreted (cf the example discussed in 6.7) by saying that a certain part of the mass in our distributions »escapes towards infinity» when we pass to the limit.

A straightforward generalization of 6.7 will show that a sequence of distributions converges to a distribution when and only when the corresponding distribution functions $F_1, F_2, \ldots$ tend to a distribution function F in all »non-excluded» (cf 8.3) points of the latter. A further criterion for deciding whether a given sequence of distributions converges to a distribution or not will be given in 10.7.

As in 6.8, we shall further say that a sequence of distribution functions $F_1, F_2, \ldots$ is convergent, if there is a function F, non-decreasing in each x_ν, such that $F_n \to F$ in every »non-excluded» point of F. We then always have $0 \leqq F \leqq 1$, but according to the above F is not necessarily a distribution function. We then have the following generalization of the proposition proved in 6.8 for the one-dimensional case: *Every sequence of distribution functions contains a convergent sub-sequence.* — This may be proved by a fairly straightforward generalization of the proof in 6.8, and we shall not give the proof here.

8.6. Distributions in a product space. — Consider two spaces $\boldsymbol{R}_m$ and $\boldsymbol{R}_n$, with the variable points $\boldsymbol{x} = (x_1, \ldots, x_m)$ and $\boldsymbol{y} = (y_1, \ldots, y_n)$ respectively. Suppose that in each space a distribution is given, and let P_1 and F_1 denote the probability function and the distribution function of the distribution in $\boldsymbol{R}_m$, while P_2 and F_2 have the analogous significance for the distribution in $\boldsymbol{R}_n$.

In the *product space* (cf 3.5) $\boldsymbol{R}_m \cdot \boldsymbol{R}_n$ of $m + n$ dimensions, we denote the variable point by $\boldsymbol{z} = (\boldsymbol{x}, \boldsymbol{y}) = (x_1, \ldots, x_m, y_1, \ldots, y_n)$. If S_1 and S_2 are sets in $\boldsymbol{R}_m$ and $\boldsymbol{R}_n$ respectively, we denote by S the *rectangle set* (cf 3.5) of all points $\boldsymbol{z} = (\boldsymbol{x}, \boldsymbol{y})$ in the product space such that $\boldsymbol{x} < S_1$ and $\boldsymbol{y} < S_2$.

It is almost evident that we can always find an infinite number of distributions in the product space, such that for each of them the marginal distributions (cf 8.4) corresponding to the subspaces $\boldsymbol{R}_m$ and $\boldsymbol{R}_n$ coincide with the two given distributions in these spaces. Among these distributions in the product space we shall particularly note one, which is of special importance for the applications. This is the distribution given by the following theorem.

There is one and only one distribution in the product space $\boldsymbol{R}_m \cdot \boldsymbol{R}_n$ *such that*

(8.6.1) $$P(S) = P_1(S_1)\, P_2(S_2)$$

for all rectangle sets S *defined by the relations* $\boldsymbol{x} < S_1$ *and* $\boldsymbol{y} < S_2$. *This is the distribution defined by the distribution function*

8.6.2) $$F(\boldsymbol{z}) = F_1(\boldsymbol{x})\, F_2(\boldsymbol{y})$$

for all points $\boldsymbol{z} = (\boldsymbol{x}, \boldsymbol{y})$.

We first observe that $F(\boldsymbol{z})$ as given by (8.6.2) is certainly a distribution function in $\boldsymbol{R}_m \cdot \boldsymbol{R}_n$, since it satisfies the characteristic properties of a distribution function given in 8.4. Consider now the distribution defined by $F(\boldsymbol{z})$. By means of (8.3.3) it follows that we have

$$P(I) = P_1(I_1)\, P_2(I_2)$$

for any half-open interval $I = (I_1, I_2)$ defined by inequalities of the type $a_\nu < x_\nu \leqq b_\nu$, $c_\nu < y_\nu \leqq d_\nu$. Now any Borel set S_1 may be formed from intervals I_1 by repetitions of the operations of addition and subtraction. (By (1.3.1), the operation of multiplication may be reduced to additions and subtractions.) By the additive property of P_1, it follows that for any rectangle set of the form $S = (S_1, I_2)$ we have

$$P(S) = P_1(S_1)\, P_2(I_2).$$

and finally we obtain (8.6.1) by operating in the same way on intervals I_2. — On the other hand, any distribution satisfying (8.6.1) also satisfies (8.6.2), the latter relation being, in fact, merely a particular case of the former. Since a distribution is uniquely determined by its distribution function, there can thus be only one distribution satisfying (8.6.1).

If, in (8.6.1), we put $S_2 = \boldsymbol{R}_n$, it follows from (8.4.2) that the marginal distribution corresponding to the subspace $\boldsymbol{R}_m$ coincides with the given distribution in this space, with the probability function P_1. Similarly, by putting $S_1 = \boldsymbol{R}_m$, we find that the marginal distribution in $\boldsymbol{R}_n$ coincides with the given distribution in this space.

We finally remark that the theorem may be generalized to distributions in the product space of any number of spaces. The proof is quite similar to the above, and the relations (8.6.1) and (8.6.2) are replaced by the obvious generalizations

$$P = P_1 P_2 \dots P_k \quad \text{and} \quad F = F_1 F_2 \dots F_k.$$

CHAPTER 9.

The Lebesgue-Stieltjes Integral for Functions of n Variables.

9.1. The Lebesgue-Stieltjes integral. — The theory of the Lebesgue-Stieltjes integral for functions of one variable developed in Ch. 7 may be directly generalized to functions of n variables. If, in the expressions (7.1.1) of the Darboux sums, we allow $P(S)$ to denote a non-negative and additive set function in $\boldsymbol{R}_n$, while m_ν and M_ν are the lower and upper bounds of a given function $g(\boldsymbol{x}) = g(x_1, \dots, x_n)$ in the n-dimensional set S_ν, the *Lebesgue-Stieltjes integral*

(9.1.1) $$\int_S g(\boldsymbol{x})\, dP = \int_S g(x_1, \dots, x_n)\, dP$$

is defined in the same way as in the one-dimensional case.

The function $g(\boldsymbol{x})$ is said to be B-measurable in the set S if the subset of all points $\boldsymbol{x}$ in S such that $g(\boldsymbol{x}) \leqq k$ is a Borel set for every real value of k. All remarks on B-measurable functions given in 5.2 extend themselves without difficulty to functions of n variables.

If $g(\boldsymbol{x})$ is bounded and B-measurable in a set S of finite P-measure, it is integrable over S with respect to P. The definitions of integral and integrability in the case of an unbounded function $g(\boldsymbol{x})$, and a set S of infinite P-measure, require only a straightforward generalization of 7.2. All properties of the integral mentioned in 7.1—7.3 readily extend themselves to the case of n variables, all proofs being strictly analogous to those given in the case $n = 1$.

In the particular case when $P(S)$ is the n-dimensional Lebesgue measure $L(S)$, we obtain the *Lebesgue integral* of the function $g(\boldsymbol{x})$, which is also often written in the ordinary multiple integral notation:

$$\int_S g(\boldsymbol{x})\, dL = \int_S g(x_1, \dots, x_n)\, dx_1 \dots dx_n.$$

If S is an interval, and $g(\boldsymbol{x})$ is integrable in the Riemann sense over the interval, the Lebesgue integral coincides with the ordinary multiple Riemann integral, as we have observed for the one-dimensional case in 5.1.

9.2. Lebesgue-Stieltjes integrals with respect to a distribution. — The remarks made on this subject in 7.4 evidently apply also in the case $n > 1$.

The *moments* of a distribution in $\boldsymbol{R}_n$ are the integrals

$$\alpha_{\nu_1 \ldots \nu_n} = \int\limits_{\boldsymbol{R}_n} x_1^{\nu_1} \ldots x_n^{\nu_n} \, d\,P,$$

where the ν_i are non-negative integers. As in the one-dimensional case, we shall say that the above moment *exists*, whenever the function $x_1^{\nu_1} \ldots x_n^{\nu_n}$ is integrable over $\boldsymbol{R}_n$ with respect to P.

We shall now consider the integral

$$\int\limits_{\boldsymbol{R}_n} g(x_1, \ldots, x_n) \, d\,P \tag{9.2.1}$$

in the case when the function g only depends on a certain number of the variables, say $x_1, \ldots, x_k$, where $k < n$. We denote by $\boldsymbol{R}_k$ the k-dimensional subspace of these variables. Let us first assume g bounded, and consider the divisions

$$\boldsymbol{R}_k = S_1' + \cdots + S_q',$$
$$\boldsymbol{R}_n = S_1 + \cdots + S_q,$$

where the S_ν' are Borel sets in $\boldsymbol{R}_k$ such that $S_\mu' S_\nu' = 0$ for $\mu \neq \nu$, while S_ν denotes the cylinder set (cf 3.5) in $\boldsymbol{R}_n$ which has the base S_ν'.

The upper Darboux sum

$$Z = M_1 P(S_1) + \cdots + M_q P(S_q)$$

corresponding to the integral (9.2.1) is then by (8.4.2) identical with the sum

$$Z = M_1 P_{1, \ldots, k}(S_1') + \cdots + M_q P_{1, \ldots, k}(S_q'),$$

where $P_{1, \ldots, k}$ denotes the probability function of the marginal distribution of the variables $x_1, \ldots, x_k$. This is, however, the upper Darboux sum corresponding to the k-dimensional integral

$$\int\limits_{\boldsymbol{R}_k} g \, d\,P_{1, \ldots, k}.$$

As the same relation holds for the lower Darboux sums, it follows that we have for any bounded $g(x_1, \ldots, x_k)$

(9.2.2) $$\int_{R_n} g(x_1, \ldots, x_k)\, d\,P = \int_{R_k} g(x_1, \ldots, x_k)\, d\,P_{1, \ldots, k},$$

so that in this case the n-dimensional integral reduces to a k-dimensional integral.

It is easily seen that the same relation holds whenever g is integrable over $\boldsymbol{R}_k$ with respect to $P_{1, \ldots, k}$, even if g is not bounded. We may also assume g complex-valued.

9.3. A theorem on repeated integrals. — If $g(x, y)$ is continuous in the rectangle $a \leqq x \leqq b$, $c \leqq y \leqq d$, we know that the relation

$$\int_a^b\!\!\int_c^d g(x, y)\, d\,x\, d\,y = \int_a^b \left(\int_c^d g(x, y)\, d\,y\right) d\,x = \int_c^d \left(\int_a^b g(x, y)\, d\,x\right) d\,y$$

holds, so that the double integral can be expressed in two ways as a repeated integral. — There is a corresponding theorem for the Lebesgue-Stieltjes integral in any number of dimensions, and we shall now prove this theorem in a certain special case.

Using the same notations as in 8.6, we consider two probability functions P_1 and P_2 in the spaces $\boldsymbol{R}_m$ and $\boldsymbol{R}_n$ respectively, and the uniquely determined probability function P in the product space $\boldsymbol{R}_m \cdot \boldsymbol{R}_n$ which satisfies (8.6.1). Let S_1 and S_2 denote given sets in $\boldsymbol{R}_m$ and $\boldsymbol{R}_n$ respectively, while $S = (S_1, S_2)$ is the rectangle set in the product space with the »sides» S_1 and S_2. Let further $g(\boldsymbol{x})$ and $h(\boldsymbol{y})$ be given point functions in $\boldsymbol{R}_m$ and $\boldsymbol{R}_n$ respectively, such that $g(\boldsymbol{x})$ is integrable over S_1 with respect to P_1, while $h(\boldsymbol{y})$ is integrable over S_2 with respect to P_2.

Then $g(\boldsymbol{x})\, h(\boldsymbol{y})$ is integrable over $S = (S_1, S_2)$ with respect to P, and we have

(9.3.1) $$\int_S g(\boldsymbol{x})\, h(\boldsymbol{y})\, d\,P = \int_{S_1} g(\boldsymbol{x})\, d\,P_1 \int_{S_2} h(\boldsymbol{y})\, d\,P_2.$$

Suppose first that $g(\boldsymbol{x})$ and $h(\boldsymbol{y})$ are bounded and non-negative. Consider the Darboux sums corresponding to the three integrals in (9.3.1), and to the divisions $S_1 = S_1^{(1)} + \cdots + S_1^{(\mu)}$, $S_2 = S_2^{(1)} + \cdots + S_2^{(\nu)}$, $S = \sum_{i,j} S^{(ij)}$, where $S^{(ij)}$ denotes the rectangle set $(S_1^{(i)}, S_2^{(j)})$. If these sums are denoted by z and Z for the integral in the first member, and by z_1, Z_1 and z_2, Z_2 for the two integrals in the second member, it is seen that we have

$$z_1 z_2 \leqq z \leqq Z \leqq Z_1 Z_2.$$

By the definition of the integral, (9.3.1) then follows immediately. — Replacing further g and h by $g' - g''$ and $h' - h''$, where g', g'', h' and h'' are bounded and non-negative, we obtain (9.3.1) for any real and bounded g and h. The extension to any integrable and complex-valued functions follows directly from the definition of the integral for these classes of functions.

9.4. The Riemann-Stieltjes integral. — The considerations of 7.5 may also be generalized to n variables, where we have to employ the point function $F(x_1, \ldots, x_n)$ and the difference $\Delta_n F$ instead of the point function $F(x)$ and the difference $F(x_\nu) - F(x_{\nu-1})$.

In particular it follows that, if a continuous derivative $\dfrac{\partial^n F}{\partial x_1 \ldots \partial x_n}$ exists for all points of the interval I $(a_\nu \leqq x_\nu \leqq b_\nu,\ \nu = 1, \ldots, n)$, and if $g(\boldsymbol{x})$ is continuous in I, then the integral (9.1.1) may, for $S = I$, be expressed as a multiple Riemann integral

$$\int_I g(\boldsymbol{x})\, dP = \int_{a_1}^{b_1} \cdots \int_{a_n}^{b_n} g(x_1, \ldots, x_n) \frac{\partial^n F}{\partial x_1 \ldots \partial x_n} d x_1 \ldots d x_n.$$

This property is immediately extended to the case of a complex-valued function $g(\boldsymbol{x})$, and also to infinite intervals, subject to the condition that $g(\boldsymbol{x})$ is integrable over I with respect to P.

9.5 The Schwarz inequality. — Consider two real functions $g(\boldsymbol{x})$ and $h(\boldsymbol{x})$ such that the squares g^2 and h^2 are integrable with respect to P over the set S in $\boldsymbol{R}_n$. The quadratic form

$$\int_S [u g(\boldsymbol{x}) + v h(\boldsymbol{x})]^2\, dP = u^2 \int_S g^2\, dP + 2uv \int_S gh\, dP + v^2 \int_S h^2\, dP$$

is non-negative for all real values of the variables u and v Thus (cf 11.10) the determinant of the form is non-negative, which implies that we have

$$\left(\int_S gh\, dP\right)^2 \leqq \int_S g^2\, dP \cdot \int_S h^2\, dP. \tag{9.5.1}$$

CHAPTER 10.

FOURIER INTEGRALS.

For the applications to probability theory and statistics, we shall require a certain number of theorems concerning some special classes of Fourier integrals, which will be deduced in this chapter. The general theory of the subject is treated e. g. in books by Bochner (Ref. 4), Titchmarsh (Ref. 38) and Wiener (Ref. 41).

10.1. The characteristic function of a distribution in R_1. — Let $F(x)$ denote a one-dimensional distribution function (cf 6.6), and t a real number. The function $g(x) = e^{itx} = \cos tx + i \sin tx$ is then, by 7.4, integrable over $(-\infty, \infty)$ with respect to $F(x)$, since $|e^{itx}| = 1$. The function of the real variable t

$$\varphi(t) = \int_{-\infty}^{\infty} e^{itx}\, dF(x) \tag{10.1.1}$$

will be called the *characteristic function* of the distribution corresponding to $F(x)$.

In general $\varphi(t)$ is a complex-valued function of t. Obviously we always have $\varphi(0) = 1$, and for all values of t

$$|\varphi(t)| \leqq \int_{-\infty}^{\infty} dF(x) = 1,$$

$$\varphi(-t) = \overline{\varphi(t)},$$

writing $\bar{a}$ for the conjugated complex quantity of a. It further follows from 7.3 that $\varphi(t)$ is continuous for all real t.

If the moment of order k of the distribution (cf 7.4) exists, it follows from 7.3 that we may differentiate (10.1.1) k times with respect to t, and thus obtain for $0 \leqq \nu \leqq k$

$$\varphi^{(\nu)}(t) = i^{\nu} \int_{-\infty}^{\infty} x^{\nu} e^{itx}\, dF(x). \tag{10.1.2}$$

Hence by 7.3 $\varphi^{(\nu)}(t)$ is continuous for all real t, and we have

$$\varphi^{(\nu)}(0) = i^{\nu} \int_{-\infty}^{\infty} x^{\nu}\, d\, F(x) = i^{\nu}\, \alpha_{\nu}.$$

In the neighbourhood of $t = 0$ we thus have a development in MacLaurin's series:

$$\varphi(t) = 1 + \sum_{1}^{k} \frac{\alpha_{\nu}}{\nu!} (i\, t)^{\nu} + o(t^{k}), \tag{10.1.3}$$

where the error term, divided by t^k, tends to zero as $t \to 0$ (cf 12.1).

Conversely, if it is known that the characteristic function has, for the particular value $t = 0$, a finite derivative of even order $2\,k$, this derivative is equal to the limit

$$\varphi^{(2\,k)}(0) = \lim_{t \to 0} \int_{-\infty}^{\infty} \left(\frac{e^{itx} - e^{-itx}}{2\,t}\right)^{2\,k} d\, F(x) = (-1)^{k} \lim_{t \to 0} \int_{-\infty}^{\infty} \left(\frac{\sin t\, x}{t}\right)^{2\,k} d\, F(x).$$

For any finite interval (a, b) we have, however, by (7.1.7),

$$\int_{a}^{b} x^{2\,k}\, d\, F(x) = \lim_{t \to 0} \int_{a}^{b} \left(\frac{\sin t\, x}{t}\right)^{2\,k} d\, F(x) \leqq |\, \varphi^{(2\,k)}(0)\,|.$$

It follows that the moment $\alpha_{2\,k}$ exists, and thus (10.1.2) holds for $0 \leqq \nu \leqq 2\,k$ and for all values of t.

We thus see that the differentiability properties of $\varphi(t)$ are related to the behaviour of $F(x)$ for large values of x, since it is this behaviour that decides whether the moments α_ν exist or not. It can also be shown that, conversely, the behaviour of $\varphi(t)$ at infinity is related to the continuity and differentiability properties of $F(x)$. Suppose, e. g., that $F(x)$ is everywhere continuous, and that a continuous frequency function $F'(x) = f(x)$ exists for all x, except at most in a finite number of points. We then have by (7.5.5)

$$\varphi(t) = \int_{-\infty}^{\infty} e^{itx} f(x)\, dx, \tag{10.1.4}$$

and it can be shown that $\varphi(t)$ tends to zero as $t \to \pm \infty$. If, moreover, the n:th derivative $f^{(n)}(x)$ exists for all x and is such that $|f^{(n)}(x)|$ is integrable over $(-\infty, \infty)$, a repeated partial integration shows that we have

$$|\,\varphi(t)\,| < \frac{K}{|\,t\,|^{n}}$$

for all t, where K is a constant. We shall, however, not give a detailed proof of these properties here.

Suppose, on the other hand, that $F(x)$ is a step-function with steps of the height p_ν in the points $x = x_\nu$. We then have by (7.1.8)

$$\varphi(t) = \sum_\nu p_\nu e^{itx_\nu}, \tag{10.1.5}$$

the series being absolutely and uniformly convergent for all t, since $\sum_\nu p_\nu = 1$. Each term of the series is a periodic function of t, and thus certainly does not tend to zero as $t \to \pm\infty$. It can be shown that also the sum of the series does not tend to zero as $t \to \pm\infty$. Thus e.g. the characteristic function of the distribution function $\varepsilon(x)$ defined by (6.7.1) is identically equal to 1.

Not every function $\varphi(t)$ may be the characteristic function of a distribution. Necessary conditions are, according to the above, that $\varphi(t)$ should be everywhere continuous and such that $|\varphi(t)| \leq 1$, $\varphi(0) = 1$ and $\varphi(-t) = \overline{\varphi(t)}$. These conditions are, however, not sufficient. If, e.g., $\varphi(t)$ is near $t = 0$ of the form $\varphi(t) = 1 + O(t^{2+\delta})$, where $\delta > 0$, then it follows from (10.1.3) that the distribution corresponding to $\varphi(t)$ must have $\alpha_1 = \alpha_2 = 0$, which means (cf 16.1) that the whole mass of the distribution is concentrated in the point $t = 0$. This is, however, the distribution which has the distribution function $\varepsilon(x)$ and the characteristic function $\varphi(t) = 1$. Hence in this case $\varphi(t)$ cannot be a characteristic function unless it is identically equal to 1. Thus e.g. the functions e^{-t^4} and $\dfrac{1}{1+t^4}$ are no characteristic functions, though both satisfy the above necessary conditions.

Various *necessary and sufficient* conditions are known. The simplest seem to be the following (Cramér, Ref. 71): *In order that a given, bounded and continuous function $\varphi(t)$ should be the characteristic function of a distribution, it is necessary and sufficient that $\varphi(0) = 1$ and that the function*

$$\psi(x, A) = \int_0^A \int_0^A \varphi(t-u)\, e^{ix(t-u)}\, dt\, du$$

is real and non-negative for all real x and all $A > 0$.

That these conditions are necessary is easily shown. When $\varphi(t)$ is the characteristic function corresponding to the distribution function $F(x)$ we find, in fact,

$$\psi(x, A) = 2 \int_{-\infty}^{\infty} \frac{1 - \cos A(x+y)}{(x+y)^2}\, dF(y),$$

and the last expression is evidently real and non-negative. — The proof that the conditions are sufficient depends on the properties of certain integrals analogous to those used in the two following paragraphs. It is, however, somewhat intricate and will not be given here.

10.2. Some auxiliary functions. — Consider the functions

$$s(h, T) = \frac{2}{\pi} \int_0^T \frac{\sin h t}{t} d t,$$

$$c(h, T) = \frac{2}{\pi} \int_0^T \frac{1 - \cos h t}{t^2} d t,$$

where h is real and $T > 0$. Obviously $c(h, T) \geqq 0$, and

$$s(-h, T) = -s(h, T), \quad c(-h, T) = c(h, T).$$

By simple transformations we obtain for $h > 0$

$$s(h, T) = \frac{2}{\pi} \int_0^{hT} \frac{\sin t}{t} d t,$$

$$c(h, T) = \frac{2h}{\pi} \int_0^{hT} \frac{\sin t}{t} d t - \frac{2}{\pi} \cdot \frac{1 - \cos h T}{T}.$$

Now it is proved in text-books on Integral Calculus that the integral

$$\int_0^x \frac{\sin t}{t} d t$$

is bounded for all $x > 0$ and tends to the limit $\frac{\pi}{2}$ as $x \to \infty$.

It follows that $s(h, T)$ is bounded for all real h and all $T > 0$ and that we have, uniformly for $|h| > \delta > 0$,

$$\lim_{T \to \infty} s(h, T) = \begin{cases} 1 & \text{for } h > 0, \\ 0 & \text{» } h = 0, \\ -1 & \text{» } h < 0. \end{cases} \tag{10.2.1}$$

We further obtain for all real h

$$\lim_{T \to \infty} c(h, T) = \frac{2}{\pi} \int_0^{\infty} \frac{1 - \cos h t}{t^2} d t = |h|. \tag{10.2.2}$$

10.3. Uniqueness theorems for characteristic functions in R_1. — *If $(a-h,\ a+h)$ is a continuity interval (cf 6.7) of the distribution function $F(x)$, we have*

$$(10.3.1)\qquad F(a+h)-F(a-h)=\lim_{T\to\infty}\frac{1}{\pi}\int_{-T}^{T}\frac{\sin h t}{t}\,e^{-ita}\,\varphi(t)\,dt.$$

This important theorem (Lévy, Ref. 24) shows that a distribution is uniquely determined by its characteristic function. In fact, if two distributions have the same characteristic function, the theorem shows that the two distributions agree for every interval that is a continuity interval for both distributions. Then, by 6.7, the distributions are identical.

In order to prove the theorem, we write

$$J=\frac{1}{\pi}\int_{-T}^{T}\frac{\sin h t}{t}\,e^{-ita}\,\varphi(t)\,dt=\frac{1}{\pi}\int_{-T}^{T}\frac{\sin h t}{t}\,e^{-ita}\,dt\int_{-\infty}^{\infty}e^{itx}\,dF(x).$$

Now the modulus of the function $\dfrac{\sin h t}{t}\,e^{it(x-a)}$ is at most equal to h, so that the conditions stated in 7.3 for the reversion of the order of integration are satisfied. Hence

$$J=\frac{1}{\pi}\int_{-\infty}^{\infty}dF(x)\int_{-T}^{T}\frac{\sin h t}{t}\,e^{it(x-a)}\,dt=\frac{2}{\pi}\int_{-\infty}^{\infty}dF(x)\int_{0}^{T}\frac{\sin h t}{t}\cos(x-a)t\,dt$$

$$=\int_{-\infty}^{\infty}g(x,T)\,dF(x),$$

where

$$g(x,T)=\frac{2}{\pi}\int_{0}^{T}\frac{\sin h t}{t}\cos(x-a)t\,dt=\frac{1}{\pi}\int_{0}^{T}\frac{\sin(x-a+h)t}{t}\,dt$$

$$-\frac{1}{\pi}\int_{0}^{T}\frac{\sin(x-a-h)t}{t}\,dt=\frac{1}{2}s(x-a+h,T)-\frac{1}{2}s(x-a-h,T).$$

Thus by the preceding paragraph $|g(x,T)|$ is less than an absolute constant, and we have

$$\lim_{T\to\infty} g(x,T) = \begin{cases} 0 & \text{for } x < a-h, \\ \frac{1}{2} & \text{»} \quad x = a-h, \\ 1 & \text{»} \quad a-h < x < a+h, \\ \frac{1}{2} & \text{»} \quad x = a+h, \\ 0 & \text{»} \quad x > a+h. \end{cases}$$

We may thus apply theorem (7.2.2) and so obtain, since $F(x)$ is continuous for $x = a \pm h$,

$$\lim_{T\to\infty} J = \int_{a-h}^{a+h} d\,F(x) = F(a+h) - F(a-h),$$

so that (10.3.1) is proved.

In the particular case when $|\varphi(t)|$ is integrable over $(-\infty, \infty)$, it follows from (10.3.1) that we have

$$\frac{F(x+h) - F(x-h)}{2\,h} = \frac{1}{2\pi}\int_{-\infty}^{\infty} \frac{\sin h\,t}{h\,t}\, e^{-itx}\,\varphi(t)\,d\,t,$$

as soon as F is continuous in the points $x \pm h$. When h tends to zero, the function under the integral tends to $e^{-itx}\varphi(t)$, while its modulus is dominated by the integrable function $|\varphi(t)|$. Thus we may apply (7.3.1), and find that the derivative $F'(x) = f(x)$ exists for all x, and that we have

$$f(x) = \frac{1}{2\pi}\int_{-\infty}^{\infty} e^{-itx}\,\varphi(t)\,d\,t. \tag{10.3.2}$$

Then $f(x)$ is the frequency function (cf 6.6) of the distribution, and it follows from 7.3 that $f(x)$ is continuous for all values of x. — We call attention to the mutual reciprocity between the relations (10.3.2) and (10.1.4).

In order to determine $F(x)$ by means of (10.3.1) we must know $\varphi(t)$ over the whole infinite interval $(-\infty, \infty)$. The knowledge of $\varphi(t)$ over a finite interval is, in fact, *not* sufficient for a unique determination of $F(x)$. This follows from an example given by Gnedenko (Ref. 117) of *two characteristic functions which agree over a finite interval without being identical for all t.* We shall give a somewhat simpler example due to Khintchine. The two functions

$$\varphi_1(t) = \begin{cases} 1 - |t| & \text{for } |t| \leqq 1, \\ 0 & \text{for } |t| > 1, \end{cases}$$

$$\varphi_2(t) = \tfrac{1}{2} + \frac{4}{\pi^2}\left(\frac{\cos \pi t}{1^2} + \frac{\cos 3\pi t}{3^2} + \frac{\cos 5\pi t}{5^2} + \cdots\right)$$

are both characteristic functions. $\varphi_1(t)$ is the characteristic function of the distribution defined by the frequency function

$$f_1(x) = \frac{1 - \cos x}{\pi x^2},$$

as may be seen by taking $h = 1$, $F(x) = \varepsilon(x)$ and $\varphi(t) = 1$ in (10.3.3), while $\varphi_2(t)$ corresponds to a distribution having the mass $\frac{1}{2}$ placed in the point $x = 0$, and the mass $\frac{2}{n^2 \pi^2}$ in the point $x = n\pi$, where $n = \pm 1, \pm 3, \ldots$ — By summation of the trigonometrical series for $\varphi_2(t)$ it is seen that $\varphi_1(t) = \varphi_2(t)$ for $|t| \leqq 1$. For $|t| > 1$, on the other hand, $\varphi_1(t)$ is equal to zero, while $\varphi_2(t)$ is periodical with the period 2.

We now proceed to prove a formula which is closely related to (10.3.1), but differs from it by containing an absolutely convergent integral. In the following paragraph, this formula will find an important application. — *For any real a and $h > 0$ we have*

$$(10.3.3) \qquad \int_0^h [F(a+z) - F(a-z)]\, dz = \frac{1}{\pi} \int_{-\infty}^{\infty} \frac{1 - \cos h t}{t^2} e^{-ita} \varphi(t)\, dt.$$

Transforming the integral in the second member in the same way as in the proof of (10.3.1), the reversion of the order of integration is justified by means of 7.3. Denoting the second member of (10.3.3) by J_1, we then obtain

$$J_1 = \frac{1}{\pi} \int_{-\infty}^{\infty} dF(x) \int_{-\infty}^{\infty} \frac{1 - \cos h t}{t^2} e^{it(x-a)}\, dt$$

$$= \frac{2}{\pi} \int_{-\infty}^{\infty} dF(x) \int_0^{\infty} \frac{1 - \cos h t}{t^2} \cos (x-a) t\, dt.$$

In the same way as above it then follows from (10.2.2)

$$J_1 = \int_{-\infty}^{\infty} \frac{|x - a + h| + |x - a - h| - 2|x - a|}{2}\, dF(x)$$

$$= \int_{a-h}^{a+h} (h - |x - a|)\, dF(x).$$

Applying the formula of partial integration (7.5.7) to the last integral, taken over each of the intervals $(a - h, a)$ and $(a, a + h)$ separately, it is finally seen that J_1 is identical with the expression in the first member of (10.3.3), so that this relation is proved.

10.4. Continuity theorem for characteristic functions in $\boldsymbol{R}_1$. — We have seen in the preceding paragraph that there is a one-to-one correspondence between a distribution and its characteristic function $\varphi(t)$. A distribution function $F(x)$ is thus always uniquely determined by the corresponding characteristic function $\varphi(t)$, and the transformation by which we pass from $F(x)$ to $\varphi(t)$, or conversely, is always unique. We shall now prove a theorem which shows that, subject to certain conditions, this transformation is also *continuous*, so that the relations $F_n(x) \to F(x)$ and $\varphi_n(t) \to \varphi(t)$ are equivalent.

This theorem is of the highest importance for the applications, since it affords a criterion which often permits us to decide whether a given sequence of distributions converges to a distribution or not. We have seen in 6.7 that a sequence of distributions converges to a distribution when and only when the corresponding sequence of distribution functions converges to a distribution function. In the applications it is, however, sometimes very difficult to investigate directly the convergence of a sequence of distribution functions, while the convergence problem for the corresponding sequence of characteristic functions may be comparatively easy to solve. In such situations, we shall often have occasion to use the following theorem, which is due to Levy (Ref. 24, 25) and Cramer (Ref. 11).

We are given a sequence of distributions, with the distribution functions $F_1(x), F_2(x), \ldots$, and the characteristic functions $\varphi_1(t), \varphi_2(t), \ldots$ A necessary and sufficient condition for the convergence of the sequence $\{F_n(x)\}$ to a distribution function $F(x)$ is that, for every t, the sequence $\{\varphi_n(t)\}$ converges to a limit $\varphi(t)$, which is continuous for the special value $t = 0$.

When this condition is satisfied, the limit $\varphi(t)$ is identical with the characteristic function of the limiting distribution function $F(x)$.

We shall first show that the condition is *necessary*, and that the limit $\varphi(t)$ is the characteristic function of $F(x)$. This is, in fact, an immediate corollary of (7.5.9), since the conditions of this relation are evidently satisfied if we take $g(x) = e^{itx}$.

The main difficulty lies in the proof that the condition is *sufficient*. We then assume that $\varphi_n(t)$ tends for every t to a limit $\varphi(t)$ which is continuous for $t = 0$, and we shall prove that under this hypothesis $F_n(x)$ tends to a distribution function $F(x)$. If this is proved, it follows from the first part of the theorem that the limit $\varphi(t)$ is identical with the characteristic function of $F(x)$.

By 6.8 the sequence $\{F_n(x)\}$ contains a sub-sequence $\{F_{n_\nu}(x)\}$ convergent to a non-decreasing function $F(x)$, where $F(x)$ may be determined so as to be everywhere continuous to the right. We shall first prove that $F(x)$ is a distribution function. As we obviously have $0 \leqq F(x) \leqq 1$, it is sufficient to prove that $F(+\infty) - F(-\infty) = 1$. From (10.3.3) we obtain, putting $a = 0$,

$$\int_0^h F_{n_\nu}(z)\,dz - \int_{-h}^0 F_{n_\nu}(z)\,dz = \frac{1}{\pi}\int_{-\infty}^{\infty} \frac{1-\cos h t}{t^2}\,\varphi_{n_\nu}(t)\,dt.$$

On both sides of this relation, we may allow ν to tend to infinity under the integrals. In fact, the integrals on the left are taken over finite intervals, where F_{n_ν} is uniformly bounded and tends almost everywhere to F, so that we may apply (5.3.6). On the right, the modulus of the function under the integral is dominated by the function $\frac{1-\cos h t}{t^2}$, which is integrable over $(-\infty, \infty)$, so that we may apply the more general theorem (5.5.2). We thus obtain, dividing by h,

$$\begin{aligned}\frac{1}{h}\int_0^h F(z)\,dz - \frac{1}{h}\int_{-h}^0 F(z)\,dz &= \frac{1}{\pi h}\int_{-\infty}^{\infty} \frac{1-\cos h t}{t^2}\,\varphi(t)\,dt \\ &= \frac{1}{\pi}\int_{-\infty}^{\infty} \frac{1-\cos t}{t^2}\,\varphi\left(\frac{t}{h}\right)dt.\end{aligned}$$

In this relation, we now allow h to assume a sequence of values tending to infinity. The first member then obviously tends to $F(+\infty) - F(-\infty)$. On the other hand, $\varphi(t)$ is continuous for $t = 0$, so that $\varphi\left(\frac{t}{h}\right)$ tends for every t to the limit $\varphi(0)$. We have, however, $\varphi(0) = \lim_{n\to\infty} \varphi_n(0)$, but $\varphi_n(0) = 1$ for every n, since $\varphi_n(t)$ is a characteristic function. Hence $\varphi(0) = 1$. Applying once more (5.5.2), we thus obtain from the last integral, using (10.2.2),

$$F(+\infty) - F(-\infty) = \frac{1}{\pi}\int_{-\infty}^{\infty} \frac{1-\cos t}{t^2}\,dt = 1.$$

Thus we must have $F(+\infty) = 1$, $F(-\infty) = 0$, and the limit $F(x)$ of the sequence $\{F_{n_\nu}(x)\}$ is a distribution function. — By the first part of the proof, it then follows that the limit $\varphi(t)$ of the sequence $\{\varphi_{n_\nu}(t)\}$ is identical with the characteristic function of $F(x)$.

Consider now another convergent sub-sequence of $\{F_n(x)\}$, and denote the limit of the new sub-sequence by $F^*(x)$, always assuming this function to be determined so as to be everywhere continuous to the right. In the same way as before, it is then shown that $F^*(x)$ is a distribution function. By hypothesis the characteristic functions of the new sub-sequence have, however, for all values of t the same limit $\varphi(t)$ as before, so that $\varphi(t)$ is the characteristic function of both $F(x)$ and $F^*(x)$. Then according to the uniqueness theorem (10.3.1) we have $F(x) = F^*(x)$ for all x.

Thus every convergent sub-sequence of $\{F_n(x)\}$ has the same limit $F(x)$. This is, however, equivalent to the statement that the sequence $\{F_n(x)\}$ converges to $F(x)$, and since we have shown that $F(x)$ is a distribution function, our theorem is proved.

We know from 10.1 that a characteristic function is always continuous for every t. Thus it follows from the above theorem that, as soon as the limit $\varphi(t)$ of a sequence of characteristic functions is continuous for the special value $t = 0$, it is continuous for every t. The condition that the limit should be continuous for the special value $t = 0$ is, however, essential for the truth of the theorem.

We shall, in fact, show by an example that the theorem is not true, if this condition is omitted. — Let $F_n(x)$ be the distribution function defined by

$$F_n(x) = \begin{cases} 0 & \text{for } x \leqq -n, \\ \dfrac{x+n}{2n} & \text{» } -n < x < n, \\ 1 & \text{» } x \geqq n. \end{cases}$$

The corresponding frequency function is constant equal to $\frac{1}{2n}$ in the interval $(-n, n)$, and disappears outside that interval. The corresponding characteristic function is by (10.1.4)

$$\varphi_n(t) = \frac{1}{2n} \int_{-n}^{n} e^{itx}\, dx = \frac{\sin nt}{nt}.$$

As n tends to infinity, $\varphi_n(t)$ converges for every t to the limit $\varphi(t)$ defined by

$$\varphi(t) = \begin{cases} 1 & \text{for } t = 0, \\ 0 & \text{» } t \neq 0. \end{cases}$$

Thus the limit is not continuous for $t = 0$. Accordingly, for every fixed x we have $F_n(x) \to \frac{1}{2}$, so that the limit of $F_n(x)$ is not a distribution function.

In the case $F_n(x) = \varepsilon(x - n)$ considered in 6.7, we have $\varphi_n(t) = e^{int}$, so that the sequence of characteristic functions is never convergent, except when t is a multiple of 2π. Accordingly, for every fixed x we have $F_n(x) \to 0$, so that the limit of $F_n(x)$ is not a distribution function, as we have already seen in 6.7.

10.5. Some particular integrals. — We shall now deduce some formulae that will be used in the sequel. The integral

$$\int_{-\infty}^{\infty} e^{-x^2}\,dx = \sqrt{\pi}$$

is given in text-books on Integral Calculus. Substituting $x\sqrt{h/2}$ for x, we obtain for $h > 0$

$$\int_{-\infty}^{\infty} e^{-\frac{1}{2}hx^2}\,dx = \sqrt{\frac{2\pi}{h}}.$$

By means of 7.3 it is easily seen that we may differentiate any number of times with respect to h, so that

$$\int_{-\infty}^{\infty} x^{2\nu} e^{-\frac{1}{2}hx^2}\,dx = \frac{(2\nu)!}{2^\nu \nu!}\sqrt{2\pi}\,h^{-\nu-\frac{1}{2}} \qquad (\nu = 0, 1, 2, \ldots). \tag{10.5.1}$$

Consider now the integral

$$\int_{-\infty}^{\infty} e^{itx-\frac{1}{2}hx^2}\,dx = \int_{-\infty}^{\infty} \sum_0^\infty \frac{(itx)^\nu}{\nu!} e^{-\frac{1}{2}hx^2}\,dx.$$

The partial sums of the series under the last integral are dominated by the function $e^{|tx|-\frac{1}{2}hx^2}$, which is integrable over $(-\infty, \infty)$. Thus by (5.5.2) we may integrate the series term by term and so obtain, since all terms of odd order evidently vanish,

$$\begin{aligned}\int_{-\infty}^{\infty} e^{itx-\frac{1}{2}hx^2}\,dx &= \sum_0^\infty \frac{(it)^\nu}{\nu!}\int_{-\infty}^{\infty} x^\nu e^{-\frac{1}{2}hx^2}\,dx \\ &= \sum_0^\infty \frac{(it)^{2\nu}}{(2\nu)!}\cdot\frac{(2\nu)!}{2^\nu \nu!}\sqrt{2\pi}\,h^{-\nu-\frac{1}{2}} \qquad (10.5.2) \\ &= \sqrt{\frac{2\pi}{h}}\,e^{-\frac{t^2}{2h}}.\end{aligned}$$

Taking here $h = 1$, and introducing the function

$$\Phi(x) = \frac{1}{\sqrt{2\pi}}\int_{-\infty}^{x} e^{-\frac{t^2}{2}}\,dt, \tag{10.5.3}$$

it follows that we have

$$(10.5.4) \qquad \int_{-\infty}^{\infty} e^{itx}\, d\Phi(x) = \frac{1}{\sqrt{2\pi}} \int_{-\infty}^{\infty} e^{itx - \frac{x^2}{2}}\, dx = e^{-\frac{t^2}{2}}.$$

Now (10.5.3) shows that $\Phi(x)$ is a non-decreasing and everywhere continuous function, such that $\Phi(-\infty) = 0$ and $\Phi(+\infty) = 1$. Thus $\Phi(x)$ is a distribution function, and then (10.5.4) shows that the corresponding characteristic function is $e^{-\frac{t^2}{2}}$. The distribution determined by $\Phi(x)$ is the important *normal distribution*, that will be treated in Ch. 17. — By repeated partial integration, we obtain from (10.5.4) the relation

$$(10.5.5) \qquad \int_{-\infty}^{\infty} e^{itx}\, d\Phi^{(n)}(x) = (-it)^n e^{-\frac{t^2}{2}}.$$

We shall further consider the integral

$$(10.5.6) \qquad \begin{aligned} \tfrac{1}{2}\int_{-\infty}^{\infty} e^{itx - |x|}\, dx &= \int_{0}^{\infty} \cos tx\, e^{-x}\, dx \\ &= \left[\frac{t \sin tx - \cos tx}{1 + t^2} e^{-x}\right]_0^{\infty} = \frac{1}{1 + t^2}. \end{aligned}$$

This expression may be regarded as the characteristic function corresponding to the frequency function $f(x) = \frac{1}{2} e^{-|x|}$. Since the characteristic function is integrable over $(-\infty, \infty)$, we obtain from (10.3.2) the reciprocal formula

$$(10.5\,7) \qquad \frac{1}{\pi} \int_{-\infty}^{\infty} \frac{e^{-itx}}{1 + t^2}\, dt = e^{-|x|}.$$

10.6. The characteristic function of a distribution in R_n. — If $\boldsymbol{t} = (t_1, \ldots, t_n)$ and $\boldsymbol{x} = (x_1, \ldots, x_n)$ are considered as column vectors (cf. 11.2) corresponding to points in R_n, we denote by $\boldsymbol{t}'\boldsymbol{x}$ the product formed according to the rule (11.2.1) of vector multiplication:

$$\boldsymbol{t}'\boldsymbol{x} = t_1 x_1 + \cdots + t_n x_n.$$

The definition (10.1.1) of the characteristic function of a one-dimensional distribution is then generalized by writing

$$\varphi(\boldsymbol{t}) = \varphi(t_1, \ldots, t_n) = \int_{\boldsymbol{R}_n} e^{i\boldsymbol{t}'\boldsymbol{x}}\, dP, \tag{10.6.1}$$

where $P = P(S)$ is the probability function of a distribution in $\boldsymbol{R}_n$. The characteristic function $\varphi(\boldsymbol{t})$ of the distribution is thus a function of the n real variables $t_1, \ldots, t_n$. Obviously we always have $\varphi(0, \ldots, 0) = 1$, and for all values of the variables

$$|\varphi(\boldsymbol{t})| \leqq 1, \qquad \varphi(-\boldsymbol{t}) = \overline{\varphi(\boldsymbol{t})}.$$

Further, $\varphi(\boldsymbol{t})$ is everywhere continuous. If all moments of the distribution (cf 9.2) up to a certain order exist, we have in the neighbourhood of the point $\boldsymbol{t} = 0$ an expansion of $\varphi(\boldsymbol{t})$ analogous to (10.1.3).

The following theorem, which is a direct generalization of the uniqueness theorem (10.3.1), shows that a distribution in $\boldsymbol{R}_n$ is uniquely determined by its characteristic function.

If the interval I defined by the inequalities $a_\nu - h_\nu < x_\nu < a_\nu + h_\nu$, $(\nu = 1, \ldots, n)$, is a continuity interval (cf 8.3) of $P(S)$, we have

$$P(I) = \lim_{T \to \infty} \frac{1}{\pi^n} \int_{-T}^{T} \cdots \int_{-T}^{T} \prod_{1}^{n} \frac{\sin h_\nu t_\nu}{t_\nu} e^{-i t_\nu a_\nu} \cdot \varphi(\boldsymbol{t})\, dt_1 \ldots dt_n. \tag{10.6.2}$$

The proof of this theorem is a straightforward generalization of the proof of (10.3.1). — In the particular case when $|\varphi(\boldsymbol{t})|$ is integrable over $\boldsymbol{R}_n$, we find as in (10.3.2) that the frequency function (cf 8.4) $\dfrac{\partial^n F}{\partial x_1 \ldots \partial x_n} = f(x_1, \ldots, x_n) = f(\boldsymbol{x})$ exists and is continuous for all $\boldsymbol{x}$, and that we have

$$f(\boldsymbol{x}) = \frac{1}{(2\pi)^n} \int_{-\infty}^{\infty} \cdots \int_{-\infty}^{\infty} e^{-i\boldsymbol{t}'\boldsymbol{x}} \varphi(\boldsymbol{t})\, dt_1 \ldots dt_n. \tag{10.6.3}$$

The reciprocal formula corresponding to (10.1.4):

$$\varphi(\boldsymbol{t}) = \int_{-\infty}^{\infty} \cdots \int_{-\infty}^{\infty} e^{i\boldsymbol{t}'\boldsymbol{x}} f(\boldsymbol{x})\, dx_1 \ldots dx_n \tag{10.6.4}$$

is obtained from (10.6.1) and holds whenever the frequency function $f(\boldsymbol{x})$ exists and is continuous, except possibly in certain points belonging to a finite number of hypersurfaces in $\boldsymbol{R}_n$.

We shall also want the following generalization of the theorem (10.3.3), which is proved in the same way as the one-dimensional case.

Let $I_{z_1, \ldots, z_n}$ *denote the interval defined by the inequalities*

$$a_\nu - z_\nu < x_\nu < a_\nu + z_\nu, \qquad (\nu = 1, \ldots, n).$$

For any real a_ν *and positive* h_ν *we have*

$$\int_0^{h_1} \cdots \int_0^{h_n} P(I_{z_1, \ldots, z_n})\, dz_1 \ldots dz_n =$$

$$= \frac{1}{\pi^n} \int_{-\infty}^{\infty} \cdots \int_{-\infty}^{\infty} \prod_1^n \frac{1 - \cos h_\nu t_\nu}{t_\nu^2} e^{-i t_\nu a_\nu} \cdot \varphi(\boldsymbol{t})\, dt_1 \ldots dt_n. \tag{10.6.5}$$

10.7. Continuity theorem for characteristic functions in $\boldsymbol{R}_n$. — The continuity theorem proved in 10.4 may be directly generalized to multi-dimensional distributions. By 8.5, a sequence of distributions in $\boldsymbol{R}_n$ converges to a distribution when and only when the corresponding distribution functions converge to a distribution function. As in the one-dimensional case, it is often easier in the applications to solve the convergence problem for the corresponding sequence of characteristic functions, and in such situations the following theorem will be useful.

We are given a sequence of distributions in $\boldsymbol{R}_n$, *with the distribution functions* $F_1(\boldsymbol{x}), F_2(\boldsymbol{x}), \ldots$, *and the characteristic functions* $\varphi_1(\boldsymbol{t}), \varphi_2(\boldsymbol{t}), \ldots$. *A necessary and sufficient condition for the convergence of the sequence* $\{F_n(\boldsymbol{x})\}$ *to a distribution function* $F(\boldsymbol{x})$ *is that, for every* $\boldsymbol{t}$, *the sequence* $\{\varphi_n(\boldsymbol{t})\}$ *converges to a limit* $\varphi(\boldsymbol{t})$, *which is continuous at the special point* $\boldsymbol{t} = 0$.

When this condition is satisfied, the limit $\varphi(\boldsymbol{t})$ *is identical with the characteristic function of the limiting distribution function* $F(\boldsymbol{x})$.

The proof that the condition is necessary is quite similar to the corresponding part of the proof in 10.4, and uses the generalization of (7.5.9) to integrals in $\boldsymbol{R}_n$ (cf 9.4). It then also follows that the limit $\varphi(\boldsymbol{t})$ is the characteristic function of $F(\boldsymbol{x})$. — In order to prove that the condition is sufficient, we consider a sub-sequence $\{F_{m_\mu}(\boldsymbol{x})\}$, which converges (cf 8.5) to a limit $F(\boldsymbol{x}) = F(x_1, \ldots, x_n)$ that is non-decreasing and continuous to the right in each variable x_ν. We want to show that $F(\boldsymbol{x})$ is a distribution function, i. e. that the corresponding non-negative and additive set function $P(S)$ is a probability function. For this purpose, it is sufficient to show that we have $P(\boldsymbol{R}_n) = 1$. We then apply (10.6.5) to each $\varphi_{m_\mu}(\boldsymbol{t})$, putting all the

$a_\nu = 0$. When μ tends to infinity, we obtain by the same argument as in 10.4

$$\frac{1}{h_1 \ldots h_n} \int_0^{h_1} \cdots \int_0^{h_n} P(I_{z_1, \ldots, z_n})\, dz_1 \ldots dz_n =$$

$$= \frac{1}{\pi^n} \int_{-\infty}^{\infty} \cdots \int_{-\infty}^{\infty} \prod_1^n \frac{1 - \cos t_\nu}{t_\nu^2} \varphi\left(\frac{t_1}{h_1}, \ldots, \frac{t_n}{h_n}\right) dt_1 \ldots dt_n.$$

Allowing the h_ν to tend to infinity, we then obtain, in perfect analogy with the one-dimensional case,

$$P(\boldsymbol{R}_n) = \prod_1^n \frac{1}{\pi} \int_{-\infty}^{\infty} \frac{1 - \cos t_\nu}{t_\nu^2} dt_\nu = 1,$$

so that the limit $P(S)$ of the sequence $\{P_{m_\mu}(S)\}$ is a probability function. The proof is then completed in the same way as in 10.4.

CHAPTER 11.

Matrices, Determinants and Quadratic Forms.

The subject of the present chapter is treated in several text-books in an elementary form well adapted for our purpose. We refer particularly to Aitken (Ref. 1), Bôcher (Ref. 3), and for Scandinavian readers to Bohr-Mollerup (Ref. 5). We shall here restrict ourselves to give, for the convenience of the reader, a brief survey — in many cases without complete proofs — of some fundamental definitions and properties that will be used in the sequel, adding full proofs of certain special theorems not contained in the text-books.

11.1. Matrices. — A *matrix* $\boldsymbol{A}$ of order $m \cdot n$ is a rectangular scheme of numbers or *elements* a_{ik} arranged in m rows and n columns:

$$\boldsymbol{A} = \begin{Bmatrix} a_{11} & a_{12} & \ldots & a_{1n} \\ a_{21} & a_{22} & \ldots & a_{2n} \\ \cdot & \cdot & \cdot & \cdot \\ a_{m1} & a_{m2} & \ldots & a_{mn} \end{Bmatrix}.$$

We write briefly $\boldsymbol{A} = \{a_{ik}\}$, and when we want to emphasize the order of the matrix, we write $\boldsymbol{A}_{mn}$ instead of $\boldsymbol{A}$. We shall always assume that the elements a_{ik} are real numbers.

In the particular case when $m = n = 1$, the matrix $\boldsymbol{A}$ consists of one single element a_{11}, and we shall then identify the matrix with the ordinary number a_{11}.

Two matrices $\boldsymbol{A}$ and $\boldsymbol{B}$ are called *equal*, and we write $\boldsymbol{A} = \boldsymbol{B}$, when and only when $\boldsymbol{A}$ and $\boldsymbol{B}$ are of the same order, and all corresponding elements are equal: $a_{ik} = b_{ik}$ for all i and k. — We shall now define three kinds of *operations with matrices*:

1. The *product* of a matrix $\boldsymbol{A}$ and an ordinary number c is defined as the matrix obtained by multiplying every element of $\boldsymbol{A}$ by c. Thus $c\boldsymbol{A} = \boldsymbol{A}c = \boldsymbol{B}$, where the elements of $\boldsymbol{B}$ are $b_{ik} = c a_{ik}$. When $c = -1$, we write $-\boldsymbol{A}$ instead of $(-1)\,\boldsymbol{A}$.

2. The *sum* of two matrices $\boldsymbol{A}$ and $\boldsymbol{B}$ is only defined when the two matrices are of the same order. Then the sum $\boldsymbol{C} = \boldsymbol{A} + \boldsymbol{B}$ is defined as a matrix of the same order with the elements $c_{ik} = a_{ik} + b_{ik}$.

3. The *product* of two matrices $\boldsymbol{A}$ and $\boldsymbol{B}$ is only defined when the *first factor* $\boldsymbol{A}$ is of order $m \cdot r$, and the *second factor* $\boldsymbol{B}$ is of order $r \cdot n$, so that the number of columns of the first factor agrees with the number of rows of the second factor. Then the product $\boldsymbol{C} = \boldsymbol{A}\boldsymbol{B}$, or $\boldsymbol{C}_{mn} = \boldsymbol{A}_{mr}\boldsymbol{B}_{rn}$, is defined as a matrix of order $m \cdot n$, with elements c_{ik} given by the expression

$$c_{ik} = \sum_{j=1}^{r} a_{ij}\, b_{jk}.$$

The element in the i:th row and k:th column of the product matrix is thus the sum of all products of corresponding elements from the i:th *row* of the *first* factor and the k:th *column* of the *second* factor.

The three matrix operations thus defined are *associative* and *distributive*. Moreover, the two first operations are *commutative*, while generally the third is *non-commutative*. Thus we have, e. g.,

$$(\boldsymbol{A} + \boldsymbol{B}) + \boldsymbol{C} = \boldsymbol{A} + (\boldsymbol{B} + \boldsymbol{C}), \qquad (\boldsymbol{A}\boldsymbol{B})\,\boldsymbol{C} = \boldsymbol{A}\,(\boldsymbol{B}\boldsymbol{C}),$$

$$\boldsymbol{C}\,(\boldsymbol{A} + \boldsymbol{B}) = \boldsymbol{C}\boldsymbol{A} + \boldsymbol{C}\boldsymbol{B}, \qquad (\boldsymbol{A} + \boldsymbol{B})\,\boldsymbol{C} = \boldsymbol{A}\boldsymbol{C} + \boldsymbol{B}\boldsymbol{C},$$

$$\boldsymbol{A} + \boldsymbol{B} = \boldsymbol{B} + \boldsymbol{A}, \qquad c\,(\boldsymbol{A} + \boldsymbol{B}) = c\boldsymbol{A} + c\boldsymbol{B},$$

but generally *not* $\boldsymbol{A}\boldsymbol{B} = \boldsymbol{B}\boldsymbol{A}$. Even if both products $\boldsymbol{A}\boldsymbol{B}$ and $\boldsymbol{B}\boldsymbol{A}$ are defined, they may be unequal. We are thus obliged to distinguish between *premultiplication* and *postmultiplication*. $\boldsymbol{A}\boldsymbol{B}$ means $\boldsymbol{A}$ postmultiplied by $\boldsymbol{B}$, or $\boldsymbol{B}$ premultiplied by $\boldsymbol{A}$.

From these properties, it follows e. g. that a linear combination $c_1 A_1 + \cdots + c_p A_p$ is uniquely defined as soon as all the A_i are of the same order, and that the terms may be arbitrarily rearranged. Similarly, the product $D_{mn} = A_{mr} B_{rs} C_{sn}$ is uniquely defined, but here no rearrangement of the factors is allowed. The elements d_{hk} of D are given by the expression

$$d_{hk} = \sum_{i=1}^{r} \sum_{j=1}^{s} a_{hi} b_{ij} c_{jk}.$$

The *transpose* of a matrix $A = \{a_{ik}\}$ of order $m \cdot n$ is a matrix $A' = \{a'_{ik}\}$ of order $n \cdot m$, such that $a'_{ik} = a_{ki}$. Thus the rows of A' are the columns of A, while the columns of A' are the rows of A. Obviously we have

$$(A')' = A, \qquad (A + B)' = A' + B', \qquad (AB)' = B'A'.$$

Any matrix obtained by deleting one or more of the rows and columns of A is called a *submatrix* of A. In particular every element of A is a submatrix of order $1 \cdot 1$, while the rows and columns are submatrices of order $1 \cdot n$ and $m \cdot 1$ respectively.

When $m = n$, we shall call A a *square matrix*. Owing to the associative property of matrix multiplication, the powers A^2, $A^3, \ldots$ of a square matrix are defined without ambiguity. The elements a_{11}, $a_{22}, \ldots, a_{nn}$ of a square matrix form the *main* or *principal diagonal* of the matrix, and are called the *diagonal elements*.

A square matrix which is symmetrical about its main diagonal is called a *symmetric matrix*. A symmetric matrix is identical with its transpose, so that we have $A' = A$ or $a_{ki} = a_{ik}$. For an arbitrary matrix $A = A_{mn}$, it will be seen that the products AA' and $A'A$ are symmetric, and of order $m \cdot m$ and $n \cdot n$ respectively.

A symmetric matrix with all its non-diagonal elements equal to zero is called a *diagonal matrix*. If A_{mn} is an arbitrary matrix, and if D_{mm} and D_{nn} are diagonal matrices, the product $D_{mm} A_{mn}$ is obtained by multiplying the *rows* of A by the corresponding diagonal elements of D, while the product $A_{mn} D_{nn}$ is obtained by multiplying the *columns* of A by the corresponding diagonal elements of D.

A *unit matrix* I is a diagonal matrix with all its diagonal elements equal to 1. For any matrix $A = A_{mn}$ we have

$$IA = AI = A,$$

where $\boldsymbol{I}$ denotes the unit matrix of order $m \cdot m$ in the first product, and of order $n \cdot n$ in the second.

A matrix (not necessarily square) having all its elements equal to zero is called a *zero matrix*, and is denoted by 0.

11.2. Vectors. — A *vector* is a matrix consisting of one single row or one single column, and is called a *row vector* or a *column vector*, as the case may be. Thus a row vector $\boldsymbol{x} = \{x_1, \ldots, x_n\}$ is a matrix of order $1 \cdot n$, while a column vector

$$\boldsymbol{x} = \begin{Bmatrix} x_1 \\ \vdots \\ x_n \end{Bmatrix}$$

is of order $n \cdot 1$. In order to simplify the writing we shall, however, usually write the latter vector in the form $\boldsymbol{x} = (x_1, \ldots, x_n)$, indicating by the use of ordinary instead of curled brackets that the vector is to be conceived as a column vector. The majority of vectors occurring in the applications will be of this kind.

The transpose of the column vector $\boldsymbol{x} = (x_1, \ldots, x_n)$ is the row vector $\boldsymbol{x}' = \{x_1, \ldots, x_n\}$, and conversely.

If $\boldsymbol{x} = (x_1, \ldots, x_n)$ and $\boldsymbol{y} = (y_1, \ldots, y_n)$ are two column vectors, the product $\boldsymbol{x}'\boldsymbol{y}$ is a matrix of order $1 \cdot 1$, i. e. an ordinary number:

$$\boldsymbol{x}'\boldsymbol{y} = x_1 y_1 + \cdots + x_n y_n. \tag{11.2.1}$$

In particular for $\boldsymbol{x} = \boldsymbol{y}$ we have

$$\boldsymbol{x}'\boldsymbol{x} = x_1^2 + \cdots + x_n^2.$$

The products $\boldsymbol{x}\boldsymbol{y}'$ and $\boldsymbol{x}\boldsymbol{x}'$, on the other hand, are not ordinary numbers, but matrices of order $n \cdot n$.

The vectors $\boldsymbol{x}_1, \ldots, \boldsymbol{x}_p$ are said to be *linearly dependent*, if a relation of the form $c_1 \boldsymbol{x}_1 + \cdots + c_p \boldsymbol{x}_p = 0$ exists, where the c_i are ordinary numbers which are not all equal to zero. Otherwise $\boldsymbol{x}_1, \ldots, \boldsymbol{x}_p$ are *linearly independent*. Similarly, p functions $f_1, \ldots, f_p$ of one or more variables are said to be linearly dependent, if a relation $c_1 f_1 + \cdots + c_p f_p = 0$, where the c_i are constants not all $= 0$, holds for all values of the variables. When several linear relations of this form exist, these are called *independent*, if the corresponding vectors $\boldsymbol{c} = (c_1, \ldots, c_p)$ are linearly independent.

11.3. Matrix notation for linear transformations. — A linear transformation

$$
(11.3.1)\qquad
\begin{aligned}
x_1 &= a_{11}\, y_1 + a_{12}\, y_2 + \cdots + a_{1n}\, y_n,\\
x_2 &= a_{21}\, y_1 + a_{22}\, y_2 + \cdots + a_{2n}\, y_n,\\
&\cdots\cdots\cdots\cdots\cdots\cdots\\
x_m &= a_{m1}\, y_1 + a_{m2}\, y_2 + \cdots + a_{mn}\, y_n,
\end{aligned}
$$

establishes a relation between two sets of variables, $x_1, \ldots, x_m$ and $y_1, \ldots, y_n$, where m is not necessarily equal to n. The matrix $\boldsymbol{A} = \boldsymbol{A}_{mn} = \{a_{ik}\}$ is the *transformation matrix.*

Now if $\boldsymbol{x} = (x_1, \ldots, x_m)$ and $\boldsymbol{y} = (y_1, \ldots, y_n)$ are conceived as column vectors, the right-hand sides of the equations (11.3.1) are the elements of the product matrix $\boldsymbol{A}\boldsymbol{y}$, which is of order $m \cdot 1$, i. e. a column vector. Thus (11.3.1) expresses that the corresponding elements of the column vectors $\boldsymbol{x}$ and $\boldsymbol{A}\boldsymbol{y}$ are equal, so that in matrix notation the transformation (11.3.1) takes the simple form $\boldsymbol{x} = \boldsymbol{A}\boldsymbol{y}$.

11.4. Matrix notation for bilinear and quadratic forms. — In the column vectors $\boldsymbol{x}$ and $\boldsymbol{y}$ of the preceding paragraph, we now consider the x_i and y_k as two sets of independent variables, and form the product matrix $\boldsymbol{x}'\boldsymbol{A}\boldsymbol{y}$, where $\boldsymbol{A} = \boldsymbol{A}_{mn} = \{a_{ik}\}$. This is a matrix of order $1 \cdot 1$, i. e. an ordinary number, and we find

$$
(11.4.1)\qquad \boldsymbol{x}'\boldsymbol{A}\boldsymbol{y} = \sum_{i,k} a_{ik}\, x_i\, y_k,
$$

where $i = 1, 2, \ldots, m$ and $k = 1, 2, \ldots, n$. Thus the *bilinear form* in the variables x_i and y_k that appears here in the second member has a simple expression in matrix notation.

In the important particular case when $m = n$, $\boldsymbol{x} = \boldsymbol{y}$ and $\boldsymbol{A}$ is symmetric, the bilinear form (11.4.1) becomes

$$
(11.4.2)\qquad \boldsymbol{x}'\boldsymbol{A}\boldsymbol{x} = \sum_{i,k=1}^{n} a_{ik}\, x_i\, x_k,
$$

where $a_{ki} = a_{ik}$. This expression is called a *quadratic form* in the variables $x_1, \ldots, x_n$, and will often be denoted by $Q(\boldsymbol{x})$ or $Q(x_1, \ldots, x_n)$. In matrix notation, we thus have $Q(\boldsymbol{x}) = \boldsymbol{x}'\boldsymbol{A}\boldsymbol{x}$. The symmetric matrix $\boldsymbol{A}$ is called the *matrix of the form* Q. If, in particular, $\boldsymbol{A} = \boldsymbol{I}$, we have $Q = \boldsymbol{x}'\boldsymbol{I}\boldsymbol{x} = \boldsymbol{x}'\boldsymbol{x} = x_1^2 + \cdots + x_n^2$.

The matrix expressions (11.4.1) and (11.4.2) are particularly well adapted for the study of *linear transformations* of bilinear and quadratic forms. Thus if, in the quadratic form $Q(x_1, \ldots, x_n) = \sum_{i,k=1}^{n} a_{ik}\, x_i x_k$, new variables $y_1, \ldots, y_m$ are introduced by the linear transformation $\boldsymbol{x} = \boldsymbol{C}\boldsymbol{y}$, where $\boldsymbol{C} = \boldsymbol{C}_{nm}$, the result is a quadratic form $Q_1(y_1, \ldots, y_m)$ in the new variables:

$$Q(x_1, \ldots, x_n) = Q_1(y_1, \ldots, y_m) = \sum_{i,k=1}^{m} b_{ik}\, y_i y_k,$$

and the matrix expression (11.4.2) then immediately gives

$$Q = \boldsymbol{x}'\boldsymbol{A}\boldsymbol{x} = \boldsymbol{y}'\boldsymbol{C}'\boldsymbol{A}\,\boldsymbol{C}\boldsymbol{y} = \boldsymbol{y}'\boldsymbol{B}\boldsymbol{y},$$

where $\boldsymbol{B} = \boldsymbol{C}'\boldsymbol{A}\boldsymbol{C}$. By transposition it is seen that this is a symmetric matrix, and thus the matrix of the transformed form is $\boldsymbol{C}'\boldsymbol{A}\boldsymbol{C}$. The order is, of course, $m \cdot m$.

11.5. Determinants. — To every square matrix $\boldsymbol{A} = \boldsymbol{A}_{nn} = \{a_{ik}\}$ corresponds a number A known as the *determinant* of the matrix, which is denoted

$$A = |\boldsymbol{A}| = |a_{ik}| = \begin{vmatrix} a_{11} & a_{12} & \ldots & a_{1n} \\ a_{21} & a_{22} & \ldots & a_{2n} \\ \cdot & \cdot & \cdot & \cdot \\ a_{n1} & a_{n2} & \ldots & a_{nn} \end{vmatrix}$$

The determinant is defined as the sum

$$A = \sum \pm\, a_{1r_1} a_{2r_2} \ldots a_{nr_n},$$

where the second subscripts $r_1, \ldots, r_n$ run through all the $n!$ possible permutations of the numbers $1, 2, \ldots, n$, while the sign of each term is $+$ or $-$ according as the corresponding permutation is even or odd. The number n is called the order of the determinant.

The determinants of a square matrix $\boldsymbol{A}$ and of its transpose $\boldsymbol{A}'$ are equal: $A = A'$. If two rows or two columns in $\boldsymbol{A}$ are interchanged, the determinant changes its sign. Hence if two rows or two columns in $\boldsymbol{A}$ are identical, the determinant is zero. If $\boldsymbol{A}$, $\boldsymbol{B}$ and $\boldsymbol{C}$ are square matrices such that $\boldsymbol{A}\boldsymbol{B} = \boldsymbol{C}$, the corresponding determinants satisfy the relation $AB = C$.

When $\boldsymbol{A}$ is an arbitrary matrix (not necessarily square), the determinant of any square submatrix of $\boldsymbol{A}$ is called a *minor* of $\boldsymbol{A}$. When $\boldsymbol{A}$ is square, a *principal minor* is a minor, the diagonal elements of which are diagonal elements of $\boldsymbol{A}$.

In a square matrix $\boldsymbol{A} = \{a_{ik}\}$, the *cofactor* A_{ik} of the element a_{ik} is the particular minor obtained by deleting the i:th row and the k:th column, multiplied with $(-1)^{i+k}$. We have the important identities

$$\sum_{j=1}^{n} a_{ij} A_{kj} = \begin{cases} A & \text{for } i = k, \\ 0 & \text{for } i \neq k, \end{cases} \tag{11.5.1}$$

$$\sum_{j=1}^{n} a_{ji} A_{jk} = \begin{cases} A & \text{for } i = k, \\ 0 & \text{for } i \neq k, \end{cases} \tag{11.5.2}$$

and further

$$A = a_{11} A_{11} - \sum_{i,k=2}^{n} a_{i1} a_{1k} A_{11.ik}, \tag{11.5.3}$$

where $A_{11.ik}$ is the cofactor of a_{ik} in A_{11}.

11.6. Rank. — The *rank of a matrix* $\boldsymbol{A}$ (not necessarily square) is the greatest integer r such that $\boldsymbol{A}$ contains at least one minor of order r which is not equal to zero. If all minors of $\boldsymbol{A}$ are zero, $\boldsymbol{A}$ is a zero matrix, and we put $r = 0$. When $\boldsymbol{A} = \boldsymbol{A}_{mn}$, the rank r is at most equal to the smaller of the numbers m and n.

Let the rows and columns of $\boldsymbol{A}$ be considered as vectors. If $\boldsymbol{A}$ is of rank r, it is possible to find r linearly independent rows of $\boldsymbol{A}$, while any $r+1$ rows are linearly dependent. The same holds true for columns.

If $\boldsymbol{A}_1, \boldsymbol{A}_2, \ldots, \boldsymbol{A}_p$ are of ranks $r_1, r_2, \ldots, r_p$, the rank of the sum $\boldsymbol{A}_1 + \cdots + \boldsymbol{A}_p$ is at most equal to the *sum* $r_1 + \cdots + r_p$, while the rank of the product $\boldsymbol{A}_1 \ldots \boldsymbol{A}_p$ is at most equal to the *smallest* of the ranks $r_1, \ldots, r_p$.

If a square matrix $\boldsymbol{A} = \boldsymbol{A}_{nn}$ is such that $A \neq 0$, then $\boldsymbol{A}$ is of rank n. Such a matrix is said to be *non-singular*, while a square matrix with $A = 0$ is of rank $r < n$ and is called a *singular* matrix. If an arbitrary matrix $\boldsymbol{B}$ is multiplied (pre- or post-) by a non-singular matrix $\boldsymbol{A}$, the product has the same rank as $\boldsymbol{B}$. When the matrix of a linear transformation is singular or non-singular, the corresponding adjectives are also applied to the transformation.

If A is symmetric and of rank r, there is at least one *principal* minor of order r in A which is not zero. Hence in particular the rank of a diagonal matrix is equal to the number of diagonal elements which are different from zero.

The *rank of a quadratic form* $Q = \boldsymbol{x}'\boldsymbol{A}\boldsymbol{x} = \sum_{i,k=1}^{n} a_{ik} x_i x_k$ is, by definition, equal to the rank of the matrix A of the form. According as A is singular or non-singular, the same expressions are used with respect to Q. A non-singular linear transformation does not affect the rank of the form. If, by such a transformation, Q is changed into $\sum_1^r \varkappa_i y_i^2$, where $\varkappa_i \neq 0$ for $i = 1, 2, \ldots, r$, it follows that Q is of rank r. The rank is the smallest number of independent variables, on which Q may be brought by a non-singular linear transformation.

A proposition which is often useful is the following: If Q may be written in the form $Q = L_1^2 + \cdots + L_p^2$, where the L_i are linear functions of $x_1, \ldots, x_n$, and if there are exactly h independent linear relations (cf 11.2) between the L_i, then the rank of Q is $p - h$. It follows that, if we know that there are *at least* h such linear relations, the rank of Q is $\leqq p - h$.

11.7. Adjugate and reciprocal matrices. — Let $A = \{a_{ik}\}$ be a square matrix, and let as before A_{ik} denote the cofactor of the element a_{ik}. If we form a matrix $\{A_{ik}\}$ with the cofactors as elements, and then transpose, we obtain a new matrix $\boldsymbol{A}^* = \{a_{ik}^*\}$, where $a_{ik}^* = A_{ki}$. We shall call $\boldsymbol{A}^*$ the *adjugate* of $\boldsymbol{A}$. By the identities (11.5.1) and (11.5.2) we find

$$\text{(11.7.1)} \qquad \boldsymbol{A}\boldsymbol{A}^* = \boldsymbol{A}^*\boldsymbol{A} = A\boldsymbol{I} = \begin{Bmatrix} A & 0 & \ldots & 0 \\ 0 & A & \ldots & 0 \\ \cdot & & \cdot & \cdot \\ 0 & 0 & \ldots & A \end{Bmatrix}.$$

For the cofactor A_{ik}^* of the element $a_{ik}^* = A_{ki}$ in $\boldsymbol{A}^*$ we have

$$\text{(11.7.2)} \qquad A_{ik}^* = A^{n-2} a_{ki}.$$

This is only a particular case of a general relation which expresses any minor of $\boldsymbol{A}^*$ in terms of A and its minors. We shall here only quote the further particular case

$$(11.7.3)\qquad \begin{vmatrix} A_{11} & A_{i1} \\ A_{1k} & A_{ik} \end{vmatrix} = A_{11} A_{ik} - A_{i1} A_{1k} = A A_{11.ik}.$$

When A is non-singular, the matrix $A^{-1} = \frac{1}{A} A^* = \left\{ \frac{A_{ki}}{A} \right\}$ is called the *reciprocal* of A. We obtain from (11.7.1)

$$(11.7.4)\qquad AA^{-1} = A^{-1}A = I.$$

The matrix equations $AX = I$ and $XA = I$ then both have a unique solution, viz. $X = A^{-1}$. It follows that the determinant of A^{-1} is A^{-1}. Further $(A^{-1})^{-1} = A$, so that the relation of reciprocity is mutual. The transpose of a reciprocal is equal to the reciprocal of the transpose: $(A^{-1})' = (A')^{-1}$. For the reciprocal of a product we have the rule $(AB)^{-1} = B^{-1} A^{-1}$.

When A is symmetric, we have $A_{ki} = A_{ik}$, so that the adjugate A^* and the reciprocal A^{-1} are also symmetric. The reciprocal of a diagonal matrix D with the diagonal elements $d_1, \ldots, d_n$ is another diagonal matrix D^{-1} with the diagonal elements $d_1^{-1}, \ldots, d_n^{-1}$.

If $Q = x'Ax$ is a non-singular quadratic form, the form $Q^{-1} = x'A^{-1}x$ is called the *reciprocal form* of Q. Obviously $(Q^{-1})^{-1} = Q$.

Let $x = (x_1, \ldots, x_n)$ and $t = (t_1, \ldots, t_n)$ be variable column vectors. If new variables $y = (y_1, \ldots, y_m)$ and $u = (u_1, \ldots, u_m)$ are introduced by the transformations

$$(11.7.5)\qquad y = Cx, \qquad t = C'u,$$

where $C = C_{mn}$, we have

$$(11.7.6)\qquad t'x = u'Cx = u'y.$$

The bilinear form $t'x = t_1 x_1 + \cdots + t_n x_n$ is thus transformed into the analogous form $u'y = u_1 y_1 + \cdots + u_m y_m$ in the new variables. Two sets of variables x_i and t_i which are transformed according to (11.7.5) are called *contragredient* sets of variables. In the particular case when $m = n$ and C is non-singular, (11.7.5) may be written

$$(11.7.7)\qquad y = Cx, \qquad u = (C')^{-1} t.$$

11.8. Linear equations. — We shall here only consider some particular cases. The *non-homogeneous* system

$$
(11.8.1)\qquad
\begin{aligned}
a_{11} x_1 + a_{12} x_2 + \cdots + a_{1n} x_n &= h_1, \\
\cdots\cdots\cdots\cdots\cdots\cdots \\
a_{n1} x_1 + a_{n2} x_2 + \cdots + a_{nn} x_n &= h_n,
\end{aligned}
$$

is equivalent to the matrix relation $\boldsymbol{A}\boldsymbol{x} = \boldsymbol{h}$, where $\boldsymbol{A} = \{a_{ik}\}$, $\boldsymbol{x} = (x_1, \ldots, x_n)$ and $\boldsymbol{h} = (h_1, \ldots, h_n)$. If $\boldsymbol{A}$ is non-singular, we may premultiply both sides by the reciprocal matrix $\boldsymbol{A}^{-1}$, and so obtain the unique solution $\boldsymbol{x} = \boldsymbol{A}^{-1}\boldsymbol{h}$, or in explicit form

$$
(11.8.2)\qquad x_k = \frac{1}{A}\sum_{i=1}^{n} h_i A_{ik} \qquad (k = 1, 2, \ldots, n).
$$

Thus x_k is expressed by a fraction with the denominator A and the numerator equal to the determinant obtained from A when the elements of the k:th column are replaced by the second members $h_1, \ldots, h_n$. This is the classical solution due to Cramer (1750).

Consider now the *homogeneous* system

$$
(11.8.3)\qquad
\begin{aligned}
a_{11} x_1 + a_{12} x_2 + \cdots + a_{1n} x_n &= 0, \\
\cdots\cdots\cdots\cdots\cdots\cdots \\
a_{m1} x_1 + a_{m2} x_2 + \cdots + a_{mn} x_n &= 0,
\end{aligned}
$$

or in matrix notation $\boldsymbol{A}\boldsymbol{x} = 0$, where m is not necessarily equal to n. By 11.6, the matrix $\boldsymbol{A}$ is of rank $r \leqq n$. If $r = n$, the system (11.8.3) has only the trivial solution $\boldsymbol{x} = 0$. On the other hand, if $r < n$, it is possible to find $n - r$ linearly independent vectors $\boldsymbol{c}_1, \ldots, \boldsymbol{c}_{n-r}$ such that the general solution of (11.8.3) may be written in the form $\boldsymbol{x} = t_1 \boldsymbol{c}_1 + \cdots + t_{n-r} \boldsymbol{c}_{n-r}$, where the t_i are arbitrary constants.

11.9. Orthogonal matrices. Characteristic numbers. — An *orthogonal* matrix is a square matrix $\boldsymbol{C} = \{c_{ik}\}$ such that $\boldsymbol{C}\boldsymbol{C}' = \boldsymbol{I}$. Hence $C^2 = 1$, so that the determinant $C = |\boldsymbol{C}| = \pm 1$. Obviously the transpose $\boldsymbol{C}'$ of an orthogonal $\boldsymbol{C}$ is itself orthogonal. Further $\boldsymbol{C}^{-1} = \boldsymbol{C}'$, and thus by the definition of the reciprocal matrix $C_{ik} = C c_{ik}$ for all i and k, and hence by the identities (11.5.1) and (11.5.2)

$$
(11.9.1)\qquad \sum_{j=1}^{n} c_{ij}\, c_{kj} = \begin{cases} 1 & \text{for } i = k, \\ 0 & \text{for } i \neq k, \end{cases}
$$

$$
(11.9.2)\qquad \sum_{j=1}^{n} c_{ji}\, c_{jk} = \begin{cases} 1 & \text{for } i = k, \\ 0 & \text{for } i \neq k. \end{cases}
$$

The product $C_1 C_2$ of two orthogonal matrices of the same order is itself orthogonal. — If any number $p < n$ of rows $c_{i1}, c_{i2}, \ldots, c_{in}$ $(i = 1, 2, \ldots, p)$ are given, such that the relations (11.9.1) are satisfied, we can always find $n - p$ further rows such that the resulting matrix of order $n \cdot n$ is orthogonal. The same holds, of course, for columns.

The linear transformation $\boldsymbol{x} = \boldsymbol{C}\boldsymbol{y}$, where $\boldsymbol{C}$ is orthogonal, is called an *orthogonal transformation*. The quadratic form $\boldsymbol{x}'\boldsymbol{x} = x_1^2 + \cdots + x_n^2$ is *invariant* under this transformation, i. e. it is transformed into the form $\boldsymbol{y}'\boldsymbol{C}'\boldsymbol{C}\boldsymbol{y} = \boldsymbol{y}'\boldsymbol{y} = y_1^2 + \cdots + y_n^2$, which has the same matrix $\boldsymbol{I}$. — The reciprocal transformation $\boldsymbol{y} = \boldsymbol{C}^{-1}\boldsymbol{x}$ is also orthogonal, since $\boldsymbol{C}^{-1} = \boldsymbol{C}'$ is orthogonal.

The orthogonal transformations have an important geometrical significance. In fact, any orthogonal transformation may be regarded as the analytical expression of the transformation of coordinates in an euclidean space of n dimensions which is effected by a rotation of a rectangular system of coordinate axes about a fixed origin. The distance $(x_1^2 + \cdots + x_n^2)^{\frac{1}{2}}$ from the origin to the point $(x_1, \ldots, x_n)$ is invariant under any such rotation.

If $\boldsymbol{A}$ is an arbitrary symmetric matrix, it is always possible to find an orthogonal matrix $\boldsymbol{C}$ such that the product $\boldsymbol{C}'\boldsymbol{A}\boldsymbol{C}$ is a diagonal matrix:

$$(11.9.3) \qquad \boldsymbol{C}'\boldsymbol{A}\boldsymbol{C} = \boldsymbol{K} = \left\{ \begin{matrix} \varkappa_1 & 0 & \ldots & 0 \\ 0 & \varkappa_2 & \ldots & 0 \\ \cdot & \cdot & \cdot & \cdot \\ 0 & 0 & \ldots & \varkappa_n \end{matrix} \right\}.$$

Any other orthogonal matrix satisfying the same condition yields the same diagonal elements $\varkappa_1, \ldots, \varkappa_n$, though possibly in another arrangement. The numbers $\varkappa_1, \ldots, \varkappa_n$, which thus depend only on the matrix $\boldsymbol{A}$, are called the *characteristic numbers* of $\boldsymbol{A}$. They are the n roots of the *secular equation*

$$(11.9.4) \qquad |\boldsymbol{A} - \varkappa \boldsymbol{I}| = \begin{vmatrix} a_{11} - \varkappa & a_{12} & \ldots & a_{1n} \\ a_{21} & a_{22} - \varkappa & \ldots & a_{2n} \\ \cdot & \cdot & \cdot & \cdot \\ a_{n1} & a_{n2} & \ldots & a_{nn} - \varkappa \end{vmatrix} = 0,$$

and are all real. Since $\boldsymbol{C}$ is non-singular, $\boldsymbol{A}$ and $\boldsymbol{K}$ have the same rank (cf 11.6). Hence the rank of $\boldsymbol{A}$ is equal to the number of the roots $\varkappa_i$ which are not zero. From (11.9.3) we obtain, taking the determinants on both sides and paying regard to the relation $C^2 = 1$,

(11.9.5) $$A = \varkappa_1 \varkappa_2 \ldots \varkappa_n.$$

If $\boldsymbol{A}$ is non-singular, the identity

(11.9.6) $$|\boldsymbol{A}^{-1} - \varkappa \boldsymbol{I}| = (-\varkappa)^n A^{-1} |\boldsymbol{A} - \frac{1}{\varkappa}\boldsymbol{I}|$$

shows that the characteristic numbers of $\boldsymbol{A}^{-1}$ are the reciprocals of the characteristic numbers of $\boldsymbol{A}$.

Finally, let $\boldsymbol{B}$ be a matrix of order $m \cdot n$, where $m \leqq n$. If $\boldsymbol{B}$ is of rank m, the symmetric matrix $\boldsymbol{BB}'$ of order $m \cdot m$ has all its characteristic numbers positive. It follows, in particular, that $\boldsymbol{BB}'$ is non-singular. — This is proved without difficulty if, in (11.9.3), we take $\boldsymbol{A} = \boldsymbol{BB}'$ and express an arbitrary characteristic number $\varkappa_i$ by means of the multiplication rule.

11.10. Non-negative quadratic forms. — If, for all real values of the variables $x_1, \ldots, x_n$, we have

$$Q(x_1, \ldots, x_n) = \sum_{i,k=1}^{n} a_{ik} x_i x_k \geqq 0,$$

where $a_{ki} = a_{ik}$, the form Q will be called a *non-negative* quadratic form. If, in addition, the sign of equality in the last relation holds only when all the x_i are equal to zero, we shall say that Q is *definite positive*. A form Q which is non-negative without being definite positive, will be called *semi-definite positive*. Each of the properties of being non-negative, definite positive or semi-definite positive, is obviously invariant under any non-singular linear transformation.

The symmetric matrix $\boldsymbol{A} = \{a_{ik}\}$ will be called non-negative, definite positive or semi-definite positive, according as the corresponding quadratic form $Q = \boldsymbol{x}'\boldsymbol{A}\boldsymbol{x}$ has these properties.

The orthogonal transformation $\boldsymbol{x} = \boldsymbol{C}\boldsymbol{y}$, where $\boldsymbol{C}$ is the orthogonal matrix occurring in the special transformation (11.9.3), changes the form Q into a form containing only quadratic terms:

(11.10.1) $$Q(x_1, \ldots, x_n) = \varkappa_1 y_1^2 + \varkappa_2 y_2^2 + \cdots + \varkappa_n y_n^2,$$

or in matrix notation $\boldsymbol{x}'\boldsymbol{A}\boldsymbol{x} = \boldsymbol{y}'\boldsymbol{K}\boldsymbol{y}$, where the $\varkappa_i$ are the characteristic numbers of $\boldsymbol{A}$, while $\boldsymbol{K}$ is the corresponding diagonal matrix occurring in (11.9.3). By the same orthogonal transformation, the form $Q - \varkappa(x_1^2 + \cdots + x_n^2)$ is transformed into $(\varkappa_1 - \varkappa) y_1^2 + \cdots + (\varkappa_n - \varkappa) y_n^2$. If $\varkappa \leqq$

the smallest characteristic number of $\boldsymbol{A}$, the last form is obviously non-negative, and it follows that the form $Q - \varkappa(x_1^2 + \cdots + x_n^2)$, with the matrix $\boldsymbol{A} - \varkappa \boldsymbol{I}$, has the same property.

If the form Q is definite positive, the form in the second member of (11.10.1) has the same property, and it follows that in this case all the characteristic numbers $\varkappa_i$ are positive. Hence by (11.9.5) we have $A > 0$, so that $\boldsymbol{A}$ is non-singular.

If, on the other hand, Q is semi-definite positive, the same argument shows that at least one of the characteristic numbers is zero, so that $A = 0$. If Q is of rank r, there are exactly r positive characteristic numbers, while the $n - r$ others are equal to zero. In this case, there are exactly $n-r$ linearly independent vectors $\boldsymbol{x}_p = (x_1^{(p)}, \ldots, x_n^{(p)})$ such that $Q(\boldsymbol{x}_p) = 0$.

The geometrical significance of the orthogonal transformation considered above is that, by a suitable rotation of the coordinate system, the quadric $Q(x_1, \ldots, x_n) = \text{const.}$ is referred to its principal axes. If Q is definite positive, the equation $Q = \text{const.}$ represents an ellipsoid in n dimensions, with the semi-axes $\varkappa_i^{-\frac{1}{2}}$. For semi-definite forms Q, we obtain various classes of elliptic cylinders.

If Q is definite positive, any form obtained by putting one or more of the x_i equal to zero must be definite positive. Hence any principal minor of Q is positive. For a semi-definite positive Q, the same argument shows that any principal minor is non-negative. — It follows in particular that if, in a non-negative form Q, the quadratic term x_i^2 does not occur, then Q must be wholly independent of x_i. Otherwise, in fact, the principal minor $a_{ii} a_{kk} - a_{ik}^2$ would be negative for some k. — Conversely, if the quantities $A, A_{11}, A_{11.22}, \ldots, A_{11.22\ldots n-1,\,n-1}$ are all positive, Q is definite positive.

The substitution $\boldsymbol{x} = \boldsymbol{A}^{-1}\boldsymbol{y}$ changes the form $Q = \boldsymbol{x}'\boldsymbol{A}\boldsymbol{x}$ into the reciprocal form $Q^{-1} = \boldsymbol{y}'\boldsymbol{A}^{-1}\boldsymbol{y}$. Thus if Q is definite positive, so is Q^{-1}, and conversely. This can also be seen directly from (11.9.6). — Consider now the relation (11.5.3) for a definite positive symmetric matrix $\boldsymbol{A}$. Since any principal submatrix of $\boldsymbol{A}$ is also definite positive, it follows that the last term in the second member of (11.5.3) is a definite positive quadratic form in the variables $a_{12}, \ldots, a_{1n}$, so that we have $0 < A \leqq a_{11} A_{11}$, and generally

(11.10.2) $$0 < A \leqq a_{ii} A_{ii} \qquad (i = 1, 2, \ldots, n).$$

By repeated application of the same argument we obtain

$$0 < A \leqq a_{11}\, a_{22} \ldots a_{nn}. \tag{11.10.3}$$

The sign of equality holds here only when $\boldsymbol{A}$ is a diagonal matrix. — For a general non-negative matrix, the relation (11.10.3) holds, of course, if we replace the sign $<$ by $\leqq$.

11.11. Decomposition of $\sum_{1}^{n} x_i^2$. — In certain statistical applications we are concerned with various relations of the type

$$\sum_{1}^{n} x_i^2 = Q_1 + \cdots + Q_k, \tag{11.11.1}$$

where Q_i is for $i = 1, 2, \ldots, k$, a non-negative quadratic form in $x_1, \ldots, x_n$ of rank r_i.

Consider first the particular case $k = 2$, and suppose that there exists an orthogonal transformation changing Q_1 into a sum of r_1 squares: $Q_1 = \sum_{1}^{r_1} y_i^2$. Applying this transformation to both sides of (11.11.1), the left-hand side becomes $\sum_{1}^{n} y_i^2$, and it follows that Q_2 is changed into $\sum_{r_1+1}^{n} y_i^2$. Thus the rank of Q_2 is $r_2 = n - r_1$, and all its characteristic numbers are 0 or 1. — As an example, we consider the identity

$$\sum_{1}^{n} x_i^2 = n\bar{x}^2 + \sum_{1}^{n} (x_i - \bar{x})^2, \tag{11.11.2}$$

where $\bar{x} = \frac{1}{n}\sum_{1}^{n} x_i$. Any orthogonal transformation $\boldsymbol{y} = \boldsymbol{C}\boldsymbol{x}$ such that the first row of $\boldsymbol{C}$ is $\frac{1}{\sqrt{n}}, \frac{1}{\sqrt{n}}, \ldots, \frac{1}{\sqrt{n}}$, will change the form $n\bar{x}^2 = \left(\frac{x_1}{\sqrt{n}} + \frac{x_2}{\sqrt{n}} + \cdots + \frac{x_n}{\sqrt{n}}\right)^2$ into y_1^2. Thus the same transformation changes $\sum_{1}^{n} (x_i - \bar{x})^2$ into $\sum_{2}^{n} y_i^2$. In the decomposition of $\sum_{1}^{n} x_i^2$ according to (11.11.2), the two terms in the second member are thus of ranks 1 and $n - 1$ respectively.

Consider now the relation (11.11.1) for an arbitrary $k > 1$. We shall prove the following proposition due to Cochran (Ref. 66; cf also Madow, Ref. 154):

If $\sum_{1}^{k} r_i = n$, *there exists an orthogonal transformation* $\boldsymbol{x} = \boldsymbol{C}\boldsymbol{y}$ *changing each* Q_i *into a sum of squares according to the relations*

$$Q_1 = \sum_{1}^{r_1} y_i^2, \quad Q_2 = \sum_{r_1+1}^{r_1+r_2} y_i^2, \ldots, \quad Q_k = \sum_{n-r_k+1}^{n} y_i^2,$$

i. e. such that no two Q_i *contain a common variable* y_i.

We shall prove this theorem by induction. For $k = 1$, the truth of the theorem is evident. We thus have to show that, if the theorem holds for a decomposition in $k - 1$ terms, it also holds for k terms. In order to show this, we first apply to (11.11.1) an orthogonal transformation $\boldsymbol{x} = \boldsymbol{C}_1 \boldsymbol{z}$ changing Q_1 into $\sum_{1}^{r_1} \varkappa_i z_i^2$. This gives us

$$\sum_{1}^{r_1} (1 - \varkappa_i) z_i^2 + \sum_{r_1+1}^{n} z_i^2 = Q_2' + \cdots + Q_k',$$

where $Q_2', \ldots, Q_k'$ denote the transforms of $Q_2, \ldots, Q_k$. We now assert that all the $\varkappa_i$ are equal to 1. Suppose, in fact, that p of the $\varkappa_i$ are different from 1, while the rest are equal to 1. Both members of the last relation are quadratic forms in $z_1, \ldots, z_n$. The rank of the first member is $n - r_1 + p$, while by 11.6 the rank of the second member is at most equal to $r_2 + \cdots + r_k = n - r_1$. Thus $p = 0$, and all $\varkappa_i = 1$, so that we obtain

$$\sum_{r_1+1}^{n} z_i^2 = Q_2' + \cdots + Q_k'. \tag{11.11.3}$$

Here, the variables $z_1, \ldots, z_r$ do not occur in the first member, and we shall now show that these variables do not occur in any term in the second member. If, e. g., Q_2' would not be independent of z_1, then by the preceding paragraph Q_2' must contain a term $c z_1^2$ with $c > 0$. Since the coefficients of z_1^2 in $Q_3', \ldots, Q_k'$ are certainly non-negative, this would, however, imply a contradiction with (11.11.3).

Thus (11.11.3) gives a representation of $\sum_{r_1+1}^{n} z_i^2$ as a sum of $k - 1$

non-negative forms in $z_{r_1+1}, \ldots, z_n$. By hypothesis the Cochran theorem holds for this decomposition. Thus there exists an orthogonal transformation in $n-r_1$ variables, replacing $z_{r_1+1}, \ldots, z_n$ by new variables $y_{r_1+1}, \ldots, y_n$ such that

$$(11.11.4) \qquad Q_2' = \sum_{r_1+1}^{r_1+r_2} y_i^2, \ldots, Q_k' = \sum_{n-r_k+1}^{n} y_i^2.$$

If we complete this transformation by the r_1 equations $z_1 = y_1, \ldots, z_{r_1} = y_{r_1}$, we obtain an orthogonal transformation in n variables, $\boldsymbol{z} = \boldsymbol{C}_2 \boldsymbol{y}$, such that (11.11.4) holds.

The result of performing successively the transformations $\boldsymbol{x} = \boldsymbol{C}_1 \boldsymbol{z}$ and $\boldsymbol{z} = \boldsymbol{C}_2 \boldsymbol{y}$ will be a composed transformation $\boldsymbol{x} = \boldsymbol{C}_1 \boldsymbol{C}_2 \boldsymbol{y}$ which is orthogonal, since the product of two orthogonal matrices is itself orthogonal. This transformation has all the required properties, and thus the theorem is proved.

Let us remark that if, in (11.11.1), we only know that every Q_i is non-negative and that the rank of Q_i is *at most* equal to r_i, where $\sum_1^k r_i = n$, we can at once infer that Q_i is effectively of rank r_i, so that the conditions of the Cochran theorem are satisfied. In fact, since the rank of a sum of quadratic forms is at most equal to the sum of the ranks, we have, denoting by r_i' the rank of Q_i,

$$n \leqq \sum_1^k r_i' \leqq \sum_1^k r_i = n.$$

Thus $\sum r_i' = \sum r_i$, and $r_i' \leqq r_i$. This evidently implies $r_i' = r_i$ for all i.

We finally remark that the Cochran theorem evidently holds true if, in (11.11.1), *the first member is replaced by a quadratic form Q in any number of variables which, by an orthogonal transformation, may be transformed into* $\sum_1^n x_i^2$.

11.12. Some integral formulae. — We shall first prove the important formula

$$(11.12.1\text{ a}) \qquad \int_{-\infty}^{\infty} \cdots \int_{-\infty}^{\infty} e^{i\boldsymbol{t}'\boldsymbol{x} - \frac{1}{2}\boldsymbol{x}'\boldsymbol{A}\boldsymbol{x}}\, d x_1 \ldots d x_n = \frac{(2\pi)^{\frac{n}{2}}}{\sqrt{A}}\, e^{-\frac{1}{2}\boldsymbol{t}'\boldsymbol{A}^{-1}\boldsymbol{t}},$$

or in ordinary notation

(11.12.1 b) $$\int_{-\infty}^{\infty} \cdots \int_{-\infty}^{\infty} e^{i\sum_1^n t_j x_j - \frac{1}{2} Q(x_1, \ldots, x_n)} dx_1 \ldots dx_n = \frac{(2\pi)^{\frac{n}{2}}}{\sqrt{A}} e^{-\frac{1}{2} Q^{-1}(t_1, \ldots, t_n)},$$

where Q is a definite positive quadratic form of matrix $\boldsymbol{A}$, while $\boldsymbol{t} = (t_1, \ldots, t_n)$ is a real vector. As in the preceding paragraphs, A is the determinant $|\boldsymbol{A}|$, while Q^{-1} is the reciprocal form defined in 11.7. — For $n = 1$, the formula reduces to (10.5.2).

In order to prove (11.12.1 a) we introduce new variables $\boldsymbol{y} = (y_1, \ldots, y_n)$ by the substitution $\boldsymbol{x} = \boldsymbol{C}\boldsymbol{y}$, where $\boldsymbol{C}$ is the orthogonal matrix of (11.9.3), so that $\boldsymbol{C}'\boldsymbol{A}\boldsymbol{C} = \boldsymbol{K}$, where $\boldsymbol{K}$ is the diagonal matrix formed by the characteristic numbers $\varkappa_j$ of $\boldsymbol{A}$. At the same time we replace the vector $\boldsymbol{t}$ by a new vector $\boldsymbol{u} = (u_1, \ldots, u_n)$ by means of the contragredient substitution (cf 11.7.7) $\boldsymbol{t} = (\boldsymbol{C}')^{-1}\boldsymbol{u}$, which in this case reduces to $\boldsymbol{t} = \boldsymbol{C}\boldsymbol{u}$, since $\boldsymbol{C}$ is orthogonal. By (11.7.6) we then have $\boldsymbol{t}'\boldsymbol{x} = \boldsymbol{u}'\boldsymbol{y}$. Denoting the integral in the first member of (11.12.1 a) by J, we then obtain, since $C = \pm 1$,

$$J = \int_{-\infty}^{\infty} \cdots \int_{-\infty}^{\infty} e^{i\boldsymbol{u}'\boldsymbol{y} - \frac{1}{2}\boldsymbol{y}'\boldsymbol{K}\boldsymbol{y}} dy_1 \ldots dy_n = \prod_{j=1}^{n} \int_{-\infty}^{\infty} e^{iu_j y_j - \frac{1}{2}\varkappa_j y_j^2} dy_j.$$

Applying (10.5.2) to every factor of the last expression, we obtain

$$J = \frac{(2\pi)^{\frac{n}{2}}}{\sqrt{\varkappa_1 \varkappa_2 \ldots \varkappa_n}} e^{-\frac{1}{2}\sum_1^n \frac{u_j^2}{\varkappa_j}} = \frac{(2\pi)^{\frac{n}{2}}}{\sqrt{A}} e^{-\frac{1}{2}\boldsymbol{u}'\boldsymbol{K}^{-1}\boldsymbol{u}},$$

since by 11.7 the diagonal matrix with the diagonal elements $\frac{1}{\varkappa_j}$ is identical with the reciprocal $\boldsymbol{K}^{-1}$, while by (11.9.5) we have $A = \varkappa_1 \varkappa_2 \ldots \varkappa_n$. We have, however, $\boldsymbol{K}^{-1} = (\boldsymbol{C}'\boldsymbol{A}\boldsymbol{C})^{-1} = \boldsymbol{C}^{-1}\boldsymbol{A}^{-1}(\boldsymbol{C}')^{-1} = \boldsymbol{C}'\boldsymbol{A}^{-1}\boldsymbol{C}$, since $\boldsymbol{C}$ is orthogonal. Hence $\boldsymbol{u}'\boldsymbol{K}^{-1}\boldsymbol{u} = \boldsymbol{u}'\boldsymbol{C}'\boldsymbol{A}^{-1}\boldsymbol{C}\boldsymbol{u} = \boldsymbol{t}'\boldsymbol{A}^{-1}\boldsymbol{t}$, and thus finally

$$J = \frac{(2\pi)^{\frac{n}{2}}}{\sqrt{A}} e^{-\frac{1}{2}\boldsymbol{t}'\boldsymbol{A}^{-1}\boldsymbol{t}},$$

i. e. the formula (11.12.1 a). — Putting in particular $t = 0$, we obtain the formula

$$\int_{-\infty}^{\infty} \cdots \int_{-\infty}^{\infty} e^{-\frac{1}{2} Q(x_1, \ldots, x_n)} \, dx_1 \ldots dx_n = \frac{(2\pi)^{\frac{n}{2}}}{\sqrt{A}}. \tag{11.12.2}$$

This holds even for a matrix A with complex elements, provided that the matrix formed by the real parts of the elements is definite positive.

We further consider the integral

$$V = \int_{Q(x_1, \ldots, x_n) < c^2} \cdots \int dx_1 \ldots dx_n,$$

which represents the n-dimensional »volume» of the domain bounded by the ellipsoid $Q = c^2$. The orthogonal transformation used above, followed by the simple substitution $y_i = \frac{c}{\sqrt{\varkappa_i}} z_i$, shows that we have

$$V = \frac{c^n}{\sqrt{A}} \int_{\sum_1^n z_i^2 < 1} \cdots \int dz_1 \ldots dz_n.$$

The last integral represents the volume of the n-dimensional »unit sphere», and it will be shown below that its value is $\frac{\pi^{\frac{n}{2}}}{\Gamma\left(\frac{n}{2} + 1\right)}$, so that

$$V = \frac{\pi^{\frac{n}{2}}}{\Gamma\left(\frac{n}{2} + 1\right)} \cdot \frac{c^n}{\sqrt{A}}. \tag{11.12.3}$$

We shall finally require the value of the integral

$$B_{ik} = \int_{Q < c^2} \cdots \int x_i x_k \, dx_1 \ldots dx_n,$$

extended over the same domain as the integral V. Making the same substitutions as in the case of V, we find by some calculation that the matrix $\boldsymbol{B}$ with the elements B_{ik} is

$$\boldsymbol{B} = g_n \boldsymbol{C} \boldsymbol{K}^{-1} \boldsymbol{C}' = g_n \boldsymbol{A}^{-1},$$

where

$$g_n = \frac{c^{n+2}}{\sqrt{A}} \int \cdots \int_{\Sigma z_i^2 < 1} z_1^2 \, dz_1 \ldots dz_n .$$

It will be shown below that we have

$$g_n = \frac{c^{n+2}}{\sqrt{A}} \cdot \frac{\pi^{\frac{n}{2}}}{2\,\Gamma\left(\frac{n}{2}+2\right)} = \frac{c^2 V}{n+2},$$

so that

$$B_{ik} = \frac{c^2 V}{n+2} \cdot \frac{A_{ki}}{A}. \tag{11.12.4}$$

The *Dirichlet integrals* used above:

$$j_1 = \int \ldots \int dz_1 \ldots dz_n \text{ and } j_2 = \int \ldots \int z_1^2 \, dz_1 \ldots dz_n,$$

extended over the n-dimensional unit sphere $\sum_1^n z_i^2 < 1$, can be calculated by means of the transformation

$$\begin{aligned} z_1 &= \cos \varphi_1, \\ z_2 &= \sin \varphi_1 \cos \varphi_2, \\ z_3 &= \sin \varphi_1 \sin \varphi_2 \cos \varphi_3, \\ &\ldots\ldots\ldots\ldots\ldots \\ z_n &= \sin \varphi_1 \ldots \sin \varphi_{n-1} \cos \varphi_n, \end{aligned}$$

which establishes a one-to-one correspondence between the domains $\sum z_i^2 < 1$ and $0 < \varphi_i < \pi$ $(i = 1, 2, \ldots, n)$. The Jacobian of the transformation is $(-1)^n (\sin \varphi_1)^n \cdot (\sin \varphi_2)^{n-1} \ldots \sin \varphi_n$. With the aid of the relation

$$\int_0^{\pi} (\sin \varphi)^n \, d\varphi = 2 \int_0^{\frac{\pi}{2}} (\sin \varphi)^n \, d\varphi = \frac{\Gamma\left(\frac{n+1}{2}\right)}{\Gamma\left(\frac{n+2}{2}\right)} \sqrt{\pi},$$

which is proved by substituting $x = \sin^2 \varphi$ and using (12.4.2), we then obtain

$$j_1 = \int_0^{\pi} (\sin \varphi_1)^n d\varphi_1 \ldots \int_0^{\pi} \sin \varphi_n \, d\varphi_n = \frac{\pi^{\frac{n}{2}}}{\Gamma\left(\frac{n}{2}+1\right)},$$

$$j_2 = \int_0^{\pi} (\sin \varphi_1)^n \cos^2 \varphi_1 \, d\varphi_1 \int_0^{\pi} (\sin \varphi_2)^{n-1} \, d\varphi_2 \ldots \int_0^{\pi} \sin \varphi_n \, d\varphi_n = \frac{\pi^{\frac{n}{2}}}{2\Gamma\left(\frac{n}{2}+2\right)}.$$

CHAPTER 12.

MISCELLANEOUS COMPLEMENTS.

12.1. The symbols O, o and $\sim$. — When we are investigating the behaviour of a function $f(x)$ as x tends to zero, or infinity, or some other specified limit, it is often desirable to compare the *order of magnitude* of $f(x)$ with the order of magnitude of some known simple function $g(x)$. In such situations we shall often use the following notations.

1) When $\frac{f(x)}{g(x)}$ remains bounded as x tends to its limit, we write $f(x) = O(g(x))$, which may be read: »$f(x)$ is at most of the order $g(x)$».

2) When $\frac{f(x)}{g(x)}$ tends to zero, we write $f(x) = o(g(x))$, which may be read: »$f(x)$ is of a smaller order than $g(x)$».

3) When $\frac{f(x)}{g(x)}$ tends to unity, we write $f(x) \sim g(x)$, which may be read: »$f(x)$ is asymptotically equal to $g(x)$».

Thus as $x \to \infty$ we have e.g. $ax + b = O(x)$, $x^n = o(e^x)$, $\frac{x^2}{x + \log x} \sim x$.

Symbols like $O(x)$, $o(1)$ etc. will often be used without reference to a specified function $f(x)$. Thus e.g. $O(x)$ will stand for »any function which is at most of order x», while $O(1)$ signifies »any bounded function», and $o(1)$ »any function tending to zero».

As a further example we consider a function $f(x)$ which, in some neighbourhood of $x = 0$, has n continuous derivatives. We then have the Mac Laurin expansion

$$f(x) = \sum_0^n \frac{f^{(\nu)}(0)}{\nu!} x^\nu + R_n(x),$$

where

$$R_n(x) = \frac{f^{(n)}(\theta x) - f^{(n)}(0)}{n!} x^n, \qquad (0 < \theta < 1).$$

Now by hypothesis $f^{(n)}(\theta x) - f^{(n)}(0)$ tends to zero with x. According to the above we may thus write, as x tends to zero,

$$f(x) = \sum_0^n \frac{f^{(\nu)}(0)}{\nu!} x^\nu + o(x^n).$$

This relation, which holds even when $f(x)$ is complex, has already been used in (10.1.3).

12.2. The Euler-MacLaurin sum formula. — We define a sequence of auxiliary functions $P_1(x)$, $P_2(x)$, . . . by the trigonometric expansions

$$(12.2.1)\qquad \begin{aligned} P_{2k}(x) &= \sum_{\nu=1}^{\infty} \frac{\cos 2\nu\pi x}{2^{2k-1}(\nu\pi)^{2k}}, \\ P_{2k+1}(x) &= \sum_{\nu=1}^{\infty} \frac{\sin 2\nu\pi x}{2^{2k}(\nu\pi)^{2k+1}}. \end{aligned}$$

All these functions are periodical with the period 1, so that

$$P_n(x+1) = P_n(x).$$

For $n > 1$, the series representing $P_n(x)$ is absolutely and uniformly convergent for all real x, so that $P_n(x)$ is bounded and continuous over the whole interval $(-\infty, \infty)$.

The series for $P_1(x)$, on the other hand, is only conditionally convergent, and it is well known that we have $P_1(x) = -x + \frac{1}{2}$ for $0 < x < 1$. Denoting by $[x]$ the greatest integer $\leqq x$, it follows from the periodicity that we have for all non-integral values of x

$$P_1(x) = [x] - x + \tfrac{1}{2}.$$

Thus every integer is a discontinuity point for $P_1(x)$, and we have $|P_1(x)| < \frac{1}{2}$ for all x.

For integral values of x we have

$$\begin{aligned} P_{2k}(m) &= \frac{1}{2^{2k-1}\pi^{2k}} \sum_{1}^{\infty} \frac{1}{\nu^{2k}} = (-1)^{k-1} \frac{B_{2k}}{(2k)!}, \\ P_{2k+1}(m) &= 0. \end{aligned}$$

The numbers B_ν appearing here are the *Bernoulli numbers* defined by the expansion

$$(12.2.2)\qquad \frac{x}{e^x - 1} = \sum_{0}^{\infty} \frac{B_\nu}{\nu!} x^\nu.$$

We have

$$B_0 = 1,\quad B_1 = -\tfrac{1}{2},\quad B_2 = \tfrac{1}{6},\quad B_4 = -\tfrac{1}{30},\quad B_6 = \tfrac{1}{42}, \ldots,$$

while all the B_ν of odd order $\geqq 3$ are zero. — For $n > 1$ we have

$$\frac{d}{dx} P_n(x) = (-1)^{n-1} P_{n-1}(x).$$

For $n > 2$ this relation holds for all x, while for $n = 2$ its validity is restricted to non-integral values of x.

Consider now a function $g(x)$ which is continuous and has a continuous derivative $g'(x)$ for all x in the closed interval $(a + n_1 h,\ a + n_2 h)$, where a and $h > 0$ are constants, while n_1 and n_2 are positive or negative integers. For any integer ν such that $n_1 \leqq \nu < n_2$ we then find by partial integration

$$h\int_{\nu}^{\nu+1} P_1(x)\, g'(a + hx)\, dx = -\tfrac{1}{2}\, g(a + \nu h) - \tfrac{1}{2}\, g(a + (\nu + 1) h) + \int_{\nu}^{\nu+1} g(a + hx)\, dx.$$

Hence we obtain, summing over $\nu = n_1, \ldots, n_2 - 1$,

$$\sum_{n_1}^{n_2} g(a + h\nu) = \int_{n_1}^{n_2} g(a + hx)\, dx + \tfrac{1}{2}\, g(a + n_1 h) + \tfrac{1}{2}\, g(a + n_2 h) - \tag{12.2.3}$$
$$- h\int_{n_1}^{n_2} P_1(x)\, g'(a + hx)\, dx.$$

This is the simplest case of the *Euler-MacLaurin sum formula*, which is often very useful for the summation of series. If $g(x)$ has continuous derivatives of higher orders, the last term can be transformed by repeated partial integration, and we obtain the general formula

$$\sum_{n_1}^{n_2} g(a + h\nu) = \int_{n_1}^{n_2} g(a + hx)\, dx + \tfrac{1}{2}\, g(a + n_1 h) + \tfrac{1}{2}\, g(a + n_2 h) -$$
$$- \sum_{1}^{s} \frac{B_{2\nu}}{(2\nu)!}\, h^{2\nu-1} \left[g^{(2\nu-1)}(a + n_1 h) - g^{(2\nu-1)}(a + n_2 h)\right] + \tag{12.2.4}$$
$$+ (-1)^{s+1} h^{2s+1} \int_{n_1}^{n_2} P_{2s+1}(x)\, g^{(2s+1)}(a + hx)\, dx,$$

where s may be any non-negative integer, provided that all derivatives appearing in the formula exist and are continuous.

If $\sum_{-\infty}^{\infty} g(a + h\nu)$ and $\int_{-\infty}^{\infty} g(a + hx)\, dx$ both converge, we obtain from the formula (12.2.3)

$$\sum_{-\infty}^{\infty} g(a + h\nu) = \int_{-\infty}^{\infty} g(a + hx)\, dx - h\int_{-\infty}^{\infty} P_1(x)\, g'(a + hx)\, dx, \tag{12.2.5}$$

where the last integral must also converge. If, in addition, $g^{(2\nu-1)}(x) \to 0$ as $x \to \pm\infty$ for $\nu = 1, 2, \ldots, s$, we obtain from (12.2.4)

$$\sum_{-\infty}^{\infty} g(a + h\nu) = \tag{12.2.6}$$

$$= \int_{-\infty}^{\infty} g(a + hx)\,dx + (-1)^{s+1} h^{2s+1} \int_{-\infty}^{\infty} P_{2s+1}(x)\, g^{(2s+1)}(a + hx)\,dx.$$

If, in (12.2.3), we take $g(x) = \frac{1}{x}$, $a = 0$, $h = 1$, $n_1 = 1$ and $n_2 = n$, we obtain

$$\sum_{1}^{n} \frac{1}{\nu} = \log n + \tfrac{1}{2} + \frac{1}{2n} + \int_{1}^{n} \frac{P_1(x)}{x^2}\,dx.$$

From the definition of $P_1(x)$, it is easily seen that

$$0 < \int_{n}^{\infty} \frac{P_1(x)}{x^2}\,dx < \frac{1}{8n^2},$$

so that we have

$$\sum_{1}^{n} \frac{1}{\nu} = \log n + C + \frac{1}{2n} + O\left(\frac{1}{n^2}\right), \tag{12.2.7}$$

where

$$C = \tfrac{1}{2} + \int_{1}^{\infty} \frac{P_1(x)}{x^2}\,dx = 0.5772\ldots$$

is known as *Euler's constant.*

12.3. The Gamma function. — The Gamma function $\Gamma(p)$ is defined for all real $p > 0$ by the integral

$$\Gamma(p) = \int_{0}^{\infty} x^{p-1} e^{-x}\,dx. \tag{12.3.1}$$

By 7.3, the function is continuous and has continuous derivatives of all orders:

$$\Gamma^{(r)}(p) = \int_{0}^{\infty} x^{p-1} (\log x)^r e^{-x}\,dx$$

for any $p > 0$. When p tends to 0 or to $+\infty$, $\Gamma(p)$ tends to $+\infty$. Since the second derivative is always positive, $\Gamma(p)$ has one single minimum in $(0, \infty)$. Approximate calculation shows that the minimum is situated in the point $p_0 = 1.4616$, where the function assumes the value $\Gamma(p_0) = 0.8856$.

By a partial integration, we obtain from (12.3.1) for any $p > 0$

$$\Gamma(p+1) = p\,\Gamma(p).$$

When p is equal to a positive integer n, a repeated use of the last equality gives, since $\Gamma(1) = 1$,

$$\Gamma(n+1) = n!$$

From (12.3.1) we further obtain the relation

$$\int_0^\infty x^{\lambda-1} e^{-\alpha x}\,dx = \frac{\Gamma(\lambda)}{\alpha^\lambda}, \tag{12.3.2}$$

where $\alpha > 0$, $\lambda > 0$. If we replace here α by $\alpha + i t$ and develop the factor e^{-itx} in series, it can be shown that the last relation holds true for complex values of α, provided that the real part of α is positive.[1])

By (12.3.2), the function

$$f(x;\ \alpha,\lambda) = \begin{cases} \dfrac{\alpha^\lambda}{\Gamma(\lambda)} x^{\lambda-1} e^{-\alpha x} & \text{for } x > 0, \\ 0 & \text{for } x \leqq 0, \end{cases} \tag{12.3.3}$$

has, with respect to the variable x, the fundamental properties of a frequency function (cf 6.6): the function is always non-negative, and its integral over $(-\infty, \infty)$ is equal to 1. The corresponding distribution plays an important rôle in the applications (cf e. g. 18.1 and 19.4). It has the characteristic function

$$\int_{-\infty}^{\infty} e^{itx} f(x;\ \alpha,\lambda)\,dx = \frac{\alpha^\lambda}{\Gamma(\lambda)} \int_0^\infty x^{\lambda-1} e^{-(\alpha-it)x}\,dx =$$

$$= \frac{\alpha^\lambda}{\Gamma(\lambda)} \cdot \frac{\Gamma(\lambda)}{(\alpha - i t)^\lambda} = \frac{1}{\left(1 - \dfrac{it}{\alpha}\right)^\lambda}. \tag{12.3.4}$$

12.4. The Beta function. — The Beta function $B(p, q)$ is defined for all real $p > 0$, $q > 0$ by the integral

---

[1]) A reader acquainted with Cauchy's theorem on complex integration will be able to deduce the validity of (12.3.2) for complex α by a simple application of that theorem.

$$B(p, q) = \int_0^1 x^{p-1}(1-x)^{q-1}\, dx. \tag{12.4.1}$$

We shall prove the important relation

$$B(p, q) = \frac{\Gamma(p)\,\Gamma(q)}{\Gamma(p+q)}. \tag{12.4.2}$$

The integral

$$\int_0^\infty t^{p+q-1} x^{p-1} e^{-t(1+x)}\, dx = \Gamma(p)\, t^{q-1} e^{-t},$$

regarded as a function of the parameter t, satisfies the conditions of the integration theorem of 7.3 for any interval (ε, ∞) with $\varepsilon > 0$, so that we have

$$\Gamma(p) \int_\varepsilon^\infty t^{q-1} e^{-t}\, dt = \int_0^\infty dx \int_\varepsilon^\infty t^{p+q-1} x^{p-1} e^{-t(1+x)}\, dt.$$

When ε tends to zero, the first member tends to $\Gamma(p)\,\Gamma(q)$. In the second member, the integral with respect to t tends increasingly to the limit $\Gamma(p+q) \dfrac{x^{p-1}}{(1+x)^{p+q}}$, which is integrable with respect to x over $(0, \infty)$. According to (5.5.2) we then obtain

$$\Gamma(p)\,\Gamma(q) = \Gamma(p+q) \int_0^\infty \frac{x^{p-1}}{(1+x)^{p+q}}\, dx.$$

Introducing the new variable $y = \dfrac{x}{1+x}$ in the integral, we obtain the relation (12.4.2).

Taking in particular $p = q$ in (12.4.2) we obtain, introducing the new variable $y = 2x - 1$,

$$\frac{\Gamma^2(p)}{\Gamma(2p)} = \int_0^1 x^{p-1}(1-x)^{p-1}\, dx = 2^{2-2p} \int_0^1 (1-y^2)^{p-1}\, dy. \tag{12.4.3}$$

For $p = \frac{1}{2}$ this gives

$$\Gamma^2(\tfrac{1}{2}) = 2 \int_0^1 \frac{dy}{\sqrt{1-y^2}} = \pi, \qquad \Gamma(\tfrac{1}{2}) = \sqrt{\pi}.$$

On the other hand, putting in (12.4.3) $y^2 = z$, we obtain

$$\frac{\Gamma^2(p)}{\Gamma(2p)} = 2^{1-2p} \int_0^1 (1-z)^{p-1} z^{-\frac{1}{2}} dz = 2^{1-2p} \frac{\Gamma(p)\,\Gamma(\frac{1}{2})}{\Gamma(p+\frac{1}{2})},$$

(12.4.4) $$\Gamma(2p) = \frac{2^{2p-1}}{\sqrt{\pi}} \Gamma(p)\,\Gamma(p+\tfrac{1}{2}).$$

If we define a function $\beta(x;\, p,\, q)$ by the relation

(12.4.5) $$\beta(x;\, p, q) = \frac{\Gamma(p+q)}{\Gamma(p)\,\Gamma(q)} x^{p-1} (1-x)^{q-1}$$

for $0 < x < 1$, and put $\beta(x;\, p, q) = 0$ outside that interval, it follows from (12.4.1) and (12.4.2) that this function has the fundamental properties of a frequency function. The corresponding distribution, which has its total mass confined to the interval $(0, 1)$, will be further discussed in 18.4.

12.5. Stirling's formula. — We now proceed to deduce a famous formula due to Stirling, which gives an *asymptotic expression for* $\Gamma(p)$ when p is large. We shall first prove the relation

(12.5.1) $$\Gamma(p) = \lim_{n\to\infty} \frac{n!\; n^p}{p(p+1)\ldots(p+n)}$$

for any $p > 0$.

By repeated partial integration we obtain

$$\int_0^n x^{p-1} \left(1-\frac{x}{n}\right)^n dx = \frac{n!\; n^p}{p(p+1)\ldots(p+n)}.$$

The first member of this relation may be written as $\int_0^\infty g(x, n)\, dx$, $g(x, n) = x^{p-1}\left(1-\frac{x}{n}\right)^n$ for $0 < x < n$, and $g(x, n) = 0$ for $x \geqq n$. As n tends to infinity, $g(x, n)$ tends to $x^{p-1} e^{-x}$ for every $x > 0$, and it is easily seen that we always have $0 \leqq g(x, n) < x^{p-1} e^{-x}$. Hence by (5.5.2) we obtain (12.5.1).

It follows from (12.5.1) that $\log \Gamma(p) = \lim_{n\to\infty} S_n$, where

$$S_n = p \log n + \sum_{1}^{n} \log \nu - \sum_{0}^{n} \log (p + \nu).$$

Applying the Euler-MacLaurin formula (12.2.3) to both sums in the last expression, we obtain after some reductions

$$S_n = (p - \tfrac{1}{2}) \log p - (p + n + \tfrac{1}{2}) \log \left(1 + \frac{p}{n}\right) + \\ + 1 - \int_{1}^{n} \frac{P_1(x)}{x} dx + \int_{0}^{n} \frac{P_1(x)}{p + x} dx.$$

As n tends to infinity, the second term on the right-hand side tends to $-p$, while the two integrals are convergent (though not absolutely), owing to the fluctuations of sign of $P_1(x)$. Thus we obtain

(12.5.2) $$\log \Gamma(p) = (p - \tfrac{1}{2}) \log p - p + k + R(p),$$

where k is a constant, and the remainder term $R(p)$ has the expression

$$R(p) = \int_{0}^{\infty} \frac{P_1(x)}{p + x} dx.$$

This integral may be transformed by repeated partial integration, as shown in (12.2.4), and we obtain in this way

$$R(p) = \sum_{1}^{s} \frac{B_{2\nu}}{2\nu(2\nu - 1)p^{2\nu-1}} + (-1)^s (2s)! \int_{0}^{\infty} \frac{P_{2s+1}(x)}{(p + x)^{2s+1}} dx$$

for $s = 0, 1, 2, \ldots$ For any $s > 0$, the integral appearing here is absolutely convergent, and its modulus is smaller than

$$A \int_{p}^{\infty} \frac{dx}{x^{2s+1}} = \frac{A}{2 s p^{2s}},$$

where A is a constant. It follows in particular that $R(p) \to 0$ as $p \to \infty$.

In order to find the value of the constant k in (12.5.2), we observe that by (12.4.4) we have

$$\log \Gamma(2p) = \log \Gamma(p) + \log \Gamma(p + \tfrac{1}{2}) + (2p - 1) \log 2 - \tfrac{1}{2} \log \pi.$$

Substituting here for the Γ-functions their expressions obtained from (12.5.2), and allowing p to tend to infinity, we find after some reductions

$$k = \tfrac{1}{2} \log 2\pi.$$

We have thus proved the *Stirling formula*:

$$\log \Gamma(p) = (p - \tfrac{1}{2}) \log p - p + \tfrac{1}{2} \log 2\pi + R(p), \tag{12.5.3}$$

where

$$R(p) = \int_0^\infty \frac{P_1(x)}{p+x}\,dx = \frac{1}{12p} + O\left(\frac{1}{p^3}\right)$$

$$= \frac{1}{12p} - \frac{1}{360p^3} + O\left(\frac{1}{p^5}\right)$$

$$\cdots\cdots\cdots\cdots$$

From Stirling's formula, we deduce i. a. the asymptotic expressions

$$n! = \Gamma(n+1) \sim \left(\frac{n}{e}\right)^n \sqrt{2\pi n},$$

and further, when $p \to \infty$ while h remains fixed,

$$\frac{\Gamma(p+h)}{\Gamma(p)} \sim p^h.$$

By differentiation, we obtain from Stirling's formula

$$\frac{\Gamma'(p)}{\Gamma(p)} = \log p - \frac{1}{2p} - \int_0^\infty \frac{P_1(x)}{(p+x)^2}\,dx,$$

(12.5.4)

$$\frac{\Gamma''(p)}{\Gamma(p)} - \left(\frac{\Gamma'(p)}{\Gamma(p)}\right)^2 = \frac{1}{p} + \frac{1}{2p^2} + 2\int_0^\infty \frac{P_1(x)}{(p+x)^3}\,dx.$$

For $p = 1$, the first relation gives

$$\Gamma'(1) = -\tfrac{1}{2} - \int_0^\infty \frac{P_1(x)}{(1+x)^2}\,dx = -\tfrac{1}{2} - \int_1^\infty \frac{P_1(x)}{x^2}\,dx = -C, \tag{12.5.5}$$

where C is Euler's constant defined by (12.2.7). — Differentiating the equation $\Gamma(p+1) = p\,\Gamma(p)$, we further obtain

$$\frac{\Gamma'(p+1)}{\Gamma(p+1)} = \frac{1}{p} + \frac{\Gamma'(p)}{\Gamma(p)},$$

and hence for integral values of p

$$\frac{\Gamma'(n)}{\Gamma(n)} = 1 + \tfrac{1}{2} + \cdots + \frac{1}{n-1} - C. \tag{12.5.6}$$

An application of the Euler-MacLaurin formula (12.2.3) gives

$$\sum_{n}^{\infty} \frac{1}{\nu^2} = \frac{1}{n} + \frac{1}{2n^2} + 2\int_{n}^{\infty} \frac{P_1(x)}{x^3}\,dx.$$

Taking $p = n$ in the second relation (12.5.4), we thus obtain (cf p. 123)

$$\frac{\Gamma''(n)}{\Gamma(n)} - \left(\frac{\Gamma'(n)}{\Gamma(n)}\right)^2 = \sum_{n}^{\infty} \frac{1}{\nu^2} = \frac{\pi^2}{6} - \sum_{1}^{n-1} \frac{1}{\nu^2}. \tag{12.5.7}$$

12.6. Orthogonal polynomials. — Let $F(x)$ be a distribution function with finite moments (cf 7.4) α_ν of all orders. We shall say that x_0 is a *point of increase* for $F(x)$, if $F(x_0 + h) > F(x_0 - h)$ for every $h > 0$.

Suppose first that the set of all points of increase of F is infinite. We shall then show that there exists a sequence of polynomials $p_0(x)$, $p_1(x)$, ... uniquely determined by the following conditions:

a) $p_n(x)$ is of degree n, and the coefficient of x^n in $p_n(x)$ is positive.

b) The $p_n(x)$ satisfy the orthogonality conditions

$$\int_{-\infty}^{\infty} p_m(x)\,p_n(x)\,dF(x) = \begin{cases} 1 & \text{for} \quad m = n, \\ 0 & \text{for} \quad m \neq n. \end{cases}$$

The $p_n(x)$ will be called the *orthogonal polynomials* associated with the distribution corresponding to $F(x)$.

We first observe that for any $n \geqq 0$ the quadratic form in the $n + 1$ variables $u_0, u_1, \ldots, u_n$

$$\int_{-\infty}^{\infty} (u_0 + u_1 x + \cdots + u_n x^n)^2\,dF(x) = \sum_{i,k=0}^{n} \alpha_{i+k}\,u_i\,u_k$$

is definite positive. For by hypothesis $F(x)$ has at least $n + 1$ points of increase, and at least one of these must be different from all the n zeros of $u_0 + \cdots + u_n x^n$, so that the integral is always positive as long as the u_i are not all equal to zero. It follows (cf 11.10) that the determinant of the form is positive:

$$D_n = \begin{vmatrix} \alpha_0 & \alpha_1 & \ldots & \alpha_n \\ \alpha_1 & \alpha_2 & \ldots & \alpha_{n+1} \\ \cdot & \cdot & \cdot\;\cdot\;\cdot & \cdot \\ \alpha_n & \alpha_{n+1} & \ldots & \alpha_{2n} \end{vmatrix} > 0.$$

Obviously we must have $p_0(x) = 1$. Now write

$$p_n(x) = u_0 + u_1 x + \cdots + u_n x^n,$$

where $n > 0$, and try to determine the coefficients u_i from the condi tions a) and b). Since every $p_i(x)$ is to have the precise degree i, any power x^i can be represented as a linear combination of $p_0(x), \ldots, p_i(x)$. It follows that we must have

$$\int_{-\infty}^{\infty} x^i p_n(x)\, dF(x) = 0$$

for $i = 0, 1, \ldots, n-1$. Carrying out the integrations, we thus have n linear and homogeneous equations between the $n+1$ unknowns $u_0, \ldots, u_n$, and it follows that any polynomial $p_n(x)$ satisfying our conditions must necessarily be of the form

(12.6.1) $$p_n(x) = K \begin{vmatrix} \alpha_0 & \alpha_1 & \ldots & \alpha_n \\ \cdot & \cdot & \cdot & \cdot \\ \alpha_{n-1} & \alpha_n & \ldots & \alpha_{2n-1} \\ 1 & x & \ldots & x^n \end{vmatrix},$$

where K is a constant. For $K \neq 0$, this polynomial is of precise degree n, as the coefficient of x^n in the determinant is $D_{n-1} > 0$. Thus $p_n(x)$ is uniquely determined by the conditions that $\int p_n^2\, dF = 1$ and that the coefficient of x^n should be positive.[1]) We have thus established the existence of a uniquely determined sequence of orthogonal polynomials corresponding to any distribution with an infinite number of points of increase.

If $F(x)$ has only N points of increase, it easily follows from the above proof that the $p_n(x)$ exist and are uniquely determined for $n = 0, 1, \ldots, N-1$. The determinants D_n are in this case still positive for $n = 0, 1, \ldots, N-1$, but for $n \geqq N$ we have $D_n = 0$.

Consider in particular the case of a distribution with a continuous frequency function $f(x) = F'(x)$, and let $p_0(x), \ldots$ be the corresponding orthogonal polynomials. If $g(x)$ is another frequency function, we may try to develop $g(x)$ in a series

(12.6.2) $$g(x) = b_0 p_0(x) f(x) + b_1 p_1(x) f(x) + \cdots$$

---

[1]) It can be shown that $K = (D_{n-1} D_n)^{-\frac{1}{2}}$. Cf e. g. Szegö, Ref. 36.

Multiply with $p_n(x)$ and suppose that we may integrate term by term. The orthogonality relations then give

$$b_n = \int_{-\infty}^{\infty} p_n(x)\, g(x)\, dx. \tag{12.6.3}$$

Thus in particular $b_0 = 1$. Expansions of this type may sometimes render good service for the analytic representation of distributions. — We shall now give some examples of orthogonal polynomials.

1. The *Hermite polynomials* $H_n(x)$ are defined by the relations

$$\left(\frac{d}{dx}\right)^n e^{-\frac{x^2}{2}} = (-1)^n H_n(x)\, e^{-\frac{x^2}{2}} \qquad (n = 0, 1, 2, \ldots). \tag{12.6.4}$$

$H_n(x)$ is a polynomial of degree n, and we have

$$\begin{aligned} &H_0(x) = 1, \quad H_1(x) = x, \quad H_2(x) = x^2 - 1, \\ &H_3(x) = x^3 - 3x, \quad H_4(x) = x^4 - 6x^2 + 3, \\ &H_5(x) = x^5 - 10x^3 + 15x, \quad H_6(x) = x^6 - 15x^4 + 45x^2 - 15, \\ &\ldots\ldots\ldots\ldots\ldots\ldots\ldots\ldots \end{aligned} \tag{12.6.5}$$

By repeated partial integration, we obtain the relation

$$\int_{-\infty}^{\infty} H_m(x)\, H_n(x)\, d\Phi(x) = \frac{1}{\sqrt{2\pi}} \int_{-\infty}^{\infty} H_m(x)\, H_n(x)\, e^{-\frac{x^2}{2}} dx = \begin{cases} n! \text{ for } m = n, \\ 0 \text{ for } m \neq n, \end{cases} \tag{12.6.6}$$

which shows that $\left\{\frac{1}{\sqrt{n!}} H_n(x)\right\}$ is the sequence of orthogonal polynomials associated with the normal distribution defined by (10.5.3). We also note the expansions

$$\sum_0^{\infty} \frac{H_\nu(x)}{\nu!} t^\nu = e^{-\frac{t^2}{2} + tx}, \tag{12.6.7}$$

and

$$\sum_0^{\infty} \frac{H_\nu(x)\, H_\nu(y)}{\nu!} t^\nu = \frac{1}{\sqrt{1 - t^2}} e^{-\frac{t^2 x^2 + t^2 y^2 - 2txy}{2(1 - t^2)}}, \qquad (|t| < 1). \tag{12.6.8}$$

The first of these follows simply from the definition (12.6.4). A proof of (12.6.8) given by Cramér will be found in Charlier, Ref. 9 a, p. 50—53.

2. The Laguerre polynomials $L_n^{(\lambda)}(x)$ are defined by the relations

$$\left(\frac{d}{dx}\right)^n (x^{n+\lambda-1} e^{-x}) = (-1)^n n!\, L_n^{(\lambda)}(x)\, x^{\lambda-1} e^{-x},$$

which give

$$L_0(x) = 1, \quad L_1(x) = x - \lambda, \quad L_2(x) = \frac{x^2 - 2(\lambda+1)x + \lambda(\lambda+1)}{2}, \ldots$$

By repeated partial integration we find

$$\frac{1}{\Gamma(\lambda)} \int_0^\infty L_m^{(\lambda)}(x) L_n^{(\lambda)}(x) x^{\lambda-1} e^{-x} dx = \begin{cases} \binom{n+\lambda-1}{n} & \text{for } m = n, \\ 0 & \text{for } m \neq n, \end{cases}$$

so that $\left\{ \frac{L_n^{(\lambda)}(x)}{\sqrt{\binom{n+\lambda-1}{n}}} \right\}$ is the sequence of orthogonal polynomials associated with the distribution defined by the frequency function $f(x;\, \alpha, \lambda)$ considered in (12.3.3), when we take $\alpha = 1$.

3. Consider the distribution obtained by placing the mass $\frac{1}{N}$ in each of the N points $x_1, x_2, \ldots, x_N$. The corresponding distribution function is a step-function with a step of height $\frac{1}{N}$ in each x_i. Let $p_0(x), \ldots, p_{N-1}(x)$ be the associated orthogonal polynomials, which according to the above are uniquely determined. The orthogonality relations then reduce to

$$\frac{1}{N} \sum_{i=1}^{N} p_m(x_i) p_n(x_i) = \begin{cases} 1 & \text{for } m = n, \\ 0 & \text{for } m \neq n. \end{cases}$$

These polynomials may be used with advantage e. g. in the following problem. Suppose that we have N observed points $(x_1, y_1), \ldots, (x_N, y_N)$, and want to find the parabola $y = q(x)$ of degree $n < N$, which gives the *closest fit* to the observed ordinates, in the sense of the principle of least squares, i. e. such that

$$U = \frac{1}{N} \sum_{i=1}^{N} (y_i - q(x_i))^2$$

becomes a minimum. We then write $q(x)$ in the form

$$q(x) = c_0 p_0(x) + \cdots + c_n p_n(x),$$

and the ordinary rules for finding a minimum now immediately give

$$c_r = \frac{1}{N} \sum_{i=1}^{N} y_i p_r(x_i)$$

for $r = 0, 1, \ldots, n$, while the corresponding minimum value of U is

$$U_{\min} = \frac{1}{N} \sum_{i=1}^{N} y_i^2 - c_0^2 - c_1^2 - \cdots - c_n^2.$$

The case when the points x_i are equidistant is particularly important in the applications. In that case, the numerical calculation of $q(x)$ and $U_{\min}$ may be performed with a comparatively small amount of labour. Cf e. g. Esscher (Ref. 82) and Aitken (Ref. 50). — Cf further the theory of *parabolic regression* in 21.6.

SECOND PART

RANDOM VARIABLES AND PROBABILITY DISTRIBUTIONS

CHAPTERS 13—14. FOUNDATIONS.

CHAPTER 13.

STATISTICS AND PROBABILITY.

13.1. Random experiments. — In the most varied fields of practical and scientific activity, cases occur where certain experiments or observations may be repeated a large number of times under similar circumstances. On each occasion, our attention is then directed to a *result of the observation*, which is expressed by a certain number of characteristic features.

In many cases these characteristics directly take a quantitative form: at each observation something is counted or measured. In other cases, the characteristics are qualitative: we observe e. g. the colour of a certain object, the occurrence or non-occurrence of some specified event in connection with each experiment, etc. In the latter case, it is always possible to express the characteristics in numerical form according to some conventional system of notation. Whenever it is found convenient, we may thus always suppose that the result of each observation is expressed by a certain number of quantities.

1. If we make a series of throws with an ordinary die, each throw yields as its result one of the numbers $1, 2, \ldots, 6$.

2. If we measure the length and the weight of the body of each member of a group of animals belonging to the same species, every individual gives rise to an observation, the result of which is expressed by two numbers.

3. If, in a steel factory, we take a sample from every day's production, and measure its hardness, tensile strength and percentage of coal, sulphur and phosphorus, the result of each observation is given by five numbers.

4. If we observe at regular time intervals the prices of k different commodities, the result of each observation is expressed by k numbers.

5. If we observe the sex of every child born in a certain district, the result of each observation is not directly expressed by numbers. We may, however, agree to denote the birth of a boy by 1, and the birth of a girl by 0, and thus conventionally express our results in numerical form.

In some cases we know the phenomenon under investigation sufficiently well to feel justified in making exact predictions with respect to the result of each individual observation. Thus if our experiments consist in observing, for every year, the number of eclipses of the sun visible from a given observatory, we do not hesitate to predict, on the strength of astronomical calculations, the exact value of this number. A similar situation arises in every case where it is assumed that the laws governing the phenomena are known, and these laws are sufficiently simple to be used for calculations in practice.

In the majority of cases, however, our knowledge is not precise enough to allow of exact predictions of the results of individual observations. This is the situation, e. g., in all the examples 1—5 quoted above. Even if the utmost care is taken to keep all relevant circumstances under control, the result may in such cases vary from one observation to another in an irregular way that eludes all our attempts at prediction. In such a case, we shall say that we are concerned with a sequence of *random experiments.*

Any systematic record of the results of sequences of this kind will be said to constitute a *set of statistical data* relative to the phenomenon concerned. The chief object of statistical theory is to investigate the possibility of *drawing valid inferences from statistical data*, and to work out methods by which such inferences may be obtained. As a preliminary to the discussion of these questions, we shall in the two following paragraphs consider some general properties of random experiments.

13.2. Examples. — It does not seem possible to give a precise definition of what is meant by the word »random». The sense of the word is best conveyed by some examples.

If an ordinary coin is rapidly spun several times, and if we take care to keep the conditions of the experiment as uniform as possible in all respects, we shall find that we are unable to predict whether, in a particular instance, the coin will fall »heads» or »tails». If the first throw has resulted in heads and if, in the following throw, we try to give the coin exactly the same initial state of motion, it will still appear that it is not possible to secure another case of heads. Even if we try to build a machine throwing the coin with perfect regularity, it is not likely that we shall succeed in predicting the results of individual throws. On the contrary, the result of the experiment will always fluctuate in an uncontrollable way from one instance to another.

At first, this may seem rather difficult to explain. If we accept a deterministic point of view, we must maintain that the result of each throw is uniquely determined by the initial state of motion of the coin (external conditions, such as air resistance and physical properties of the table, being regarded as fixed). Thus it would seem theoretically possible to make an exact prediction, as soon as the initial state is known, and to produce any desired result by starting from an appropriate initial state. A moment's reflection will, however, show that even extremely small changes in the initial state of motion must be expected to have a dominating influence on the result. In practice, the initial state will never be exactly known, but only to a certain approximation. Similarly, when we try to establish a perfect uniformity of initial states during the course of a sequence of throws, we shall never be able to exclude small variations, the magnitude of which depends on the precision of the mechanism used for making the throws. Between the limits determined by the closeness of the approximation, there will always be room for various initial states, leading to both the possible final results of heads and tails, and thus an exact prediction will always be practically impossible. — Similar remarks apply to the throws with a die quoted as Ex. 1 in the preceding paragraph, and generally to all ordinary games of chance with dice and cards.

According to modern biological theory, the phenomenon of heredity shows in important respects a striking analogy with a game of chance. The combinations of genes arising in the process of fertilization seem to be regulated by a mechanism more or less resembling the throwing of a coin. In a similar way as in the case of the coin, extremely small variations in the initial position and motion of the gametes may produce great differences in the properties of the offspring. Accordingly we find here, e. g. with respect to the sex of the offspring (Ex. 5 of the preceding paragraph), the same impossibility of individual prediction and the same »random fluctuations» of the results as in the case of the coin or the die.

Next, let us imagine that we observe a number of men of a given age during a period of, say, one year, and note in each case whether the man is alive at the end of the year or not. Let us suppose that, with the aid of a medical expert, we have been able to collect detailed information concerning health, occupation, habits etc. of each observed person. Nevertheless, it will obviously be impossible to make exact predictions with regard to the life or death of one particular person, since the causes leading to the ultimate result are far too numerous and too complicated to allow of any precise calculation. Even for an observer endowed with a much more advanced biological knowledge than is possible at the present epoch, the practical conclusion would be the same, owing to the multitude and complexity of the causes at work.

In the examples 2 and 4 of the preceding paragraph, the situation seems to be largely analogous to the example just discussed. The laws governing the phenomena are in neither case very well known, and even if they were known to a much greater extent than at present, the structure of each case is so complicated that an individual prediction would still seem practically impossible. Accordingly, the observations show in these cases, and in numerous other cases of a similar nature, the same kind of random irregularity as in the previous examples.

It is important to note that a similar situation may arise even in cases where we consider the laws of the phenomena as perfectly known, provided that these laws are sufficiently complicated. Consider e. g. the case of the eclipses of the sun mentioned in the preceding paragraph. We do assume that it is possible to predict the annual number of eclipses, and if the requisite tables are available, anybody can undertake to make such predictions. Without the tables, however, it would be rather a formidable task to work out the necessary calculations, and if these difficulties should be considered insurmountable, prediction would still be practically impossible, and the fluctuations in the annual number of eclipses would seem comparable to the fluctuations in a sequence of games of chance.

Suppose, finally, that our observations consist in making a series of repeated measurements of some physical constant, the method of measurement and the relevant external conditions being kept as uniform as possible during the whole series. It is well known that, in spite of all precautions taken by the observer, the successive measurements will generally yield different results. This phenomenon is commonly ascribed to the action of a large number of small disturbing factors, which combine their effects to a certain total »error» affecting each particular measurement. The amount of this error fluctuates from one observation to another in an irregular way that makes it impossible to predict the result of an individual measurement. — Similar considerations apply to cases of fluctuations of quality in manufactured articles, such as Ex. 3 of the preceding paragraph. Small and uncontrollable variations in the production process and in the quality of raw materials will combine their effects and produce irregular fluctuations in the final product.

The examples discussed above are representative of large and important groups of random experiments. Small variations in the initial state of the observed units, which cannot be detected by our instruments, may produce considerable changes in the final result. The complicated character of the laws of the observed phenomena may render exact calculation practically, if not theoretically, impossible. Uncontrollable action by small disturbing factors may lead to irregular deviations from a presumed »true value».

It is, of course, clear that there is no sharp distinction between these various modes of randomness. Whether we ascribe e. g. the fluctuations observed in the results of a series of shots at a target mainly to small variations in the initial state of the projectile, to the complicated nature of the ballistic laws, or to the action of small disturbing factors, is largely a matter of taste. The essential thing is that, in all cases where one or more of these circumstances are present, an exact prediction of the results of individual experiments becomes impossible, and the irregular fluctuations characteristic of random experiments will appear.

We shall now see that, in cases of this character, there appears amidst all irregularity of fluctuations a certain typical form of regularity, that will serve as the basis of the mathematical theory of statistics.

13.3. Statistical regularity. — We have seen that, in a sequence of random experiments, it is not possible to predict individual results. These are subject to irregular random fluctuations which cannot be submitted to exact calculation. However, as soon as we turn our attention from the individual experiments to the whole *sequence of experiments*, the situation changes completely, and an extremely important phenomenon appears: *In spite of the irregular behaviour of individual results, the average results of long sequences of random experiments show a striking regularity.*

In order to explain this important mode of regularity, we consider a determined random experiment $\mathfrak{E}$, that may be repeated a large number of times under uniform conditions. Let $\boldsymbol{S}$ denote the set of all a priori possible different results of an individual experiment, while S denotes a fixed subset of $\boldsymbol{S}$. If, in a particular experiment, we obtain a result ξ belonging to the subset S, we shall say that the *event* defined by the relation $\xi < S$, or briefly the *event* $\xi < S$, has occurred.[1]) We shall often also denote an event by a single letter E, writing $E = E(\xi < S)$, and we may then speak without distinction of »the event E» or »the event $\xi < S$».

When our experiment $\mathfrak{E}$ consists in throwing a die, the set S contains the six numbers $1, 2, \ldots, 6$. Let S denote e. g. the subset containing the three numbers $2, 4, 6$. The event $\xi < S$ then occurs at any throw resulting in an even number of points.

When we are concerned with measurements of some physical constant x, the value of which is a priori completely unknown, it may be at least theoretically possible for a measurement to yield as its result any real number, and accordingly the set S would then be the one-dimensional space R_1. Let S denote e. g. the closed interval (a, b). The event $\xi < S$ then occurs every time a measurement yields a value ξ belonging to (a, b).

Let us now repeat our experiment $\mathfrak{E}$ a large number of times, and observe each time whether the event $E = E(\xi < S)$ takes place or not. If we find that, among the n first experiments, the event E has occurred exactly ν times, the ratio ν/n will be called the *frequency ratio* or simply the *frequency* of the event E in the sequence formed by the n first experiments.

Now, if we observe the frequency ν/n of a fixed event E for increasing values of n, we shall generally find that it shows a marked tendency to become more or less constant for large values of n.

This phenomenon is illustrated by Fig. 3, which shows the variation of the frequency ν/n of the event »heads» within a sequence of throws with a coin. As shown by the figure, the frequency ratio fluctuates violently for small values of n, but gradually the amplitude of the fluctuations becomes smaller, and the graph may suggest the impression that, if the series of experiments could be infinitely continued under uniform conditions, the frequency would approach some definite ideal or limiting value very near to $\frac{1}{2}$.

It is an old experience that this *stability of frequency ratios* usually appears in long series of repeated random observations, performed under uniform conditions. For an event of the type $\xi < S$ observed in connection with such a series, we shall thus as a rule obtain a graph of the same general character as in the particular case illustrated

---

[1]) We assume here that S is some set of simple structure, so that it may be directly observed whether ξ belongs to S or not. In the following chapter, the question will be considered from a more general point of view.

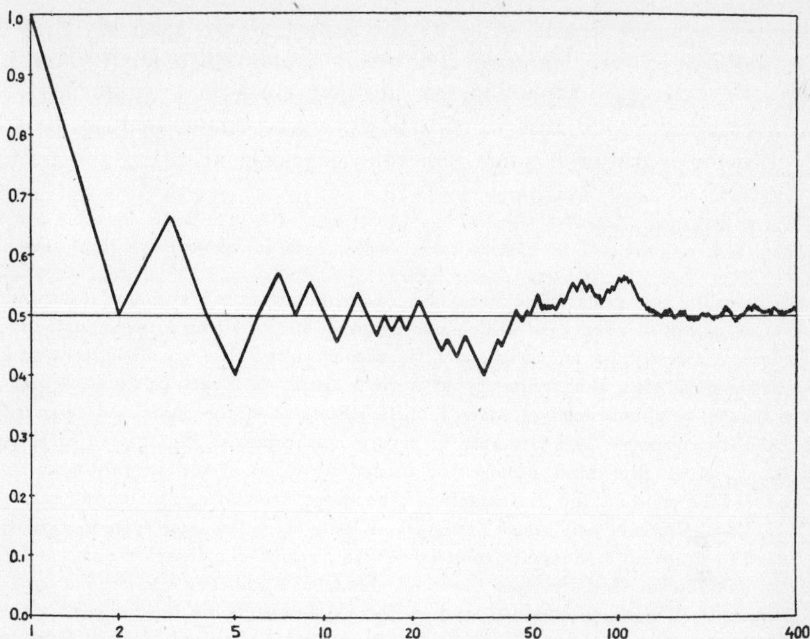

Fig. 3. Frequency ratio of »heads» in a sequence of throws with a coin. Logarithmic scale for the abscissa.

by Fig. 3. Moreover, in a case where this statement is not true, a careful examination will usually disclose some definite lack of uniformity in the conditions of the experiments. We might thus be tempted to advance a conjecture that, generally, a frequency of the type here considered would approach a definite ideal value, if the corresponding series of experiments could be infinitely continued.

A conjecture of this kind can, of course, neither be proved nor disproved by actual experience, since we can never perform an infinite sequence of experiments. The experiments do, however, strongly support the less precise conjecture that, *to any event E connected with a random experiment $\mathfrak{E}$, we should be able to ascribe a number P such that, in a long series of repetitions of $\mathfrak{E}$, the frequency of E would be approximately equal to P.*

This is the typical form of *statistical regularity* which constitutes the empirical basis of statistical theory. We must now attempt to give a precise meaning to the somewhat vague expressions used in the above statement, and we shall further have to investigate the laws that govern this mode of regularity, and to show how these laws may be applied in drawing inferences from statistical data. In order to carry out this task, we shall in the first place try to work out a *mathematical theory* of phenomena showing statistical regularity. Before attempting to do this it will, however, be convenient to give in the following paragraph some general remarks concerning the nature and object of any mathematical theory of a group of empirically observed phenomena.

Historically, this remarkable behaviour of frequency ratios was first observed in the field of games of chance, of which our example with the coin forms a particularly simple case. Already at an early epoch, it was observed that, in all current games with cards, dice etc., the frequency of a given result of a certain game seemed to cluster in the neighbourhood of some definite value, when the game was repeated a large number of times. The attempts to give a mathematical explanation of certain observed facts of this kind became the immediate cause of the origin (about 1650) and first development of the Mathematical Theory of Probability, under the hands of Pascal, Fermat, Huygens and James Bernoulli. A little later, the same type of regularity was found to occur in frequencies connected with various demographic data, and the theory of population statistics was based on this fact. Gradually, the field of application of statistical methods widened, and at the present time we may regard it as an established empirical fact that the »long run stability» of frequency ratios is a general characteristic of random experiments, performed under uniform conditions.

In some cases, especially when we are concerned with observations on individuals from human or other biological populations, this statistical regularity is often interpreted by considering the observed units as *samples* from some very large or even infinite *parent population*.

Consider first the case of a *finite* population, consisting of N individuals. For any individual that comes under observation we note a certain characteristic ξ, and we denote by E some specified event of the type $\xi < S$. The frequency of E in a sample of n observed individuals tends, as the size of the sample increases, towards the frequency of E in the total population, and actually reaches this value when we take $n = N$, which means that we observe every individual in the whole population.

The idea of an *infinite* parent population is a mathematical abstraction of the same kind as the idea that a given random experiment might be repeated an infinite number of times. We may consider this as a limiting case of a finite population, when the number N of individuals increases indefinitely. The frequency of the event E in a sample of n individuals from an infinite population will always be subject to random fluctuations, as long as n is finite, but it may seem natural to assume that, for indefinitely increasing values of n, this frequency would ultimately reach a »true» value, corresponding to the frequency of E in the total infinite population.

This mode of interpretation by means of the idea of sampling may even be extended to any type of random experiment. We may, in fact, conceive of any finite sequence of repetitions of a random experiment as a sample from the hypothetical infinite population of all experiments that might have been performed under the given conditions. — We shall return to this matter in Ch. 25, where the idea of sampling will be further discussed.

13.4. Object of a mathematical theory. — When, in some group of observable phenomena, we find evidence of a confirmed regularity, we may try to form a mathematical theory of the subject. Such a theory may be regarded as a *mathematical model* of the body of empirical facts which constitute our data.

We then choose as our starting point some of the most essential and most elementary features of the regularity observed in the data. These we express, in a simplified and idealized form, as mathematical propositions which are laid down as the basic *axioms* of our theory. From the axioms, various propositions are then obtained by purely logical deduction, without any further appeal to experience. The logically consistent system of propositions built up in this way on an axiomatic basis constitutes our mathematical theory.

Two classical examples of this procedure are provided by Geometry and Theoretical Mechanics. Geometry, e. g., is a system of purely mathematical propositions, designed to form a mathematical model of a large group of empirical facts connected with the position and configuration in space of various bodies. It rests on a comparatively small number of axioms, which are introduced without proof. Once the axioms have been chosen, the whole system of geometrical propositions is obtained from them by purely logical deductions. In the choice of the axioms we are guided by the regularities found in available empirical facts. The axioms may, however, be chosen in different ways, and accordingly there are several different systems of geometry: Euclidean, Lobatschewskian etc. Each of these is a logically consistent system of mathematical propositions, founded on its own set of axioms. — In a similar way, theoretical mechanics is a system of mathematical propositions, designed to form a mathematical model of observed facts connected with the equilibrium and motion of bodies.

Every proposition of such a system is *true*, in the mathematical sense of the word, as soon as it is correctly deduced from the axioms. On the other hand, it is important to emphasize that no proposition of any mathematical theory *proves* anything about the events that will, in fact, happen. The points, lines, planes etc. considered in pure geometry are not the perceptual things that we know from immediate experience. The pure theory belongs entirely to the conceptual sphere, and deals with abstract objects entirely defined by their properties, as expressed by the axioms. For these objects, the propositions of the theory are exactly and rigorously true. But no proposition about such conceptual objects will ever involve a logical proof of properties of the perceptual things of our experience. Mathematical arguments are fundamentally incapable of proving physical facts.

Thus the Euclidean proposition that the sum of the angles in a triangle is equal to π is rigorously true for a conceptual triangle as defined in pure geometry. But it does not follow that the sum of the angles measured in a concrete triangle will necessarily be equal to π, just as it does not follow from the theorems of classical mechanics that the sun and the planets will necessarily move in conformity with the Newtonian law of gravitation. These are questions that can only be decided by direct observation of the facts.

Certain propositions of a mathematical theory may, however, be *tested by experience.* Thus the Euclidean proposition concerning the sum of the angles in a triangle may be directly compared with actual measurements on concrete triangles. If, in systematic tests of this character, we find that the verifiable consequences of a theory really conform with sufficient accuracy to available empirical facts, we may feel more or less justified in thinking that there is some kind of resemblance between the mathematical theory and the structure of the perceptual world. We further expect that the agreement between theory and experience will continue to hold also for future events and for consequences of the theory not yet submitted to direct verification, and we allow our actions to be guided by this expectation.

Such is the case, e. g., with respect to Euclidean geometry. Whenever a proposition belonging to this theory has been compared with empirical observations, it has been found that the agreement is sufficient for all ordinary practical purposes. (It is necessary to exclude here certain applications connected with the recent development of physics.) Thus, although it can never be *logically proved* that the sum of the angles in a concrete triangle must be equal to π, we regard it as *practically certain* — i. e. sufficiently certain to act upon in practice — that our measurements will yield a sum *approximately equal* to this value. Moreover, we believe that the same kind of agreement will be found with respect to any proposition deduced from Euclidean axioms, that we may have occasion to test by experience.

Naturally, our relying on the future agreement between theory and experience will grow more confident in the same measure as the accumulated evidence of such agreement increases. The »practical certainty» felt with respect to a proposition of Euclidean geometry will be different from that connected with, say, the second law of thermodynamics. Further, the *closeness* of the agreement that we may reasonably expect will not always be the same. Whereas in some cases the most sensitive instruments have failed to discover the slightest disagreement, there are other cases where a scientific »law» only accounts for the main features of the observed facts, the deviations being interpreted as »errors» or »disturbances».

In a case where we have found evidence of a more or less accurate and permanent agreement between theory and facts, the mathematical theory acquires a *practical value*, quite apart from its purely mathematical interest. The theory may then be used for various purposes. The majority of ordinary applications of a mathematical theory may be roughly classified under the three headings: *Description*, *Analysis* and *Prediction*.

In the first place, the theory may be used for purely *descriptive* purposes. A large set of empirical data may, with the aid of the theory, be reduced to a relatively small number of characteristics which represent, in a condensed form, the relevant information supplied by the data. Thus the complicated set of astronomical observations concerning the movements of the planets is summarized in a condensed form by the Copernican system.

Further, the results of a theory may be applied as tools for a scientific *analysis* of the phenomena under observation. Almost every scientific investigation makes use of applications belonging to this class. The general principle behind such applications may be thus expressed: *Any theory which does not fit the facts must be modified.* Suppose, e. g., that we are trying to find out whether the variation of a certain factor has any influence on some phenomena in which we are interested. We may then try to work out a theory, according to which no such influence takes place, and compare the consequences of this theory with our observations. If on some point we find a manifest disagreement, this indicates that we should proceed to amend our theory in order to allow for the neglected influence.

Finally, we may use the theory in order to *predict* the events that will happen under given circumstances. Thus, with the aid of geometrical and mechanical theory, an astronomer is able to predict the date of an eclipse. This constitutes a direct application of the principle mentioned above, that the agreement between theory and facts is expected to hold true also for future events. The same principle is applied when we use our theoretical knowledge with a view to produce some determined event, as e. g. when a ballistic expert shows how to direct a gun in order to hit the target.

13.5. Mathematical probability. — We now proceed to work out a theory designed to serve as a mathematical model of phenomena showing statistical regularity. We want a theory which takes account of the fundamental facts characteristic of this mode of regularity, and which may be put to use in the various ways indicated in the preceding paragraph.

In laying the foundations of this theory, we shall try to imitate as strictly as possible the classical construction process described in the preceding paragraph. In the case of geometry, e. g., we know that by certain actions, such as the appropriate use of a ruler and a piece of chalk, we may produce things known in everyday language as points, straight lines etc. The empirical study of the properties of these things gives evidence of certain regularities. We then postulate the existence of conceptual counterparts of the things: the points, straight lines etc. of pure geometry. Further, the fundamental features of the observed regularities are stated, in an idealized form, as the geometrical axioms.

Similarly, in the case actually before us, we know that by certain actions, viz. the performance of sequences of certain experiments, we may produce sets of observed numbers known as frequency ratios. The empirical study of the behaviour of frequency ratios gives evidence of a certain typical form of regularity, as described in 13.3. Consider an event E connected with the random experiment $\mathfrak{E}$. According to 13.3, the frequency of E in a sequence of n repetitions of $\mathfrak{E}$ shows a tendency to become constant as n increases, and we have been led to express the conjecture that for large n the frequency ratio would with practical certainty be approximately equal to some assignable number P.

In our mathematical theory, we shall accordingly introduce a definite number P, which will be called the probability of the event E with respect to the random experiment $\mathfrak{E}$.

Whenever we say that the probability of an event E with respect to an experiment $\mathfrak{E}$ is equal to P, the concrete meaning of this assertion will thus simply be the following: In a long series of repetitions of $\mathfrak{E}$, it is practically certain that the frequency of E will be approximately *equal to P.*[1]) — *This statement will be referred to as the frequency interpretation of the probability P.*

The probability number P introduced in this way provides a conceptual counterpart of the empirical frequency ratios. It will be observed that, in order to define the probability P, both the type of random experiment $\mathfrak{E}$ and the event E must be specified. Usually we shall, however, regard the experiment $\mathfrak{E}$ as fixed, and we may then without ambiguity simply talk of the *probability of the event E.*

For the further development of the theory, we shall have to consider the fundamental properties of frequency ratios and express these, in an idealized form, as statements concerning the properties of the corresponding probability numbers. These statements, together with the existence postulate for the probability numbers, will serve as the axioms of our theory. — In the present paragraph, we shall only add a few preliminary remarks; the formal statement of the axioms will then be given in the following chapter.

For any frequency ratio ν/n we obviously have $0 \leqq \nu/n \leqq 1$. Since, by definition, any probability P is approximately equal to some frequency ratio, it will be natural to assume that P satisfies the corresponding inequality

$$0 \leqq P \leqq 1,$$

and this will in fact be one of the properties expressed by our axioms.

If E is an *impossible* event, i. e. an event that can *never* occur at a performance of the experiment $\mathfrak{E}$, any frequency of E must be zero; and consequently we take $P = 0$. — On the other hand, if we know that for some event E we have $P = 0$, then E is *not* necessarily an impossible event. In fact, the frequency interpretation of P only implies that the frequency ν/n of E will for large n be *approximately* equal to zero, so that in the long run E will at most occur *in a very small percentage of all cases.* The same conclusion holds not only when $P = 0$, but even under the more general assumption that $0 \leqq P < \varepsilon$, where ε is some very small number. *If E is an event of this type, and if the experiment* $\mathfrak{E}$ *is performed one single time, it can thus be considered as practically certain that E will not occur.* — This particular case of the frequency interpretation of a probability will often be applied in the sequel.

Similarly, if E is a *certain* event, i. e. an event that *always* occurs at a performance of $\mathfrak{E}$, we take $P = 1$. — On the other hand, if we

[1]) At a later stage (cf 16.3), we shall be able to give a more precise form to this statement.

know that $P = 1$, we cannot infer that E is certain, but only that in the long run E will occur in all but a very small percentage of cases. The same conclusion holds under the more general assumption that $1 - \varepsilon < P \leqq 1$, where ε is some very small number. *If E is an event of this type, and if the experiment $\mathfrak{E}$ is performed one single time, it can be considered as practically certain that E will occur.*

With respect to the foundations of the theory of probability, many different opinions are represented in the literature. None of these has so far met with universal acceptance. We shall conclude this paragraph by a very brief survey of some of the principal standpoints.

The theory of probability originated from the study of problems connected with ordinary games of chance (cf 13.3). In all these games, the results that are a priori possible may be arranged in a finite number of cases supposed to be perfectly symmetrical, such as the cases represented by the six sides of a die, the 52 cards in an ordinary pack of cards, etc. This fact seemed to provide a basis for a rational explanation of the observed stability of frequency ratios, and the 18:th century mathematicians were thus led to the introduction of the famous *principle of equally possible cases* which, after having been more or less tacitly assumed by earlier writers, was explicitly framed by Laplace in his classical work (Ref. 22) as the fundamental principle of the whole theory. According to this principle, a division in »equally possible» cases is conceivable in any kind of observations, and the probability of an event is the ratio between the number of cases favourable to the event, and the total number of possible cases.

The weakness of this definition is obvious. In the first place, it does not tell us how to decide whether two cases should be regarded as equally possible or not. Moreover, it seems difficult, and to some minds even impossible, to form a precise idea as to how a division in equally possible cases could be made with respect to observations not belonging to the domain of games of chance. Much work has been devoted to attempts to overcome these difficulties and introduce an improved form of the classical definition.

On the other hand, many authors have tried to replace the classical definition by something radically different. Modern work on this line has been largely influenced by the general tendency to build any mathematical theory on an axiomatic basis. Thus some authors try to introduce a system of axioms directly based on the properties of frequency ratios. The chief exponent of this school is von Mises (Ref. 27, 28, 159), who defines the probability of an event as the *limit of the frequency ν/n* of that event, as n tends to infinity. The existence of this limit, in a strictly mathematical sense, is postulated as the first axiom of the theory. Though undoubtedly a definition of this type seems at first sight very attractive, it involves certain mathematical difficulties which deprive it of a good deal of its apparent simplicity. Besides, the probability definition thus proposed would involve a mixture of empirical and theoretical elements, which is usually avoided in modern axiomatic theories. It would, e. g., be comparable to defining a geometrical point as the limit of a chalk spot of infinitely decreasing dimensions, which is usually not done in modern axiomatic geometry.

A further school chooses the same observational starting-point as the frequency school, but avoids postulating the existence of definite limits of frequency ratios, and introduces the probability of an event simply as a number associated with that event. The axioms of the theory, which express the rules for operating with such numbers, are idealized statements of observed properties of frequency ratios. The theory of this school has been exposed from a purely mathematical point of view by Kolmogoroff (Ref. 21). More or less similar standpoints are represented by Doob, Feller and Neyman (Ref. 75, 84, 30). A work of the present author (Ref. 11) belongs to the same order of ideas, and the present book constitutes an attempt to build the theory of statistics on the same principles.

So far, we have throughout been concerned with the theory of probability, conceived as a mathematical theory of phenomena showing statistical regularity. According to this point of view, the probabilities have their counterparts in observable frequency ratios, and any probability number assigned to a specified event must, in principle, be liable to empirical verification. The differences between the various schools mentioned above are mainly restricted to the foundations and the mathematical exposition of the subject, whereas from the point of view of the applications the various theories are largely equivalent.

In radical opposition to all the above approaches stands the more general conception of probability theory as a theory of *degrees of reasonable belief* represented e. g. by Keynes (Ref. 20) and Jeffreys (Ref. 18). According to this theory in its most advanced form given by Jeffreys, any proposition has a numerically measurable probability. Thus e. g. we should be able to express in definite numerical terms the degree of »practical certainty» felt with respect to the future agreement between some mathematical theory and observed facts (cf 13.4). Similarly there would be a definite numerical probability of the truth of any statement such as: »The 'Masque de Fer' was the brother of Louis XIV», »The present European war will end within a year», or »There is organic life on the planet of Mars». Probabilities of this type have no direct connection with random experiments, and thus no obvious frequency interpretation. In the present book, we shall not attempt to discuss the question whether such probabilities are numerically measurable and, if this question could be answered in the affirmative, whether such measurement would serve any useful purpose.

CHAPTER 14.

Fundamental Definitions and Axioms.

14.1. Random variables. (Axioms 1–2.) — Consider a determined random experiment $\mathfrak{E}$, which may be repeated a large number of times under uniform conditions. We shall suppose that the result of each particular experiment is given by a certain number of real quantities $\xi_1, \xi_2, \ldots, \xi_k$, where $k \geqq 1$.

We then introduce a corresponding variable point or vector $\boldsymbol{\xi} = (\xi_1, \ldots, \xi_k)$ in the k-dimensional space $\boldsymbol{R}_k$. We shall call $\boldsymbol{\xi}$ a k-dimensional *random variable.*[1]) Each performance of the experiment $\mathfrak{E}$ yields as its result an *observed value* of the variable $\boldsymbol{\xi}$, the coordinates of which are the values of $\xi_1, \ldots, \xi_k$ observed on that particular occasion.

Let S denote some simple set of points in $\boldsymbol{R}_k$, say a k-dimensional interval (cf 3.1), and let us consider the event $\boldsymbol{\xi} < S$, which may or may not occur at any particular performance of $\mathfrak{E}$. We shall assume that this event has a definite probability P, in the sense explained in 13.5. The number P will obviously depend on the set S, and will accordingly be denoted by any of the expressions

$$P = P(S) = P(\boldsymbol{\xi} < S).$$

It is thus seen that the probability may be regarded as a *set function*, and that it seems reasonable to require that this set function should be uniquely defined at least for all k-dimensional intervals. However, it would obviously not be convenient to restrict ourselves to the consideration of intervals. We may also want to consider the probabilities of events that correspond e. g. to sets obtained from intervals by means of the operations of addition, subtraction and multiplication (cf 1.3). We have seen in 2.3 and 3.3 that, by such operations, we are led to the class of Borel sets in $\boldsymbol{R}_k$ as a natural extension of the class of all intervals. It thus seems reasonable directly to extend our considerations to this class, and assume that $P(S)$ is defined for any Borel set. It is true that when S is some Borel set of complicated structure, the event $\boldsymbol{\xi} < S$ may not be directly observable, and the introduction of probabilities of events of this type must be regarded as a theoretical idealization. Some of the consequences of the theory will, however, always be directly observable, and the practical value of the theory will have to be judged from the agreement between its observable consequences and empirical facts. — We may thus state our first axiom:

Axiom 1. — *To any random variable* $\boldsymbol{\xi}$ *in* $\boldsymbol{R}_k$ *there corresponds a set function* $P(S)$ *uniquely defined for all Borel sets* S *in* $\boldsymbol{R}_k$, *such that* $P(S)$ *represents the probability of the event (or relation)* $\boldsymbol{\xi} < S$.

---

[1]) Throughout the exposition of the general theory, random variables will preferably be denoted by the letters ξ and η. We use heavy-faced types for multi-dimensional variables ($k > 1$), and ordinary types for one-dimensional variables.

As we have seen in 13.5, it will be natural to assume that any probability P satisfies the inequality $0 \leqq P \leqq 1$. Further, at any performance of the experiment $\mathfrak{E}$, the observed value of ξ must lie *somewhere* in $\boldsymbol{R}_k$, so that the event $\xi < \boldsymbol{R}_k$ is a *certain* event, and in accordance with 13.5 we then take $P(\boldsymbol{R}_k) = 1$.

Let now S_1 and S_2 be two sets in $\boldsymbol{R}_k$ without a common point.[1]) Consider a sequence of n repetitions of $\mathfrak{E}$, and let

ν_1 denote the number of occurrences of the event $\xi < S_1$,

ν_2 » » » » » » » » $\xi < S_2$,

ν » » » » » » » » $\xi < S_1 + S_2$.

We then obviously have $\nu = \nu_1 + \nu_2$, and hence the corresponding frequency ratios satisfy the relation

$$\frac{\nu}{n} = \frac{\nu_1}{n} + \frac{\nu_2}{n}.$$

For large values of n it is, by assumption, practically certain that the frequencies $\frac{\nu}{n}$, $\frac{\nu_1}{n}$ and $\frac{\nu_2}{n}$ are approximately equal to $P(S_1 + S_2)$, $P(S_1)$ and $P(S_2)$ respectively. It thus seems reasonable to require that the probability P should possess the additive property

$$P(S_1 + S_2) = P(S_1) + P(S_2).$$

The argument extends itself immediately to any finite number of sets. In order to obtain a simple and coherent mathematical theory we shall, however, now introduce a further idealization. We shall, in fact, assume that the additive property of $P(S)$ may be extended even to an enumerable sequence of sets $S_1, S_2, \ldots$, no two of which have a common point, so that we have $P(S_1 + S_2 + \cdots) = P(S_1) + P(S_2) + \cdots$ (As in the case of Axiom 1 this implies, of course, the introduction of relations that are not directly observable.) Using the terminology introduced in 6.2 and 8.2, we may now state our second axiom:

Axiom 2. — *The function $P(S)$ is a non-negative and additive set function in $\boldsymbol{R}_k$ such that $P(\boldsymbol{R}_k) = 1$.*

According to 6.6 and 8.4, any set function $P(S)$ with the properties stated in Axiom 2 defines a *distribution* in $\boldsymbol{R}_k$, that may be concretely interpreted by means of a distribution of a mass unit over

[1]) As already stated in 5.1, we only consider Borel sets.

the space $\boldsymbol{R}_k$, such that any set S carries the mass $P(S)$. This distribution will be called the *probability distribution* of the random variable ξ, and the set function $P(S)$ will be called the *probability function* (abbreviated *pr.f.*) of ξ. Similarly, the point function $F(\boldsymbol{x}) = F(x_1, \ldots, x_k)$ corresponding to $P(S)$, which is defined by (6.6.1) in the case $k = 1$, and by (8.4.1) in the general case, will be called the *distribution function* (abbreviated *d.f.*) of ξ. As shown in 6.6 and 8.4, the distribution may be uniquely defined either by the set function $P(S)$ or by the point function $F(\boldsymbol{x})$.

Finally, we observe that the Axioms 1 and 2 may be summed up in the following statement: *Any random variable has a unique probability distribution.*

If, e. g., the experiment $\mathfrak{E}$ consists in making a throw with a die, and observing the number of points obtained, the corresponding random variable ξ is a number that may assume the values $1, 2, \ldots, 6$, and these values only. Our axioms then assert the existence of a distribution in $\boldsymbol{R}_1$ with certain masses $p_1, p_2, \ldots, p_6$ placed in the points $1, 2, \ldots, 6$, such that p_r represents the probability of the event $\xi = r$, while $\sum_1^6 p_r = 1$. On the other hand, it is important to observe that it does *not* follow from the axioms that $p_r = \frac{1}{6}$ for every r. The numbers p_r should, in fact, be regarded as physical constants of the particular die that we are using, and the question as to their numerical values cannot be answered by the axioms of probability theory, any more than the size and the weight of the die are determined by the geometrical and mechanical axioms. However, experience shows that in a well made die the frequency of any event $\xi = r$ in a long series of throws usually approaches $\frac{1}{6}$, and accordingly we shall often assume that all the p_r are equal to $\frac{1}{6}$, when the example of the die is used for purposes of illustration. This is, however, an assumption and not a logical consequence of the axioms.

If, on the other hand, $\mathfrak{E}$ consists in observing the stature ξ of a man belonging to some given group, ξ may assume any value within a certain part of the scale, and our axioms now assert the existence of a non-negative and additive set function $P(S)$ in $\boldsymbol{R}_1$ such that $P(S)$ represents the probability that ξ takes a value belonging to the set S.

The Axioms 1 and 2 are, for the class of random variables here considered, equivalent to the axioms given by Kolmogoroff (Ref. 21). The axioms of Kolmogoroff are, however, applicable to random variables defined in spaces of a more general character than those here considered. The same axioms as above were used in a work of the present author (Ref. 11).

14.2. Combined variables. (Axiom 3.) — We shall first consider a particular case. Let the random experiments $\mathfrak{E}$ and $\mathfrak{F}$ be connected with the one-dimensional random variables ξ and η respectively. Thus the result of $\mathfrak{E}$ is represented by one single quantity ξ, while the result of $\mathfrak{F}$ is another quantity η. It often occurs that we have occasion to consider a *combined experiment* $(\mathfrak{E}, \mathfrak{F})$ which consists in making, in accordance with some given rule, one performance of each of the experiments $\mathfrak{E}$ and $\mathfrak{F}$, and observing jointly the results of both.

This means that we are observing a variable point (ξ, η), the coordinates of which are the results ξ and η of the experiments $\mathfrak{E}$ and $\mathfrak{F}$. We may then consider the point (ξ, η) as representing a two-dimensional variable, that will be called a *combined variable* defined by ξ and η. The space of the combined variable is the two dimensional product space (cf 3.5) of the one-dimensional spaces of ξ and η.

Let the experiment $\mathfrak{E}$ consist in a throw with a certain die, while $\mathfrak{F}$ consists in a throw with another die, and the combined experiment $(\mathfrak{E}, \mathfrak{F})$ consists in a throw with both dice. The result of $\mathfrak{E}$ is a number ξ that may assume the values $1, 2, \ldots, 6$, and the same holds for the result η of $\mathfrak{F}$. The combined variable (ξ, η) then expresses the joint results for both dice, and its possible »values» are the 36 pairs of numbers $(1, 1), \ldots, (6, 6)$.

If, on the other hand, the experiment $\mathfrak{E}$ consists in observing the stature ξ of a married man, while $\mathfrak{F}$ consists in observing the stature η of a married woman, the combined experiment $(\mathfrak{E}, \mathfrak{F})$ may consist e. g. in observing both statures (ξ, η) of a married couple. The point (ξ, η) may in this case assume any position within a certain part of the plane.

The principle of combination of variables may be applied to more general cases. Let the random experiments $\mathfrak{E}_1, \ldots, \mathfrak{E}_n$ be connected with the random variables $\mathfrak{x}_1, \ldots, \mathfrak{x}_n$ of $k_1, \ldots, k_n$ dimensions respectively, and consider a combined experiment $(\mathfrak{E}_1, \ldots, \mathfrak{E}_n)$ which consists in making one performance of each $\mathfrak{E}_\nu$, and observing jointly all the results. We then obtain a combined variable $(\mathfrak{x}_1, \ldots, \mathfrak{x}_n)$ represented by a point in the $(k_1 + \cdots + k_n)$-dimensional product space (cf 3.5) of the spaces of all the $\mathfrak{x}_\nu$.

The empirical study of frequency ratios connected with combined experiments discloses a statistical regularity of the same kind as in the case of the component experiments. Any experiment composed of random experiments shows, in fact, the character of a random experiment, and we may accordingly state our third axiom:

Axiom 3. — *If* $\mathfrak{x}_1, \ldots, \mathfrak{x}_n$ *are random variables, any combined variable* $(\mathfrak{x}_1, \ldots, \mathfrak{x}_n)$ *is also a random variable.*

It then follows from the preceding axioms that any combined variable has a unique probability distribution in its space of $k_1 + \cdots + k_n$ dimensions. This distribution will often be called the *joint* or *simultaneous distribution* of the variables $\mathfrak{x}_1, \ldots, \mathfrak{x}_n$.

Consider now the case of two random variables ξ and η, of k_1 and k_2 dimensions respectively. Let P_1 and P_2 denote the pr. f:s of ξ and η, while P denotes the pr. f. of the combined variable (ξ, η). If S denotes a set in the space of the variable ξ, the expression $P(\xi < S)$ represents the probability that the combined variable (ξ, η) takes a value belonging to the cylinder set (cf. 3.5) defined by the relation $\xi < S$, or in other words the probability that ξ takes a value belonging to S, irrespective of the value of η. Similarly, if T is a set in the space of η, the expression $P(\eta < T)$ represents the probability that η takes a value belonging to T, irrespective of the value of ξ. We thus have

$$(14.2.1) \qquad P(\xi < S) = P_1(S), \qquad P(\eta < T) = P_2(T),$$

and according to (8.4.2) this shows that the *marginal distributions* of the $(k_1 + k_2)$-dimensional combined distribution, relative to the subspaces of the variables ξ and η, are identical with the distributions of ξ and η respectively. — Obviously this may be generalized to any number of component variables. When the mass in the combined distribution is projected on the subspace of any of the component variables, the marginal distribution thus obtained will always be identical with the distribution of the corresponding variable.

An important case of combination of variables arises when we consider a sequence of repetitions of a random experiment $\mathfrak{E}$. Let us form a combined experiment by performing n times the same experiment $\mathfrak{E}$, and observing all the results $\xi_1, \ldots, \xi_n$ of the n repetitions. The result of this combined experiment will then be an observed value of the combined variable $(\xi_1, \ldots, \xi_n)$, which expresses the joint results of all the n repetitions of $\mathfrak{E}$.

If, e. g., $\mathfrak{E}$ consists in a throw with a die, the corresponding one-dimensional random variable ξ has the six possible values $1, 2, \ldots, 6$. The combined variable $(\xi_1, \ldots, \xi_n)$ then expresses the joint results of n successive throws, and its »values» are the 6^n systems of n numbers $(1, \ldots, 1), \ldots, (6, \ldots, 6)$. According to Axiom 3, there exists a corresponding probability distribution in $\boldsymbol{R}_n$, with determined probabilities $p_{1,\ldots,1}, \ldots, p_{6,\ldots,6}$ corresponding to the various possible values of the combined variable.

In problems where several random variables are considered simultaneously, we shall always assume that a rule of combination is given for all the variables that enter into the question, so that the combined variable is defined. We shall then as a rule use the symbol $P(S)$ to denote the pr. f. of the combined variable.

14.3. Conditional distributions. — Let ξ and η be random variables of k_1 and k_2 dimensions, attached to the random experiments $\mathfrak{E}$ and $\mathfrak{F}$. Let P denote the pr. f. of the combined variable (ξ, η), while S and T are sets in the spaces of ξ and η respectively. The expression $P(\xi < S,\ \eta < T)$ then represents the probability of the event defined by the joint relations $\xi < S$, $\eta < T$, or, in other words, the probability that the combined variable (ξ, η) takes a value belonging to the rectangle set (cf 3.5) with the sides S and T.

Suppose now that $P(\xi < S) > 0$. We then introduce a new quantity $P(\eta < T \mid \xi < S)$ defined by the relation

$$P(\eta < T \mid \xi < S) = \frac{P(\xi < S,\ \eta < T)}{P(\xi < S)}. \tag{14.3.1}$$

Similarly, supposing that $P(\eta < T) > 0$, we introduce another new quantity $P(\xi < S \mid \eta < T)$ by writing

$$P(\xi < S \mid \eta < T) = \frac{P(\xi < S,\ \eta < T)}{P(\eta < T)}. \tag{14.3.2}$$

In order to justify the names that will presently be given to these quantities, we shall now deduce some important properties of the latter.

In the first place, let us in (14.3.2) consider T as a fixed set, while S is variable in the space $\boldsymbol{R}_{k_1}$ of the variable ξ. The second member of (14.3.2) then becomes a non-negative and additive function of the set S. When $S = \boldsymbol{R}_{k_1}$, the rectangle set $\xi < \boldsymbol{R}_{k_1}$, $\eta < T$ is identical with the cylinder set (cf 3.5) $\eta < T$, so that the second member of (14.3.2) then assumes the value 1. Thus $P(\xi < S \mid \eta < T)$ is, for fixed T, a non-negative and additive function of the set S which for $S = \boldsymbol{R}_{k_1}$ assumes the value 1. In other words, $P(\xi < S \mid \eta < T)$ *is, for fixed T, the probability function of a certain distribution in* $\boldsymbol{R}_{k_1}$. In the same way it is shown that $P(\eta < T \mid \xi < S)$ is, for fixed S, the pr. f. of a certain distribution in the space $\boldsymbol{R}_{k_2}$ of the variable η. — We shall now show that, in a certain generalized sense, these quantities may in fact be regarded as probabilities having a determined frequency interpretation.

Consider a sequence $\boldsymbol{Z}$ of n repetitions of the combined experiment $(\mathfrak{E}, \mathfrak{F})$. Each of the n experiments which are the elements of $\boldsymbol{Z}$ yields as its result an observed »value» of the combined variable (ξ, η). In the sequence $\boldsymbol{Z}$, let

ν_1 denote the number of occurrences of the event $\xi < S$,
ν_2 » » » » » » » » $\eta < T$,
ν » » » » » » » » $\xi < S, \eta < T$,

while Z_1, Z_2 and Z are the corresponding sub-sequences of $\mathbf{Z}$. — Obviously the third event occurs when and only when the first and second events both occur, so that Z consists precisely of the elements common to Z_1 and Z_2.

According to the frequency interpretation of a probability (cf 13.5), it is practically certain that the relations

$$P(\xi < S) = \frac{\nu_1}{n}, \quad P(\eta < T) = \frac{\nu_2}{n}, \quad P(\xi < S, \eta < T) = \frac{\nu}{n}$$

will, for large n, be approximately satisfied. By (14.3.1) and (14.3.2) we then have, approximately,

$$(14.3.3) \qquad P(\eta < T \mid \xi < S) = \frac{\nu}{\nu_1}, \quad P(\xi < S \mid \eta < T) = \frac{\nu}{\nu_2}.$$

Consider now the ν_1 elements of the sub-sequence Z_1. These are all cases among our n repetitions, where the event $\xi < S$ has occurred. Among these, there are exactly ν cases where, in addition, the event $\eta < T$ has occurred, viz. the ν cases forming the sub-sequence Z. Thus the ratio $\frac{\nu}{\nu_1}$ is the frequency of the event $\eta < T$ in the sub-sequence Z_1 or, as we may express it, $\frac{\nu}{\nu_1}$ *is the conditional frequency of the event* $\eta < T$, *relative to the hypothesis* $\xi < S$. The corresponding property of the ratio $\frac{\nu}{\nu_2}$ is obtained by simple permutation. — The approximate relations (14.3.3) now provide a frequency interpretation of the expressions $P(\eta < T \mid \xi < S)$ and $P(\xi < S \mid \eta < T)$, which will justify the introduction of the following definitions:

The quantity $P(\eta < T \mid \xi < S)$ *defined by* (14.3.1) *will be called the conditional probability of the event* $\eta < T$, *relative to the hypothesis* $\xi < S$. *Accordingly, the distribution in* $\mathbf{R}_{k_2}$ *defined by* (14.3.1) *for fixed* S *will be called the conditional distribution of* η, *relative to the hypothesis* $\xi < S$. — *With respect to the quantity* $P(\xi < S \mid \eta < T)$ *defined by* (14.3.2), *we shall use the denominations obtained by permutation of symbols.*

It should be well observed that each conditional probability is hereby defined only in the case when the probability of the corresponding hypothesis is different from zero.

When $P(\xi < S)$ and $P(\eta < T)$ are both different from zero, we obtain from (14.3.1) and (14.3.2) the relation

$$P(\xi < S,\, \eta < T) = P(\xi < S)\, P(\eta < T \mid \xi < S) = \\ = P(\eta < T)\, P(\xi < S \mid \eta < T). \tag{14.3.4}$$

In the example considered in the preceding paragraph, where ξ is the stature of a married man, and η the stature of his wife, the data corresponding to *all observed values* of ξ determine the distribution of ξ. Thus e.g. the probability of the relation $a < \xi \leqq b$ will be approximately determined by the frequency of the corresponding event in the totality of our data.

Suppose now that we select from our data the subgroup of all cases where η is larger than some given constant c. The data corresponding to the values of ξ *in the cases belonging to this subgroup* determine the conditional distribution of ξ, relative to the hypothesis $\eta > c$. Thus e.g. the frequency of the event $a < \xi \leqq b$ within the subgroup is a conditional frequency as defined above, and for a large number of observations this becomes, with practical certainty, approximately equal to the conditional probability of the relation $a < \xi \leqq b$, relative to the hypothesis $\eta > c$. Here the set S is the interval $a < \xi \leqq b$, while the set T is the interval $\eta > c$.

It is evident that, in this case, we have reason to suppose that the conditional probability will differ from the probability in the totality of the data, since the taller women corresponding to the hypothesis $\eta > c$ may on the average be expected to choose, or be chosen by, taller husbands than the shorter women.

On the other hand, let ξ still stand for the stature of a married man, while η denotes the stature of the wife *belonging to the couple immediately following* ξ in the population register from which our data are taken. In this case, there will be no obvious reason to expect the conditional probability of the relation $a < \xi \leqq b$, relative to the hypothesis $\eta > c$, to be different from the unconditional probability $P(a < \xi \leqq b)$. On the contrary, we should expect the conditional distribution of ξ to be *independent of any hypothesis made with respect to* η, and conversely. If this condition is satisfied, we are concerned with the case of *independent variables*, that will be discussed in the following paragraph.

14.4. Independent variables. — An important particular case of the concepts introduced in the preceding paragraph arises when the multiplicative relation

$$P(\xi < S,\; \eta < T) = P(\xi < S)\, P(\eta < T) \tag{14.4.1}$$

is satisfied for any sets S and T. The relations (14.3.1) and (14.3.2) show that this implies

$$P(\xi < S \mid \eta < T) = P(\xi < S) \qquad \text{if } P(\eta < T) > 0, \tag{14.4.2}$$

$$P(\eta < T \mid \xi < S) = P(\eta < T) \qquad \text{if } P(\xi < S) > 0, \tag{14.4.3}$$

so that *the conditional distribution of* ξ *is independent of any hypothesis made with respect to* η, *and conversely.*

In this case we shall say that ξ and η are *independent random variables*, and that the events $\xi < S$ and $\eta < T$ are *independent events.*

Conversely, suppose that one of the two last relations, say (14.4.2), is satisfied for all sets S and T such that the conditional probability on the left-hand side is defined, i. e. for $P(\eta < T) > 0$. It then follows from (14.3.2) that the multiplicative relation (14.4.1) holds in all these cases. (14.4.1) is, however, trivial in the case $P(\eta < T) = 0$, since both members are then equal to zero. Thus (14.4.1) holds for all S and T, and hence we infer (14.4.3). *Thus either relation* (14.4.2) *or* (14.4.3) *constitutes a necessary and sufficient condition of independence.*

We shall now give another necessary and sufficient condition. Let P_1 and P_2 denote the probability functions of ξ and η, while the distribution functions of ξ, η and (ξ, η) are

$$F_1(\boldsymbol{x}) = F_1(x_1, \ldots, x_{k_1}) = P_1(\xi_1 \leqq x_1, \ldots, \xi_{k_1} \leqq x_{k_1}),$$

$$F_2(\boldsymbol{y}) = F_2(y_1, \ldots, y_{k_2}) = P_2(\eta_1 \leqq y_1, \ldots, \eta_{k_2} \leqq y_{k_2}),$$

$$F(\boldsymbol{x}, \boldsymbol{y}) = F(x_1, \ldots, x_{k_1}, y_1, \ldots, y_{k_2}) = P(\xi_i \leqq x_i,\ \eta_j \leqq y_j),$$

for all $i = 1, 2, \ldots, k_1$ and $j = 1, 2, \ldots, k_2$. According to (14.2.1), the multiplicative relation (14.4.1) may be written

$$P(\xi < S, \eta < T) = P_1(S)\, P_2(T). \tag{14.4.4}$$

Now it has been shown in 8.6 that, when P_1 and P_2 are given pr. f:s in the spaces of ξ and η, there is one and only one distribution in the product space satisfying (14.4.4), viz. the distribution defined by the d. f.

$$F(\boldsymbol{x}, \boldsymbol{y}) = F_1(\boldsymbol{x})\, F_2(\boldsymbol{y}). \tag{14.4.5}$$

Thus (14.4.5) *is a necessary and sufficient condition for the independence of the variables* ξ and η.

Consider now the case of n random variables $\xi_1, \ldots, \xi_n$, with pr. f:s $P_1, \ldots, P_n$ and d. f:s $F_1, \ldots, F_n$. Let P and F denote the pr. f. and the d. f. of the combined variable $(\xi_1, \ldots, \xi_n)$. In direct generalization of the above, we shall say that $\xi_1, \ldots \xi_n$ are *independent random variables*, if the multiplicative relation

$$(14.4.6) \qquad P(\xi_1 < S_1, \ldots, \xi_n < S_n) = \prod_{r=1}^{n} P(\xi_r < S_r) = \prod_{r=1}^{n} P_r(S_r)$$

is satisfied for any sets $S_1, \ldots, S_n$. Using the final remark of 8.6, we find that the condition (14.4.5) may be directly generalized, so that in the present case the relation $F = F_1 F_2 \cdots F_n$ is a necessary and sufficient condition of independence. — If ξ_r and the combined variable $(\xi_1, \ldots, \xi_{r-1})$ are independent for $r = 2, 3, \ldots, n$, then $\xi_1, \ldots, \xi_n$ are independent. This follows directly from the independence definition (14.4.6).

If, in a sequence $\xi_1, \xi_2, \ldots$, any group $\xi_1, \ldots, \xi_n$ of n variables are independent, we shall briefly say that $\xi_1, \xi_2, \ldots$ form a *sequence of independent variables.* — An important case of a sequence of this type arises when we consider a sequence of repetitions of a random experiment $\mathfrak{E}$. If the conditions of the successive experiments are strictly uniform, the probability P of any specified event connected with, say, the n:th experiment cannot be supposed to be in any way influenced by the results of the $n - 1$ preceding experiments. This implies, however, that the distribution of the random variable ξ_n connected with the n:th experiment is independent of any hypothesis made with respect to the value assumed by the combined variable $(\xi_1, \ldots, \xi_{n-1})$, so that ξ_n and $(\xi_1, \ldots, \xi_{n-1})$ are independent. According to the above, it then follows that $\xi_1, \xi_2, \ldots$ form a sequence of independent variables. A sequence of repetitions of a random experiment $\mathfrak{E}$ showing a uniformity of this character will be briefly denoted as a sequence of *independent repetitions* of $\mathfrak{E}$. When nothing is said to the contrary, we shall always assume that any sequence of repetitions that we may consider is of this type.

Consider a combined experiment consisting of two throws with a certain die. Let us repeat this combined experiment a large number of times, the conditions of each single throw being kept as uniform as possible. We may then study the behaviour of the conditional frequency of any given result of the second throw, relative to any hypothesis made with respect to the result of the first throw. Long experience has failed to detect any kind of influence of such hypotheses on the behaviour of the conditional frequency, and it seems reasonable to assume that the random variables connected with the two throws are independent. The same situation arises when we consider a combined experiment consisting of n throws, where n may have any value, and accordingly we assume that a sequence of throws made under uniform conditions form a sequence of independent repetitions, in the sense stated above.

Suppose now that, in each throw, all the six possible results have the probability $\frac{1}{6}$. Then by (14.4.6) each of the 6^n possible results of n consecutive throws will have the probability $(\frac{1}{6})^n$.

Finally, let us consider n independent variables $\xi_1, \ldots, \xi_n$. If, in the multiplicative relation (14.4.6), we allow a certain number of the sets S_r to coincide with the whole spaces of the corresponding variables, it follows that *any group of $n_1 < n$ of the variables are independent.*

The converse of the last proposition is not true. We shall, in fact, give an example due to S. Bernstein of three one-dimensional variables ξ, η, ζ, such that any two of the variables are independent, while the three variables ξ, η, ζ are not independent. Let the three-dimensional distribution of the combined variable (ξ, η, ζ) be such that each of the four points

$$(1, 0, 0)$$
$$(0, 1, 0)$$
$$(0, 0, 1)$$
$$(1, 1, 1)$$

carries the mass $\frac{1}{4}$. It is then easily verified that any one-dimensional marginal distribution has a mass equal to $\frac{1}{2}$ in each of the two points 0 and 1, while any two-dimensional marginal distribution has a mass equal to $\frac{1}{4}$ in each of the four points $(0, 0)$, $(1, 0)$, $(0, 1)$ and $(1, 1)$. It follows that any two of the variables are independent. We have e. g.

$$P(\xi = 1,\ \eta = 1) = P(\xi = 1)\, P(\eta = 1) = (\tfrac{1}{2})^2 = \tfrac{1}{4},$$

and it is seen without difficulty that the analogous relation holds for any events $\xi < S$ and $\eta < T$, so that (14.4.1) is satisfied. *But the three variables ξ, η, ζ are not independent,* as we have

$$P(\xi = 1,\ \eta = 1,\ \zeta = 1) = \tfrac{1}{4}$$

but

$$P(\xi = 1)\ P(\eta = 1)\ P(\zeta = 1) = (\tfrac{1}{2})^3 \neq \tfrac{1}{4}.$$

14.5. Functions of random variables. — Consider first the case of a one-dimensional random variable ξ with the pr. f. P. Suppose that, at each performance of the random experiment to which ξ is attached, we do not observe directly the variable ξ itself, but a certain real-valued function $g(\xi)$, which is finite and uniquely defined for all real ξ. As usual we assume that $g(\xi)$ is B-measurable (cf 5.2).

The equation $\eta = g(\xi)$ defines a correspondence between the variables ξ and η. Denote by Y a given set on the η-axis, and by X the corresponding set of all ξ such that $\eta = g(\xi) < Y$. It has been shown in 5.2 that the set X corresponding to any Borel set Y is a Borel set. When X and Y are corresponding sets, we have $\eta < Y$ when and only when $\xi < X$, so that the two events $\eta < Y$ and $\xi < X$ are completely equivalent. The latter event has, by Axiom 1, a definite probability $P(X)$, and thus the event $\eta < Y$ has the same probability.

We thus see that any function $\eta = g(\xi)$ *of the random variable* ξ *is itself a random variable, with a probability distribution determined by the distribution of* ξ. In fact, if Q denotes the pr. f. of η, it follows from the above that we have for any Borel set Y

$$Q(Y) = P(X), \tag{14.5.1}$$

where X is the set corresponding to Y. If, in particular, we choose for the set Y the closed interval $(-\infty, y)$, and denote by S_y the set of all ξ such that $\eta = g(\xi) \leqq y$, it follows that the d. f. of the variable η is

$$G(y) = Q(\eta \leqq y) = P(S_y). \tag{14.5.2}$$

Let the ξ-distribution be interpreted in the usual way as a distribution of mass on the ξ-axis. Let us imagine that every mass particle in this distribution is moved from its original place on the ξ-axis, first in a vertical direction until it reaches the curve $\eta = g(\xi)$, and then horizontally towards the η-axis. The distribution on the η-axis generated in this way will be the distribution defined by (14.5.1).

The above considerations are immediately extended to any number of dimensions. Let $\boldsymbol{\xi} = (\xi_1, \ldots, \xi_j)$ be a random variable in a j-dimensional space $\boldsymbol{R}_j$, with the pr. f. P. Consider a k-dimensional vector function $\boldsymbol{\eta} = g(\boldsymbol{\xi}) = (\eta_1, \ldots, \eta_k)$, which is finite and uniquely defined for all $\boldsymbol{\xi}$ in $\boldsymbol{R}_j$, and is itself represented by a point in a k-dimensional space $\boldsymbol{R}_k$. We assume that any component η_ν of $\boldsymbol{\eta}$ is a B-measurable function (cf 9.1) of the variables $\xi_1, \ldots, \xi_j$. It then follows as in the one-dimensional case that $\boldsymbol{\eta}$ is a random variable in $\boldsymbol{R}_k$, with a pr. f. Q determined by the relation (14.5.1) where, now, Y denotes any given set in $\boldsymbol{R}_k$, while X is the corresponding set of all $\boldsymbol{\xi}$ in $\boldsymbol{R}_j$ such that $\boldsymbol{\eta} = g(\boldsymbol{\xi}) < Y$.

For a set Y such that the corresponding set X is empty, we obtain, of course, $Q(Y) = 0$. — The condition that $g(\boldsymbol{\xi})$ should be finite and uniquely defined for all $\boldsymbol{\xi}$ in $\boldsymbol{R}_j$ may obviously be replaced by the more general condition that the points $\boldsymbol{\xi}$ where $g(\boldsymbol{\xi})$ is not finite or not uniquely defined, should form a set S such that $P(S) = 0$.

As an example, we may take $g(\boldsymbol{\xi}) = (\xi_1, \ldots, \xi_r)$, where $r < j$, so that $g(\boldsymbol{\xi})$ is simply the projection of the point $\boldsymbol{\xi}$ on a certain subspace (cf 3.5) of r dimensions. The pr. f. of $g(\boldsymbol{\xi})$ is then $Q(Y) = P(X)$, where Y is a set in the subspace, while X is the cylinder set (cf 3.5) in $\boldsymbol{R}_j$ defined by the relation $(\xi_1, \ldots, \xi_r, 0, \ldots, 0) < Y$. The corresponding distribution is the marginal distribution (cf 8.4) of $(\xi_1, \ldots, \xi_r)$, which is obtained by projecting the original distribution on the r-dimensional subspace. Taking, in particular, $r = 1$, it is seen that every component ξ_ν of the random variable ξ is itself a random variable, with a marginal distribution obtained by projecting the original distribution on the axis of ξ_ν.

A function $\eta = g(\xi_1, \ldots, \xi_n)$ of n random variables may be regarded as a function of the combined variable $(\xi_1, \ldots, \xi_n)$. Thus according to the above η is always a random variable, with a probability distribution uniquely determined by the simultaneous distribution of $\xi_1, \ldots, \xi_n$.

If $\xi_1, \ldots, \xi_n$ are independent variables, it is immediately seen that the variables $g_1(\xi_1), \ldots, g_n(\xi_n)$ are also independent.

14.6. Conclusion. — The contents of the present chapter may be briefly summed up in the following way. — From the domain of empirical data connected with random experiments, we have selected the fundamental fact of statistical regularity, viz. the long run stability of frequency ratios. In our mathematical theory, we have idealized this fact by postulating the existence of conceptual counterparts of the frequency ratios: the *mathematical probabilities.* The process of idealization has then been carried one step further by our assumption that the additive property of the probabilities may be extended from a finite to an enumerable sequence of »events». In this way, we have reached the concept of a *random variable* and its *probability distribution.*

We have further introduced the assumption that any number of random experiments may be joined to form a combined random experiment, showing the same kind of statistical regularity as the component experiments. Thus we have obtained the idea of the *joint probability distribution* of a number of random variables.

The study of certain conditional frequencies has led us to introduce their conceptual counterparts, under the name of *conditional probabilities.* These are connected with a certain *conditional distribution* of a random variable, which in a particular case gives rise to the important concept of *independent random variables.*

Finally, it has been shown that a B-measurable function of any number of random variables is itself a random variable, with a probability distribution uniquely determined by the joint distribution of the arguments.

We have thus laid the foundations for a purely mathematical theory of random variables and probability distributions. Our next object will now be to work out this theory in detail, and the rest of

Part II will be devoted to this purpose. In Chs 15—20 we shall mainly be concerned with variables and distributions in one dimension, while the multi-dimensional case will be dealt with in Chs 21—24.

In Part III, we shall then turn to questions of testing the mathematical theory by experience, and using the results of the theory for purposes of statistical inference.

Chapters 15–20. Variables and Distributions in R_1.

CHAPTER 15.

General Properties.

15.1. Distribution function and frequency function. — Consider a one-dimensional random variable ξ. By Axioms 1 and 2 of 14.1, ξ possesses a definite *probability distribution* in R_1. This distribution may be concretely interpreted as the distribution of a unit of mass over R_1, in such a way that the mass quantity $P(S)$ allotted to any Borel set S represents the probability that the variable ξ takes a value belonging to S.

As we have seen in 6.6, we are at liberty to define the distribution either by the non-negative and additive set function $P(S)$, which is called the *probability function* (abbreviated *pr.f.*) of the variable ξ, or by the corresponding point function $F(x)$ defined by the relation

$$P(\xi \leq x) = F(x),$$

which is called the *distribution function* (abbreviated *d.f.*) of ξ. In the present case of a one-dimensional distribution, we shall practically always use $F(x)$.

The reader is referred to the discussion of the general properties of a d.f. given in 6.6. In particular it has been shown there that any d.f. $F(x)$ is a non-decreasing function of x, which is everywhere continuous to the right, and is such that $F(-\infty) = 0$ and $F(+\infty) = 1$. The difference $F(b) - F(a)$ represents the probability that the variable ξ takes a value belonging to the interval $a < \xi \leq b$:

$$P(a < \xi \leq b) = F(b) - F(a).$$

If x_0 is a discontinuity point of $F(x)$, with a saltus equal to p_0, it follows from 6.6 that the mass p_0 is concentrated in the point x_0, which means that we have the probability p_0 that the variable ξ takes the value x_0:

$$P(\xi = x_0) = p_0.$$

If, on the other hand, the derivative $F'(x) = f(x)$ exists in a certain point x, then $f(x)$ represents the density of mass at this point, and we shall call $f(x)$ the *probability density* or the *frequency function* (abbreviated *fr.f.*) of the variable. The probability that the variable ξ takes a value belonging to the interval $x < \xi < x + \Delta x$ is then for small Δx asymptotically equal to $f(x)\Delta x$, which is written in the usual differential notation

$$P(x < \xi < x + dx) = f(x)\,dx.$$

This differential will be called the *probability element* of the distribution.

Any function $\eta = g(\xi)$ of the random variable ξ is, by 14.5, itself a random variable, with a d.f. given by (14.5.2). We shall consider two simple examples, that will often occur in the sequel.

In the case of a linear function $\eta = a\xi + b$, the relation $\eta \leqq y$ is equivalent to $\xi \leqq (y - b)/a$ or to $\xi \geqq (y - b)/a$, according as $a > 0$ or $a < 0$. It then follows from (14.5.2) that η has the d.f.

$$G(y) = \begin{cases} F\left(\dfrac{y-b}{a}\right) & \text{if } a > 0, \\ 1 - F\left(\dfrac{y-b}{a}\right) & \text{if } a < 0, \end{cases} \tag{15.1.1}$$

where $F(x)$ denotes the d.f. of ξ. The formula for $G(y)$ in the case $a < 0$ is, however, only valid if $(y - b)/a$ is a continuity point of F. In a discontinuity point, the function should, according to our usual convention, be so determined as to be always continuous to the right. If the fr.f. $f(x) = F'(x)$ exists for all values of x, it follows that η has the fr.f.

$$g(y) = G'(y) = \frac{1}{|a|} f\left(\frac{y-b}{a}\right). \tag{15.1.2}$$

Next, we consider the function $\eta = \xi^2$. The variable η is here always non-negative, and for $y > 0$ the relation $\eta \leqq y$ is equivalent to $-\sqrt{y} \leqq \xi \leqq \sqrt{y}$. Consequently η has the d.f.

$$G(y) = \begin{cases} 0 & \text{for } y < 0, \\ F(\sqrt{y}) - F(-\sqrt{y}) & \text{for } y \geqq 0. \end{cases} \tag{15.1.3}$$

This time, the last expression is valid only if $-\sqrt{y}$ is a continuity point of F. If the fr. f. $f(x) = F'(x)$ exists for all x, it follows that η has the fr. f.

$$(15.1.4) \quad g(y) = G'(y) = \begin{cases} 0 & \text{for } y < 0, \\ \dfrac{1}{2\sqrt{y}}\left(f(\sqrt{y}) + f(-\sqrt{y})\right) & \text{for } y > 0. \end{cases}$$

Other simple functions may be treated in a similar way.

15.2. Two simple types of distributions. — In the majority of problems occurring in statistical applications, we are concerned with distributions belonging to one of the two simple types known as the *discrete* and the *continuous* type.

1. *The discrete type.* A random variable ξ will be said to be of the discrete type, or to possess a distribution of this type, if the total mass of the distribution is concentrated in discrete mass points[1]) and if, moreover, any finite interval contains at most a finite number of the mass points. By 6.2, the set of all mass points is finite or enumerable. Let us denote the mass points by $x_1, x_2, \ldots$, and the corresponding masses by $p_1, p_2, \ldots$. The distribution of ξ is then completely described by saying that, for every ν, we have the probability p_ν that ξ takes the value x_ν:

$$P(\xi = x_\nu) = p_\nu.$$

For a set S not containing any point x_ν we have, on the other hand,

$$P(\xi < S) = 0.$$

Since the total mass in the distribution must be unity, we always have

$$\sum_\nu p_\nu = 1.$$

The d. f. $F(x)$ is then given by

$$(15.2.1) \qquad F(x) = P(\xi \leqq x) = \sum_{x_\nu \leqq x} p_\nu,$$

the summation being extended to all values of ν such that $x_\nu \leqq x$. Thus $F(x)$ is a step-function (cf 6.2 and 6.6), which is constant over

[1]) This corresponds to the case $c_1 = 1$, $c_2 = 0$ in (6.6.2).

every interval not containing any point x_ν, but has in each x_ν a step of the height p_ν.

A distribution of the discrete type may be graphically represented by means of a diagram of the function $F(x)$, or by a diagram showing an ordinate of the height p_ν over each point x_ν, as illustrated by Figs 4 and 5.

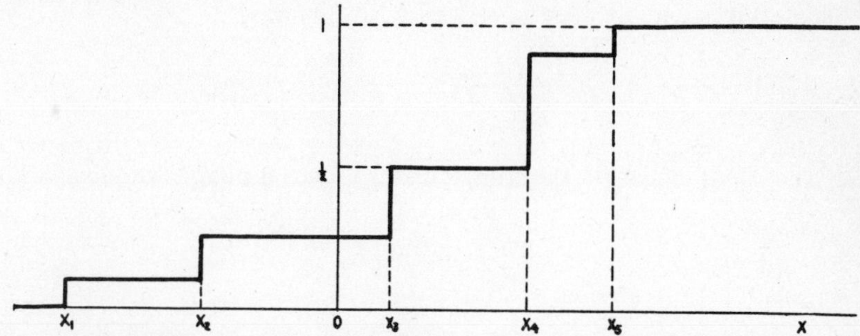

Fig. 4. Distribution function of the discrete type. (Note that the median is indeterminate; cf p. 178.)

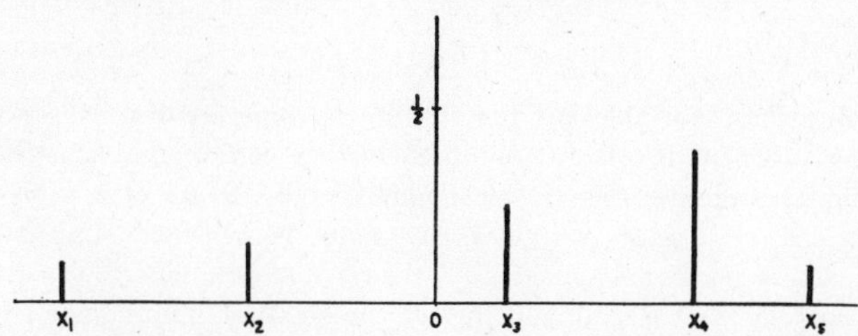

Fig. 5. Probabilities corresponding to the distribution in Fig. 4.

In statistical applications, variables of the discrete type occur e. g. in cases where the variable represents a certain number of units of some kind. Examples are: the number of pigs in a litter, the number of telephone calls at a given station during one hour, the number of business failures during one year. In such cases, the mass points x_ν are simply the natural numbers 0, 1, 2, ...

2. *The continuous type.* A variable ξ will be said to be of the continuous type, or to possess a distribution of this type, if the d. f. $F(x)$ is everywhere continuous[1]) and if, moreover, the fr. f. $f(x) = F'(x)$ exists and is continuous for all values of x, except possibly in certain points, of which any finite interval contains at most a finite number. The d. f. $F(x)$ is then

$$F(x) = P(\xi \leqq x) = \int_{-\infty}^{x} f(t)\, dt.$$

[1]) This corresponds to the case $c_1 = 0$, $c_2 = 1$ in (6.6.2).

The distribution has no discrete mass points, and consequently the probability that ξ takes a particular value x_0 is zero for every x_0:

$$P(\xi = x_0) = 0.$$

The probability that ξ takes a value belonging to the finite or infinite interval (a, b) has thus the same value, whether we consider the interval as closed, open or half-open, and is given by

$$P(a < \xi < b) = F(b) - F(a) = \int_a^b f(t)\,dt.$$

Since the total mass in the distribution must be unity, we always have

$$\int_{-\infty}^{\infty} f(t)\,dt = 1.$$

A distribution of the continuous type may be graphically represented by diagrams showing the d. f. $F(x)$ or the fr. f. $f(x)$, as illustrated by Figs 6—7. The curve $y = f(x)$ is known as the *frequency curve* of the distribution.

In statistical applications, variables of the continuous type occur when we are concerned with the measurement of quantities which, within certain limits, may assume any value. Examples are: the price of a commodity, the stature of a man, the yield of a corn field. In such cases variables are treated as continuous, although strictly speaking the actual data are practically always discontinuous, since every measurement is expressed by an integral multiple of the smallest unit registered in our observations. Thus prices are expressed in money units, lengths may be expressed in cm and weights in kg, etc. When, for theoretical purposes, variables of this kind are considered as continuous, a certain mathematical idealization of actually observed facts is thus already implied.

15.3. Mean values. — Consider a random variable ξ with the d. f. $F(x)$, and let $g(\xi)$ be a function integrable over $(-\infty, \infty)$ with respect to F (cf 7.2). The integral

$$\int_{-\infty}^{\infty} g(x)\,dF(x)$$

has, in 7.4, been interpreted as a weighted mean of the values of $g(x)$ for all values of x, the weights being furnished by the mass quantities dF situated in the neighbourhood of each point x.

Accordingly we shall denote this integral as the *mean value* or *mathematical expectation* of the random variable $g(\xi)$, and write

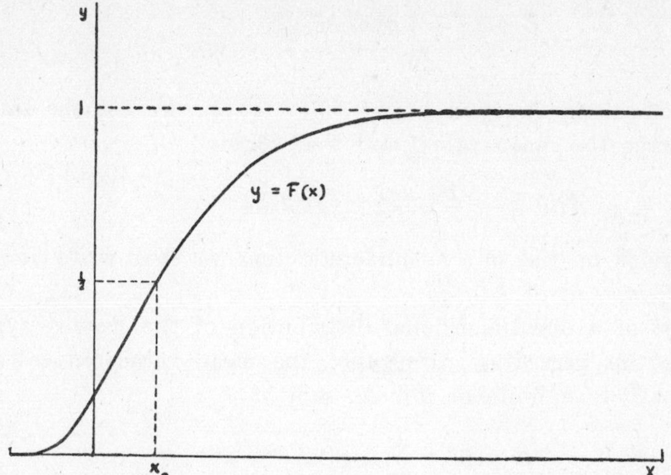

Fig. 6. Distribution function of the continuous type. (Note that the distribution has a unique median at x_0; cf p. 178.)

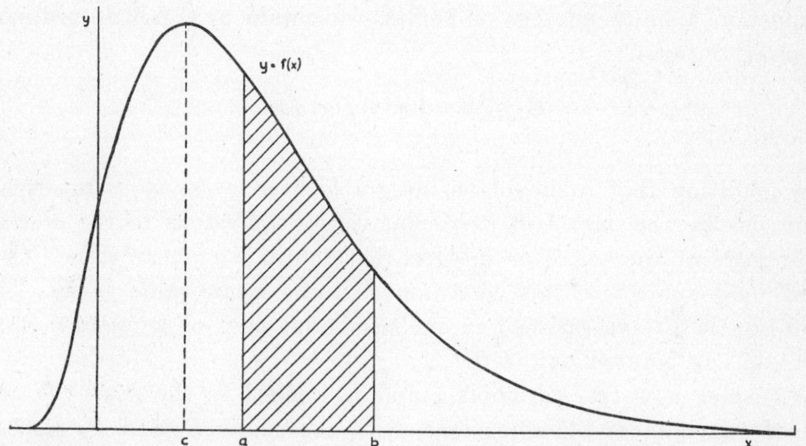

Fig. 7. Frequency function of the distribution in Fig. 6. The shaded area corresponds to the probability $P(a < \xi \leq b)$. The distribution has a unique mode (cf p. 179) at c. The skewness (cf p. 184) is positive.

$$\boldsymbol{E}(g(\xi)) = \int_{-\infty}^{\infty} g(x)\, dF(x). \tag{15.3.1}$$

More generally, if ξ is a j-dimensional random variable with the probability function $P(S)$, and if $g(\xi)$ is a one-dimensional function (particular case $k = 1$ of 14.5) of ξ which is integrable over $\boldsymbol{R}_j$ with respect to $P(S)$, we define the mean value of $g(\xi)$ by the relation

$$(15.3.2) \qquad \boldsymbol{E}(g(\xi)) = \int_{\boldsymbol{R}_j} g(\boldsymbol{x})\, d P(S).$$

For a complex-valued function $g(\xi) = a(\xi) + i\, b(\xi)$, we use the same formula to define the mean value, and thus obtain

$$\boldsymbol{E}(g(\xi)) = \boldsymbol{E}(a(\xi)) + i\, \boldsymbol{E}(b(\xi)).$$

When there is no risk of a misunderstanding, we shall write simply $\boldsymbol{E}\, g(\xi)$ or $\boldsymbol{E}(g)$ instead of $\boldsymbol{E}(g(\xi))$.

In the case of a one-dimensional distribution of the *discrete* type, as defined in the preceding paragraph, the mean value reduces according to (7.1.8) to a finite or infinite sum:

$$\boldsymbol{E}(g(\xi)) = \sum_{\nu} p_\nu\, g(x_\nu),$$

while for the *continuous* type, assuming $g(x)$ to be continuous except at most in a finite number of points, we obtain by (7.5.5) an ordinary Riemann integral:

$$\boldsymbol{E}(g(\xi)) = \int_{-\infty}^{\infty} g(x) f(x)\, dx.$$

The condition that g should be integrable over $(-\infty, \infty)$ with respect to F is, in the last two particular cases, equivalent to the *absolute convergence* of the series or integral representing the mean value. Thus it is only subject to this condition that the mean value exists. The condition is always satisfied in the particular case of a *bounded* function $g(\xi)$, as pointed out in 7.4.

Consider now two variables ξ and η, defined in the spaces $\boldsymbol{R}'$ and $\boldsymbol{R}''$ of any number of dimensions, with the pr. f:s P_1 and P_2 respectively. Let $g(\xi)$ and $h(\eta)$ be two real or complex functions such that the mean values $\boldsymbol{E}\, g(\xi)$ and $\boldsymbol{E}\, h(\eta)$ both exist. We shall consider the sum $g(\xi) + h(\eta)$. By 14.5, this sum is a random variable, which may be regarded as a function of the combined variable (ξ, η). If $\boldsymbol{R}$ denotes the space of the combined variable, while P is the corresponding pr. f., the mean value of the sum has the expression

$$\boldsymbol{E}(g(\xi) + h(\eta)) = \int_{\boldsymbol{R}} (g(\boldsymbol{x}) + h(\boldsymbol{y}))\, d P = \int_{\boldsymbol{R}} g(\boldsymbol{x})\, d P + \int_{\boldsymbol{R}} h(\boldsymbol{y})\, d P.$$

By (9.2.2) the last two integrals reduce, however, to

$$\int_{\boldsymbol{R}'} g(\boldsymbol{x})\,dP_1 = \boldsymbol{E}\,g(\xi) \quad \text{and} \quad \int_{\boldsymbol{R}''} h(\boldsymbol{y})\,dP_2 = \boldsymbol{E}\,h(\eta)$$

respectively, so that we obtain

$$\boldsymbol{E}(g(\xi) + h(\eta)) = \boldsymbol{E}\,g(\xi) + \boldsymbol{E}\,h(\eta). \tag{15.3.3}$$

The extension of this relation to an arbitrary finite number of terms is immediate, and we thus have the following important theorem: *The mean value of a sum of random variables is equal to the sum of the mean values of the terms, provided that the latter mean values exist.*

It should be observed that this theorem has been proved without any assumption concerning the nature of the dependence between the terms of the sum. In the case of the mean value of a *product*, it is not possible to obtain an equally general result. Using the same notations as above, we have

$$\boldsymbol{E}(g(\xi)\,h(\eta)) = \int_{\boldsymbol{R}} g(\boldsymbol{x})\,h(\boldsymbol{y})\,dP.$$

In order to reduce this integral to a simple form, *we now suppose that* ξ *and* η *are independent*, so that the pr. f. P satisfies the multiplicative relation (14.4.4). By the final remark of 14.5, the variables $g(\xi)$ and $h(\eta)$ are then also independent. On this hypothesis, the formula for the mean value reduces according to (9.3.1) to

$$\boldsymbol{E}(g(\xi)\,h(\eta)) = \int_{\boldsymbol{R}'} g(\boldsymbol{x})\,dP_1 \cdot \int_{\boldsymbol{R}''} h(\boldsymbol{y})\,dP_2 = \boldsymbol{E}g(\xi)\,\boldsymbol{E}h(\eta). \tag{15.3.4}$$

The extension to an arbitrary finite number of factors is immediate, so that we have the following theorem: *The mean value of a product of independent random variables is equal to the product of the mean values of the factors, provided that the latter mean values exist.*

We finally consider some simple particular cases of the preceding general relations. — If ξ is a one-dimensional random variable, such that the mean value $\boldsymbol{E}(\xi)$ obtained by taking $g(\xi) = \xi$ in (15.3.1) exists, we have for any constant a and b

$$\boldsymbol{E}(a\,\xi + b) = a\boldsymbol{E}(\xi) + b. \tag{15.3.5}$$

Putting $\boldsymbol{E}(\xi) = m$ we have, in particular,

$$\boldsymbol{E}(\xi - m) = m - m = 0. \tag{15.3.6}$$

Taking $g(\xi) = \xi$, $h(\eta) = \eta$ in the addition theorem (15.3.3), we obtain

$$E(\xi + \eta) = E(\xi) + E(\eta). \tag{15.3.7}$$

If ξ and η are independent, the multiplication theorem (15.3.4) gives

$$E(\xi\eta) = E(\xi)E(\eta). \tag{15.3.8}$$

15.4. Moments. — The *moments* of a one-dimensional distribution have been introduced in 7.4. If, for a positive integer ν, the function x^ν is integrable over $(-\infty, \infty)$ with respect to $F(x)$, the mean value

$$\alpha_\nu = E(\xi^\nu) = \int_{-\infty}^{\infty} x^\nu \, dF(x) \tag{15.4.1}$$

is called the moment of order ν, or simply the ν:th moment, of the variable or the distribution, and we say that the ν:th moment is finite or *exists*. Obviously α_0 always exists and is equal to unity.

If α_ν exists, the function $|x|^\nu$ is also integrable, so that the ν:th *absolute moment*

$$\beta_\nu = E(|\xi|^\nu) = \int_{-\infty}^{\infty} |x|^\nu \, dF(x) \tag{15.4.2}$$

exists. It follows that, if α_k exists, then α_ν and β_ν exist for $0 \leqq \nu \leqq k$.

For a distribution of the discrete type, the moments are according to 15.3 expressed by the series

$$\alpha_\nu = \sum_i p_i x_i^\nu,$$

and for a distribution of the continuous type by the Riemann integral

$$\alpha_\nu = \int_{-\infty}^{\infty} x^\nu f(x) \, dx.$$

It is only in the case when the series or integral representing the moment is *absolutely convergent* that the moment is said to exist.

The first moment α_1 is equal to the mean value, or briefly the *mean*, of the variable, and will often be denoted by the letter m:

$$\alpha_1 = E(\xi) = m.$$

If c denotes any constant, the quantities

$$E[(\xi - c)^\nu] = \int_{-\infty}^{\infty} (x-c)^\nu \, dF(x),$$

are called the *moments about the point c.* For $c = 0$, we obtain the ordinary moments. The *absolute* moments about c are, of course, defined in an analogous way. The *moments about the mean m* are often called the *central moments.* These are particularly important and deserve a special notation. We shall write

$$\mu_\nu = E[(\xi - m)^\nu] = \int_{-\infty}^{\infty} (x-m)^\nu \, dF(x). \tag{15.4.3}$$

Developing the factor $(x-m)^\nu$, we find

$$\begin{aligned} \mu_0 &= 1, \\ \mu_1 &= 0, \\ \mu_2 &= \alpha_2 - m^2, \\ \mu_3 &= \alpha_3 - 3\,m\,\alpha_2 + 2\,m^3, \\ \mu_4 &= \alpha_4 - 4\,m\,\alpha_3 + 6\,m^2\,\alpha_2 - 3\,m^4, \\ &\cdots\cdots\cdots\cdots\cdots \end{aligned} \tag{15.4.4}$$

For the second moment about any point c, we have

$$\begin{aligned} E[(\xi - c)^2] &= E[(\xi - m + m - c)^2] \\ &= \mu_2 + (c-m)^2 \geqq \mu_2, \end{aligned}$$

so that *the second moment becomes a minimum when taken about the mean.*

The moments of any function $g(\xi)$ are the mean values of the successive powers of $g(\xi)$. In the particular case of a linear function $g(\xi) = a\,\xi + b$, the moment α'_ν is given by the expression

$$\alpha'_\nu = E[(a\,\xi + b)^\nu] = a^\nu \alpha_\nu + \binom{\nu}{1} a^{\nu-1}\, b\, \alpha_{\nu-1} + \cdots + b^\nu.$$

In 7.4, we have given a simple sufficient condition for the existence of the moment of a given order k. We remark further that, when the variable ξ is *bounded,* i. e. when finite a and b can be found such that $P(a < \xi < b) = 1$, all moments are finite, and $|\alpha_\nu| \leqq |a|^\nu + |b|^\nu$.

We shall now prove an important inequality for the absolute moments β_ν defined by (15.4.2). The quadratic form in u and v

$$\int_{-\infty}^{\infty} \left(u\,|x|^{\frac{\nu-1}{2}} + v\,|x|^{\frac{\nu+1}{2}}\right)^2 dF(x) = \beta_{\nu-1}u^2 + 2\,\beta_\nu uv + \beta_{\nu+1}v^2$$

is evidently non-negative. Thus by 11.10 the determinant of the form is non-negative, so that we have $\beta_{\nu-1}\beta_{\nu+1} - \beta_\nu^2 \geqq 0$, or

$$\beta_\nu^{2\nu} \leqq \beta_{\nu-1}^\nu \beta_{\nu+1}^\nu. \tag{15.4.5}$$

Replacing here ν successively by 1, 2, . . ., ν, and multiplying all the inequalities thus formed, we obtain $\beta_\nu^{\nu+1} \leqq \beta_{\nu+1}^\nu$, or finally

$$\beta_\nu^{\frac{1}{\nu}} \leqq \beta_{\nu+1}^{\frac{1}{\nu+1}} \qquad (\nu = 1, 2, \ldots). \tag{15.4.6}$$

It is often important to know whether a distribution is *uniquely determined by the sequence of its moments.* We shall not enter upon a complete discussion of this difficult problem, but shall content ourselves with proving the following criterion that is often useful.

Let $\alpha_0 = 1$, α_1, α_2, . . . be the moments of a certain d. f. $F(x)$, all of which are assumed to be finite. Suppose that the series $\sum_0^\infty \frac{\alpha_\nu}{\nu!} r^\nu$ is absolutely convergent for some $r > 0$. Then $F(x)$ is the only d. f. that has the moments α_0, α_1, α_2, ...

We shall first show that $\frac{\beta_n}{n!} r^n \to 0$ as $n \to \infty$. If n is restricted to even values, this follows directly from our hypothesis, and for odd values of n we have by (15.4.5)

$$\frac{\beta_n}{n!} r^n \leqq \left(\frac{\beta_{n-1}}{(n-1)!} r^{n-1}\right)^{\frac{1}{2}} \cdot \left(\frac{\beta_{n+1}}{(n+1)!} r^{n+1}\right)^{\frac{1}{2}} \sqrt{\frac{n+1}{n}},$$

which completes the proof of our assertion. — For any integer $n > 0$ and for any real z we have the MacLaurin expansion

$$e^{iz} = \sum_0^{n-1} \frac{(iz)^\nu}{\nu!} + \vartheta \frac{z^n}{n!},$$

where ϑ denotes a real or complex quantity of modulus not exceeding unity. Hence we obtain by means of (10.1.2) the following expansion for the c. f. $\varphi(t)$ of $F(x)$:

$$\varphi(t+h) = \int_{-\infty}^{\infty} e^{ihx} \cdot e^{itx}\, dF(x)$$

$$= \sum_{0}^{n-1} \frac{(ih)^\nu}{\nu!} \int_{-\infty}^{\infty} x^\nu e^{itx}\, dF(x) + \vartheta \frac{h^n}{n!} \int_{-\infty}^{\infty} |x|^n\, dF(x)$$

$$= \sum_{0}^{n-1} \frac{h^\nu}{\nu!} \varphi^{(\nu)}(t) + \vartheta \frac{\beta_n h^n}{n!}.$$

For $|h| < r$ the remainder tends to zero, so that *for any t the c.f. $\varphi(t+h)$ can be developed in Taylor's series, convergent for $|h| < r$.*

Taking first $t = 0$, we find that the series (where we have written t in the place of h)

$$\varphi(t) = \sum_{0}^{\infty} \frac{\alpha_\nu}{\nu!} (it)^\nu \tag{15.4.7}$$

represents the function $\varphi(t)$ at least in the interval $-r < t < r$. In this interval, $\varphi(t)$ is thus uniquely determined by the moments α_ν. In the points $t = \pm \frac{1}{2} r$, the series obtained by differentiating (15.4.7) any number of times is convergent, so that all the derivatives $\varphi^{(\nu)}(\pm \frac{1}{2} r)$ can be calculated from (15.4.7), i.e. from the moments α_ν. These derivatives appear as coefficients in the Taylor developments of $\varphi(\pm \frac{1}{2} r + h)$, which converge and represent $\varphi(t)$ for $|h| < r$, so that the domain where $\varphi(t)$ is known is now extended to the interval $-\frac{3}{2} r < t < \frac{3}{2} r$. From the last developments, we can now calculate the derivatives $\varphi^{(\nu)}(t)$ in the points $t = \pm r$, and use these as coefficients in the Taylor developments of $\varphi(\pm r + h)$, etc. In this way we may go on as long as we please, and it will be seen that by this procedure *the c.f. $\varphi(t)$ is uniquely defined by the moments α_ν for all values of t.*[1]) It then follows from the uniqueness theorem (10.3.1) that the d. f. $F(x)$ is also uniquely determined by the α_ν, and our theorem is proved.

In the particular case when $F(x)$ is the d. f. of a *bounded* variable, it follows from the remark made above that the conditions of the theorem are always satisfied.

15.5. Measures of location. — In practical applications it is important to be able to describe the main features of a distribution by

[1]) This is the method known as *analytic continuation* in the Theory of Analytic Functions.

means of a few simple parameters. In the first place, we often want to *locate* a distribution by finding some *typical value* of the variable, which may be conceived as a *central point* of the distribution. There are various ways of calculating such a typical parameter, and we shall here discuss the three most important cases, viz. the *mean*, the *median*, and the *mode*.

The *mean* $\boldsymbol{E}(\xi) = m$ is the first moment of the distribution, and has already been defined in the preceding paragraph. In terms of our mechanical interpretation of the probability distribution as a distribution of mass, the mean has an important concrete significance: it is the abscissa of the *centre of gravity* of the distribution (cf 7.4). This property gives the mean an evident claim of being regarded as a typical parameter.

The *median.* — If x_0 is a point which divides the whole mass of the distribution into two equal parts, each containing the mass $\frac{1}{2}$, x_0 is called a *median* of the distribution. Thus any root of the equation $F(x) = \frac{1}{2}$ is a median of the distribution. In order to discuss the possible cases, we consider the curve $y = F(x)$, regarding any vertical step as part of the curve, so that we have a single connected, never decreasing curve (cf Figs 4 and 6). This curve has at least one point of intersection with the straight line $y = \frac{1}{2}$. If there is only one point of intersection, the abscissa of this point is the unique median of the distribution (cf Fig. 6). It may, however, occur that the curve and the line have a whole closed interval in common (cf. Fig. 4). In this case the abscissa of every point in the interval satisfies the equation $F(x) = \frac{1}{2}$, and may thus be taken as a median of the distribution.

We thus see that *every distribution has at least one median.* In the *determinate case*, the median is uniquely defined; in the *indeterminate case*, every point in a certain closed interval is a median.

The mean, on the other hand, does not always exist. Even in cases when the mean does exist, the median is sometimes preferable as a typical parameter, since the value of the mean may be largely influenced by the occurrence of very small masses situated at a very large distance from the bulk of the distribution.

As shown in the preceding paragraph, the mean is characterized by a certain minimum property: the second moment becomes a minimum when taken about the mean. There is an analogous property of the median: *the first absolute moment* $\boldsymbol{E}(|\xi - c|)$ *becomes a minimum when* c *is equal to the median.* This property holds even in the indeterminate case, and the moment has then the same value for c equal to any of the possible median values. Denoting the median (or, in the indeterminate case, any median value) by μ, we have in fact the relations

$$E(|\xi - c|) = \begin{cases} E(|\xi - \mu|) + 2\int\limits_{\mu}^{c} (c - x)\, dF(x) & \text{for } c > \mu, \\ E(|\xi - \mu|) + 2\int\limits_{c}^{\mu} (x - c)\, dF(x) & \text{»} \quad c < \mu. \end{cases}$$

The second terms on the right hand sides are evidently positive, except in the case when c is another median value (indeterminate case), when the corresponding term is zero.[1]) The proof of these relations will be left as an exercise for the reader.

The *mode* of a distribution will only be defined for distributions of the two simple types introduced in 15.2. For a distribution of the *continuous* type, any maximum point x_0 of the frequency function $f(x)$ is called a *mode* of the distribution. A unique mode thus only exists for frequency curves $y = f(x)$ having a single maximum (cf Fig. 7); such *unimodal* distributions occur, however, often in statistical applications. When the frequency curve has more than one maximum, the distribution is called *bimodal* or *multimodal*, as the case may be. — For a distribution of the *discrete* type, we may suppose the mass points x_ν arranged in increasing order of magnitude. The point x_ν is then called a *mode* of the distribution, if $p_\nu > p_{\nu-1}$ and $p_\nu > p_{\nu+1}$. The expressions unimodal, bimodal and multimodal distributions are here defined in a similar way as for continuous distributions.

In the particular case when the distribution is *symmetric* about a certain point a, we have $F(a + x) + F(a - x) = 1$ as soon as $a \pm x$ are continuity points of F. It is then seen that the mean (if existent) and the median are both equal to a. If, in addition, the distribution is unimodal, the mode is also equal to a.

15.6. Measures of dispersion. — When we know a typical value for a random variable, it is often required to calculate some parameter giving an idea of how widely the values of the variable are spread on either side of the typical value. A parameter of this kind is called a measure of spread or *dispersion*. It is sometimes also called a measure of *concentration*. Dispersion and concentration vary, of course,

---

[1]) In the particular case when μ is a discontinuity point of F, the ordinary definition of the integrals in the second members must be somewhat modified, as the integrals should then in both cases include *half* the contribution arising from the discontinuity.

in inverse sense: the greater the dispersion, the smaller the concentration, and conversely.

If our typical value is the mean m of the distribution, it seems natural to consider the second moment about the mean, μ_2, as a dispersion measure. This is called the *variance* of the variable, and represents the *moment of inertia* of the mass distribution with respect to a perpendicular axis through the centre of gravity (cf 7.4). We have, of course, always $\mu_2 \geqq 0$. When $\mu_2 = 0$, it follows from the definition of μ_2 that the whole mass of the distribution must be concentrated in the single point m (cf 16.1).

In order to obtain a quantity of the first dimension in units of the variable, it is, however, often preferable to use the non-negative square root of μ_2, which is called the *standard deviation* (abbreviated *s. d.*) of the variable, and is denoted by $\boldsymbol{D}(\xi)$ or sometimes by the single letter σ. We then have for any variable such that the second moment exists

$$\begin{aligned}\boldsymbol{D}^2(\xi) = \sigma^2 = \mu_2 &= \boldsymbol{E}[(\xi - \boldsymbol{E}(\xi))^2] \\ &= \boldsymbol{E}(\xi^2) - \boldsymbol{E}^2(\xi).\end{aligned}$$

It then follows from (15.3.5) that we have for any constant a and b

$$\boldsymbol{D}(a\xi + b) = |a|\,\boldsymbol{D}(\xi).$$

When ξ is a variable with the mean m and the s. d. σ, we shall often have occasion to consider the corresponding *standardized variable* $\frac{\xi - m}{\sigma}$, which represents the deviation of ξ from its mean m, expressed in units of the s. d. σ. It follows from the last relation and from (15.3.5) that the standardized variable has zero mean and unit s. d.:

$$\boldsymbol{E}\left(\frac{\xi - m}{\sigma}\right) = 0, \qquad \boldsymbol{D}\left(\frac{\xi - m}{\sigma}\right) = 1.$$

If ξ and η are independent variables, it further follows from (15.3.8) that we have

$$\boldsymbol{D}^2(\xi + \eta) = \boldsymbol{D}^2(\xi) + \boldsymbol{D}^2(\eta). \tag{15.6.1}$$

This relation is immediately extended to any finite number of terms. If $\xi_1, \ldots \xi_n$ are independent variables, we thus obtain

$$\boldsymbol{D}^2(\xi_1 + \cdots + \xi_n) = \boldsymbol{D}^2(\xi_1) + \cdots + \boldsymbol{D}^2(\xi_n). \tag{15.6.2}$$

We have seen that the second moment is a minimum when taken about the mean, and the first absolute moment when taken about the median (cf 15.4 and 15.5). If we use the median μ as our typical value, it thus seems natural to use the first absolute moment

$$E(|\xi - \mu|)$$

as measure of dispersion. This is called the *mean deviation* of the variable. Sometimes the name of mean deviation is used for the first absolute moment taken about the mean, but this practice is not to be recommended.

In the same way as we have defined the median by means of the equation $F(x) = \frac{1}{2}$, we may define a quantity ζ_p by the equation $F(\zeta_p) = p$, where p is any given number such that $0 < p < 1$. The quantity ζ_p will be called the *quantile* of order p of the distribution. Like the median, any quantile ζ_p may sometimes be indeterminate. The quantile $\zeta_{\frac{1}{2}}$ is, of course, identical with the median. The knowledge of ζ_p for some set of conveniently chosen values of p, such as $p = \frac{1}{4}, \frac{1}{2}, \frac{3}{4}$, or $p = 0.1, 0.2, \ldots .. 0.9$, will obviously give a good idea of the location and dispersion of the distribution. The quantities $\zeta_{\frac{1}{4}}$ and $\zeta_{\frac{3}{4}}$ are called the *lower* and *upper quartiles*, while the quanties $\zeta_{0.1}, \zeta_{0.2}, \ldots$ are known as the *deciles*. The halved difference $\dfrac{\zeta_{\frac{3}{4}} - \zeta_{\frac{1}{4}}}{2}$ is sometimes used as a measure of dispersion under the name of *semi-interquartile range.*

If the whole mass of the distribution is situated within finite distance, there is an upper bound g of all points x such that $F(x) = 0$, and a lower bound G of all x such that $F(x) = 1$. The interval (g, G) then contains the whole mass of the distribution. The length $G - g$ of this interval is called the *range* of the distribution, and may be used as a measure of dispersion.

The word range is sometimes also used to denote the interval (g, G) itself. If we know this interval, we have a fairly good idea both of the location and of the dispersion of the distribution. For a distribution where the range is not finite, intervals such as $(m - \sigma, m + \sigma)$ or $(\zeta_{\frac{1}{4}}, \zeta_{\frac{3}{4}})$, although they do not contain the whole mass of the distribution, may be used in a similar way, as a kind of geometrical representation of the location and dispersion of the distribution (cf 21.10).

All measures of location and dispersion, and of other similar properties, are to a large extent arbitrary. This is quite natural, since the properties to be described by such parameters are too vaguely defined to admit of unique measurement by means of a single number.

Each measure has advantages and disadvantages of its own, and a measure which renders excellent service in one case may be more or less useless in another.

If, in particular, we choose the variance σ^2 or the s. d. σ as our measure of dispersion, this means that the dispersion of the mass in a distribution with the mean $m = 0$ is measured by the mean square

$$\boldsymbol{E}(\xi^2) = \int_{-\infty}^{\infty} x^2 \, dF(x).$$

The concentration of the variable ξ about the point $m = 0$ will be measured by the same quantity: the smaller the mean square, the greater the concentration, and conversely. Thus the mean square of a variable quantity is considered as a measure of the deviation of this quantity from zero. This is a way of expressing the famous *principle of least squares*, that we shall meet in various connections in the sequel. — It follows from the above that there is no logical necessity prompting us to adopt this principle. On the contrary, it is largely a matter of convention whether we choose to do so or not. The main reason in favour of the principle lies in the relatively simple nature of the rules of operation to which it leads. We have, e. g., the simple addition rule (15.6.2) for the variance, while there is no analogue for the other dispersion measures discussed above.

15.7. Tchebycheff's theorem. — We shall now prove the following generalization of a theorem due to Tchebycheff:

Let $g(\xi)$ be a non-negative function of the random variable ξ. For every $K > 0$ we then have

$$P[g(\xi) \geqq K] \leqq \frac{\boldsymbol{E}\, g(\xi)}{K}, \tag{15.7.1}$$

where P denotes as usual the pr. f. of ξ.

If we denote by S the set of all ξ satisfying the inequality $g(\xi) \geqq K$, the truth of the theorem follows directly from the relation

$$\boldsymbol{E}\, g(\xi) = \int_{-\infty}^{\infty} g(x)\, dF \geqq K \int_S dF = K\, P(S).$$

It is evident that the theorem holds, with the same proof, even when ξ is replaced by a random variable $\boldsymbol{\xi}$ in any number of dimensions.

Taking in particular $g(\xi) = (\xi - m)^2$, $K = k^2 \sigma^2$, where m and σ

denote the mean and the s. d. of ξ, we obtain for every $k > 0$ the *Bienaymé-Tchebycheff inequality:*

$$P(|\xi - m| \geqq k\sigma) \leqq \frac{1}{k^2}. \tag{15.7.2}$$

This inequality shows that the quantity of mass in the distribution situated outside the interval $m - k\sigma < \xi < m + k\sigma$ is at most equal to $\frac{1}{k^2}$, and thus gives a good idea of the sense in which σ may be used as a measure of dispersion or concentration.

For the particular distribution of mean m and s. d. σ which has a mass $\frac{1}{2k^2}$ in each of the points $x = m \pm k\sigma$, and a mass $1 - \frac{1}{k^2}$ in the point $x = m$, we have $P(|\xi - m| \geqq k\sigma) = \frac{1}{k^2}$, and it is thus seen that the upper limit of the probability given by (15.7.2) cannot generally be improved.

On the other hand, if we restrict ourselves to certain classes of distributions, it is sometimes possible to improve the inequality (15.7.2). Thus it was already shown by Gauss in 1821 that for a *unimodal* distribution (cf 15.5) of the continuous type we have for every $k > 0$

$$P(|\xi - x_0| \geqq k\tau) \leqq \frac{4}{9k^2}, \tag{15.7.3}$$

where x_0 is the mode, and $\tau^2 = \sigma^2 + (x_0 - m)^2$ is the second order moment about the mode. A simple proof of this relation will be indicated in Ex. 4 on p. 256. Hence we obtain the following inequality for the deviation from the mean:

$$P(|\xi - m| \geqq k\sigma) \leqq \tfrac{4}{9} \cdot \frac{1 + s^2}{(k - |s|)^2} \tag{15.7.4}$$

for every $k > |s|$, where s denotes the Pearson measure of skewness defined by (15.8.3). For moderate values of $|s|$, this inequality often gives a lower value to the limit than (15.7.2). Thus if $|s| < 0.25$, the probability of a deviation exceeding 3σ is by (15.7.4) smaller than 0.0624, while (15.7.2) gives the less precise limit 0.1111. For the probability of a deviation exceeding 4σ, the corresponding figures are 0.0336 by (15.7.4), and 0.0625 by (15.7.2).

15.8. Measures of skewness and excess. — In a symmetric distribution, every moment of odd order about the mean (if existent) is evidently equal to zero. Any such moment which is not zero may thus be considered as a measure of the *asymmetry* or *skewness* of the distribution. The simplest of these measures is μ_3, which is of the third dimension in units of the variable. In order to reduce this to zero dimension, and so construct an *absolute* measure, we divide by σ^3 and regard the ratio

$$\gamma_1 = \frac{\mu_3}{\sigma^3} \tag{15.8.1}$$

as a measure of the skewness. We shall call γ_1 the *coefficient of skewness.*

In statistical applications, we often meet unimodal continuous distributions of the type shown in Fig. 7, where the frequency curve forms a »long tail» on one side of the mode, and a »short tail» on the other side. In the curve shown in Fig. 7, the long tail is on the positive side, and in μ_3 the cubes of the positive deviations will then generally outweigh the negative cubes, so that γ_1 will be positive. We shall call this a distribution of *positive skewness.* Similarly we have *negative skewness* when γ_1 is negative; the long tail will then generally be on the negative side.

Reducing the fourth moment μ_4 to zero dimension in the same way as above, we define the *coefficient of excess*

$$\gamma_2 = \frac{\mu_4}{\sigma^4} - 3, \tag{15.8.2}$$

which is sometimes used as a measure of the degree of flattening of a frequency curve near its centre. For the important normal distribution (cf 17.2), γ_2 is equal to zero. Positive values of γ_2 are supposed to indicate that the frequency curve is more tall and slim than the normal curve in the neighbourhood of the mode, and conversely for negative values. In the former case, it is usual to talk of a *positive excess*, as compared with the normal curve, in the latter case of a *negative excess.* This usage is, however, open to certain criticism (cf 17.6).

In the literature, the quantities $\beta_1 = \gamma_1^2$ and $\beta_2 = \gamma_2 + 3$ are often used instead of γ_1 and γ_2.

Many other measures of skewness and excess have been proposed. Thus K. Pearson introduced the difference between the mean and the mode, divided by the s. d.:

$$s = \frac{m - x_0}{\sigma}, \tag{15.8.3}$$

as a measure of skewness. For the class of distributions belonging to the Pearson system (cf 19.4), it can be shown that

$$s = \frac{\gamma_1 (\gamma_2 + 6)}{2(5\gamma_2 - 6\gamma_1^2 + 6)}.$$

When γ_1 and γ_2 are small, this gives approximately

$$s = \tfrac{1}{2}\gamma_1 \quad \text{or} \quad x_0 = m - \tfrac{1}{2}\gamma_1 \sigma.$$

The last relation also holds approximately for distributions given by the Edgeworth or Charlier expansions (cf 17.6—17.7). Charlier used the coefficient $S = -\frac{1}{2}\gamma_1$ as measure of skewness, and $E = \frac{1}{8}\gamma_2$ as measure of excess.

15.9. Characteristic functions. — The mean value of the particular function $e^{it\xi}$ will be written

$$\varphi(t) = \boldsymbol{E}(e^{it\xi}) = \int_{-\infty}^{\infty} e^{itx}\, dF(x). \tag{15.9.1}$$

This is a function of the real variable t, and will be called the *characteristic function* (abbreviated *c. f.*) of the variable ξ, or of the corresponding distribution. The reader is referred to the discussion of the mathematical theory of characteristic functions given in Ch. 10.

It follows in particular from this discussion that there is a one-to-one correspondence between distributions and characteristic functions. If two distributions are identical, so are their c. f:s, and conversely. This property has important consequences. In many problems where it is required to find the distribution of some given random variable, it is relatively easy to find the c. f. of the variable. If this is found to agree with the c. f. of some already known distribution, we may conclude that the latter must be identical with the required distribution.

The c. f. of any function $g(\xi)$ is the mean value of $e^{itg(\xi)}$. In the particular case of a linear function $g(\xi) = a\xi + b$ the c. f. becomes

$$\boldsymbol{E}(e^{it(a\xi+b)}) = e^{bit}\varphi(at). \tag{15.9.2}$$

Thus e. g. the variable $-\xi$ has the c. f. $\varphi(-t) = \overline{\varphi(t)}$. Further, the *standardized variable* $(\xi - m)/\sigma$ has the c. f.

$$\boldsymbol{E}\left(e^{it\frac{\xi-m}{\sigma}}\right) = e^{-\frac{mit}{\sigma}}\varphi\left(\frac{t}{\sigma}\right).$$

15.10. Semi-invariants. — If the k:th moment of the distribution exists, the c. f. may according to (10.1.3) be developed in MacLaurin's series for small values of t:

$$\varphi(t) = 1 + \sum_{1}^{k} \frac{\alpha_\nu}{\nu!}(it)^\nu + o(t^k). \tag{15.10.1}$$

For the function $\log(1 + z)$ we have the corresponding development

$$\log(1 + z) = \frac{z}{1} - \frac{z^2}{2} + \cdots \pm \frac{z^k}{k} + o(z^k).$$

Replacing here $1 + z$ by $\varphi(t)$, we obtain after rearrangement of the terms a development of the form

$$\log \varphi(t) = \sum_{1}^{k} \frac{\varkappa_\nu}{\nu!} (i\,t)^\nu + o(t^k). \tag{15.10.2}$$

The coefficients $\varkappa_\nu$ were introduced by Thiele (Ref. 37), and are called the *semi-invariants* or *cumulants* of the distribution.

In order to deduce the relations between the moments α_ν and the semi-invariants $\varkappa_\nu$, we may use the identities

$$\log \varphi(t) = \log \left(1 + \sum_{1}^{\infty} \frac{\alpha_\nu}{\nu!} (i\,t)^\nu\right) = \sum_{1}^{\infty} \frac{\varkappa_\nu}{\nu!} (i\,t)^\nu,$$

$$\varphi(t) = 1 + \sum_{1}^{\infty} \frac{\alpha_\nu}{\nu!} (i\,t)^\nu = e^{\sum_{1}^{\infty} \frac{\varkappa_\nu}{\nu!} (i\,t)^\nu}$$

in a purely formal way, without paying any attention to questions of existence of moments or convergence of series. It is seen that $\varkappa_n$ is a polynomial in $\alpha_1, \ldots, \alpha_n$, and conversely α_n is a polynomial in $\varkappa_1, \ldots, \varkappa_n$. In particular we have

$$\begin{aligned}
\varkappa_1 &= \alpha_1 = m,\\
\varkappa_2 &= \alpha_2 - \alpha_1^2 = \sigma^2,\\
\varkappa_3 &= \alpha_3 - 3\,\alpha_1\,\alpha_2 + 2\,\alpha_1^3,\\
\varkappa_4 &= \alpha_4 - 3\,\alpha_2^2 - 4\,\alpha_1\,\alpha_3 + 12\,\alpha_1^2\,\alpha_2 - 6\,\alpha_1^4,\\
&\cdots\cdots\cdots\cdots
\end{aligned} \tag{15.10.3}$$

and conversely

$$\begin{aligned}
\alpha_1 &= \varkappa_1,\\
\alpha_2 &= \varkappa_2 + \varkappa_1^2,\\
\alpha_3 &= \varkappa_3 + 3\,\varkappa_1\,\varkappa_2 + \varkappa_1^3,\\
\alpha_4 &= \varkappa_4 + 3\,\varkappa_2^2 + 4\,\varkappa_1\,\varkappa_3 + 6\,\varkappa_1^2\,\varkappa_2 + \varkappa_1^4,\\
&\cdots\cdots\cdots\cdots
\end{aligned} \tag{15.10.4}$$

In terms of the central moments μ_ν, the expressions of the $\varkappa_\nu$ become

$$
\begin{aligned}
\varkappa_1 &= m, \\
\varkappa_2 &= \mu_2 = \sigma^2, \\
\varkappa_3 &= \mu_3, \\
\varkappa_4 &= \mu_4 - 3\,\mu_2^2, \\
\varkappa_5 &= \mu_5 - 10\,\mu_2\,\mu_3, \\
\varkappa_6 &= \mu_6 - 15\,\mu_2\,\mu_4 - 10\,\mu_3^2 + 30\,\mu_2^3, \\
&\cdots\cdots\cdots\cdots
\end{aligned}
\tag{15.10.5}
$$

so that the coefficients of skewness and excess introduced in 15.8 are $\gamma_1 = \frac{\varkappa_3}{\varkappa_2^{3/2}}$ and $\gamma_2 = \frac{\varkappa_4}{\varkappa_2^2}$.

The semi-invariants $\varkappa'_\nu$ of a linear function $g(\xi) = a\,\xi + b$ are, by (15.9.2), found from the development

$$\log\,[e^{b\,i\,t}\,\varphi\,(a\,t)] = \sum_1^k \frac{\varkappa'_\nu}{\nu\,!}(i\,t)^\nu + o\,(t^k).$$

Comparing with (15.10.2), we obtain the expressions

$$\varkappa'_1 = a\,\varkappa_1 + b, \quad \text{and} \quad \varkappa'_\nu = a^\nu\,\varkappa_\nu \quad \text{for} \quad \nu > 1.$$

15.11. Independent variables. Let ξ and η be random variables with the d.f:s F_1 and F_2, and the joint pr. f. P. By (14.4.5) a necessary and sufficient condition for the independence of ξ and η is that the joint d. f. of the variables is, for all x and y, given by the expression[1])

$$F(x, y) = P(\xi \leqq x, \eta \leqq y) = F_1(x)\,F_2(y). \tag{15.11.1}$$

When both variables have distributions belonging to the same simple type, the independence condition may be expressed in a more convenient form, as we are now going to show.

Consider first the case of two variables of the *discrete* type, with distributions given by

$$P(\xi = x_\nu) = p_\nu, \quad P(\eta = y_\nu) = q_\nu,$$

where $\nu = 1, 2, \ldots$ It is then easily seen that the independence condition (15.11.1) is equivalent to

$$P(\xi = x_\mu,\; \eta = y_\nu) = p_\mu\,q_\nu \tag{15.11.2}$$

for all values of μ and ν.

[1]) Another necessary and sufficient condition will be given in 21.3.

In the case of two variables of the *continuous* type, the independence condition (15.11.1) may be differentiated with respect to x and y, and we obtain

$$f(x, y) = \frac{\partial^2 F}{\partial x \, \partial y} = f_1(x) f_2(y), \qquad (15.11.3)$$

where f_1 and f_2 are the fr. f:s of ξ and η, while f is according to 8.4 the fr. f. of the joint distribution, or the *joint fr. f.* of ξ and η. Conversely, from (15.11.3) we obtain (15.11.1) by direct integration.

Thus a necessary and sufficient condition for independence is given by (15.11.2) *in the case of two discrete variables, and by* (15.11.3) *in the case of two continuous variables. Both conditions immediately extend themselves to an arbitrary finite number of variables.*

15.12. Addition of independent variables. — Let ξ and η be independent random variables with known distributions. By 14.5, the sum $\xi + \eta$ has a distribution uniquely determined by the distributions of ξ and η. In many problems it is required to express the d. f., the c. f., the moments etc. of this distribution in terms of the corresponding functions and quantities of the given distributions of ξ and η. The problem may, of course, be generalized to a sum of more than two independent variables.

We shall first consider the c. f:s. Let $\varphi_1(t)$, $\varphi_2(t)$ and $\varphi(t)$ denote the c. f:s of ξ, η and $\xi + \eta$ respectively. We then have, by the theorem (15.3.4) on the mean value of a product of independent factors,

$$\begin{aligned} \varphi(t) &= \boldsymbol{E}\left(e^{it(\xi+\eta)}\right) = \boldsymbol{E}\left(e^{it\xi} e^{it\eta}\right) \\ &= \boldsymbol{E}\left(e^{it\xi}\right) \boldsymbol{E}\left(e^{it\eta}\right) = \varphi_1(t)\, \varphi_2(t). \end{aligned}$$

This relation is immediately extended to an arbitrary finite number of variables. If $\xi_1, \ldots, \xi_n$ are independent variables with the c. f:s $\varphi_1(t), \ldots, \varphi_n(t)$, the c. f. $\varphi(t)$ of the sum $\xi_1 + \cdots + \xi_n$ is thus given by the relation

$$\varphi(t) = \varphi_1(t)\, \varphi_2(t) \ldots \varphi_n(t), \qquad (15.12.1)$$

so that we have the following important theorem, which expresses a fundamental property of the c. f:s.

The characteristic function of a sum of independent variables is equal to the product of the characteristic functions of the terms.

We now want to express the d. f. of the sum $\xi + \eta$ by means of the d. f:s F_1 and F_2 of the terms. This problem will be treated as an example of the general method (cf 10.3 and 15.9) of finding a d.f. with the aid of its c.f. Consider the integral

$$F(x) = \int_{-\infty}^{\infty} F_1(x - z)\, dF_2(z).$$

Since F_1 is bounded, this integral has by 7.1 a finite and determined value for every x. Now $F_1(x - z)$ is, for every fixed z, a never decreasing function of x which is everywhere continuous to the right, and tends to 1 as $x \to +\infty$, and to 0 as $x \to -\infty$. Consider the difference $F(x + h) - F(x)$, where $h > 0$. It follows from (7.1.4) that this difference is non-negative, and from (7.3.1) that it tends to zero with h. It further follows from (7.3.1) that $F(x)$ tends to 1 as $x \to +\infty$, and to 0 as $x \to -\infty$. Thus $F(x)$ is a d.f. The corresponding c.f.

$$\int_{-\infty}^{\infty} e^{itx} dF(x)$$

is, by (7.5.6), the limit as $n \to \infty$ of a sum s_n of the form

$$s_n = \sum_1^n e^{itx_\nu} [F(x_\nu) - F(x_{\nu-1})],$$

provided that the maximum length of the sub-intervals $(x_{\nu-1}, x_\nu)$ tends to zero, while $x_0 \to -\infty$ and $x_n \to +\infty$. Introducing here the integral expression of $F(x)$, we obtain

$$s_n = \int_{-\infty}^{\infty} s_n' \, e^{itz} \, dF_2(z),$$

where

$$s_n' = \sum_1^n e^{itx_\nu'} [F_1(x_\nu') - F_1(x_{\nu-1}')],$$

$$x_\nu' = x_\nu - z.$$

As $n \to \infty$, s_n' tends for every fixed z to the limit

$$\lim s_n' = \int_{-\infty}^{\infty} e^{itx} \, dF_1(x) = \varphi_1(t).$$

Further, s_n' is uniformly bounded, since we have

$$|s_n'| \leqq \sum_1^n [F_1(x_\nu') - F_1(x_{\nu-1}')] \leqq 1$$

According to (7.1.7) it then follows that

$$\lim s_n = \varphi_1(t) \int_{-\infty}^{\infty} e^{itz}\, dF_2(z) = \varphi_1(t)\, \varphi_2(t).$$

Thus the c. f. of $F(x)$ is identical with the c. f. $\varphi(t) = \varphi_1(t)\,\varphi_2(t)$ of the sum $\xi + \eta$, so that $F(x)$ is the required d. f. Since the functions F_1 and F_2 may evidently be interchanged without affecting the proof, we have established the following theorem:

The distribution function $F(x)$ of the sum of two independent variables is given by the expression

$$F(x) = \int_{-\infty}^{\infty} F_1(x-z)\, dF_2(z) = \int_{-\infty}^{\infty} F_2(x-z)\, dF_1(z), \tag{15.12.2}$$

where F_1 and F_2 are the distribution functions of the terms.[1])

When three d. f:s satisfy (15.12.2), we shall say that F is *composed* of the *components* F_1 and F_2, and we shall use the abbreviation

$$F(x) = F_1(x) * F_2(x) = F_2(x) * F_1(x). \tag{15.12.2 a}$$

By (15.12.1), this symbolical multiplication of the d. f:s corresponds to a genuine multiplication of the c. f:s.

If the three variables ξ_1, ξ_2 and ξ_3 are independent, an evident modification of the proof of (15.12.2) shows that the sum $\xi_1 + \xi_2 + \xi_3$ has the d. f. $(F_1 * F_2) * F_3 = F_1 * (F_2 * F_3)$. Obviously this may be generalized to any number of components, and it is seen that the operation of composition is commutative and associative. For the sum $\xi_1 + \cdots + \xi_n$ of n independent variables we have the d. f.

$$F = F_1 * F_2 * \cdots * F_n. \tag{15.12.3}$$

Let us now consider the following two particular cases of the composition of two components according to (15.12.2):

a) Both components belong to the discrete type (cf 15.2).

b) Both components belong to the continuous type, and at least one of the fr. f:s, say $f_1 = F_1'$, is bounded for all x.

In case a), let $x_1, x_2, \ldots$ and $y_1, y_2, \ldots$ denote the discontinuity points of F_1 and F_2 respectively. It is then evident that the total

---

[1]) The reader should try to construct a direct proof of this theorem, without the use of characteristic functions. It is to be proved that, in the two-dimensional distribution of the independent variables ξ and η, the mass quantity $F(x)$ situated in the half-plane $\xi + \eta \leqq x$ is given by (15.12.2). Cf. Cramér, Ref. 11, p. 35.

mass of the composed distribution is concentrated in the points $x_r + y_s$, where r and s independently assume the values 1, 2, ... If the set of all these points has no finite limiting point, the composed d. f. thus also belongs to the discrete type. This is the case e. g. when all the x_r and y_s are non-negative, or when at least one of the sequences $\{x_r\}$ and $\{y_s\}$ is finite.

In case b), the first integral in (15.12.2) satisfies the conditions for derivation with respect to x (cf 7.3.2). Further, by (7.3.1) and (7.5.5), the derivative $F'(x) = f(x)$ is continuous for all x, and may be expressed as a Riemann integral

$$(15.12.4) \qquad f(x) = \int_{-\infty}^{\infty} f_1(x-z) f_2(z)\, dz = \int_{-\infty}^{\infty} f_2(x-z) f_1(z)\, dz.$$

Thus the composed distribution belongs to the continuous type, and the fr. f. $f(x)$ is everywhere continuous.

Returning to the general case, we denote by m_1, m_2 and m the means, and by σ_1, σ_2 and σ the s. d:s of ξ, η and $\xi + \eta$ respectively. Since ξ and η are independent, we then have by (15.3.7) and (15.6.1)

$$(15.12.5) \qquad m = m_1 + m_2, \qquad \sigma^2 = \sigma_1^2 + \sigma_2^2.$$

For the higher moments about the mean, a general expression is deduced from the relation

$$\mu_\nu = \boldsymbol{E}\,[(\xi + \eta - m)^\nu] = \boldsymbol{E}\,[(\xi - m_1 + \eta - m_2)^\nu].$$

Since any first order moment about a mean is zero, we have in particular, using easily understood notations,

$$(15.12.6) \qquad \begin{aligned} \mu_3 &= \mu_3^{(1)} + \mu_3^{(2)}, \\ \mu_4 &= \mu_4^{(1)} + 6\,\mu_2^{(1)}\,\mu_2^{(2)} + \mu_4^{(2)}, \\ &\cdots\cdots\cdots\cdots \end{aligned}$$

The composition formulae for moments are directly extended to the case of more than two variables. For the addition of n independent variables, we thus have the following simple expressions for the moments of the three lowest orders:

$$(15.12.7) \qquad \begin{aligned} m &= m_1 + m_2 + \cdots + m_n, \\ \sigma^2 &= \sigma_1^2 + \sigma_2^2 + \cdots + \sigma_n^2, \\ \mu_3 &= \mu_3^{(1)} + \mu_3^{(2)} + \cdots + \mu_3^{(n)}. \end{aligned}$$

For the higher moments ($\nu > 3$), the formulae become more complicated.

Finally, we shall consider the semi-invariants of the composed distribution. The multiplication theorem for characteristic functions gives us

$$\log \varphi(t) = \log \varphi_1(t) + \log \varphi_2(t).$$

Hence we obtain by (15.10.2) $\varkappa_\nu = \varkappa_\nu^{(1)} + \varkappa_\nu^{(2)}$. This simple composition rule is the chief reason for introducing the semi-invariants. The extension to the case of n independent variables is immediate and gives

$$\varkappa_\nu = \varkappa_\nu^{(1)} + \varkappa_\nu^{(2)} + \cdots + \varkappa_\nu^{(n)}. \tag{15.12.8}$$

CHAPTER 16.

Various Discrete Distributions.

16.1. The function $\varepsilon(x)$. — The simplest discrete distribution has the total mass 1 concentrated in one single point, say in the point $x = 0$. This is the distribution of a variable ξ which is »almost always» equal to zero, i. e. such that $P(\xi = 0) = 1$. The corresponding d. f. is the function $\varepsilon(x)$ defined by (6.7.1):

$$\varepsilon(x) = \begin{cases} 0 & \text{for} \quad x < 0, \\ 1 & \text{»} \quad x \geqq 0. \end{cases} \tag{16.1.1}$$

The c. f. is identically equal to 1, as we have already remarked in 10.1.

More generally, a »variable» which is almost always equal to x_0 has the d. f. $\varepsilon(x - x_0)$ and the c. f. e^{itx_0}. The mean of this variable is x_0, and the s. d. is zero. Conversely, if it is known that the s. d. of a certain variable is equal to zero, it follows (cf 15.6) that the whole mass of the distribution is concentrated in one single point, so that the d. f. must be of the form $\varepsilon(x - x_0)$.

The general d. f. of the discrete type as given by (15.2.1) may be written

$$F(x) = \sum_\nu p_\nu \, \varepsilon(x - x_\nu). \tag{16.1.2}$$

Let us consider the particular case of a discrete variable ξ, the distribution of which is specified in the following way:

$$\xi = \begin{cases} 1 & \text{with the probability} \quad p, \\ 0 & \text{»} \quad \text{»} \quad \text{»} \quad q = 1 - p. \end{cases} \tag{16.1.3}$$

In the following paragraph, we shall make an important use of variables possessing this distribution. From (16.1.2) we obtain the d. f. of ξ

$$F(x) = p\,\varepsilon(x-1) + q\,\varepsilon(x).$$

and hence the c. f.

$$\varphi(t) = p\,e^{it} + q = 1 + p\,(e^{it} - 1). \tag{16.1.4}$$

The mean and variance of ξ are

$$\begin{aligned} \mathbf{E}(\xi) &= p \cdot 1 + q \cdot 0 = p, \\ \mathbf{D}^2(\xi) &= \mathbf{E}((\xi - p)^2) = p\,(1-p)^2 + q\,(0-p)^2 = pq. \end{aligned} \tag{16.1.5}$$

16.2. The binomial distribution. — Let $\mathfrak{E}$ be a given random experiment, and denote by E an event having a definite probability p to occur at each performance of $\mathfrak{E}$. Consider a series of n independent repetitions of $\mathfrak{E}$ (cf 14.4), and let us define a random variable ξ_r attached to the r:th experiment by writing

$$\xi_r = \begin{cases} 1 & \text{when } E \text{ occurs at the } r\text{:th experiment (probability} = p), \\ 0 & \text{otherwise (probability} = q = 1 - p). \end{cases}$$

Then each ξ_r has the probability distribution (16.1.3) considered in the preceding paragraph, and the variables $\xi_1, \ldots, \xi_n$ are independent.

Obviously ξ_r denotes the *number of occurrences* of E in the r:th experiment, so that the sum

$$\nu = \xi_1 + \xi_2 + \cdots + \xi_n$$

denotes *the total number of occurrences of the event E in our series of n repetitions of the experiment $\mathfrak{E}$.*

Since ν is a sum of n independent random variables, it is itself a random variable[1]), the distribution of which may be found by the methods developed in 15.12. Thus we obtain by (15.12.7) and (16.1.5) the following expressions for the mean, the variance and the s. d. of ν:

$$\mathbf{E}(\nu) = np, \quad \mathbf{D}^2(\nu) = npq, \quad \mathbf{D}(\nu) = \sqrt{npq}. \tag{16.2.1}$$

[1]) Throughout the general theory developed in the preceding chapters, we have systematically used the letters ξ and η to denote random variables. From now on it would, however, be inconvenient to adhere strictly to this rule. We shall thus often find it practical to allow any other letters (Greek or italic) to denote random variables. It will thus always be necessary to observe with great care the significance of the various letters used in the formulae.

The ratio ν/n expresses the *frequency* of E in our series of n repetitions. For the mean and the s. d. of ν/n, we have

$$(16.2.2) \qquad \boldsymbol{E}\left(\frac{\nu}{n}\right) = p, \quad \boldsymbol{D}\left(\frac{\nu}{n}\right) = \sqrt{\frac{pq}{n}}.$$

The c. f. of ν is by (15.12.1) equal to the product of the c. f:s of all the ξ_r, and thus we obtain from (16.1.4)

$$(16.2.3) \qquad \boldsymbol{E}(e^{it\nu}) = (p\,e^{it} + q)^n = (1 + p\,(e^{it} - 1))^n.$$

Developing the first expression by the binomial theorem, we find

$$\boldsymbol{E}(e^{it\nu}) = \sum_{r=0}^{n} \binom{n}{r} p^r q^{n-r} e^{itr}.$$

By (10.1.5) this is, however, the c. f. of a variable which may assume the values $r = 0, 1, \ldots, n$ with the probabilities $P_r = \binom{n}{r} p^r q^{n-r}$. Owing to the one-to-one correspondence between distributions and characteristic functions, we may thus conclude (cf 15.9) that the probability distribution of ν is specified by the relation

$$(16.2.4) \qquad P(\nu = r) = P_r = \binom{n}{r} p^r q^{n-r} \qquad (r = 0, 1, \ldots, n).$$

This is the *binomial distribution*, the simplest properties of which we assume to be already known. It is a distribution of the discrete type, involving two parameters n and p, where n is a positive integer, while $0 < p < 1$. (The cases $p = 0$ and $p = 1$ are trivial and will be excluded from our discussion.) The corresponding d. f.

$$(16.2.5) \qquad B_n(x; p) = P(\nu \leqq x) = \sum_{r \leqq x} \binom{n}{r} p^r q^{n-r}$$

is a step-function, with steps of the height P_r in the $n + 1$ discrete mass points $r = 0, 1, \ldots, n$.

In order to find the moments μ_r about the mean of the binomial distribution, we consider the c. f. of the deviation $\nu - np$. This is

$$\begin{aligned} \mathbf{E}\left(e^{it(\nu-np)}\right) &= e^{-npit}(p\,e^{it}+q)^n \\ &= (p\,e^{qit}+q\,e^{-pit})^n \\ &= \left[\sum_{r=0}^{\infty}(p\,q^r+q(-p)^r)\frac{(i\,t)^r}{r!}\right]^n. \end{aligned}$$

Thus all moments μ_r are finite and may be found by equating coefficients in the relation

$$\sum_0^\infty \mu_r \frac{t^r}{r!} = \left[\sum_0^\infty (p\,q^r+q(-p)^r)\frac{t^r}{r!}\right]^n.$$

In particular, we find

$$\begin{aligned} &\mu_2 = \sigma^2 = n\,p\,q, \\ (16.2.6)\qquad &\mu_3 = n\,p\,q\,(q-p), \\ &\mu_4 = 3\,n^2\,p^2\,q^2 + n\,p\,q\,(1-6\,p\,q), \\ &\cdots\cdots\cdots\cdots \end{aligned}$$

For the coefficients of skewness and excess, we thus have the expressions

$$\gamma_1 = \frac{\mu_3}{\sigma^3} = \frac{q-p}{\sqrt{n\,p\,q}} = \frac{1-2\,p}{\sqrt{n\,p\,q}}, \quad \gamma_2 = \frac{\mu_4}{\sigma^4} - 3 = \frac{1-6\,p\,q}{n\,p\,q}.$$

The skewness is positive for $p < \frac{1}{2}$, negative for $p > \frac{1}{2}$, and zero for $p = \frac{1}{2}$. Both coefficients γ_1 and γ_2 tend to zero as $n \to \infty$.

Let ν_1 and ν_2 denote two independent variables, both having binomial distributions with the same value of the parameter p, and with the values n_1 and n_2 of the parameter n. We may, e. g., take ν_1 and ν_2 equal to the number of occurrences of the event E in two independent series of n_1 and n_2 repetitions of the experiment $\mathfrak{E}$.

The sum $\nu_1 + \nu_2$ is then equal to the number of occurrences of E in a series of $n_1 + n_2$ repetitions. Accordingly the c. f. of $\nu_1 + \nu_2$ is (cf 15.12)

$$\begin{aligned} \mathbf{E}\left(e^{it(\nu_1+\nu_2)}\right) &= \mathbf{E}\left(e^{it\nu_1}\right)\mathbf{E}\left(e^{it\nu_2}\right) \\ &= (p\,e^{it}+q)^{n_1}(p\,e^{it}+q)^{n_2} \\ &= (p\,e^{it}+q)^{n_1+n_2}. \end{aligned}$$

This is the c. f. of a binomial distribution with the parameters p and $n_1 + n_2$. Thus the addition of two independent variables with the d. f:s $B_{n_1}(x; p)$ and $B_{n_2}(x; p)$ gives (as may, of course, also be directly perceived) a variable with the d.f. $B_{n_1+n_2}(x;\,p)$. In the abbreviated notation of (15.12.2 a) this may be written

$$B_{n_1}(x;\,p) \ast B_{n_2}(x;\,p) = B_{n_1+n_2}(x;\,p).$$

Thus the binomial distribution *reproduces itself* by addition of independent variables. We shall call this an *addition theorem* for the binomial distribution. Later, we shall see that similar (but less evident) addition theorems hold also for certain other important distributions.

16.3. Bernoulli's theorem. — For the frequency ratio ν/n considered in the preceding paragraph, we have by (16.2.2)

$$\boldsymbol{E}\left(\frac{\nu}{n}\right) = p, \quad \boldsymbol{D}\left(\frac{\nu}{n}\right) = \sqrt{\frac{pq}{n}}.$$

We now apply the Bienaymé-Tchebychef inequality (15.7.2), taking $k = \varepsilon\sqrt{\frac{n}{pq}}$, where ε denotes a given positive quantity. Denoting by P the probability function of the variable ν, we then obtain the following result:

$$P\left(\left|\frac{\nu}{n} - p\right| \geqq \varepsilon\right) \leqq \frac{pq}{n\,\varepsilon^2} \leqq \frac{1}{4\,n\,\varepsilon^2}. \tag{16.3.1}$$

If δ denotes another given positive quantity, it follows that, as soon as we take $n > \frac{1}{4\,\delta\,\varepsilon^2}$, the probability on the left hand side of (16.3.1) becomes smaller than δ. Since δ is arbitrarily small, we have proved the following theorem.

The probability that the frequency ν/n differs from its mean value p by a quantity of modulus at least equal to ε tends to zero as $n \to \infty$, however small $\varepsilon > 0$ is chosen.

This is, in modern terminology, the classical *Bernoulli theorem*, originally proved by James Bernoulli, in his posthumous work *Ars Conjectandi* (1713), in a quite different way. Bernoulli considered the two complementary probabilities

$$\varpi = P\left(\left|\frac{\nu}{n} - p\right| \geqq \varepsilon\right) = \sum_{|r-np| \geqq n\varepsilon} \binom{n}{r} p^r q^{n-r},$$

$$1 - \varpi = P\left(\left|\frac{\nu}{n} - p\right| < \varepsilon\right) = \sum_{|r-np| < n\varepsilon} \binom{n}{r} p^r q^{n-r},$$

and proved by a direct evaluation of the terms of the binomial expansion that, for any given $\varepsilon > 0$, the ratio $\frac{1-\varpi}{\varpi}$ may be made to exceed any given quantity by choosing n sufficiently large.

The variable ν is, according to the preceding paragraph, attached to a combined experiment, consisting in a series of n repetitions of the original experiment $\mathfrak{E}$. Thus by 13.5 any probability statement with respect to ν is a statement concerning the approximate value of the frequency of some specified event in a series of repetitions of the combined experiment. The *frequency interpretation* (cf 13.5) of any such probability statement thus always refers to a series of repetitions of the *combined experiment.*

Consider e. g. the frequency interpretation of the probability ϖ defined above. We begin by making a series of n repetitions of the experiment $\mathfrak{E}$, and noting the number ν of occurrences of the event E. This is our first performance of the combined experiment. If the observed number ν satisfies the relation $\left|\frac{\nu}{n} - p\right| \geqq \varepsilon$, we say that *the event E'* occurs in the first combined experiment. The event E' has then the probability ϖ.

We then repeat the whole series of n experiments a large number n' of times, so that we finally obtain a series of n' repetitions of the combined experiment. The total number of performances of $\mathfrak{E}$ required will then, of course, be $n'n$. Let ν' denote the number of occurrences of E' in the whole series of n' repetitions of the combined experiment. The frequency interpretation of the probability ϖ then consists in the following statement: For large values of n', it is practically certain that the frequency $\frac{\nu'}{n'}$ will be approximately equal to ϖ.

Now the Bernoulli theorem as expressed by (16.3.1) shows that, as soon as we take $n > \frac{1}{4\delta\varepsilon^2}$, we have $\varpi < \delta$, where δ is given and arbitrarily small. In a long series of repetitions of the combined experiment (i. e. for large n'), we should then expect the event $\left|\frac{\nu}{n} - p\right| \geqq \varepsilon$ to occur with a frequency smaller than δ. Choosing for δ some very small number, and making one single performance of the combined experiment, i. e. *one single series of n repetitions of the experiment* $\mathfrak{E}$, we may then (cf 13.5) consider it as practically certain that the event $\left|\frac{\nu}{n} - p\right| \geqq \varepsilon$ will *not* occur.

What value of δ we should choose in order to realize a satisfactory degree of »practical certainty» depends on the risk that we are willing to run with respect to a failure of our predictions. Suppose, however, that we have agreed to consider a certain value δ_0 as sufficiently small for our purpose. Returning to the original event E with the probability p, we may then give the following more precise statement of the frequency interpretation of this probability, as given in 13.5:

Let $\varepsilon > 0$ be given. If we choose $n > \frac{1}{4\delta_0\varepsilon^2}$, it is practically certain that, in one single series of n repetitions of the experiment $\mathfrak{E}$, we shall have $\left|\frac{\nu}{n} - p\right| < \varepsilon$.

This statement may be called the *frequency interpretation of the Bernoulli theorem.* Like all frequency interpretations, this is not a mathematical theorem, but a statement concerning certain observable facts, which must hold true if the mathematical theory is to be of any practical value.

16.4. De Moivre's theorem. — The random variable

$$\nu = \xi_1 + \xi_2 + \cdots + \xi_n \tag{16.4.1}$$

considered in the two preceding paragraphs has, by (16.2.1), the mean np and the standard deviation $\sqrt{npq}$. The standardized variable (cf 15.6)

$$\lambda = \frac{\nu - np}{\sqrt{npq}} \tag{16.4.2}$$

thus has the mean 0 and the s. d. 1. The transformation by which we pass from ν to λ consists, of course, only in a change of origin and scale of the variable. The ordinates in the diagram of the probability distribution have the same values for both variables. We have, in fact, using the same notations as in the preceding paragraphs,

$$P\left(\lambda = \frac{r - np}{\sqrt{npq}}\right) = P(\nu = r) = \binom{n}{r} p^r q^{n-r}$$

for $r = 0, 1, \ldots, n$.

The d. f. and the c. f. of the variable ν are given by (16.2.5) and (16.2.3). Denoting by $F_n(x)$ and $\varphi_n(t)$ the corresponding functions of the standardized variable λ, we obtain (cf 15.9)

$$\begin{aligned} F_n(x) &= B_n(np + x\sqrt{npq};\, p), \\ \varphi_n(t) &= \left(p\, e^{\frac{qit}{\sqrt{npq}}} + q\, e^{-\frac{pit}{\sqrt{npq}}}\right)^n. \end{aligned} \tag{16.4.3}$$

We shall now consider the behaviour of the probability distribution of λ for increasing values of n, when p has a fixed value. We begin by making a transformation of the above expression for the c.f. $\varphi_n(t)$.

For any integer $k > 0$ and for any real z we have the MacLaurin expansion

$$e^{iz} = \sum_{0}^{k-1} \frac{(iz)^r}{r!} + \vartheta \frac{z^k}{k!}, \tag{16.4.4}$$

where we use ϑ as a general symbol for a real or complex quantity of modulus not exceeding unity. Using this development with $k = 3$, we obtain

$$p e^{\frac{q i t}{\sqrt{n p q}}} = p + \frac{p q i t}{\sqrt{n p q}} - \frac{p q^2 t^2}{2 n p q} + \vartheta \frac{p q^3 t^3}{3!(n p q)^{3/2}},$$

$$q e^{-\frac{p i t}{\sqrt{n p q}}} = q - \frac{p q i t}{\sqrt{n p q}} - \frac{p^2 q t^2}{2 n p q} + \vartheta \frac{p^3 q t^3}{3!(n p q)^{3/2}},$$

and hence, introducing in (16.4.3),

$$\varphi_n(t) = \left(1 - \frac{t^2}{2 n} + \vartheta \frac{t^3}{(n p q)^{3/2}}\right)^n.$$

Writing

$$y = -\frac{t^2}{2} + \vartheta \frac{t^3}{(p q)^{3/2} \sqrt{n}}$$

this gives us

$$\log \varphi_n(t) = y \cdot \frac{n}{y} \log \left(1 + \frac{y}{n}\right).$$

Now as n tends to infinity while t remains fixed, it is obvious that y tends to $-\frac{t^2}{2}$. Hence $\frac{y}{n}$ tends to zero, and $\frac{n}{y} \log \left(1 + \frac{y}{n}\right)$ tends to unity. It then follows that $\log \varphi_n(t)$ tends to $-\frac{t^2}{2}$, and finally that

$$\varphi_n(t) \to e^{-\frac{t^2}{2}}$$

for every t.

We are now in a position to apply the continuity theorem 10.4 for c.f:s. We have just proved that the sequence $\{\varphi_n(t)\}$ of c.f:s defined by (16.4.3) converges, for every t, to the limit $e^{-\frac{t^2}{2}}$ which is continuous for all t. By the continuity theorem we then infer 1) that the limit $e^{-\frac{t^2}{2}}$ is itself the c.f. of a certain d.f., and 2) that the sequence of d.f:s $\{F_n(x)\}$ defined by (16.4.3) converges to the d.f. which corresponds to the c.f. $e^{-\frac{t^2}{2}}$.

Now we have by (10.5.3) and (10.5.4)

$$e^{-\frac{t^2}{2}} = \int_{-\infty}^{\infty} e^{i t x}\, d\,\Phi(x),$$

where

$$\Phi(x) = \frac{1}{\sqrt{2\pi}} \int_{-\infty}^{x} e^{-\frac{t^2}{2}} dt,$$

so that $e^{-\frac{t^2}{2}}$ is the c.f. of the d.f. $\Phi(x)$ given by the last expression. This is the important *normal distribution function* that will be separately treated in the following chapter. For our present purpose we only observe that $\Phi(x)$ is continuous for every x. We have thus proved the following *limit theorem for the binomial distribution* first obtained by De Moivre in 1733:

For every fixed x and p, we have

$$\lim_{n \to \infty} B_n(np + x\sqrt{npq};\, p) = \Phi(x). \tag{16.4.5}$$

Thus the binomial distribution of the variable $\nu = \xi_1 + \cdots + \xi_n$, appropriately standardized by the mean and the s.d. according to (16.4.2), tends to the normal distribution as n tends to infinity. We shall see later (cf 17.4) that this is only a particular case of a very general and important theorem concerning the distribution of the sum of a large number of independent random variables. — The method of proof used above has been chosen with a view to prepare the reader for the proof of this general theorem. In the present particular case of the binomial distribution it is, however, possible to reach the same result also by a more direct method, without the use of characteristic functions. This is the method usually found in text-books, and we shall here content ourselves with some brief indications on the subject, referring for further detail to some standard treatise on probability theory.

The relation (16.4.5) is equivalent to

$$\sum_{np+\lambda_1\sqrt{npq} < \nu \leqq np+\lambda_2\sqrt{npq}} \binom{n}{\nu} p^\nu q^{n-\nu} \to \Phi(\lambda_2) - \Phi(\lambda_1) = \frac{1}{\sqrt{2\pi}} \int_{\lambda_1}^{\lambda_2} e^{-\frac{t^2}{2}} dt \tag{16.4.6}$$

for any fixed interval (λ_1, λ_2). Now (16.4.6) may be proved by means of a direct evaluation of the terms in the binomial expansion. For this purpose, we express the factorials in the binomial coefficient appearing in (16.4.6) by means of the Stirling formula (12.5.3). We then obtain after some calculations the expression

$$\binom{n}{\nu} p^\nu q^{n-\nu} = \frac{1}{\sqrt{2\pi npq}} e^{-\frac{1}{2}\left(\frac{\nu - np}{\sqrt{npq}}\right)^2} + \vartheta \frac{C}{n}, \tag{16.4.7}$$

where C is a quantity depending on p, but not on ν or n, while ϑ has the same significance as before. The first member of (16.4.6) is thus equal to

$$\frac{1}{\sqrt{2\pi n p q}} \sum e^{-\frac{1}{2}\left(\frac{\nu - n p}{\sqrt{n p q}}\right)^2} + \vartheta \frac{(\lambda_2 - \lambda_1)\, C}{\sqrt{n}},$$

the sum being extended over the same values of ν as in (16.4.6). As

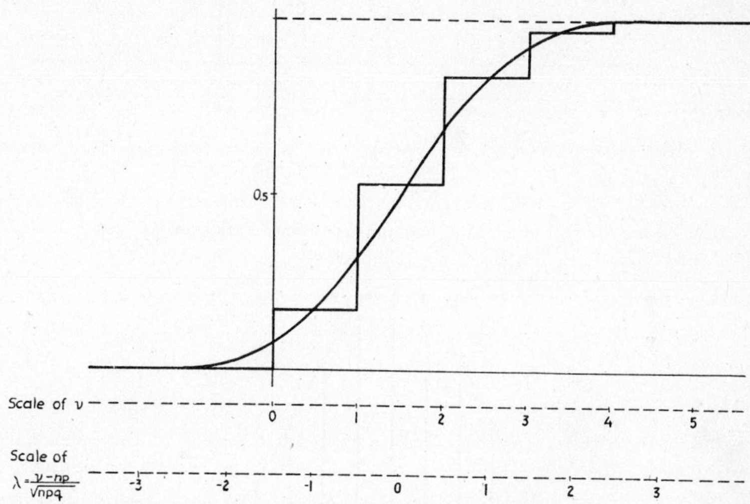

Fig. 8. Distribution function of ν (or λ) and normal distribution function. $p = 0.3$, $n = 5$.

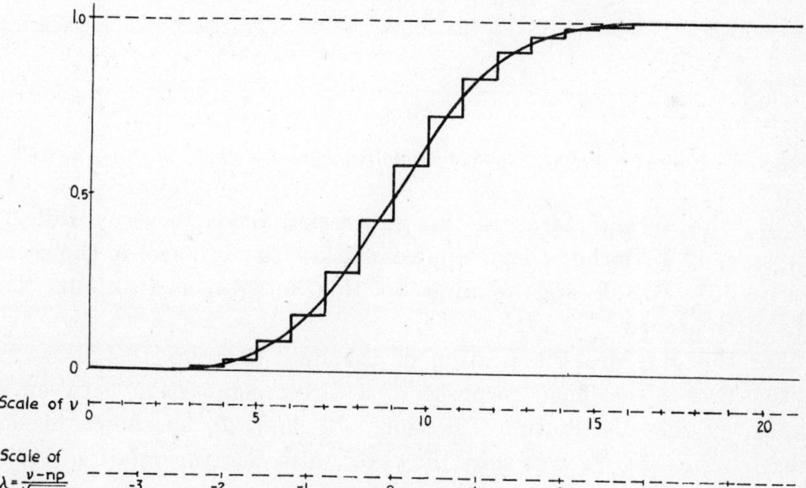

Fig. 9. Distribution function of ν (or λ) and normal distribution function. $p = 0.3$, $n = 30$.

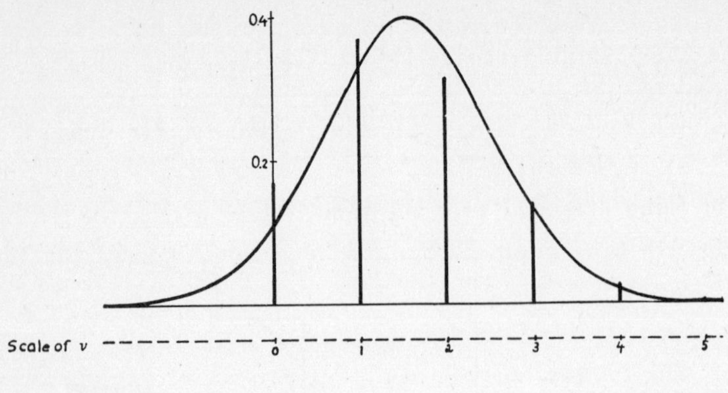

Fig. 10. $\sqrt{n p q} \cdot \binom{n}{\nu} p^{\nu} q^{n-\nu}$ and normal frequency function. $p = 0.3$, $n = 5$.

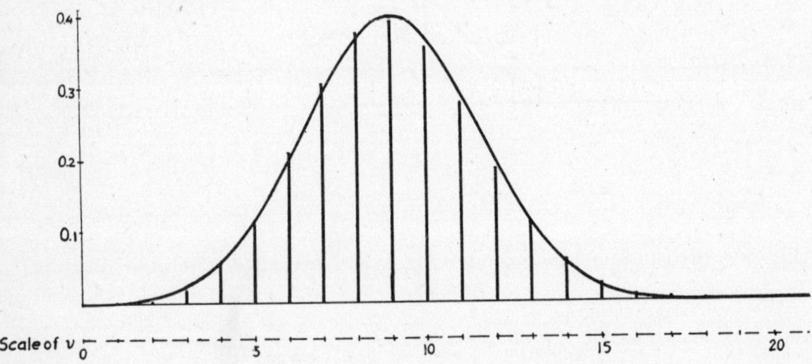

Fig. 11. $\sqrt{n p q} \cdot \binom{n}{\nu} p^{\nu} q^{n-\nu}$ and normal frequency function. $p = 0.3$, $n = 30$.

$n \to \infty$, the second term in this expression tends to zero, while the first term is a Darboux sum approximating the integral in the second member of (16.4.6) and tending to this integral as its limit. Thus (16.4.6) is proved.

For the graphical illustration of the limit theorem (16.4.5), we may in the first place have recourse to a direct comparison between the graphs of the distribution functions B_n and Φ, as shown in some cases by Figs. 8—9. We may, however, also use the relation (16.4.7). If we allow here ν to tend to infinity with n, in such a way that $\frac{\nu - n p}{\sqrt{n p q}}$ tends to a finite limit x, we obtain

$$\sqrt{npq}\cdot\binom{n}{\nu}p^{\nu}q^{n-\nu}\rightarrow\frac{1}{\sqrt{2\pi}}e^{-\frac{x^2}{2}}.$$

If the scale of ν is transformed by choosing the mean np as origin and the s. d. $\sqrt{npq}$ as unit, and if at the same time every probability P_ν is multiplied by $\sqrt{npq}$, the upper end-points of the corresponding ordinates will thus approach the frequency-curve $y=\frac{1}{\sqrt{2\pi}}e^{-\frac{x^2}{2}}$ of the normal distribution, as $n\rightarrow\infty$. This is illustrated by Figs. 10—11.

16.5. The Poisson distribution. — In the preceding paragraph, we have seen that the discrete binomial distribution may, by a limit passage, be transformed into a new distribution of the continuous type, viz. the normal distribution.

By an appropriate modification of the limit passage, we may also obtain a limiting distribution of the discrete type. Suppose that, in the binomial distribution, we allow the probability p to depend on n in such a way that p tends to zero when n tends to infinity. More precisely, we shall suppose that

(16.5.1)
$$p=\frac{\lambda}{n},$$

where λ is a positive constant. For the probability P_r given by (16.2.4) we then obtain, as $n\rightarrow\infty$,

$$P_r=\frac{n(n-1)\cdots(n-r+1)}{r!}\left(\frac{\lambda}{n}\right)^r\left(1-\frac{\lambda}{n}\right)^{n-r}$$

$$=\frac{\lambda^r}{r!}\left(1-\frac{\lambda}{n}\right)^n\frac{\left(1-\frac{1}{n}\right)\cdots\left(1-\frac{r-1}{n}\right)}{\left(1-\frac{\lambda}{n}\right)^r}\rightarrow\frac{\lambda^r}{r!}e^{-\lambda}$$

for every fixed $r=0, 1, 2, \ldots$. The sum of all the limiting values is unity, since we have

$$\sum_{r=0}^{\infty}\frac{\lambda^r}{r!}e^{-\lambda}=e^{\lambda}\cdot e^{-\lambda}=1.$$

If the probability distribution of a random variable ξ is specified by

(16.5.2)
$$P(\xi=r)=\frac{\lambda^r}{r!}e^{-\lambda}\quad\text{for}\quad r=0, 1, 2, \ldots,$$

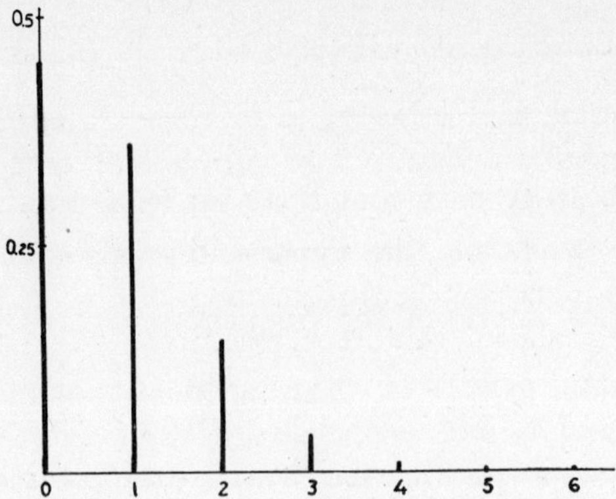

Fig. 12. Poisson distribution, $\lambda = 0.8$.

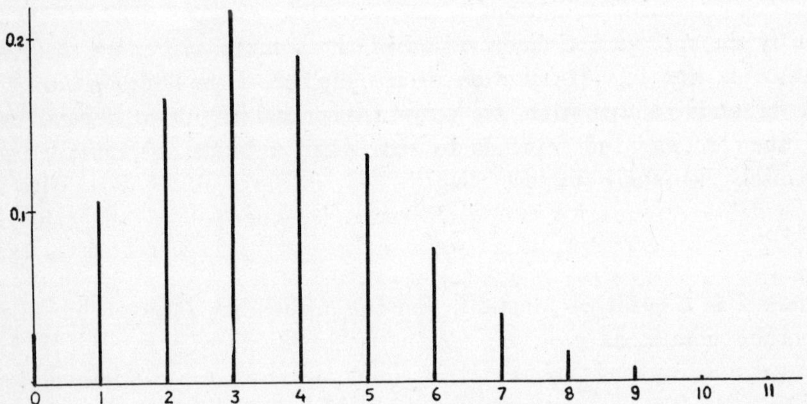

Fig. 13. Poisson distribution, $\lambda = 3.5$.

ξ is said to possess a *Poisson distribution*. This is a discrete distribution with one parameter λ, which is always positive. All points $r = 0, 1, 2, \ldots$ are discrete mass points. Two cases of the distribution are illustrated by Figs. 12—13.

The c. f. of the Poisson distribution is

$$\boldsymbol{E}\left(e^{it\xi}\right) = \sum_{r=0}^{\infty} \frac{\lambda^r}{r!} e^{-\lambda} \cdot e^{itr} = e^{\lambda\left(e^{it}-1\right)}. \tag{16.5.3}$$

According to (15.10.2), this shows that the semi-invariants of the distribution are all finite and equal to λ. From the two first semi-invariants, we find the mean and the s. d. of the Poisson distribution:

$$\boldsymbol{E}(\xi) = \lambda, \quad \boldsymbol{D}(\xi) = \sqrt{\lambda}.$$

Writing $p = \frac{\lambda}{n}$ in the second expression (16.2.3) of the c. f. of the binomial distribution, and allowing n to tend to infinity, it is readily seen that this function tends to the c. f. (16.5.3) of the Poisson distribution. By the continuity theorem 10.4, it then follows that the binomial distribution tends to the Poisson distribution, which confirms the result already obtained by direct study of the probability P_r.

It is also easily shown that the condition (16.5.1) can be replaced by the more general condition $np \to \lambda$, without modifying the result.

Finally, if ξ_1 and ξ_2 are independent Poisson-distributed variables, with the parameters λ_1 and λ_2, the sum $\xi_1 + \xi_2$ has the c. f.

$$e^{\lambda_1 (e^{it}-1)} \cdot e^{\lambda_2 (e^{it}-1)} = e^{(\lambda_1+\lambda_2)(e^{it}-1)}.$$

This is the c. f. of a Poisson distribution with the parameter $\lambda_1 + \lambda_2$. Thus the sum $\xi_1 + \xi_2$ has a Poisson distribution with the parameter $\lambda_1 + \lambda_2$, and we see that the Poisson distribution, like the binomial, has the property of reproducing itself by addition of independent variables. Denoting by $F(x; \lambda)$ the d. f. of the Poisson distribution, the *addition theorem* for this distribution is expressed by the relation

$$F(x; \lambda_1) * F(x; \lambda_2) = F(x; \lambda_1 + \lambda_2). \tag{16.5.4}$$

In statistical applications, the Poisson distribution often appears when we are concerned with the number of occurrences of a certain event in a very large number of observations, the probability for the event to occur in each observation being very small. Examples are: the annual number of suicides in a human population, the number of yeast cells in a small sample from a large quantity of suspension, etc. Cf e. g. Bortkiewicz, Ref. 63 a.

In an important group of applications, the fundamental random experiment consists in observing the number of occurrences of a certain event during a time interval of duration t, where the choice of t is at our liberty. This situation occurs e. g. in problems of telephone traffic, where we are concerned with the number of telephone calls during time intervals of various durations. — Suppose that, in such a case, the numbers of occurrences during non-overlapping time intervals are always independent. Suppose further that the probability that exactly one event occurs in an interval of duration Δt is, for small Δt, equal to

$$\lambda \Delta t + o(\Delta t),$$

where λ is a constant, while the corresponding probability for the occurrence of more than one event is $o(\Delta t)$. — Dividing a time interval of duration t in n equal parts, we may consider the n parts as representing n repetitions of a random experiment, where the probability for the event to occur in each instance is

$$\frac{\lambda t}{n} + o\left(\frac{1}{n}\right).$$

Allowing n to tend to infinity, we find that the total number of events occurring during the time t will be distributed in a Poisson distribution with the parameter λt. — Variables of this type are, besides the number of telephone calls already mentioned, the number of disintegrated radioactive atoms, the number of claims in an insurance company, etc.

16.6. The generalized binomial distribution of Poisson. — Suppose that $\mathfrak{E}_1, \ldots, \mathfrak{E}_n$ are n random experiments, such that the random variables attached to the experiments are independent. With each experiment $\mathfrak{E}_r$, we associate an event E_r having the probability $p_r = 1 - q_r$ to occur in a performance of $\mathfrak{E}_r$.

Let us make one performance of each experiment $\mathfrak{E}_1, \ldots, \mathfrak{E}_n$, and note in each case whether the associated event occurs or not. We shall call this a series of *independent trials*. If, in the experiment $\mathfrak{E}_r$, the associated event E_r occurs, we shall say that the r:th trial is a *success*; in the opposite case we have a *failure*. Let ν be the total number of successes in all n trials. What is the probability distribution of ν?

In the particular case when all the experiments $\mathfrak{E}_r$ and all the events E_r are identical, ν reduces to the variable considered in 16.2, and the required distribution is the binomial distribution. The general case was considered by Poisson (Ref. 32).

In the same way as in 16.2, we define a variable ξ_r attached to the r:th trial, and taking the value 1 for a success (probability p_r), and 0 for a failure (probability $q_r = 1 - p_r$). The variables $\xi_1, \ldots, \xi_n$ are independent, and each has a distribution of the form (16.1.3). As in the previous case, the total number of successes is $\nu = \xi_1 + \xi_2 + \cdots + \xi_n$.

The c. f. of the random variable ν is the product of the c. f:s of all the ξ_r:

$$\boldsymbol{E}\left(e^{it\nu}\right) = \prod_{r=1}^{n} (p_r e^{it} + q_r).$$

The possible values for ν are $\nu = 0, 1, \ldots, n$, and the probability that ν takes any particular value r is equal to the coefficient of e^{itr} in the development of the product.

For the mean value and the variance of ν we have the expressions

$$(16.6.1)\qquad \begin{aligned} \boldsymbol{E}(\nu) &= \sum_1^n \boldsymbol{E}(\xi_r) = \sum_1^n p_r, \\ \boldsymbol{D}^2(\nu) &= \sum_1^n \boldsymbol{D}^2(\xi_r) = \sum_1^n p_r q_r. \end{aligned}$$

Denoting by P the probability function of ν, and writing p for the arithmetic mean $\frac{1}{n}\sum_1^n p_r$, an application of the Bienaymé-Tchebycheff inequality (15.7.2) now gives the result analogous to (16.3.1)

$$(16.6.2)\qquad P\left(\left|\frac{\nu}{n} - p\right| \geqq \varepsilon\right) \leqq \frac{\Sigma p_r q_r}{n^2 \varepsilon^2} \leqq \frac{1}{4 n \varepsilon^2}.$$

We thus have the following generalization of Bernoulli's theorem found by Poisson:

The probability that the frequency of successes ν/n differs from the arithmetic mean of the probabilities p_r by a quantity of modulus at least equal to ε tends to zero as $n \to \infty$, however small $\varepsilon > 0$ is chosen.

The frequency interpretation of the generalized theorem is quite similar to the one given in 16.3 for the Bernoulli theorem. Consider in particular the case when all the probabilities p_r are equal to p. *We then see that in a long series of independent trials, where the probability of a success is constantly equal to p, though all trials may be different experiments, it is practically certain that the frequency of successes will be approximately equal to p.*

There is also a generalization of De Moivre's theorem (16.4.5) to the present case. This will, however, not be proved here, but will be deduced later as a particular case of a still more general theorem to be proved in 17.4.

For the variance of ν, we have found the value $\boldsymbol{D}^2(\nu) = \sum p_r q_r$. In a series of n trials with the constant probability $p = \frac{1}{n}\sum p_r$, the corresponding variance is npq, where $q = 1 - p = \frac{1}{n}\sum q_r$. In order to compare the two variances we write

$$\begin{aligned} \sum p_r q_r &= \sum (p + p_r - p)(q + q_r - q) \\ &= \sum (p + p_r - p)(q + p - p_r) \\ &= npq - \sum (p_r - p)^2. \end{aligned}$$

Thus the »Poisson variance» $\sum p_r q_r$ is always smaller than the corresponding »Bernoulli variance» npq. At first sight, this result may seem a little surprising. It becomes more natural if we consider the extreme case when all the probabilities p_r are equal to 0 or 1, both values being represented. The Poisson variance is then equal to zero, while the Bernoulli variance is necessarily positive.

CHAPTER 17.

The Normal Distribution.

17.1. The normal functions. — The *normal distribution function*, which has already appeared in 10.5 and 16.4, is defined by the relation

$$\Phi(x) = \frac{1}{\sqrt{2\pi}} \int_{-\infty}^{x} e^{-\frac{t^2}{2}}\, dt.$$

The corresponding *normal frequency function* is

$$\Phi'(x) = \frac{1}{\sqrt{2\pi}} e^{-\frac{x^2}{2}}.$$

Diagrams of these functions are given in Figs. 14—15, and some numerical values are found in Table 1, p. 557.

The mean value of the distribution is 0, and the s. d. is 1, as shown by (10.5.1):

$$(17.1.1)\qquad \begin{aligned} \int_{-\infty}^{\infty} x\, d\,\Phi(x) &= \frac{1}{\sqrt{2\pi}} \int_{-\infty}^{\infty} x e^{-\frac{x^2}{2}}\, dx = 0, \\ \int_{-\infty}^{\infty} x^2\, d\,\Phi(x) &= \frac{1}{\sqrt{2\pi}} \int_{-\infty}^{\infty} x^2 e^{-\frac{x^2}{2}}\, dx = 1. \end{aligned}$$

Generally, all moments of odd order vanish, while the moments of even order are according to (10.5.1)

$$(17.1.2)\qquad \int_{-\infty}^{\infty} x^{2\nu}\, d\,\Phi(x) = \frac{1}{\sqrt{2\pi}} \int_{-\infty}^{\infty} x^{2\nu} e^{-\frac{x^2}{2}}\, dx = 1 \cdot 3 \cdot \ldots \cdot (2\nu - 1).$$

Finally, the c. f. is by (10.5.4)

$$(17.1.3)\qquad \int_{-\infty}^{\infty} e^{itx}\, d\,\Phi(x) = \frac{1}{\sqrt{2\pi}} \int_{-\infty}^{\infty} e^{itx - \frac{x^2}{2}}\, dx = e^{-\frac{t^2}{2}}.$$

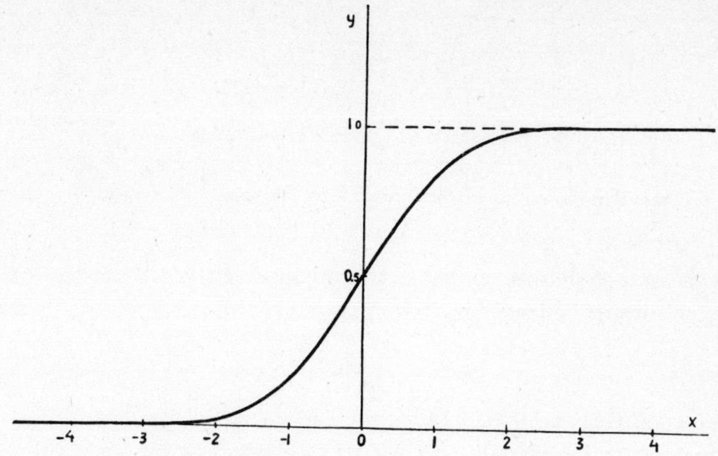

Fig. 14. The normal distribution function.

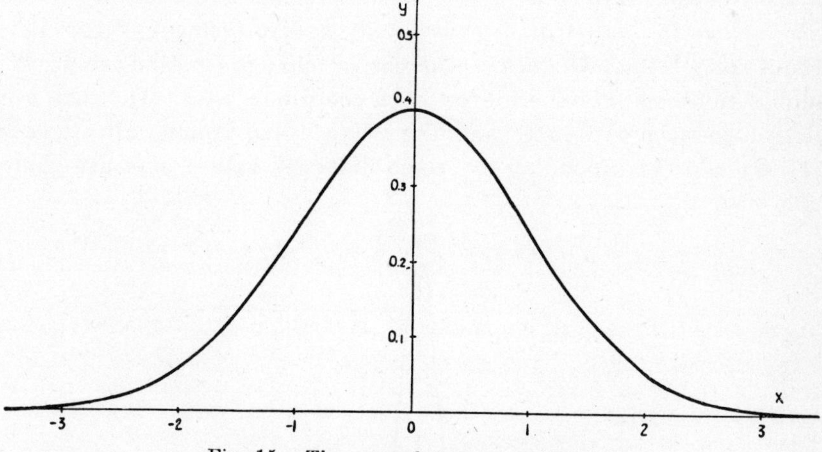

Fig. 15. The normal frequency function.

17.2. The normal distribution. — A random variable ξ will be said to be *normally distributed with the parameters m and* σ; or briefly *normal* (m, σ), if the d. f. of ξ is $\Phi\left(\frac{x-m}{\sigma}\right)$, where $\sigma > 0$ and m are constants. The fr. f. is then

$$\frac{1}{\sigma}\Phi'\left(\frac{x-m}{\sigma}\right) = \frac{1}{\sigma\sqrt{2\pi}} e^{-\frac{(x-m)^2}{2\sigma^2}},$$

and we obtain from (17.1.1)

$$\boldsymbol{E}(\xi) = \frac{1}{\sigma\sqrt{2\pi}} \int_{-\infty}^{\infty} x\, e^{-\frac{(x-m)^2}{2\sigma^2}}\, dx = \frac{1}{\sqrt{2\pi}} \int_{-\infty}^{\infty} (m + \sigma x)\, e^{-\frac{x^2}{2}}\, dx = m,$$

$$\boldsymbol{D}^2(\xi) = \frac{1}{\sigma\sqrt{2\pi}} \int_{-\infty}^{\infty} (x - m)^2\, e^{-\frac{(x-m)^2}{2\sigma^2}}\, dx = \frac{\sigma^2}{\sqrt{2\pi}} \int_{-\infty}^{\infty} x^2\, e^{-\frac{x^2}{2}}\, dx = \sigma^2,$$

so that m and σ denote as usual the mean and the s. d. of the variable.

The frequency curve

$$y = \frac{1}{\sigma\sqrt{2\pi}}\, e^{-\frac{(x-m)^2}{2\sigma^2}}$$

is symmetric and unimodal (cf 15.5), and reaches its maximum at the point $x = m$, so that m is simultaneously mean, median and mode of the distribution. For $x = m \pm \sigma$, the curve has two inflexion points. A change in the value of m causes only a displacement of the curve, without modifying its form, whereas a change in the value of σ amounts to a change of scale on both coordinate axes. The total area included between the curve and the x-axis is, of course, always equal to 1. Curves corresponding to some different values of σ are shown in Fig. 16.

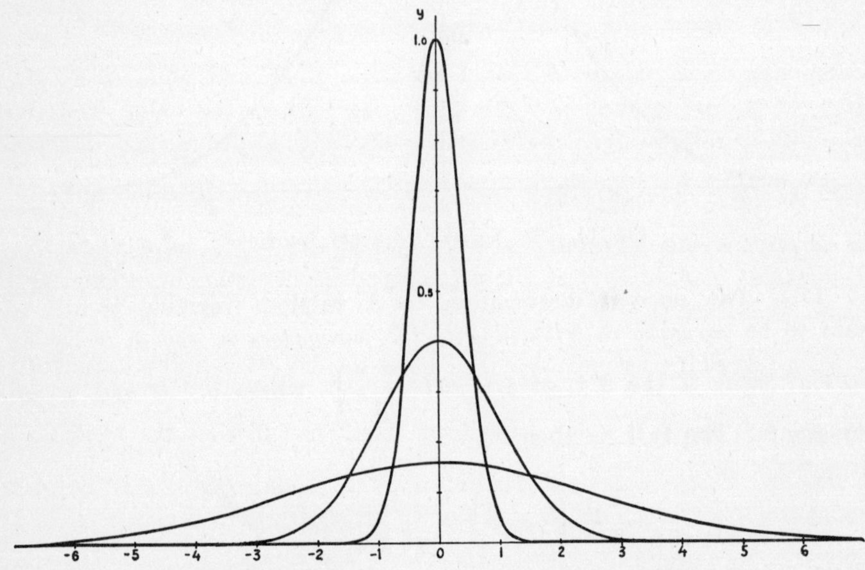

Fig. 16. Normal frequency curves. $m = 0$, $\sigma = 0.4$, 1.0, 2.5.

The smaller we take σ, the more we concentrate the mass of the distribution in the neighbourhood of $x = m$. In the limiting case $\sigma = 0$, the whole mass is concentrated in the point $x = m$, and consequently (cf 16.1) the d. f. is equal to $\varepsilon(x - m)$. This case will be regarded as a degenerate limiting case and called a *singular* normal distribution. The corresponding d. f. $\Phi\left(\frac{x-m}{0}\right)$ will always be interpreted as $\varepsilon(x - m)$.

It is often important to find the probability that a normally distributed variable differs from its mean m in either direction by more than a given multiple $\lambda\sigma$ of the s. d. This probability is equal to the joint area of the two »tails» of the frequency curve that are cut off by ordinates through the points $x = m \pm \lambda\sigma$. Owing to the symmetry of the distribution, this is

$$P = P(|\xi - m| > \lambda\sigma) = 2(1 - \Phi(\lambda)) = \frac{2}{\sqrt{2\pi}} \int_{\lambda}^{\infty} e^{-\frac{x^2}{2}}\, dx.$$

Conversely, we may regard λ as a function of P, defined by this equation. Then λ expresses, in units of the s. d. σ, that deviation from the mean value m, which is exceeded with the given probability P. When P is expressed as a percentage, say $P = p/100$, the corresponding $\lambda = \lambda_p$ is called the *p percent value* of the *normal deviate* $\frac{\xi - m}{\sigma}$. Some numerical values of p as a function of λ_p, and of λ_p as a function of p, are given in Table 2, p. 558. From the value of λ_p for $p = 50$, it follows that the quartiles (cf 15.6) of the normal distribution are $m \pm 0.6745\,\sigma$. It is further seen that the 5 % value of $\frac{\xi - m}{\sigma}$ is about 2.0, the 1 % value about 2.6, and the 0.1 % value about 3.3. Deviations exceeding four times the standard deviation have extremely small probabilities.

The standardized variable $\frac{\xi - m}{\sigma}$ has the d. f. $\Phi(x)$ and consequently by (17.1.3) the c. f. $e^{-\frac{t^2}{2}}$. It follows from (15.9.2) that the variable ξ has the c. f.

$$E(e^{it\xi}) = e^{mit - \frac{1}{2}\sigma^2 t^2}. \tag{17.2.1}$$

From this expression, the semi-invariants are found by (15.10.2), and we obtain

(17.2.2) $$\varkappa_1 = m, \quad \varkappa_2 = \sigma^2, \quad \varkappa_3 = \varkappa_4 = \cdots = 0.$$

The moments about the mean of the variable ξ are

(17.2.3) $$\mu_{2\nu+1} = 0, \quad \mu_{2\nu} = 1 \cdot 3 \cdot \ldots (2\nu - 1)\sigma^{2\nu}.$$

In particular, the coefficients of skewness and excess (cf 15.8) are

$$\gamma_1 = \frac{\mu_3}{\sigma^3} = 0, \quad \gamma_2 = \frac{\mu_4}{\sigma^4} - 3 = 0.$$

Finally we observe that, if the variable ξ is normal (m, σ), it follows from (15.1.1) that any linear function $a\xi + b$ is normal $(am + b, |a|\sigma)$.

17.3. Addition of independent normal variables. — Let $\xi_1, \ldots, \xi_n$ be independent normally distributed variables, the parameters of ξ_ν being m_ν and σ_ν. Consider the sum

$$\xi = \xi_1 + \xi_2 + \cdots + \xi_n.$$

Denoting by m and σ the mean and the s. d. of ξ, we then have by (15.12.7)

(17.3.1) $$\begin{aligned} m &= m_1 + m_2 + \cdots + m_n, \\ \sigma^2 &= \sigma_1^2 + \sigma_2^2 + \cdots + \sigma_n^2. \end{aligned}$$

By the multiplication rule (15.12.1), the c. f. of ξ is the product of the c. f:s of all the ξ_ν. From the expression (17.2.1) for the c. f. of the normal distribution, we obtain

$$\boldsymbol{E}(e^{it\xi}) = \prod_{\nu=1}^{n} e^{m_\nu it - \frac{1}{2}\sigma_\nu^2 t^2} = e^{mit - \frac{1}{2}\sigma^2 t^2}.$$

This is, however, the c. f. of a normal distribution with the parameters m and σ, and so we have proved the following important *addition theorem* for the normal distribution:

The sum of any number of independent normally distributed variables is itself normally distributed:

(17.3.2) $$\Phi\left(\frac{x - m_1}{\sigma_1}\right) * \Phi\left(\frac{x - m_2}{\sigma_2}\right) * \cdots * \Phi\left(\frac{x - m_n}{\sigma_n}\right) = \Phi\left(\frac{x - m}{\sigma}\right),$$

where m and σ are given by (17.3.1).

We mention without proof the following converse (Cramér, Ref. 11) of this theorem: *If the sum* $\xi = \xi_1 + \cdots + \xi_n$ *of n independent variables is normally distributed, then each component variable* ξ_ν *is itself normally distributed.* Thus it is not only true that the normal distribution reproduces itself by composition, but, moreover, a normal distribution can never be *exactly* produced by the composition of non-normal components. On the other hand, we shall see in the following paragraph that, under very general conditions, the composition of a large number of non-normal components produces an *approximately* normal distribution.

Since any linear function of a normal variable is, by the preceding paragraph, itself normal, it follows from (17.3.2) that a linear function $a_1 \xi_1 + a_2 \xi_2 + \cdots + a_n \xi_n + b$ of independent normal variables is itself normal, with parameters m and σ given by $m = a_1 m_1 + \cdots + a_n m_n + b$, and $\sigma^2 = a_1^2 \sigma_1^2 + \cdots + a_n^2 \sigma_n^2$. *In particular, we have the important theorem that, if* $\xi_1, \ldots, \xi_n$ *are independent and all normal* (m, σ), *the arithmetic mean* $\bar{\xi} = \frac{1}{n} \sum_1^n \xi_\nu$ *is itself normal* $\left(m, \frac{\sigma}{\sqrt{n}}\right)$.

17.4. The Central Limit Theorem. — Consider a sum

$$\xi = \xi_1 + \xi_2 + \cdots + \xi_n \tag{17.4.1}$$

of n independent variables, where ξ_ν has the mean m_ν and the s. d. σ_ν. The mean m and the s. d. σ of the sum ξ are then given by the usual expressions (17.3.1).

In the preceding paragraph we have seen that, if the ξ_ν are normally distributed, the sum ξ is itself normal. On the other hand, De Moivre's theorem (cf 16.4) shows that, in the particular case when the ξ_ν are variables having the simple distribution (16.1.3), the distribution of the sum is *approximately* normal for large values of n. In fact, De Moivre's theorem asserts that in this particular case the d. f. of the standardized variable $\frac{\xi - m}{\sigma}$ tends to the normal function $\Phi(x)$ as n tends to infinity.

It is a highly remarkable fact that the result thus established by De Moivre's theorem for a special case holds true under much more general circumstances.

It will be convenient to introduce the following terminology. Generally, if the distribution of a random variable X depends on a parameter n, and if two quantities m_0 and σ_0 (which may or may not depend on n) can be found such that the d. f. of the variable $\frac{X - m_0}{\sigma_0}$

tends to $\Phi(x)$ as $n \to \infty$, we shall say that X is *asymptotically normal* (m_0, σ_0). This does not imply that the mean and the s. d. of X tend to m_0 and σ_0, nor even that these moments exist, but is simply equivalent to saying that we have for any interval (a, b) not depending on n

$$\lim_{n \to \infty} P(m_0 + a\sigma_0 < X < m_0 + b\sigma_0) = \Phi(b) - \Phi(a).$$

Thus e. g. the variable ν considered in De Moivre's theorem is asymptotically normal $(np, \sqrt{npq})$.

The so called *Central Limit Theorem* in the mathematical theory of probability may now be expressed in the following way: *Whatever be the distributions of the independent variables* ξ_ν — *subject to certain very general conditions* — *the sum* $\xi = \xi_1 + \cdots + \xi_n$ *is asymptotically normal* (m, σ), *where* m *and* σ *are given by* (17.3.1).

This fundamental theorem was first stated by Laplace (Ref. 22) in 1812. A rigorous proof under fairly general conditions was given by Liapounoff (Ref. 146, 147) in 1901. The problem of finding the most general conditions of validity has been solved by Feller, Khintchine and Lévy (Ref. 85, 86, 140, 145). We shall here only prove the theorem in two particular cases that will be sufficient for most statistical applications.

Let us first consider the *case of equal components*, i. e. the case when all the ξ_ν in (17.4.1) have the same distribution. In this case we have $m = n m_1$, $\sigma = \sigma_1 \sqrt{n}$, and the standardized variable may be written

$$\frac{\xi - m}{\sigma} = \frac{\xi - n m_1}{\sigma_1 \sqrt{n}} = \frac{1}{\sigma_1 \sqrt{n}} \sum_1^n (\xi_\nu - m_1),$$

where all the deviations $\xi_\nu - m_1$ have the same distribution. Denote by $\varphi_1(t)$ the c.f. of any of these deviations, while $F(x)$ and $\varphi(t)$ are the d. f. and the c. f. of the standardized variable $\frac{\xi - m}{\sigma}$ It then follows from (15.9.2) and (15.12.1) that we have

$$\varphi(t) = \left[\varphi_1\left(\frac{t}{\sigma_1 \sqrt{n}}\right)\right]^n. \tag{17.4.2}$$

The two first moments of the variable $\xi_\nu - m_1$ are 0 and σ_1^2, so that by (10.1.3) we have for the corresponding c. f. the expansion

$$\varphi_1(t) = 1 - \tfrac{1}{2}\sigma_1^2 t^2 + o(t^2).$$

Substituting $\frac{t}{\sigma_1 \sqrt{n}}$ for t, we then obtain from (17.4.2)

$$\varphi(t) = \left(1 - \frac{t^2}{2n} + \frac{\zeta(n, t)}{n}\right)^n,$$

where for every fixed t the quantity $\zeta(n, t)$ tends to zero as $n \to \infty$. It follows that $\varphi(t) \to e^{-\frac{t^2}{2}}$ for every t, and hence we infer as in 16.4 that the corresponding d. f. $F(x)$ tends to $\Phi(x)$ for every x. We thus have the following case of the Central Limit Theorem, first proved by Lindeberg and Lévy (Ref. 24, 148):

If $\xi_1, \xi_2, \ldots$ are independent random variables all having the same probability distribution, and if m_1 and σ_1 denote the mean and the s. d. of every ξ_ν, then the sum $\xi = \sum_1^n \xi_\nu$ is asymptotically normal $(n m_1, \sigma_1 \sqrt{n})$. It follows that the arithmetic mean $\bar{\xi} = \frac{1}{n} \sum_1^n \xi_\nu$ is asymptotically normal $(m_1, \sigma_1/\sqrt{n})$.

In the case of equal components, it is thus sufficient for the validity of the Central Limit Theorem to assume that the common distribution of the ξ_ν has a finite moment of the second order. When we proceed to the general case of variables ξ_ν that are not supposed to be equally distributed it is, however, no longer sufficient to assume that each ξ_ν has a finite second order moment, and thus we have to impose some further conditions. The object of such additional conditions is, generally speaking, to reduce the probability that an individual ξ_ν will yield a relatively large contribution to the total value of the sum ξ. An interesting sufficient condition of this type has been found by Lindeberg. We shall, however, here only give the following somewhat less general theorem due to Liapounoff:

Let $\xi_1, \xi_2, \ldots$ be independent random variables, and denote by m_ν and σ_ν the mean and the s. d. of ξ_ν. Suppose that the third absolute moment of ξ_ν about its mean

$$\varrho_\nu^3 = \boldsymbol{E}(|\xi_\nu - m_\nu|^3)$$

is finite for every ν, and write

$$\varrho^3 = \varrho_1^3 + \varrho_2^3 + \cdots + \varrho_n^3.$$

If the condition

$$\lim_{n \to \infty} \frac{\varrho}{\sigma} = 0 \tag{17.4.3}$$

is satisfied, then the sum $\xi = \sum_{1}^{n} \xi_\nu$ *is asymptotically normal* (m, σ), *where* m *and* σ *are given by* (17.3.1).

In the particular case when all the ξ_ν are equally distributed, we have $\varrho^3 = n \varrho_1^3$, $\sigma^2 = n \sigma_1^2$, and thus $\frac{\varrho}{\sigma} = \frac{\varrho_1}{\sigma_1 \sqrt[6]{n}}$, so that the condition is satisfied. It should not be inferred, however, that the Lindeberg-Lévy theorem proved above is a particular case of the Liapounoff theorem, since the former does not assume the existence of the third moment.

In order to prove the Liapounoff theorem, we denote by $\varphi_\nu(t)$ the c. f. of the ν:th deviation $\xi_\nu - m_\nu$, and by $\varphi(t)$ the c. f. of the standardized sum $\frac{\xi - m}{\sigma} = \frac{1}{\sigma} \sum_{1}^{n} (\xi_\nu - m_\nu)$. From (15.9.2) and (15.12.1) it then follows that we have

$$\varphi(t) = \prod_{1}^{n} \varphi_\nu\left(\frac{t}{\sigma}\right). \tag{17.4.4}$$

As before, it is sufficient to prove that for every fixed t we have $\varphi(t) \to e^{-\frac{t^2}{2}}$ when $n \to \infty$, as the theorem then directly follows from the continuity theorem 10.4. — Using the expansion (16.4.4) with $k = 3$, we obtain

$$\varphi_\nu(t) = \boldsymbol{E}\left(e^{it(\xi_\nu - m_\nu)}\right) = 1 - \tfrac{1}{2} \sigma_\nu^2 t^2 + \tfrac{1}{6} \vartheta \varrho_\nu^3 t^3,$$

where, as in 16.4, we use ϑ as a general notation for a quantity of modulus not exceeding unity. We further obtain

$$\log \varphi_\nu\left(\frac{t}{\sigma}\right) = \log\left(1 - \frac{\sigma_\nu^2 t^2}{2 \sigma^2} + \vartheta \frac{\varrho_\nu^3 t^3}{6 \sigma^3}\right) = \log(1 + z),$$

where

$$z = -\frac{\sigma_\nu^2 t^2}{2 \sigma^2} + \vartheta \frac{\varrho_\nu^3 t^3}{6 \sigma^3}.$$

Owing to the condition (17.4.3) we have, however, for all sufficiently large values of n

$$\frac{\varrho_\nu}{\sigma} \leqq \frac{\varrho}{\sigma} < 1,$$

and thus, observing that by (15.4.6) we have $\sigma_\nu \leqq \varrho_\nu$ for every ν,

$$z = \vartheta \frac{\varrho_\nu^2 t^2}{2\sigma^2} + \vartheta \frac{\varrho_\nu^3 t^3}{6\sigma^3} = \vartheta \frac{\varrho_\nu^2}{\sigma^2}\left(\frac{t^2}{2} + \frac{|t|^3}{6}\right).$$

The condition (17.4.3) now shows that for every fixed t we have $z \to 0$ as $n \to \infty$. Thus certainly $|z| < \frac{1}{2}$ for all sufficiently large n. For $|z| < \frac{1}{2}$ we have, however,

$$\begin{aligned}\log(1+z) &= \frac{z}{1} - \frac{z^2}{2}\left(1 - \frac{2}{3}z + \frac{2}{4}z^2 - \dots\right)\\ &= z + \frac{1}{2}\vartheta z^2\left(1 + \frac{1}{2} + \frac{1}{2^2} + \dots\right)\\ &= z + \vartheta z^2,\end{aligned}$$

and hence

$$\begin{aligned}\log \varphi_\nu\left(\frac{t}{\sigma}\right) &= -\frac{\sigma_\nu^2}{\sigma^2}\cdot\frac{t^2}{2} + \vartheta\frac{\varrho_\nu^3}{\sigma^3}\cdot\frac{t^3}{6} + \vartheta\frac{\varrho_\nu^4}{\sigma^4}\left(\frac{t^2}{2} + \frac{|t|^3}{6}\right)^2\\ &= -\frac{\sigma_\nu^2}{\sigma^2}\cdot\frac{t^2}{2} + \vartheta\frac{\varrho_\nu^3}{\sigma^3}\left(\frac{1}{6}|t|^3 + \left(\frac{1}{2}t^2 + \frac{1}{6}|t|^3\right)^2\right).\end{aligned}$$

Summing over $\nu = 1, 2, \dots, n$, we now obtain by (17.4.4)

$$\log \varphi(t) = -\frac{t^2}{2} + \vartheta\frac{\varrho^3}{\sigma^3}\left(\frac{1}{6}|t|^3 + \left(\frac{1}{2}t^2 + \frac{1}{6}|t|^3\right)^2\right).$$

As n tends to infinity, it now follows from the condition (17.4.3) that $\log \varphi(t)$ tends to $-\frac{t^2}{2}$ for every fixed t, and thus the Liapounoff theorem is proved.

In the case (cf. 16.6) of the variable $\nu = \sum_1^n \xi_r$ which expresses the number of successes in a series of n independent trials with the probabilities $p_1, \dots, p_n$, we have

$$\varrho_r^3 = \boldsymbol{E}(|\xi_r - p_r|^3) = p_r q_r (p_r^2 + q_r^2) \leqq p_r q_r,$$

$$\varrho^3 \leqq \sum_1^n p_r q_r, \quad \sigma^2 = \sum_1^n p_r q_r,$$

and thus

$$\frac{\varrho}{\sigma} \leqq \left(\sum_1^n p_r q_r\right)^{-\frac{1}{6}}.$$

If the series $\sum_1^\infty p_r q_r$ is *divergent*, the Liapounoff condition (17.4.3) is satisfied, and thus the variable ν is asymptotically normal

$$\left(\sum_1^n p_r, \sqrt{\sum_1^n p_r q_r}\right).$$

A sufficient condition for the divergence of $\sum p_r q_r$ is, e. g., that a number $c > 0$ can be found such that $c < p_r < 1-c$ for all r. — If, on the other hand, $\sum p_r q_r$ is *convergent*, it can be proved (Ref. 11) that the variable ν is *not* asymptotically normal.

17.5. Complementary remarks to the Central Limit Theorem. — The Central Limit Theorem has been modified and extended in various directions. In this paragraph, we shall give a few brief remarks on some of these questions, while the following paragraphs will be devoted to a particular problem belonging to the same order of ideas.

1. The theorems of the preceding paragraph are exclusively concerned with the *distribution functions* of the variables. It is the d. f. of the standardized sum $\frac{\xi - m}{\sigma}$ that is shown to tend to the normal d. f. $\Phi(x)$. If the component variables ξ_ν all belong to the continuous type, the question arises if the *frequency function* of $\frac{\xi - m}{\sigma}$ tends to the normal fr. f. $\Phi'(x) = \frac{1}{\sqrt{2\pi}} e^{-\frac{x^2}{2}}$. It can, in fact, be shown (Cramér, Ref. 11, 70) that this is true if certain general regularity conditions are imposed on the components (cf 17.7.4).

2. In problems of theoretical statistics it often occurs that we are concerned with a function $g(\xi_1, \ldots, \xi_n)$ of n independent random variables, where n may be considered as a large number. If the function g has continuous derivatives of the first and second orders in the neighbourhood of the point $\boldsymbol{m} = (m_1, \ldots, m_n)$, where m_ν denotes the mean of ξ_ν, we may write a Taylor expansion

$$g(\xi_1, \ldots, \xi_n) = g(m_1, \ldots, m_n) + \sum_1^n c_\nu (\xi_\nu - m_\nu) + R, \tag{17.5.1}$$

where c_ν is the value of $\frac{\partial g}{\partial \xi_\nu}$ in the point $\boldsymbol{m}$, while the remainder R contains derivatives of the second order. The first term on the right hand side is a constant, while the second term is the sum of n independent random variables, each having the mean zero. By the central limit theorem we can then say that, under general conditions, the sum of the two first terms is asymptotically normal, with a mean equal to the first term. In many important cases it is possible to show that, in the limit as $n \to \infty$, the presence of the term R has no influence on the distribution, so that the function g is, for large values of n, approximately normally distributed (Cf von Mises, Ref. 157, 158). We shall return to this question in Ch. 28.

3. The central limit theorem may be extended to various cases when the variables ξ_ν in the sum are *not independent*. We shall here only indicate one of these extensions (Cramér, Ref. 10, p. 145), which has a considerable importance for various applications, especially to biological problems. For further information, the reader may be referred to a book by Lévy (Ref. 25), and to papers by Bernstein, Kapteyn and Wicksell (Ref. 63, 135, 230). It will be convenient to use here a terminology directly connected with some of the biological applications. If our random variable is the size of some specified organ that we are observing, the actual size of this organ in a particular individual may often be regarded as the joint effect of a large number of mutually independent causes, acting in an ordered sequence during the time of growth of the individual. If these causes simply add their effects, which are assumed to be random variables, we infer by the central limit theorem that the sum is asymptotically normally distributed.

In general it does not, however, seem plausible that the causes co-operate by simple addition. It seems more natural to suppose that each cause gives an impulse, the effect of which depends both on the strength of the impulse and on the size of the organ already attained at the instant when the impulse is working.

Suppose that we have n impulses $\xi_1, \ldots, \xi_n$, acting in the order of their indices. These we consider as independent random variables. Denote by x_ν the size of the organ which is produced by the impulses $\xi_1, \ldots, \xi_\nu$. We may then suppose e. g. that the increase caused by the impulse $\xi_{\nu+1}$ is proportional to $\xi_{\nu+1}$ and to some function $g(x_\nu)$ of the momentary size of the organ:

$$x_{\nu+1} = x_\nu + \xi_{\nu+1}\, g(x_\nu). \tag{17.5.2}$$

It follows that we have

$$\xi_1 + \xi_2 + \cdots + \xi_n = \sum_{0}^{n-1} \frac{x_{\nu+1} - x_\nu}{g(x_\nu)}.$$

If each impulse only gives a slight contribution to the growth of the organ, we thus have approximately

$$\xi_1 + \xi_2 + \cdots + \xi_n = \int_{x_0}^{x} \frac{d\,t}{g(t)},$$

where $x = x_n$ denotes the final size of the organ. By hypothesis $\xi_1, \ldots, \xi_n$ are independent variables, and n may be considered as a large number. Under the general regularity conditions of the central limit theorem it thus follows that, in the limit, the function of the random variable x appearing in the second member is normally distributed.

Consider, e. g., the case $g(t) = t$. The effect of each impulse is then directly proportional to the momentary size of the organ. In this case we thus find that $\log x$ is normally distributed. If, more generally, $\log(x - a)$ is normal (m, σ), it is easily seen that the variable x itself has the fr. f.

$$\frac{1}{\sigma(x-a)\sqrt{2\pi}} e^{-\frac{(\log(x-a)-m)^2}{2\sigma^2}} \tag{17.5.3}$$

for $x > a$, while for $x \leqq a$ the fr. f. is zero. The corresponding frequency curve, which is unimodal and of positive skewness, is illustrated in Fig. 17. This *logarithmico-normal distribution* may be used as the basic function of expansions in series, analogous to those derived from the normal distribution, which are discussed in the following paragraphs.

Similar arguments may be applied also in other cases, e. g. in certain branches of economic statistics. Consider the distribution of incomes or property values in a certain population. The position of an individual on the property scale might be regarded as the effect of a large number of impulses, each of which causes a certain increase of his wealth. It might be argued that the effect of such an impulse would not unreasonably be expected to be proportional to the wealth already attained. If this argument is accepted, we should expect distributions of incomes or property values to be approximately logarithmico-normal. For low values of the income, the logarithmico-normal curve seems, in fact, to agree fairly well with actual income curves (Quensel, Ref. 201, 202). For moderate and large incomes, however, the Pareto distribution discussed in 19.3 generally seems to give a better fit.

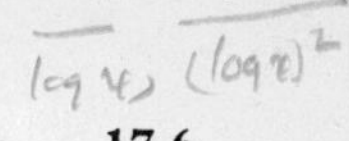

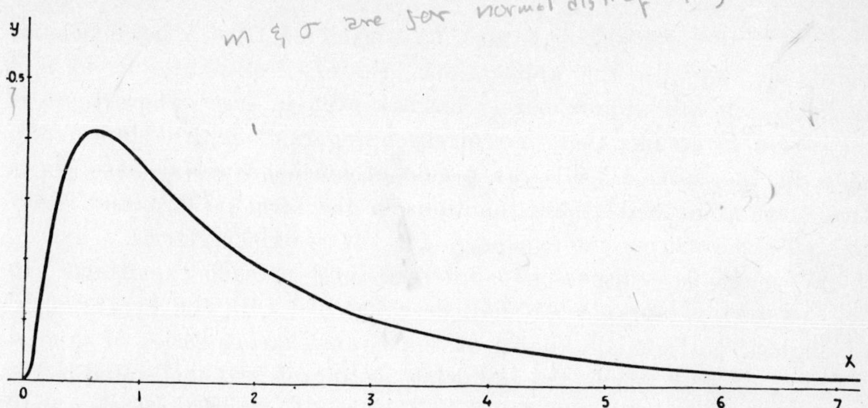

Fig. 17. The logarithmico-normal distribution, frequency curve for $a = 0$, $m = 0.46$, $\sigma = 1$.

17.6. Orthogonal expansion derived from the normal distribution. — Consider a random variable ξ which is the sum

$$\xi = \xi_1 + \xi_2 + \cdots + \xi_n \tag{17.6.1}$$

of n independent random variables. Under the conditions of the central limit theorem, the d. f. $F(x)$ of the standardized variable $\frac{\xi - m}{\sigma}$ is for large n approximately equal to $\Phi(x)$. Further, if all the components ξ_ν have distributions of the continuous type, the fr. f. $f(x) = F'(x)$ will (cf 17.5) under certain general regularity conditions be approximately equal to the normal fr. f.[1] $\varphi(x) = \Phi'(x)$. — Writing

$$\begin{aligned} F(x) &= \Phi(x) + R(x), \\ f(x) &= \varphi(x) + r(x), \end{aligned} \tag{17.6.2}$$

this implies that $R(x)$ and $r(x) = R'(x)$ are small for large values of n, so that $\Phi(x)$ and $\varphi(x)$ may be regarded as first approximations to $F(x)$ and $f(x)$ respectively. It is then natural to ask if, by further analysis of the remainder terms $R(x)$ and $r(x)$, we can find more accurate approximations, e. g. in the form of some expansion of $R(x)$ and $r(x)$ in series.

[1]) As a rule we use the letter φ to denote a characteristic function. In the paragraphs 17.6 and 17.7, however, $\varphi(x)$ will denote the normal frequency function $\varphi(x) = \Phi'(x) = \frac{1}{\sqrt{2\pi}} e^{-\frac{x^2}{2}}$, while the letter ψ will be used for c. f:s.

The same problem may also be considered from a more general point of view. In the applications, we often encounter fr. f:s and d. f:s which are approximately normal, even in cases where there is no reason to assume that the corresponding random variable is generated in the form (17.6.1), as a sum of independent variables. It is then natural to write these functions in the form (17.6.2), and to try to find some convenient expansion for the remainder terms.

We shall here discuss two different types of such expansions. In the present paragraph, we shall be concerned with the expansion in orthogonal polynomials known as the Gram-Charlier series of type A (Ref. 9, 65, 118), while the following paragraph will be devoted to the asymptotic expansion introduced by Edgeworth. In both cases we shall have to content ourselves with some formal developments and some brief indications of the main results obtained, as the complete proofs are rather complicated.

Let us first consider any random variable ξ with a distribution of the continuous type, without assuming that there is a representation of the form (17.6.1). As usual we denote the mean and the s. d. of ξ by m and σ, while μ_ν denotes the ν:th order central moment (cf 15.4) of ξ, which is supposed to be finite for all ν. We shall consider the *standardized variable* $\frac{\xi - m}{\sigma}$, and denote its d. f. and fr. f. by $F(x)$ and $f(x) = F'(x)$.

For any fr. f. $f(x)$, we may consider an expansion of the form

$$(17.6.3) \qquad f(x) = c_0 \varphi(x) + \frac{c_1}{1!} \varphi'(x) + \frac{c_2}{2!} \varphi''(x) + \dots,$$

where the c_ν are constant coefficients. According to (12.6.4), we have $\varphi^{(\nu)}(x) = (-1)^\nu H_\nu(x) \varphi(x)$, where $H_\nu(x)$ is the Hermite polynomial of degree ν, and thus (17.6.3) is in reality an expansion in orthogonal polynomials of the type (12.6.2). We shall now determine the coefficients in the same way as in 12.6, assuming that the series may be integrated term by term. Multiplying with $H_\nu(x)$ and integrating, we directly obtain from the orthogonality relations (12.6.6)

$$(17.6.4) \qquad c_\nu = (-1)^\nu \int_{-\infty}^{\infty} H_\nu(x) f(x)\, dx.$$

Now $f(x)$ is the fr. f. of the standardized variable $\frac{\xi - m}{\sigma}$, which has zero mean and unit s. d., while its ν:th moment is $\frac{\mu_\nu}{\sigma^\nu}$. Accordingly we find $c_0 = 1$, $c_1 = c_2 = 0$, so that the development (17.6.3), and the development obtained by formal integration, may be written

$$(17.6.5)\qquad \begin{aligned} F(x) &= \Phi(x) + \frac{c_3}{3!}\Phi^{(3)}(x) + \frac{c_4}{4!}\Phi^{(4)}(x) + \cdots, \\ f(x) &= \varphi(x) + \frac{c_3}{3!}\varphi^{(3)}(x) + \frac{c_4}{4!}\varphi^{(4)}(x) + \cdots, \end{aligned}$$

where the c_ν are given by (17.6.4). From the expressions (12.6.5) of the first Hermite polynomials, we obtain in particular, denoting by γ_1 and γ_2 the coefficients of skewness and excess (cf 15.8) of the variable ξ,

$$(17.6.6)\qquad \begin{aligned} c_3 &= -\frac{\mu_3}{\sigma^3} = -\gamma_1, \\ c_4 &= \frac{\mu_4}{\sigma^4} - 3 = \gamma_2, \\ c_5 &= -\frac{\mu_5}{\sigma^5} + 10\frac{\mu_3}{\sigma^3}, \\ c_6 &= \frac{\mu_6}{\sigma^6} - 15\frac{\mu_4}{\sigma^4} + 30. \end{aligned}$$

With any standardized variable $\frac{\xi - m}{\sigma}$ having finite moments of all orders, we may thus formally associate the expansions (17.6.5), the coefficients of which are given by (17.6.4). But do these expansions really converge and represent $f(x)$ and $F(x)$?

It can in fact be shown (cf e. g. Cramér, Ref. 69, 70) that, whenever the integral

$$(17.6.6a)\qquad \int_{-\infty}^{\infty} e^{\frac{x^2}{4}}\, dF(x)$$

is convergent, the first series (17.6.5) will converge for every x to the sum $F(x)$. If, in addition, the fr. f. $f(x)$ is of bounded variation in $(-\infty, \infty)$, the second series (17.6.5) will converge to $f(x)$ in every continuity point of $f(x)$. — On the other hand, it can be shown by examples (cf Ex. 18, p. 258) that, if these conditions are not satisfied, the expansions may be divergent. Thus it is in reality only for a comparatively small class of distributions that we can assert the validity of the expansions (17.6.5). In fact, the majority of the important distributions treated in the two following chapters are not included in this class.

However, in practical applications it is in most cases only of little value to know the convergence properties of our expansions. *What we really want to know is whether a small number of terms — usually not more than two or three — suffice to give a good approximation to* $f(x)$ *and* $F(x)$. If we know this to be the case, it does not concern us much whether the infinite series is convergent or divergent. And conversely, if we know that one of the series (17.6.5) is convergent, this knowledge is of little practical value if it will be necessary to calculate a large number of the coefficients c_ν in order to have the sum of the series determined to a reasonable approximation.

It is particularly when we are dealing with a variable ξ generated in the form (17.6.1) that the question thus indicated becomes important. As pointed out above, we know that under certain general conditions $F(x)$ and $f(x)$ are approximately equal to $\Phi(x)$ and $\varphi(x)$ when n is large. Will the approximation be improved if we include the term involving the third derivative in (17.6.5)? And will the consideration of further terms of the expansions yield a still better approximation? It will be seen that we are here in reality concerned with a question relating to the *asymptotic properties* of our expansions for large values of n.

In order to simplify the algebraical calculations, we shall consider the *case of equal components* (cf 17.4), when all the components $\xi_1, \ldots, \xi_n$ in (17.6.1) have the same distribution, with the mean m_1 and the s. d. σ_1, so that we have $m = n m_1$, $\sigma = \sigma_1 \sqrt{n}$. In this case, we now propose to study the behaviour of the coefficients c_ν of the A-series for large values of n.

Let $\psi(t)$ denote the c. f. of the standardized sum $\frac{\xi - m}{\sigma}$, while $\psi_1(t)$ is the c. f. of the deviation $\xi_1 - m_1$. According to (17.4.2) we then have

$$\psi(t) = \left[\psi_1\left(\frac{t}{\sigma_1 \sqrt{n}}\right)\right]^n.$$

For $\nu = 1, 2, \ldots$, let $\varkappa_\nu$ denote the semi-invariants of $\xi - m = \sum_1^n (\xi_\nu - m_1)$, while $\varkappa'_\nu$ are the semi-invariants of $\xi_1 - m_1$, and put

$$\lambda_\nu = \frac{\varkappa_\nu}{\sigma^\nu}, \quad \lambda'_\nu = \frac{\varkappa'_\nu}{\sigma_1^\nu}. \tag{17.6.7}$$

We then have by (15.12.8)

$$\varkappa_\nu = n\,\varkappa'_\nu, \quad \lambda_\nu = \frac{\lambda'_\nu}{n^{\frac{\nu}{2}-1}}. \tag{17.6.8}$$

By the definition of the c. f. $\psi(t)$ we have

$$e^{\frac{t^2}{2}}\,\psi(t) = \int_{-\infty}^{\infty} e^{\frac{t^2}{2}+itx} f(x)\,dx,$$

and hence obtain according to (12.6.7) the expansion

$$e^{\frac{t^2}{2}}\,\psi(t) = \sum_0^\infty \frac{c_\nu}{\nu!}(-it)^\nu \tag{17.6.9}$$

or

$$\psi(t) = e^{-\frac{t^2}{2}} + \frac{c_3}{3!}(-it)^3 e^{-\frac{t^2}{2}} + \frac{c_4}{4!}(-it)^4 e^{-\frac{t^2}{2}} + \cdots, \tag{17.6.10}$$

where c_ν is given by (17.6.4).

It should be observed that we cannot in general assert that the power series in the second member is convergent, but only that it holds as an asymptotic expansion for small values of t in the same sense as (10.1.3).

If we compare (17.6.10) with the expansion

$$f(x) = \varphi(x) + \frac{c_3}{3!}\varphi^{(3)}(x) + \frac{c_4}{4!}\varphi^{(4)}(x) + \cdots, \tag{17.6.11}$$

it will be seen that the terms of the two expansions correspond by means of the following relation obtained from (10.5.5):

$$\int_{-\infty}^{\infty} e^{itx}\varphi^{(\nu)}(x)\,dx = (-it)^\nu e^{-\frac{t^2}{2}}, \qquad (\nu = 0, 1, 2, \ldots). \tag{17.6.12}$$

As remarked in an analogous case in 15.10, we may use power series of the type (17.6.9) in a purely formal way, without paying any attention to questions of convergence, as long as we are only concerned with the deduction of the algebraic relations between the various parameters, such as the c_ν and the λ'_ν. Thus we may write, in accordance with 15.10 and using (17.6.7),

$$\psi_1(t) = e^{\sum\limits_1^{\infty} \frac{\varkappa'_\nu}{\nu!}(it)^\nu}$$

$$\psi(t) = \left[\psi_1\left(\frac{t}{\sigma_1 \sqrt{n}}\right)\right]^n = e^{n \sum\limits_1^{\infty} \frac{\lambda'_\nu}{\nu!}\left(\frac{it}{\sqrt{n}}\right)^\nu}.$$

Now $\xi_1 - m_1$ has the mean zero and the s. d. σ_1. Thus $\varkappa'_1 = 0$ and $\varkappa'_2 = \sigma_1^2$, so that $\lambda'_1 = 0$ and $\lambda'_2 = 1$. Hence we may write the last relation

$$e^{\frac{t^2}{2}} \psi(t) = e^{n \sum\limits_3^{\infty} \frac{\lambda'_\nu}{\nu!}\left(\frac{it}{\sqrt{n}}\right)^\nu}. \tag{17.6.13}$$

In order to obtain an explicit expression for c_ν in terms of the λ'_ν, it now only remains to develop this expression in powers of t, and identify the resulting series with (17.6.9). In this way we obtain

$$\begin{aligned} c_3 &= -\frac{\lambda'_3}{n^{1/2}}, \\ c_4 &= \frac{\lambda'_4}{n}, \\ c_5 &= -\frac{\lambda'_5}{n^{3/2}}, \\ c_6 &= \frac{\lambda'_6}{n^2} + \frac{10\,\lambda'^2_3}{n}, \end{aligned} \tag{17.6.14}$$

and generally

$$\sum_{\nu=0}^{\infty} \frac{c_\nu}{\nu!}(-it)^\nu = \sum_{h=0}^{\infty} \frac{n^h}{h!}\left[\sum_{\nu=3}^{\infty} \frac{\lambda'_\nu}{\nu!}\left(\frac{it}{\sqrt{n}}\right)^\nu\right]^h,$$

which shows that c_ν is of the form

$$c_\nu = \frac{a_{\nu 1} n + a_{\nu 2} n^2 + \cdots + a_{\nu [\nu/3]} n^{[\nu/3]}}{n^{\frac{\nu}{2}}}, \tag{17.6.15}$$

where $[\nu/3]$ denotes the greatest integer $\leqq \nu/3$, while the $a_{\nu h}$ are polynomials in the λ'_ν, which are independent of n. Thus

$$c_\nu = O\left(n^{[\nu/3] - \nu/2}\right)$$

as n tends to infinity. The following table shows the order of magnitude of c_ν for the first values of ν.

Subscript ν.	Order of c_ν.
3	$n^{-1/2}$
4, 6	n^{-1}
5, 7, 9	$n^{-3/2}$
8, 10, 12	n^{-2}
11, 13, 15	$n^{-5/2}$

Thus the order of magnitude of the terms of the A-series is not steadily decreasing as ν increases. Suppose, e. g., that we want to calculate a partial sum of the series (17.6.11), taking account of all terms involving corrections to $\varphi(x)$ of order $n^{-1/2}$ or n^{-1}. It then follows from the table that we must consider the terms up to $\nu = 6$ inclusive. In order to calculate the coefficients c_ν of these terms according to (17.6.6) or (17.6.14), we shall require the moments μ_ν or the semi-invariants λ'_ν up to the sixth order. An inspection of (17.6.14) shows, however, that the contributions of order $n^{-1/2}$ and n^{-1} really do not contain any semi-invariants of order higher than the fourth, so that in reality it ought not to be necessary to go beyond this order. If we want to proceed further and include terms containing the factors $n^{-3/2}$, n^{-2} etc., it is easily seen that we shall encounter precisely similar inadequacies.

Thus the Gram-Charlier A-series cannot be considered as a satisfactory solution of the expansion problem for $F(x)$ and $f(x)$. We want, in fact, a series which gives a straightforward expansion in powers of $n^{-1/2}$, and is such that the calculation of the terms up to a certain order of magnitude does not require the knowledge of any moments or semi-invariants that are not really necessary. These conditions are satisfied by Edgeworth's series, which will be treated in the following paragraph.

17.7. Asymptotic expansion derived from the normal distribution. — In the preceding paragraph, the expansion of the function

$$e^{\frac{t^2}{2}} \psi(t) = e^{n \sum_{3}^{\infty} \frac{\lambda'_\nu}{\nu!} \left(\frac{it}{\sqrt{n}}\right)^\nu} \tag{17.7.1}$$

in powers of t furnished expressions of the coefficients c_ν in the A-

series. The same function (17.7.1) can however, also be expanded in a different way, viz. in powers of $n^{-1/2}$. Writing

$$e^{\frac{t^2}{2}}\psi(t) = e^{(it)^2\sum_1^\infty \frac{\lambda'_{\nu+2}}{(\nu+2)!}\left(\frac{it}{\sqrt{n}}\right)^\nu}$$

$$= \sum_{h=0}^{\infty} \frac{(it)^{2h}}{h!}\left[\sum_{\nu=1}^{\infty} \frac{\lambda'_{\nu+2}}{(\nu+2)!}\left(\frac{it}{\sqrt{n}}\right)^\nu\right]^h,$$

we obtain after development

$$\psi(t) = e^{-\frac{t^2}{2}} + \sum_1^\infty \frac{b_{\nu,\nu+2}(it)^{\nu+2} + b_{\nu,\nu+4}(it)^{\nu+4} + \cdots + b_{\nu,3\nu}(it)^{3\nu}}{n^{\nu/2}} e^{-\frac{t^2}{2}},$$

where $b_{\nu,\nu+2h}$ is a polynomial in $\lambda'_3, \ldots, \lambda'_{\nu-h+3}$ which is independent of n. By the integral relation (17.6.12), this corresponds to the expansion in powers of $n^{-1/2}$:

$$(17.7.2)\quad f(x) = \varphi(x) + \sum_1^\infty (-1)^\nu \frac{b_{\nu,\nu+2}\varphi^{(\nu+2)}(x) + \cdots + b_{\nu,3\nu}\varphi^{(3\nu)}(x)}{n^{\nu/2}},$$

the first terms of which are, writing all terms of a certain order with respect to n on the same line,

$$\begin{aligned} f(x) &= \varphi(x) \\ &- \frac{1}{3!}\cdot\frac{\lambda'_3}{n^{1/2}}\varphi^{(3)}(x) \\ &+ \frac{1}{4!}\cdot\frac{\lambda'_4}{n}\varphi^{(4)}(x) + \frac{10}{6!}\frac{\lambda'^2_3}{n}\varphi^{(6)}(x) \\ &- \frac{1}{5!}\cdot\frac{\lambda'_5}{n^{3/2}}\varphi^{(5)}(x) - \frac{35}{7!}\cdot\frac{\lambda'_3\lambda'_4}{n^{3/2}}\varphi^{(7)}(x) - \frac{280}{9!}\cdot\frac{\lambda'^3_3}{n^{3/2}}\varphi^{(9)}(x) \\ &+ \cdots\cdots\cdots\cdots\cdots \end{aligned}$$

By (17.6.7) and (17.6.8) the coefficients may be expressed in terms of the semi-invariants $\varkappa_\nu$, which in their turn may be replaced by the central moments μ_ν by means of (15.10.5). In this way we obtain the series introduced by Edgeworth (Ref. 80):

$$f(x) = \varphi(x)$$
$$- \frac{1}{3!} \cdot \frac{\mu_3}{\sigma^3} \varphi^{(3)}(x)$$
$$(17.7.3) \qquad + \frac{1}{4!}\left(\frac{\mu_4}{\sigma^4} - 3\right) \varphi^{(4)}(x) + \frac{10}{6!} \cdot \left(\frac{\mu_3}{\sigma^3}\right)^2 \varphi^{(6)}(x)$$
$$- \frac{1}{5!}\left(\frac{\mu_5}{\sigma^5} - 10\frac{\mu_3}{\sigma^3}\right) \varphi^{(5)}(x) - \frac{35}{7!}\frac{\mu_3}{\sigma^3}\left(\frac{\mu_4}{\sigma^4} - 3\right) \varphi^{(7)}(x) - \frac{280}{9!}\left(\frac{\mu_3}{\sigma^3}\right)^3 \varphi^{(9)}(x)$$
$$+ \cdots\cdots\cdots\cdots\cdots ,$$

where the terms on each line are of the same order of magnitude. In order to obtain a corresponding expansion for the d. f. $F(x)$ we have only to replace $\varphi(x)$ by $\Phi(x)$.

The asymptotic properties of these series have been investigated by Cramér (Ref. 11, 70) who has shown that, under fairly general conditions, the series (17.7.2) really gives an asymptotic expansion of $f(x)$ in powers of $n^{-1/2}$, with a remainder term of the same order as the first term neglected. Analogous results hold true for $F(x)$. If we consider only the first term of the series, it follows in particular that we have in these cases

$$(17.7.4) \qquad |F(x) - \Phi(x)| < \frac{A}{\sqrt{n}}, \quad |f(x) - \varphi(x)| < \frac{B}{\sqrt{n}},$$

where A and B are constants.[1])

The terms of order $n^{-\nu/2}$ in Edgeworth's series contain the moments $\mu_3, \ldots, \mu_{\nu+2}$, which are precisely the moments necessarily required for an approximation to this order. In practice it is usually not advisable to go beyond the third and fourth moments. The terms containing these moments will, however, often be found to give a good approximation to the distribution. For the numerical calculations, tables of the derivatives $\varphi^{(\nu)}(x)$ will be required. These are given in Table 1, p. 557.

Introducing the coefficients γ_1 and γ_2 of skewness and excess (cf 15.8), we may write the expression for $f(x)$ up to terms of order n^{-1}

$$(17.7.5) \qquad f(x) = \varphi(x) - \frac{\gamma_1}{3!}\varphi^{(3)}(x) + \frac{\gamma_2}{4!}\varphi^{(4)}(x) + \frac{10\gamma_1^2}{6!}\varphi^{(6)}(x).$$

---

[1]) It has been shown by Esseen (Ref. 83) and Bergström (Ref. 62) that the inequality for $|F - \Phi|$ holds under the sole condition that $\varkappa_3'$ is finite.

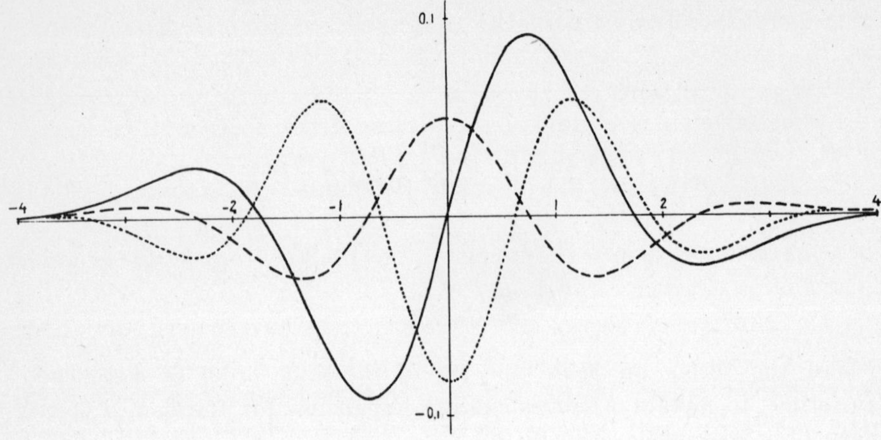

Fig. 18. Derivatives of the normal frequency function $\varphi(x) = \frac{1}{\sqrt{2\pi}} e^{-x^2/2}$.

$\frac{1}{3!} \varphi^{(3)}(x)$ ————————

$\frac{1}{4!} \varphi^{(4)}(x)$ - - - - - - - -

$\frac{10}{6!} \varphi^{(6)}(x)$ ……………………

Diagrams of the derivatives $\varphi^{(3)}$, $\varphi^{(4)}$ and $\varphi^{(6)}$, with the numerical coefficients appearing in (17.7.5), are shown in Fig. 18. The curves for $\varphi^{(4)}$ and $\varphi^{(6)}$ are symmetric about $x = 0$, while the third derivative $\varphi^{(3)}$ introduces an asymmetric element into the expression.

For large x, the expression (17.7.5) will sometimes yield small negative values for $f(x)$. This is, of course, quite consistent with the fact that (17.7.5) gives an *approximate*, but not an *exact*, expression for the frequency function.

For the mode x_0 of the fr. f., we obtain from (17.7.5) the approximate expression $x_0 = -\frac{1}{2}\gamma_1$, which is Charlier's measure of skewness. We further have

$$\frac{f(0) - \varphi(0)}{\varphi(0)} = \tfrac{1}{8}\gamma_2 - \tfrac{5}{24}\gamma_1^2.$$

The first member represents the relative excess of the frequency curve $y = f(x)$ over the normal curve $y = \varphi(x)$ at the point $x = 0$.[1]) For

[1]) If, instead of comparing the *ordinates in the mean* $x = 0$, we compare the *ordinates in the modes* of the two curves, we obtain in the first approximation

$$\frac{f(x_0) - \varphi(0)}{\varphi(0)} = \tfrac{1}{8}\gamma_2 - \tfrac{1}{12}\gamma_1^2.$$

this quantity, Charlier gave the expression $\frac{1}{8}\gamma_2$, which he introduced as his measure of excess. However, it follows from the above that the term in γ_1^2 must be included in order to have an expression of the excess which is correct up to terms of the order n^{-1} (cf 15.8).

17.8. The rôle of the normal distribution in statistics. — The normal distribution was first found in 1733 by De Moivre (Ref. 29), in connection with his discussion of the limiting form of the binomial distribution treated in 16.4.

De Moivre's discovery seems, however, to have passed unnoticed, and it was not until long afterwards that the normal distribution was rediscovered by Gauss (Ref. 16, 1809) and Laplace (Ref. 22, 1812). The latter did, in fact, touch the subject already in some papers about 1780, though he did not go deeper into it before his great work of 1812. Gauss and Laplace were both led to the normal function in connection with their work on the theory of errors of observation. Laplace gave, moreover, the first (incomplete) statement of the general theorem studied above under the name of the Central Limit Theorem, and made a great number of important applications of the normal distribution to various questions in the theory of probability.

Under the influence of the great works of Gauss and Laplace, it was for a long time more or less regarded as an axiom that statistical distributions of practically all kinds would approach the normal distribution as an ideal limiting form, if only we could dispose of a sufficiently large number of sufficiently accurate observations. The deviation of any random variable from its mean was regarded as an »error», subject to the »law of errors» expressed by the normal distribution.

Even if this view was definitely exaggerated and has had to be considerably modified, it is undeniable that, in a large number of important applications, we meet distributions which are at least approximately normal. Such is the case, e. g., with the distributions of errors of physical and astronomical measurements, a great number of demographical and biological distributions, etc.

The central limit theorem affords a theoretical explanation of these empirical facts. According to the »hypothesis of elementary errors introduced by Hagen and Bessel, the total error committed at a physical or astronomical measurement is regarded as the sum of a large number of mutually independent elementary errors. By the central limit theorem, the total error should then be approximately normally distributed. — In a similar way, it often seems reasonable to regard a random variable observed e. g. in some biological investigation as being the total effect of a large number of independent causes, which sum up their effects. The same point of view may be applied to the variables occurring in many technical and economical questions. Thus the total consumption of electric energy delivered by a certain producer is the sum of the quantities consumed by the various customers, the total gain or loss on the risk business of an insurance company is the sum of the gains or losses on each single policy, etc.

In cases of this character, we should expect to find at least approximately normal distributions. If the number of components is not sufficiently large, or if the various components cannot be regarded as strictly additive and independent, the modifications of the central limit theorem indicated in 17.5—17.7 may still show that the distribution is approximately normal, or they may indicate the use of some distribution closely related to the normal, such as the asymptotic expansion (17.7.3) or the logarithmico-normal distribution (17.5.3).

Under the conditions of the central limit theorem, the arithmetic mean of a large number of independent variables is approximately normally distributed. The remarks made in connection with (17.5.1) imply that this property holds true even for certain functions of a more general character than the mean. These properties are of a fundamental importance for many methods used in statistical practice, where we are largely concerned with means and other similar functions of the observed values of random variables (cf Ch. 28).

There is a famous remark by Lippman (quoted by Poincaré, Ref. 31) to the effect that »everybody believes in the law of errors, the experimenters because they think it is a mathematical theorem, the mathematicians because they think it is an experimental fact». — It seems appropriate to comment that both parties are perfectly right, provided that their belief is not too absolute: mathematical proof tells us that, *under certain qualifying conditions*, we are justified in expecting a normal distribution, while statistical experience shows that, in fact, distributions are often *approximately normal*.

CHAPTER 18.

Various Distributions Related to the Normal.

In this chapter, we shall consider the distributions of some simple functions of normally distributed variables. All these distributions have important statistical applications, and will reappear in various connections in Part III.

18.1. The χ^2 distribution. — Let ξ be a random variable which is normal (0, 1). The fr. f. of the square ξ^2 is, by (15.1.4), equal to

$$\frac{1}{\sqrt{2\pi x}} e^{-\frac{x}{2}}$$

for $x > 0$. For $x \leqq 0$, the fr. f. is zero. The c. f. corresponding to this fr. f. is obtained by putting $\alpha = \lambda = \frac{1}{2}$ in (12.3.4), and is

$$\int_0^\infty e^{itx} \cdot \frac{1}{\sqrt{2\pi x}} e^{-\frac{x}{2}} dx = (1 - 2it)^{-\frac{1}{2}}.$$

Let now $\xi_1, \ldots, \xi_n$ be n independent random variables, each of which is normal (0, 1), and consider the variable

$$\chi^2 = \sum_1^n \xi_\nu^2. \tag{18.1.1}$$

Each ξ_ν^2 has the c. f. $(1 - 2it)^{-\frac{1}{2}}$, and thus by the multiplication theorem (15.12.1) the sum χ^2 has the c. f.

$$\boldsymbol{E}(e^{it\chi^2}) = (1 - 2it)^{-\frac{n}{2}}. \tag{18.1.2}$$

This is, however, the c. f. obtained by putting $\alpha = \frac{1}{2}$, $\lambda = \frac{1}{2}n$ in (12.3.4), and the corresponding distribution is thus defined by the fr. f. $f(x; \frac{1}{2}, \frac{1}{2}n)$ as given by (12.3.3). We shall introduce a particular notation for this fr. f., writing for any $n = 1, 2, \ldots$

$$k_n(x) = \begin{cases} \dfrac{1}{2^{\frac{n}{2}}\Gamma\left(\dfrac{n}{2}\right)} x^{\frac{n}{2}-1} e^{-\frac{x}{2}} & \text{for } x > 0, \\ 0 & \text{for } x \leqq 0. \end{cases} \tag{18.1.3}$$

Thus $k_n(x)$ is the fr. f. of the variable χ^2, so that we have

$$k_n(x)\,dx = P(x < \chi^2 < x + dx).$$

The corresponding d. f. is zero for $x \leqq 0$, while for $x > 0$ it is

$$(18.1.4) \qquad K_n(x) = P(\chi^2 \leqq x) = \frac{1}{2^{\frac{n}{2}}\,\Gamma\left(\frac{n}{2}\right)} \int_0^x t^{\frac{n}{2}-1}\, e^{-\frac{t}{2}}\, dt.$$

The distribution defined by the fr. f. $k_n(x)$ or the d. f. $K_n(x)$ is known as the χ^2-*distribution*, a name referring to an important statistical application of the distribution. This will be treated in Ch. 30. The χ^2-distribution contains a parameter n, which is often denoted as the *number of degrees of freedom* in the distribution. The meaning of this term will be explained in Ch. 29. The χ^2-distribution was first found by Helmert (Ref. 125) and K. Pearson (Ref. 183).

For $n \leqq 2$, the fr. f. $k_n(x)$ is steadily decreasing for $x > 0$, while for $n > 2$ there is a unique maximum at the point $x = n - 2$. Diagrams of the function $k_n(x)$ are shown for some values of n in Fig. 19.

The moments α_ν and the semi-invariants $\varkappa_\nu$ of the χ^2-distribution are finite for all ν, and their general expressions may be obtained e. g. from the c. f. (18.1.2), using the formulae in 10.1 and 15.10:

$$(18.1.5) \qquad \begin{aligned} \alpha_\nu &= n(n+2)\cdots(n+2\nu-2), \\ \varkappa_\nu &= 2^{\nu-1}(\nu-1)!\,n. \end{aligned}$$

Hence in particular

$$(18.1.6) \qquad \mathbf{E}(\chi^2) = \alpha_1 = n, \qquad \mathbf{D}^2(\chi^2) = \alpha_2 - \alpha_1^2 = 2\,n.$$

Let χ_1^2 and χ_2^2 be two independent variables distributed according to (18.1.4) with the values n_1 and n_2 of the parameter. The expression (18.1.2) of the c. f. of the χ^2-distribution then shows that the c. f. of the sum $\chi_1^2 + \chi_2^2$ is

$$(1-2\,i\,t)^{-\frac{n_1}{2}} \cdot (1-2\,i\,t)^{-\frac{n_2}{2}} = (1-2\,i\,t)^{-\frac{n_1+n_2}{2}}.$$

Thus the χ^2 distribution, like the binomial, the Poisson and the normal, reproduces itself by composition, and we have the *addition theorem:*

$$(18.1.7) \qquad K_{n_1}(x) * K_{n_2}(x) = K_{n_1+n_2}(x).$$

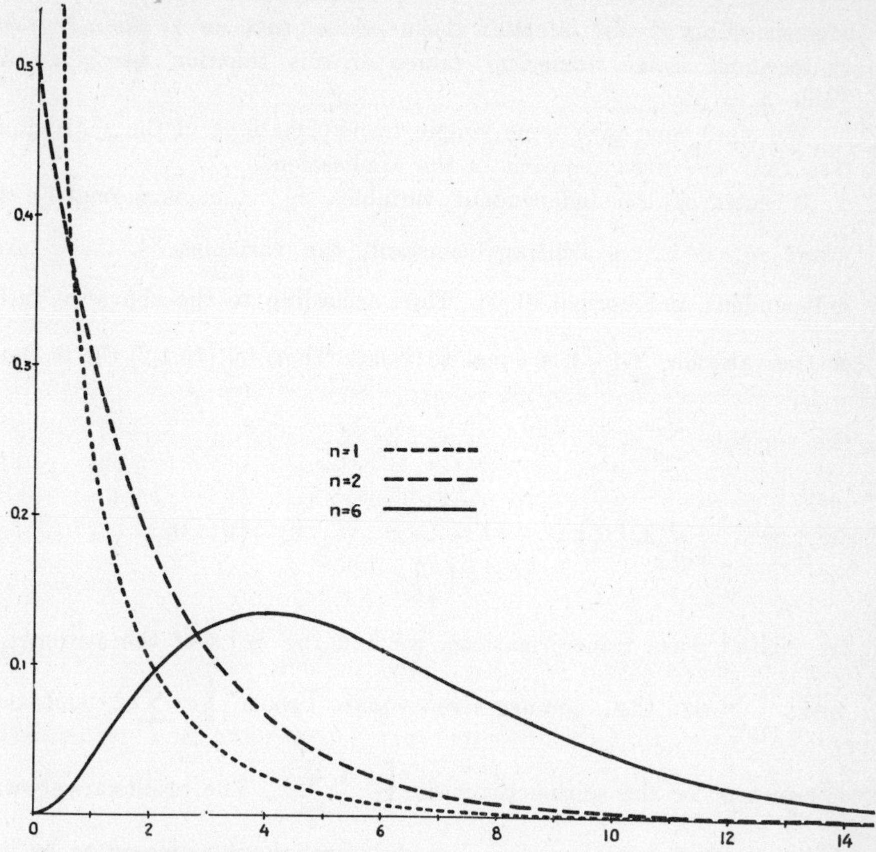

Fig. 19. The χ^2 distribution, frequency curves for $n = 1, 2, 6$.

This may, in fact, be regarded as an evident consequence of the definition (18.1.1) of the variable χ^2, since the sum $\chi_1^2 + \chi_2^2$ is the sum of $n_1 + n_2$ independent squares.

Extensive tables of the χ^2-distribution are available (Ref. 262, 264, 265). In many applications, it is important to find the probability P that the variable χ^2 assumes a value exceeding a given quantity χ_0^2. This probability is equal to the area of the tail of the frequency curve situated to the right of an ordinate through the point $x = \chi_0^2$. Thus

$$P = P(\chi^2 > \chi_0^2) = \int_{\chi_0^2}^{\infty} k_n(x)\, dx = 1 - K_n(\chi_0^2).$$

Usually it is most convenient to tabulate χ_0^2 as a function of the probability P. When P is expressed in percent, say $P = p/100$, the corresponding $\chi_0^2 = \chi_p^2$ is called the *p percent value* of χ^2 for n degrees of freedom. Some numerical values of this function are given in Table 3, p. 559.

We shall now give some simple transformations of the χ^2-distribution that are often required in the applications.

If each of the independent variables $x_1, \ldots, x_n$ is normal $(0, \sigma)$, where $\sigma > 0$ is an arbitrary constant, the variables $\frac{x_1}{\sigma}, \ldots, \frac{x_n}{\sigma}$ are independent and normal (0, 1). Thus according to the above the fr. f. of the variable $\sum_1^n \left(\frac{x_\nu}{\sigma}\right)^2$ is equal to $k_n(x)$. Then by (15.1.2) the fr. f. of the variable $\sum_1^n x_\nu^2$ is

$$\frac{1}{\sigma^2} k_n\left(\frac{x}{\sigma^2}\right) = \frac{1}{2^{\frac{n}{2}} \sigma^n \Gamma\left(\frac{n}{2}\right)} x^{\frac{n}{2}-1} e^{-\frac{x}{2\sigma^2}}, \qquad (x > 0). \tag{18.1.8}$$

By similar easy transformations, we find the fr. f:s of the arithmetic mean $\frac{1}{n}\sum_1^n x_\nu^2$, the non-negative square root $\sqrt{\sum_1^n x_\nu^2}$, and the square root of the arithmetic mean $\sqrt{\frac{1}{n}\sum_1^n x_\nu^2}$. The results are shown in the following table. $x_1, \ldots, x_n$ are throughout supposed to be independent and normal $(0, \sigma)$. For $x < 0$, the fr. f:s are all equal to zero.

Variable.	*Frequency function* $(x > 0)$.
$\sum_1^n x_\nu^2$	$\frac{1}{\sigma^2} k_n\left(\frac{x}{\sigma^2}\right) = \frac{1}{2^{\frac{n}{2}} \sigma^n \Gamma\left(\frac{n}{2}\right)} x^{\frac{n}{2}-1} e^{-\frac{x}{2\sigma^2}}$
$\frac{1}{n}\sum_1^n x_\nu^2$	$\frac{n}{\sigma^2} k_n\left(\frac{nx}{\sigma^2}\right) = \frac{\left(\frac{n}{2}\right)^{\frac{n}{2}}}{\sigma^n \Gamma\left(\frac{n}{2}\right)} x^{\frac{n}{2}-1} e^{-\frac{nx}{2\sigma^2}}$
$\sqrt{\sum_1^n x_\nu^2}$	$\frac{2x}{\sigma^2} k_n\left(\frac{x^2}{\sigma^2}\right) = \frac{2}{2^{\frac{n}{2}} \sigma^n \Gamma\left(\frac{n}{2}\right)} x^{n-1} e^{-\frac{x^2}{2\sigma^2}}$

$$\sqrt{\frac{1}{n}\sum_{1}^{n} x_\nu^2} \qquad \frac{2\,n\,x}{\sigma^2}\,k_n\left(\frac{n\,x^2}{\sigma^2}\right) = \frac{2\left(\frac{n}{2}\right)^{\frac{n}{2}}}{\sigma^n\,\Gamma\left(\frac{n}{2}\right)}\,x^{n-1}\,e^{-\frac{n}{2\sigma^2}x^2}$$

If the horizontal and vertical deviations u and v of a shot from the centre of the target are independent and normal $(0, \sigma)$, the distance $r = \sqrt{u^2 + v^2}$ from the centre will have the fr. f.

$$\frac{2\,x}{\sigma^2}\,k_2\left(\frac{x^2}{\sigma^2}\right) = \frac{x}{\sigma^2}\,e^{-\frac{x^2}{2\sigma^2}}.$$

If the components u, v and w of the velocity of a molecule with respect to a system of rectangular axes are independent and normal $(0, \sigma)$, the velocity $r = \sqrt{u^2 + v^2 + w^2}$ will have the fr. f.

$$\frac{2\,x}{\sigma^2}\,k_3\left(\frac{x^2}{\sigma^2}\right) = \sqrt{\frac{2}{\pi}}\,\frac{x^2}{\sigma^3}\,e^{-\frac{x^2}{2\sigma^2}}.$$

18.2. Student's distribution. — Suppose that the $n+1$ random variables ξ and $\xi_1, \ldots, \xi_n$ are independent and normal $(0, \sigma)$. Let us write $\eta = \sqrt{\frac{1}{n}\sum_{1}^{n}\xi_\nu^2}$, where the square root is taken positively, and consider the variable

$$t = \frac{\xi}{\eta} = \frac{\xi}{\sqrt{\frac{1}{n}\sum_{1}^{n}\xi_\nu^2}}. \tag{18.2.1}$$

Let $S_n(x)$ denote the d. f. of the variable t, so that we have

$$S_n(x) = P(t \leqq x) = P\left(\frac{\xi}{\eta} \leqq x\right).$$

By hypothesis ξ and η are independent variables, and thus according to (15.11.3) their joint fr. f. is the product of the fr. f:s of ξ and η. Now ξ is normal $(0, \sigma)$, and η has the fr. f. given in the last line of the table in the preceding paragraph, so that the joint fr. f. is[1])

[1]) As a rule we have hitherto used corresponding letters from different alphabets to denote a random variable and the variable in its d. f. or fr. f., and have thus employed expressions such as: »The random variable ξ has the fr. f. $f(x)$». When dealing with many variables simultaneously it is, however, sometimes practical to depart from this rule and use the same letter in both places. We shall thus occasionally use expressions such as: »The random variable ξ has the fr. f. $f(\xi)$» or »The random variables ξ and η have the joint fr. f. $f(\xi, \eta)$».

$$\frac{1}{\sigma}\Phi'\left(\frac{\xi}{\sigma}\right)\cdot\frac{2n\eta}{\sigma^2}k_n\left(\frac{n\eta^2}{\sigma^2}\right)=c_n\eta^{n-1}e^{-\frac{\xi^2+n\eta^2}{2\sigma^2}}$$

where $\eta > 0$ and

$$c_n=\sqrt{\frac{2}{\pi}}\frac{\left(\frac{n}{2}\right)^{\frac{n}{2}}}{\sigma^{n+1}\Gamma\left(\frac{n}{2}\right)}.$$

The probability of the relation $\frac{\xi}{\eta}\leqq x$ is the integral of the joint fr. f. over the domain defined by the inequalities $\eta > 0$, $\xi < x\eta$:

$$S_n(x)=c_n\iint\limits_{\substack{\eta>0\\ \xi<x\eta}}\eta^{n-1}e^{-\frac{\xi^2+n\eta^2}{2\sigma^2}}\,d\xi\,d\eta.$$

Introducing new variables u, v by the substitution

(18.2.2) $$\xi=uv,\qquad \eta=v,$$

the Jacobian of which is $\frac{\partial(\xi,\eta)}{\partial(u,v)}=v$, we obtain

$$S_n(x)=c_n\int\limits_{-\infty}^{x}du\int\limits_{0}^{\infty}v^n e^{-\frac{n+u^2}{2\sigma^2}v^2}\,dv$$

(18.2.3) $$=2^{\frac{n-1}{2}}\sigma^{n+1}\Gamma\left(\frac{n+1}{2}\right)c_n\int\limits_{-\infty}^{x}\frac{du}{(n+u^2)^{\frac{n+1}{2}}}$$

$$=\frac{1}{\sqrt{n\pi}}\frac{\Gamma\left(\frac{n+1}{2}\right)}{\Gamma\left(\frac{n}{2}\right)}\int\limits_{-\infty}^{x}\frac{du}{\left(1+\frac{u^2}{n}\right)^{\frac{n+1}{2}}}.$$

The corresponding fr. f. $s_n(x)=S_n'(x)$ exists for all values of x and is given by the expression

(18.2.4) $$s_n(x)=\frac{1}{\sqrt{n\pi}}\frac{\Gamma\left(\frac{n+1}{2}\right)}{\Gamma\left(\frac{n}{2}\right)}\left(1+\frac{x^2}{n}\right)^{-\frac{n+1}{2}}.$$

The distribution defined by the fr. f. $s_n(x)$ or the d. f. $S_n(x)$ is known under the name of *Student's distribution* or the *t-distribution*. It was first used in an important statistical problem by W. S. Gosset, writing under the pen-name of »Student» (Ref. 221). As in the case of the χ^2-distribution, the parameter n is often denoted as the *number of degrees of freedom* in the distribution (cf. 29.2).

From the expression of the fr. f. $s_n(x)$, it is seen that the distribution is independent of the s. d. σ of the basic variables ξ and ξ_ν. This was, of course, to be expected since the variable t is a homogeneous function of degree zero in the basic variables. — It is further seen that the distribution is unimodal and symmetric about $x = 0$. The ν:th moment of the distribution is finite for $\nu < n$. In particular, the mean is finite for $n > 1$, and the s. d. for $n > 2$. Owing to the symmetry of the distribution, all existing moments of odd order are zero, while a simple calculation gives

$$\boldsymbol{D}^2(t) = \int_{-\infty}^{\infty} x^2 s_n(x)\,dx = \frac{n}{n-2},$$

and generally for $2\nu < n$

$$\mu_{2\nu} = \alpha_{2\nu} = \frac{1 \cdot 3 \cdot \cdots (2\nu - 1)\, n^\nu}{(n-2)(n-4)\cdots(n-2\nu)}.$$

The probability that the variable t differs from its mean zero in either direction by more than a given quantity t_0 is, as in the case of the normal distribution equal to the joint area of the two tails of the frequency curve cut off by ordinates through the points $\pm t_0$. On account of the symmetry of the t-distribution, this is

$$(18.2.5) \qquad P = P(|t| > t_0) = 2\int_{t_0}^{\infty} s_n(x)\,dx = 2\,(1 - S_n(t_0)).$$

From this relation, the deviation t_0 may be tabulated as a function of the probability P. When $P = p/100$, the corresponding $t_0 = t_p$ is called the *p percent value* of t for n degrees of freedom. Some numerical values of this function are given in Table 4, p. 560.

For large values of n, the variable t is asymptotically normal (0, 1), in accordance with the relations

$$\lim_{n\to\infty} S_n(x) = \Phi(x), \quad \lim_{n\to\infty} s_n(x) = \Phi'(x) = \frac{1}{\sqrt{2\pi}} e^{-\frac{x^2}{2}},$$

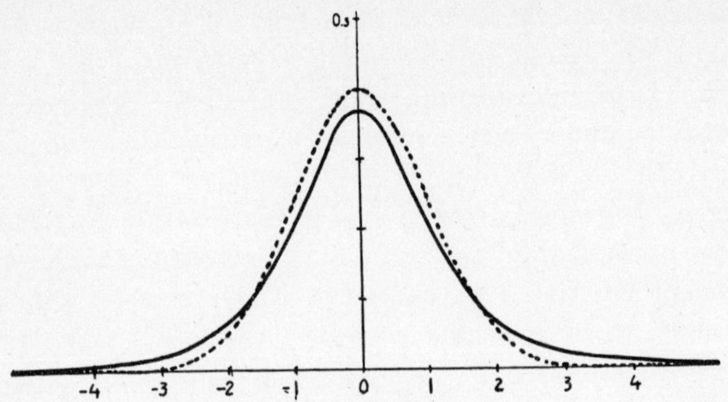

Fig. 20. Student's distribution, frequency curve for $n = 3$: ———. Normal frequency curve, $m = 0$, $\sigma = 1$: ......

which will be proved in 20.2. For small n the t-distribution differs, however, considerably from the limiting normal distribution, as seen from Table 4, where the figures for the limiting case are found under $n = \infty$. A diagram of Student's distribution for $n = 3$, compared with the normal curve, is given in Fig. 20. It is evident from the diagram that the probability of a large deviation from the mean is considerably greater in the t-distribution than in the normal.

If, instead of the variable t as defined by (18.2.1), we consider the variable

$$\tau = \frac{\xi_1}{\eta} = \frac{\xi_1}{\sqrt{\frac{1}{n}\sum_1^n \xi_\nu^2}} \qquad (n > 1), \tag{18.2.6}$$

the numerator and the denominator are no longer independent, and the distribution cannot be obtained in the same way as before. It is obvious that we always have $\tau^2 \leqq n$, so that the fr. f. of τ is certainly equal to zero outside the interval $(-\sqrt{n}, \sqrt{n})$.

Writing

$$t' = \sqrt{\frac{n-1}{n}} \cdot \frac{\tau}{\sqrt{1 - \frac{\tau^2}{n}}} = \frac{\xi_1}{\sqrt{\frac{1}{n-1}\sum_2^n \xi_\nu^2}},$$

it is seen that t' is given by an expression of the form (18.2.1), with n replaced by $n-1$. Thus t' is distributed in Student's distribution with the d. f. $S_{n-1}(x)$. When τ increases from $-\sqrt{n}$ to $+\sqrt{n}$, it is further seen that t' increases steadily from $-\infty$ to $+\infty$. It follows that the relation $\tau < x$ is equivalent to the relation

$$t' < \sqrt{\frac{n-1}{n}} \cdot \frac{x}{\sqrt{1 - \frac{x^2}{n}}},$$

and we have

$$P(\tau < x) = P\left(t' < \sqrt{\frac{n-1}{n}} \cdot \frac{x}{\sqrt{1-\frac{x^2}{n}}}\right) = S_{n-1}\left(\sqrt{\frac{n-1}{n}} \cdot \frac{x}{\sqrt{1-\frac{x^2}{n}}}\right).$$

We have thus found the d.f. of the variable τ. Differentiating with respect to x, we obtain for the fr.f. of τ the expression

$$(18.2.7)\quad \sqrt{\frac{n-1}{n}}\left(1-\frac{x^2}{n}\right)^{-\frac{3}{2}} s_{n-1}\left(\sqrt{\frac{n-1}{n}} \cdot \frac{x}{\sqrt{1-\frac{x^2}{n}}}\right) = \frac{1}{\sqrt{n\pi}} \frac{\Gamma\left(\frac{n}{2}\right)}{\Gamma\left(\frac{n-1}{2}\right)}\left(1-\frac{x^2}{n}\right)^{\frac{n-3}{2}},$$

where $|x| \leqq \sqrt{n}$. For $n = 2$, the frequency curve is »U-shaped», i.e. it has a *minimum* at the mean $x = 0$. For $n = 3$, the fr.f. is constant, and we have a *rectangular distribution* (cf 19.1). For $n > 3$, the distribution is unimodal and symmetric about $x = 0$. The mean of the distribution is 0, and the s.d. is 1 for all values of n.

18.3. Fisher's z-distribution. — Suppose that the $m + n$ random variables $\xi_1, \ldots, \xi_m, \eta_1, \ldots, \eta_n$ are independent and normal $(0, \sigma)$. Put

$$\xi = \sum_1^m \xi_\nu^2, \qquad \eta = \sum_1^n \eta_\nu^2,$$

and consider the variable

$$(18.3.1)\qquad \varkappa = \frac{\xi}{\eta} = \frac{\sum_1^m \xi_\nu^2}{\sum_1^n \eta_\nu^2},$$

Let $F_{mn}(x)$ denote the d.f. of the variable $\varkappa$. Since ξ and η are both non-negative, we have $\varkappa \geqq 0$, and $F_{mn}(x)$ is equal to zero for $x < 0$. For $x > 0$, we may use the same method as in the preceding paragraph to find $F_{mn}(x)$. Since by hypothesis ξ and η are independent, $F_{mn}(x)$ is equal to the integral of the product of the fr.f:s of ξ and η over the domain defined by the inequalities $\eta > 0$, $0 < \xi < x\eta$. The fr.f:s of ξ and η may be taken from the table in 18.1, and so we obtain

$$F_{mn}(x) = a_{mn} \iint\limits_{\substack{\eta > 0 \\ 0 < \xi < x\eta}} \xi^{\frac{m}{2}-1} \eta^{\frac{n}{2}-1} e^{-\frac{\xi+\eta}{2\sigma^2}}\, d\xi\, d\eta,$$

where

$$a_{mn} = \frac{1}{2^{\frac{m+n}{2}} \sigma^{m+n} \Gamma\left(\frac{m}{2}\right) \Gamma\left(\frac{n}{2}\right)}.$$

Introducing new variables u, v by the substitution (18.2.2), we find

$$F_{mn}(x) = a_{mn} \int_0^x u^{\frac{m}{2}-1} \, d\,u \int_0^\infty v^{\frac{m+n}{2}-1} e^{-\frac{u+1}{2\sigma^2} v} \, d\,v$$

$$= \frac{\Gamma\left(\frac{m+n}{2}\right)}{\Gamma\left(\frac{m}{2}\right) \Gamma\left(\frac{n}{2}\right)} \int_0^x \frac{u^{\frac{m}{2}-1}}{(u+1)^{\frac{m+n}{2}}} \, d\,u.$$

Hence we obtain by differentiation the fr. f. $f_{mn}(x) = F'_{mn}(x)$ of the variable $\varkappa$:

$$f_{mn}(x) = \frac{\Gamma\left(\frac{m+n}{2}\right)}{\Gamma\left(\frac{m}{2}\right) \Gamma\left(\frac{n}{2}\right)} \cdot \frac{x^{\frac{m}{2}-1}}{(x+1)^{\frac{m+n}{2}}}, \quad (x > 0). \tag{18.3.2}$$

Like the t-distribution, this is independent of σ. In the particular case $m = 1$, the variable $n\varkappa$ has an expression of the same form as the square of the variable t defined by (18.2.1).

In the *analysis of variance* introduced by R. A. Fisher (cf Ch. 36), we are concerned with a variable z defined by the relation

$$e^{2z} = \frac{n}{m} \varkappa = \frac{\frac{1}{m} \sum_1^m \xi_\nu^2}{\frac{1}{n} \sum_1^n \eta_\nu^2}. \tag{18.3.3}$$

The mean and the variance of the variable e^{2z} are easily found from the distribution of $\varkappa$:

$$\begin{aligned} \mathbf{E}(e^{2z}) &= \frac{n}{m} \mathbf{E}(\varkappa) = \frac{n}{n-2}, \quad (n > 2), \\ \mathbf{D}^2(e^{2z}) &= \left(\frac{n}{m}\right)^2 \mathbf{D}^2(\varkappa) = \frac{2n^2(m+n-2)}{m(n-2)^2(n-4)}, \quad (n > 4). \end{aligned} \tag{18.3.4}$$

For $m > 2$, the distribution of e^{2z} has a unique mode at the point $x = \frac{m-2}{m} \cdot \frac{n}{n+2}$.

In order to find the distribution of the variable z itself, we observe that when $\varkappa$ increases from 0 to ∞, (18.3.3) shows that z increases steadily from $-\infty$ to $+\infty$. Thus the relation $z < x$ is equivalent to $\varkappa < \frac{m}{n} e^{2x}$, and the d. f. of z is

$$P(z < x) = P\left(\varkappa < \frac{m}{n} e^{2x}\right) = F_{mn}\left(\frac{m}{n} e^{2x}\right).$$

Differentiating with respect to x, we obtain for the fr. f. of z the expression given by R. A. Fisher (Ref. 13, 94)

$$(18.3.5) \qquad 2\frac{m}{n} e^{2x} f_{mn}\left(\frac{m}{n} e^{2x}\right) = 2\, m^{\frac{m}{2}} n^{\frac{n}{2}} \frac{\Gamma\left(\frac{m+n}{2}\right)}{\Gamma\left(\frac{m}{2}\right)\Gamma\left(\frac{n}{2}\right)} \frac{e^{mx}}{(m\, e^{2x} + n)^{\frac{m+n}{2}}}.$$

18.4. The Beta-distribution. — Using the same notations as in the preceding paragraph, we consider the variable[1])

$$(18.4.1) \qquad \lambda = \frac{\varkappa}{1+\varkappa} = \frac{\sum_1^m \xi_\nu^2}{\sum_1^m \xi_\nu^2 + \sum_1^n \eta_\nu^2}.$$

We obviously have $0 \leqq \lambda \leqq 1$, so that the fr. f. of λ is zero outside the interval (0, 1). As $\varkappa$ increases from 0 to ∞, λ increases steadily from 0 to 1. The relation $\lambda < x$ is thus equivalent with $\varkappa < \frac{x}{1-x}$, and the d. f. of λ is

$$P(\lambda < x) = P\left(\varkappa < \frac{x}{1-x}\right) = F_{mn}\left(\frac{x}{1-x}\right).$$

Hence we obtain the fr. f. of λ:

$$(18.4.2) \qquad \frac{1}{(1-x)^2} f_{mn}\left(\frac{x}{1-x}\right) = \frac{\Gamma\left(\frac{m+n}{2}\right)}{\Gamma\left(\frac{m}{2}\right)\Gamma\left(\frac{n}{2}\right)} x^{\frac{m}{2}-1} (1-x)^{\frac{n}{2}-1}$$

---

[1]) In the particular case $m = 1$, the variable $(n+1)\lambda$ has an expression of the same form as the square of the variable τ defined by (18.2.6).

This is the particular case $p=\frac{m}{2}$, $q=\frac{n}{2}$ of the fr. f. $\beta(x; p, q)$ given by (12.4.5). In the general case, the distribution defined by the fr. f.

$$\beta(x; p, q)=\frac{\Gamma(p+q)}{\Gamma(p)\,\Gamma(q)}x^{p-1}(1-x)^{q-1}, \quad (0<x<1,\ p>0, q>0), \tag{18.4.3}$$

will be called the *Beta-distribution.* The ν:th moment of this distribution is

$$\int_0^1 x^\nu \beta(x; p, q)\,dx=\frac{\Gamma(p+\nu)}{\Gamma(p)}\cdot\frac{\Gamma(p+q)}{\Gamma(p+q+\nu)}. \tag{18.4.4}$$

Hence in particular the mean is $\frac{p}{p+q}$, while the variance is

$$\frac{p\,q}{(p+q)^2(p+q+1)}.$$

For $p>1$, $q>1$, there is a unique mode at the point $x=\frac{p-1}{p+q-2}\cdot$

CHAPTER 19.

Further Continuous Distributions.

19.1. The rectangular distribution. — A random variable ξ will be said to have a *rectangular distribution*, if its fr. f. is constantly equal to $\frac{1}{2\,h}$ in a certain finite interval $(a-h,\ a+h)$, and zero outside this interval. The frequency curve then consists of a rectangle on the range $(a-h,\ a+h)$ as base and of height $\frac{1}{2\,h}\cdot$ We shall also say in this case that ξ is *uniformly distributed* over $(a-h,\ a+h)$. The mean of this distribution is a, and the variance is $\frac{h^2}{3}\cdot$

The error introduced in a numerically calculated quantity by the »rounding off» may often be considered as uniformly distributed over the range $(-\frac{1}{2}, \frac{1}{2})$, in units of the last figure.

By a linear transformation of the variable, the range of the distribution may always be transferred to any given interval. Thus e. g.

the variable $\eta = \frac{\xi - a + h}{2h}$ is uniformly distributed over the interval $(0, 1)$. The corresponding fr. f. is

$$f_1(x) = \begin{cases} 1 & \text{in } (0, 1), \\ 0 & \text{outside } (0, 1). \end{cases}$$

If $\eta_1, \eta_2, \ldots$ are independent variables uniformly distributed over $(0,1)$, it is evident that the sum $\eta_1 + \cdots + \eta_n$ is confined to the interval $(0, n)$. If $f_n(x)$ denotes the fr. f. of $\eta_1 + \cdots + \eta_n$, it thus follows that $f_n(x)$ is zero outside $(0, n)$. It further follows from (15.12.4) that we have

$$f_{n+1}(x) = \int_{-\infty}^{\infty} f_1(x-t) f_n(t)\,dt = \int_{x-1}^{x} f_n(t)\,dt.$$

From this relation, we obtain by easy calculations

$$f_2(x) = \begin{cases} x & \text{for } 0 < x < 1, \\ x - 2(x-1) & \text{for } 1 < x < 2, \end{cases}$$

$$f_3(x) = \begin{cases} \frac{1}{2} x^2 & \text{for } 0 < x < 1, \\ \frac{1}{2}(x^2 - 3(x-1)^2) & \text{for } 1 < x < 2, \\ \frac{1}{2}(x^2 - 3(x-1)^2 + 3(x-2)^2) & \text{for } 2 < x < 3. \end{cases}$$

The general expression, which may be verified by induction, is

$$f_n(x) = \frac{1}{(n-1)!}\left[x^{n-1} - \binom{n}{1}(x-1)^{n-1} + \binom{n}{2}(x-2)^{n-1} - \cdots\right]$$

where $0 < x < n$, and the summation is continued as long as the arguments $x, x-1, x-2, \ldots$ are positive.

f_1 is a discontinuous frequency function, f_2 is continuous but has a discontinuous derivative, f_3 has a continuous derivative but a discontinuous second derivative, and so on. Diagrams of f_1, f_2 and f_3 are shown in Fig. 21. The mean and the s. d. of the sum $\eta_1 + \cdots + \eta_n$ are $\frac{n}{2}$ and $\sqrt{\frac{n}{12}}$, so that the fr. f. of the standardized sum is

$$\sqrt{\frac{n}{12}} f_n\left(\frac{n}{2} + x\sqrt{\frac{n}{12}}\right).$$

As n increases, this rapidly approaches the normal frequency function $\frac{1}{\sqrt{2\pi}} e^{-\frac{x^2}{2}}$.

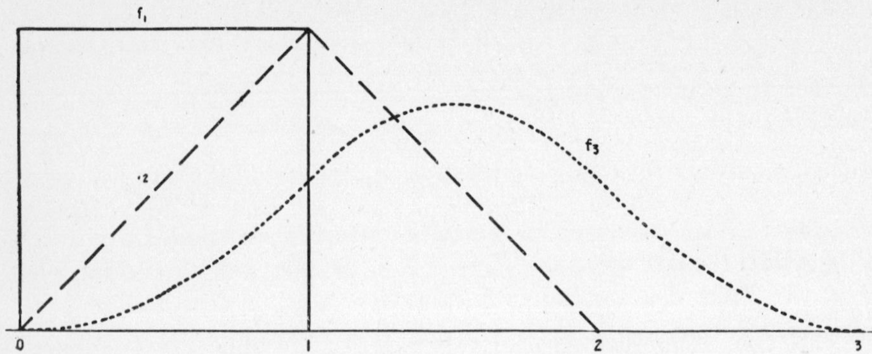

Fig. 21. Rectangular and allied distributions.

The expression of $f_2(x)$ given above may be written in the form

$$f_2(x) = 1 - |1 - x|, \qquad (0 < x < 2).$$

This fr. f., and any fr. f. obtained from it by a linear transformation, is sometimes said to define a *triangular distribution*.

19.2. Cauchy's and Laplace's distributions. — In the particular case $n = 1$, Student's distribution (18.2.4) has the fr. f.

$$\frac{1}{\pi(1 + x^2)},$$

the c. f. of which is, by (10.5.7), equal to $e^{-|t|}$. By a linear transformation, we obtain the fr. f.

$$c(x;\ \lambda,\ \mu) = \frac{1}{\pi} \cdot \frac{\lambda}{\lambda^2 + (x - \mu)^2} \tag{19.2.1}$$

with the c. f.

$$e^{\mu i t - \lambda |t|}, \tag{19.2.2}$$

where $\lambda > 0$. The distribution defined by the fr. f. $c(x;\ \lambda,\ \mu)$, or by the corresponding d. f. $C(x;\ \lambda,\ \mu)$, is called *Cauchy's distribution.* The distribution is unimodal and symmetric about the point $x = \mu$, which is the mode and the median of the distribution. No moment of positive order, not even the mean, is finite. The quartiles (cf 15.6) are $\mu \pm \lambda$, so that the semi-interquartile range is equal to λ.

If a variable ξ is distributed according to (19.2.1), any linear function $a\xi + b$ has a distribution of the same type, with parameters $\lambda' = |a|\lambda$ and $\mu' = a\mu + b$.

The form (19.2.2) of the c. f. immediately shows that this distribution reproduces itself by composition, so that we have the *addition theorem*:

$$(19.2.3) \qquad C(x;\ \lambda_1,\ \mu_1) * C(x;\ \lambda_2,\ \mu_2) = C(x;\ \lambda_1 + \lambda_2,\ \mu_1 + \mu_2),$$

Hence we deduce the following interesting property of the Cauchy distribution: *If* $\xi_1, \ldots, \xi_n$ *are independent, and all have the same Cauchy distribution, the arithmetic mean* $\bar{\xi} = \frac{1}{n}\sum_1^n \xi_\nu$ *has the same distribution as every* ξ_ν.

The two reciprocal Fourier integrals (10.5.6) and (10.5.7) connect the Cauchy distribution with the *Laplace distribution*, which has the fr. f. $\frac{1}{2} e^{-|x|}$. The latter fr. f. has finite moments of every order, while its derivative is discontinuous at $x = 0$. By a linear transformation, we obtain the fr. f.

$$(19.2.4) \qquad \frac{1}{2\lambda} e^{-\frac{|x-\mu|}{\lambda}}$$

with the c. f.

$$\frac{e^{\mu i t}}{1 + \lambda^2 t^2}.$$

19.3. Truncated distributions. — Suppose that we are concerned with a random variable ξ, attached to the random experiment $\mathfrak{E}$. Let as usual P and F denote the pr. f. and the d. f. of ξ. From a sequence of repetitions of $\mathfrak{E}$, we select the sub-sequence where the observed value of ξ belongs to a fixed set S_0. The distribution of ξ in the group of selected cases will then be the *conditional distribution of* ξ, *relative to the hypothesis* $\xi < S_0$. According to (14.3.1) or (14.3.2), the conditional probability of the event $\xi < S$, where S is any subset of S_0, may be written

$$P(\xi < S \mid \xi < S_0) = \frac{P(\xi < S)}{P(\xi < S_0)}.$$

The case when S_0 is an interval $a < \xi \leq b$ often presents itself in the applications. This means that we *discard* all observations where the observed value is $\leq a$ or $> b$. The remaining cases then yield a *truncated distribution* with the d. f.

$$F(x \mid a < \xi \leq b) = \begin{cases} 0 & \text{for} \quad x \leq a, \\ \dfrac{F(x) - F(a)}{F(b) - F(a)} & \text{for } a < x \leq b, \\ 1 & \text{for} \quad x > b. \end{cases}$$

If a fr. f. $f(x) = F'(x)$ exists, the truncated distribution has a fr. f. equal to

$$f(x \mid a < \xi \leqq b) = \frac{f(x)}{\int\limits_a^b f(t)\,dt}$$

for all x in (a, b), and zero outside (a, b). Either a or b may, of course, be infinite.

1. *The truncated normal distribution.* Suppose that the stature of an individual presenting himself for military inscription may be regarded as a random variable which is normal (m, σ). If only those cases are passed where the stature exceeds a fixed limit x_0, the statures of the selected individuals will yield a *truncated normal* distribution, with the d. f.

$$\frac{\Phi\left(\frac{x-m}{\sigma}\right) - \Phi\left(\frac{x_0-m}{\sigma}\right)}{1-\Phi\left(\frac{x_0-m}{\sigma}\right)}, \qquad (x > x_0).$$

Writing $\lambda = \dfrac{\Phi'\left(\frac{x_0-m}{\sigma}\right)}{1-\Phi\left(\frac{x_0-m}{\sigma}\right)}$, the two first moments of the truncated distribution are

$$\alpha_1 = m + \lambda\sigma, \qquad \alpha_2 = m^2 + \lambda\sigma(x_0 + m) + \sigma^2.$$

If x_0, α_1 and α_2 are given, while m and σ are unknown, two equations are thus available for the determination of the two unknown quantities. Tables for the numerical solution of these equations have been published by K. Pearson (Ref. 264).

2. *Pareto's distribution.* In certain kinds of economic statistics, we often meet truncated distributions. Thus e. g. in income statistics the data supplied are usually concerned with the distribution of the incomes of persons *whose income exceeds a certain limit* x_0 fixed by taxation rules. This distribution, and certain analogous distributions of property values, sometimes agree approximately with the *Pareto distribution* defined by the relation

$$P(\xi > x) = \left(\frac{x_0}{x}\right)^{\alpha}, \qquad (x > x_0, \quad \alpha > 0).$$

The fr. f. of this distribution is $\dfrac{\alpha}{x_0}\left(\dfrac{x_0}{x}\right)^{\alpha+1}$ for $x > x_0$, and zero for $x \leqq x_0$. The mean is finite for $\alpha > 1$, and is then equal to $\dfrac{\alpha}{\alpha-1}x_0$. The median of the distribution is $2^{\frac{1}{\alpha}}x_0$. — With respect to the Pareto distribution, we refer to some papers by Hagstroem (Ref. 121, 122).

19.4. The Pearson system. — In the majority of the continuous distributions treated in Chs. 17—19, the frequency function $y = f(x)$ satisfies a differential equation of the form

$$y' = \frac{x + a}{b_0 + b_1 x + b_2 x^2}\, y, \tag{19.4.1}$$

where a and the b:s are constants. It will be easily verified that this is true e. g. of the normal distribution, the χ^2 distribution, Student's distribution, the distribution of Fisher's ratio e^{2z}, the Beta distribution, and Pareto's distribution. Any distribution obtained from one of these by a linear transformation of the random variable will, of course, satisfy an equation of the same form.

The differential equation (19.4.1) forms the base of the system of frequency curves introduced by K. Pearson (Ref. 180, 181, 184 etc.). It can be shown that the constants of the equation (19.4.1) may be expressed in terms of the first four moments of the fr. f., if these are finite. The solutions are classified according to the nature of the roots of the equation $b_0 + b_1 x + b_2 x^2 = 0$, and in this way a great variety of possible types of frequency curves $y = f(x)$ are obtained. The knowledge of the first four moments of any fr. f. belonging to the system is sufficient to determine the function completely. A full account of the Pearson types has been given by Elderton (Ref. 12), to which the reader is referred. Here we shall only mention a few of the most important types. The multiplicative constant A appearing in all the equations below should in every case be so determined that the integral with respect to x over the range indicated becomes equal to unity.

Type I. $y = A\,(x - a)^{p-1}\,(b - x)^{q-1}; \qquad a < x < b; \quad p > 0,\ q > 0.$

For $a = 0$, $b = 1$ we obtain the Beta distribution (18.4.3) as a particular case. Taking $p = q = \frac{1}{2} b^2$, $a = -b$, and allowing b to tend to infinity, we have the normal distribution as a limiting form. Another limiting form is reached by taking $q = b\alpha$; when $b \to \infty$ we obtain after changing the notations the following

Type III. $y = A\,(x - \mu)^{\lambda - 1}\,e^{-\alpha (x - \mu)}; \qquad x > \mu; \quad \alpha > 0,\ \lambda > 0.$

This is a generalization of the fr. f. $f(x;\, \alpha, \lambda)$ defined by (12.3.3), and thus a fortiori a generalization of the χ^2-distribution (18.1.3).

Type VI. $y = A\,(x - a)^{p-1}\,(x - b)^{q-1}; \quad x > b; \ a < b,\ q > 0,\ p + q < 1.$

This contains the distribution (18.3.2) as a particular case ($a = -1$. $b = 0$).

Type VII. $y = \dfrac{A}{((x - \alpha)^2 + \beta^2)^m}; \qquad -\infty < x < \infty; \quad m > \frac{1}{2}.$

This contains Student's distribution (18.2.4) as a particular case.

CHAPTER 20.

SOME CONVERGENCE THEOREMS.

20.1. Convergence of distributions and variables. — If we are given a sequence of random variables $\xi_1, \xi_2, \ldots$ with the d. f:s $F_1(x), F_2(x), \ldots$, it is often important to know whether the sequence of d. f:s converges, in the sense of 6.7, to a limiting d. f. $F(x)$. Thus e. g. the central limit theorem asserts that certain sequences of d. f:s converge to the normal d. f. $\Phi(x)$. — In the next paragraph, we shall give some further important examples of cases of convergence to the normal distribution.

It is important to observe that any statement concerning the convergence of the *sequence of d. f:s* $\{F_n(x)\}$ should be well distinguished from a statement concerning the convergence of the *sequence of variables* $\{\xi_n\}$. We shall not have occasion to enter in this book upon a full discussion of the convergence properties of sequences of random variables. In this respect, the reader may be referred to the books by Fréchet (Ref. 15) and Lévy (Ref. 25). We shall here only use the conception of *convergence in probability*, which will be treated in the paragraphs 3—6 of the present chapter.

20.2. Convergence of certain distributions to the normal. —

1. *The Poisson distribution.* — By 16.5, a variable ξ distributed in Poisson's distribution has the mean λ, the s. d. $\sqrt{\lambda}$ and the c. f. $e^{\lambda(e^{it}-1)}$. The standardized variable $\dfrac{\xi-\lambda}{\sqrt{\lambda}}$ thus has the c. f.

$$e^{-it\sqrt{\lambda}+\lambda\left(e^{\frac{it}{\sqrt{\lambda}}}-1\right)} = e^{-\frac{t^2}{2}+\frac{(it)^3}{3!\sqrt{\lambda}}+\cdots}$$

As λ tends to infinity, this tends to $e^{-\frac{t^2}{2}}$, and by the continuity theorem 10.4 the corresponding d. f. then tends to $\Phi(x)$. Thus ξ is asymptotically normal $(\lambda, \sqrt{\lambda})$.

2. *The χ^2 distribution.* — For n degrees of freedom, the variable χ^2 has by (18.1.6) and (18.1.2) the mean n, the s. d. $\sqrt{2n}$, and the c. f. $(1-2it)^{-\frac{n}{2}}$. Thus the standardized variable $\dfrac{\chi^2-n}{\sqrt{2n}}$ has the c. f.

$$e^{-it\sqrt{\frac{n}{2}}}\left(1 - it\sqrt{\frac{2}{n}}\right)^{-\frac{n}{2}},$$

and for every fixed t we may choose n so large that this may be written in the form

$$\left(1 + \frac{t^2}{n} + \vartheta\left(\frac{2}{n}\right)^{\frac{3}{2}} |t|^3\right)^{-\frac{n}{2}},$$

where $|\vartheta| \leqq 1$.

As $n \to \infty$, this evidently tends to $e^{-t^2/2}$, and thus the d. f. of $\frac{\chi^2 - n}{\sqrt{2n}}$ tends to $\Phi(x)$, so that χ^2 is asymptotically normal $(n, \sqrt{2n})$.

Consider now the probability of the inequality $\sqrt{2\chi^2} < \sqrt{2n} + x$, which may also be written

$$\chi^2 < n + \left(x + \frac{x^2}{2\sqrt{2n}}\right)\sqrt{2n}.$$

As $n \to \infty$, while x remains fixed, $\frac{x^2}{2\sqrt{2n}}$ tends to zero, so that the probability of the above inequality tends to the same limit as the probability of the inequality $\chi^2 < n + x\sqrt{2n}$, i. e. to $\Phi(x)$. Thus the variable $\sqrt{2\chi^2}$ is asymptotically normal $(\sqrt{2n}, 1)$. — According to R. A. Fisher (Ref. 13), the approximation will be improved if we replace here $2n$ by $2n - 1$, and consider $\sqrt{2\chi^2}$ as normally distributed with the mean $\sqrt{2n-1}$ and unit s. d. As soon as $n \geqq 30$, this gives an approximation which is often sufficient for practical purposes.

3. *Student's distribution.* — The fr. f. (18.2.4) of Student's distribution may be written

$$s_n(x) = \frac{\Gamma\left(\frac{n+1}{2}\right)}{\sqrt{\frac{n}{2}}\,\Gamma\left(\frac{n}{2}\right)} \cdot \frac{1}{\sqrt{2\pi}}\left(1 + \frac{x^2}{n}\right)^{-\frac{n+1}{2}} \qquad (20.2.1)$$

By Stirling's formula (12.5.3), the first factor tends to unity as $n \to \infty$, and for every fixed x we have

$$-\frac{n+1}{2}\log\left(1 + \frac{x^2}{n}\right) \to -\frac{x^2}{2},$$

so that

$$s_n(x) \to \frac{1}{\sqrt{2\pi}} e^{-\frac{x^2}{2}}. \tag{20.2.2}$$

Further, let r denote the greatest integer contained in $\frac{n+1}{2}$. Then $r \geqq \frac{n}{2}$, and thus we have for all $n \geqq 1$ and for all real x

$$\left(1 + \frac{x^2}{n}\right)^{\frac{n+1}{2}} \geqq \left(1 + \frac{x^2}{n}\right)^r \geqq 1 + r\frac{x^2}{n} \geqq 1 + \frac{x^2}{2}.$$

Thus the sequence $\{s_n(x)\}$ is uniformly dominated by a function of the form $A(1 + \frac{1}{2}x^2)^{-1}$, so that (5.5.2) gives

$$S_n(x) = \int_{-\infty}^{x} s_n(t)\,dt \to \frac{1}{\sqrt{2\pi}} \int_{-\infty}^{x} e^{-\frac{t^2}{2}}\,dt = \Phi(x). \tag{20.2.3}$$

4. *The Beta distribution.* — Let ξ be a variable distributed in the Beta distribution (18.4.3), with the values np and nq of the parameters. The mean and the variance of ξ are then, by 18.4, $\frac{p}{p+q}$ and $\frac{pq}{(p+q)^2(np+nq+1)}$. Let now n tend to infinity, while p and q remain fixed. By calculations similar to those made above, it can then be proved that the fr. f. of the standardized variable tends to the normal fr. f. $\frac{1}{\sqrt{2\pi}} e^{-\frac{x^2}{2}}$, and that the corresponding d. f. tends to the normal d. f. $\Phi(x)$.

20.3. Convergence in probability. — Let $\xi_1, \xi_2, \ldots$ be a sequence of random variables, and let $F_n(x)$ and $\varphi_n(t)$ denote the d. f. and the c. f. of ξ_n. We shall say (cf Cantelli, Ref. 64, Slutsky, Ref. 214, and Fréchet, Ref. 112) that ξ_n *converges in probability to a constant* c if, for any $\varepsilon > 0$, the probability of the relation $|\xi_n - c| > \varepsilon$ tends to zero as $n \to \infty$.

Thus if ξ_n denotes the frequency ν/n of an event E in a series of n repetitions of a random experiment $\mathfrak{E}$, Bernoulli's theorem 16.3 asserts that ν/n converges in probability to p.

A necessary and sufficient condition for the convergence in probability of ξ_n to c is obviously that the d. f. $F_n(x)$ tends, for every fixed $x \neq c$, to the particular d. f. $\varepsilon(x - c)$ defined in 16.1.

By the continuity theorem 10.4, an equivalent condition is that the c. f. $\varphi_n(t)$ tends for every fixed t to the limit e^{cit}.

20.4. Tchebycheff's theorem. — We shall prove the following theorem, which is substantially due to Tchebycheff.

Let $\xi_1, \xi_2, \ldots$ be random variables, and let m_n and σ_n denote the mean and the s. d. of ξ_n. If $\sigma_n \to 0$ as $n \to \infty$, then $\xi_n - m_n$ converges in probability to zero.

In order to prove this theorem, it is sufficient to apply the Bienaymé-Tchebycheff inequality (15.7.2) to the variable $\xi_n - m_n$. We then see that the probability of the relation $|\xi_n - m_n| > \varepsilon$ is $\leqq \frac{\sigma_n^2}{\varepsilon^2}$, and by hypothesis this tends to zero as $n \to \infty$.

Let us now suppose that the variables $\xi_1, \xi_2, \ldots$ are independent, and write

$$\bar{\xi} = \frac{1}{n}\sum_{1}^{n} \xi_\nu, \quad \bar{m} = \frac{1}{n}\sum_{1}^{n} m_\nu.$$

We then have the following corollary of the theorem: *If*

$$\sum_{1}^{n} \sigma_\nu^2 = o(n^2), \tag{20.4.1}$$

then $\bar{\xi} - \bar{m}$ converges in probability to zero.

The variable $\bar{\xi}$ has, in fact, the mean $\bar{m}$ and the s. d. $\frac{1}{n}\sqrt{\sum_{1}^{n} \sigma_\nu^2}$. By hypothesis, the latter tends to zero as $n \to \infty$, and thus the truth of the assertion follows from the above theorem.

In the particular case when the ξ_ν are the variables considered in 16.6, in connection with a series of independent trials, σ_n is bounded and thus (20.4.1) is satisfied. The corollary then reduces to the Poisson generalization of Bernoulli's theorem.

20.5. Khintchine's theorem. — Even if the existence of finite standard deviations is not assumed for the variables ξ_ν considered in the preceding paragraph, it may still be possible to obtain a result corresponding to the corollary of Tchebycheff's theorem. We shall only consider the case when all the ξ_ν have the same probability distribution, and prove the following theorem due to Khintchine (Ref. 139).

Let $\xi_1, \xi_2, \ldots$ *be independent random variables all having the same d.f.* $F(x)$, *and suppose that* $F(x)$ *has a finite mean* m. *Then the variable* $\bar{\xi} = \frac{1}{n}\sum_1^n \xi_\nu$ *converges in probability to* m.

If $\varphi(t)$ is the c.f. of the common distribution of the ξ_ν, the c.f. of the variable $\bar{\xi}$ is $\left(\varphi\left(\frac{t}{n}\right)\right)^n$ According to (10.1.3), we have for $t \to 0$

$$\varphi(t) = 1 + m\,i\,t + o(t),$$

and thus for any fixed t, as $n \to \infty$,

$$\left(\varphi\left(\frac{t}{n}\right)\right)^n = \left(1 + \frac{m\,i\,t}{n} + o\left(\frac{1}{n}\right)\right)^n \to e^{m\,i\,t}.$$

According to 20.3, this proves the theorem.

20.6. A convergence theorem. — The following theorem will be useful in various applications:

Let $\xi_1, \xi_2, \ldots$ *be a sequence of random variables, with the d.f:s* $F_1, F_2, \ldots$. *Suppose that* $F_n(x)$ *tends to a d.f.* $F(x)$ *as* $n \to \infty$.

Let $\eta_1, \eta_2, \ldots$ *be another sequence of random variables, and suppose that* η_n *converges in probability to a constant* c. *Put*

$$X_n = \xi_n + \eta_n, \quad Y_n = \xi_n \eta_n, \quad Z_n = \frac{\xi_n}{\eta_n}. \tag{20.6.1}$$

Then the d.f. of X_n *tends to* $F(x - c)$. *Further, if* $c > 0$, *the d.f. of* Y_n *tends to* $F\left(\frac{x}{c}\right)$, *while the d.f. of* Z_n *tends to* $F(c\,x)$. *(The modification required when* $c < 0$ *is evident.)*

It is important to observe that, in this theorem, there is *no condition of independence* for any of the variables involved.

It is sufficient to prove one of the assertions of the theorem, as the other proofs are quite similar. Take, e.g., the case of Z_n. Let x be a continuity point of $F(c\,x)$, and denote by P_n the joint probability function of ξ_n and η_n. We then have to prove that

$$P_n\left(\frac{\xi_n}{\eta_n} \leqq x\right) \to F(c\,x)$$

as $n \to \infty$. Now the set S of all points in the (ξ_n, η_n)-plane such that

$\frac{\xi_n}{\eta_n} \leqq x$ is the sum of two sets S_1 and S_2 without common points, defined by the inequalities

$$S_1: \quad \frac{\xi_n}{\eta_n} \leqq x, \quad |\eta_n - c| \leqq \varepsilon,$$

$$S_2: \quad \frac{\xi_n}{\eta_n} \leqq x, \quad |\eta_n - c| > \varepsilon.$$

Thus we have $P_n(S) = P_n(S_1) + P_n(S_2)$. Here S_2 is a subset of the set $|\eta_n - c| > \varepsilon$, and thus by hypothesis $P_n(S_2) \to 0$ for any $\varepsilon > 0$.

Further, $P_n(S_1)$ is enclosed between the limits

$$P_n(\xi_n \leqq (c \pm \varepsilon)x, \quad |\eta_n - c| \leqq \varepsilon).$$

Each of these limits differs from the corresponding quantity

$$P_n(\xi_n \leqq (c \pm \varepsilon)x) = F_n((c \pm \varepsilon)x)$$

by less than $P_n(|\eta_n - c| > \varepsilon)$. As $n \to \infty$, the latter quantity tends to zero, and we thus see that $P_n(S)$ is enclosed between two limits, which can be made to lie as close to $F(cx)$ as we please, by choosing ε sufficiently small. Thus our theorem is proved.

Hence we deduce the following proposition due to Slutsky (Ref. 214): *If $\xi_n, \eta_n, \ldots, \varrho_n$ are random variables converging in probability to the constants $x, y, \ldots, r$ respectively, any rational function $R(\xi_n, \eta_n, \ldots, \varrho_n)$ converges in probability to the constant $R(x, y, \ldots, r)$, provided that the latter is finite. It follows that any power $R^k(\xi_n, \eta_n, \ldots, \varrho_n)$ with $k > 0$ converges in probability to $R^k(x, y, \ldots, r)$.*

Exercises to Chapters 15–20.

1. The variable ξ has the fr. f. $f(x)$. Find the fr. f:s of the variables $\eta = \frac{1}{\xi}$ and $\zeta = \cos \xi$. Give conditions of existence for the moments of η and ζ.

2. For any $k > 1$, the function $f(x) = \frac{k}{2(1 + |x|)^{k+1}}$ is a fr. f. with the range $(-\infty, \infty)$. Show that the n:th moment exists when and only when $n < k$.

3. The inequality (15.4.6) for the absolute moments β_n is a particular case of the following inequality due to Liapounoff (Ref. 147). For any non-negative n, p, q (not necessarily integers), we have

$$\log \beta_{n+p} \leqq \frac{q}{p+q} \log \beta_n + \frac{p}{p+q} \log \beta_{n+p+q}.$$

For $n = 0$, $q = 1$, this reduces to (15.4.6), since $\beta_0 = 1$. The general inequality expresses that a chord joining two points of the curve $y = \log \beta_x$, $(x > 0)$, lies entirely above the curve, so that $\log \beta_x$ is a *convex* function of x. (For a detailed proof, see e. g. Uspensky, Ref. 39, p. 265.)

4. When $g(x)$ is never increasing for $x > 0$, we have for any $k > 0$

$$k^2 \int_k^\infty g(x)\,dx \leqq \tfrac{4}{9} \int_0^\infty x^2 g(x)\,dx.$$

First prove that the inequality is true in the particular case when $g(x)$ is constant for $0 < x < c$, and equal to zero for $x > c$. Then define a function $h(x)$ which is constantly equal to $g(k)$ for $0 < x < k + a$, and equal to zero for $x > k + a$, where a is determined by the condition $a g(k) = \int_k^\infty g(x)\,dx$, and show that

$$k^2 \int_k^\infty g(x)\,dx = k^2 \int_k^\infty h(x)\,dx \leqq \tfrac{4}{9} \int_0^\infty x^2 h(x)\,dx \leqq \tfrac{4}{9} \int_0^\infty x^2 g(x)\,dx.$$

Use this result to prove the inequalities (15.7.3) and (15.7.4).

5. If $F(x)$ is a d. f. with the mean 0 and the s. d. σ, we have $F(x) \leqq \dfrac{\sigma^2}{\sigma^2 + x^2}$ for $x < 0$, and $F(x) \geqq \dfrac{x^2}{\sigma^2 + x^2}$ for $x > 0$. For $x < 0$, this follows from the inequalities

$$-x = \int_{-\infty}^\infty (y - x)\,dF \leqq \int_x^\infty (y - x)\,dF,$$

$$x^2 \leqq \Bigl(\int_x^\infty (y - x)\,dF\Bigr)^2 \leqq \int_x^\infty dF \cdot \int_x^\infty (y - x)^2\,dF \leqq (1 - F(x))(\sigma^2 + x^2).$$

For $x > 0$, the proof is similar. Show by an example that these inequalities cannot be improved.

6. The Bienaymé-Tchebycheff inequality (15.7.2) may be improved, if some central moment μ_{2n} with $n > 1$ is known. We have, e. g., for $k > 1$

$$P(|\xi - m| \geqq k\sigma) \leqq \frac{\mu_4 - \sigma^4}{\mu_4 + k^4\sigma^4 - 2k^2\sigma^4} = \frac{\gamma_2 + 2}{(k^2 - 1)^2 + \gamma_2 + 2}.$$

Apply (15.7.1) with $K = 1$ and $g(\xi) = 1 + \dfrac{\sigma^2 (k^2 - 1)((\xi - m)^2 - k^2\sigma^2)}{\mu_4 + k^4\sigma^4 - 2k^2\sigma^4}$.

7. Use (15.4.6) to show that the semi-invariant $\varkappa_n$ of an arbitrary distribution satisfies the inequality $|\varkappa_n| \leqq n^n \beta_n$. (Cramér, Ref. 11, p. 27.)

8. Prove the inequality $|a + b|^n \leqq 2^{n-1}(|a|^n + |b|^n)$. Hence deduce that, if the n:th moments of x and y exist, so does the n:th moment of $x + y$.

9. Writing $G(p, q) = \sum_{r > np} \binom{n}{r} p^r q^{n-r}$, show that the first absolute moment about the mean of the binomial distribution is

$$E(|\nu - np|) = 2pq\left(\frac{\partial G}{\partial p} - \frac{\partial G}{\partial q}\right) = 2\mu \binom{n}{\mu} p^{\mu} q^{n-\mu+1},$$

where μ is the smallest integer $> np$. For large n, it follows that

$$E(|\nu - np|) \infty \sqrt{\frac{2npq}{\pi}}.$$

10. Show that if $1 - F(x) = O(e^{-cx})$ as $x \to +\infty$, and $F(x) = O(e^{-c|x|})$ as $x \to -\infty$ $(c > 0)$, the distribution is uniquely determined by its moments.

11. The *factorial moments* (Steffensen, Ref. 217) of a discrete distribution are $\alpha_{[\nu]} = \sum_r p_r x_r^{[\nu]}$, where $x^{[\nu]}$ denotes the factorial $x(x-1)\ldots(x-\nu+1)$. Similarly the *central* factorial moments are $\mu_{[\nu]} = \sum_r p_r (x_r - m)^{[\nu]}$. Express $\alpha_{[\nu]}$ and $\mu_{[\nu]}$ by means of the ordinary moments. Show that $(x+y)^{[\nu]} = x^{[\nu]} + \binom{\nu}{1} x^{[\nu-1]} y^{[1]} + \cdots + y^{[\nu]}$, and hence deduce relations between $\alpha_{[\nu]}$ and $\mu_{[\nu]}$.

12. The c. f. of the distribution in the preceding exercise is $\varphi(t) = \sum_r p_r e^{itx_r}$. Substituting here t for e^{it}, we obtain the *generating function* $\psi(t) = \sum_r p_r t^{x_r}$. Show that $\psi^{(\nu)}(1) = \alpha_{[\nu]}$, and in particular $E(x) = \psi'(1)$, $D^2(x) = \psi''(1) + \psi'(1) - (\psi'(1))^2$. Use this result to deduce the expressions $\alpha_{[\nu]} = n^{[\nu]} p^{\nu}$ for the binomial distribution, and $\alpha_{[\nu]} = \lambda^{\nu}$ for the Poisson distribution.

13. a) We make a series of independent trials, the probability of a »success» being in each trial equal to $p = 1 - q$, and we go on until we have had an uninterrupted set of ν successes, where $\nu > 0$ is given. Let $p_{n\nu}$ denote the probability that exactly n trials will be required for this purpose. Find the generating function

$$\psi(t) = \sum_{n=1}^{\infty} p_{n\nu} t^n = \frac{p^{\nu} t^{\nu}(1 - pt)}{1 - t + p^{\nu} q t^{\nu+1}},$$

and show that $E(n) = \psi'(1) = \dfrac{1 - p^{\nu}}{p^{\nu} q}$.

b) On the other hand, let us make n trials, where n is given, and observe the length μ of the *longest uninterrupted set of successes* occurring in the course of these n trials. Denoting by $P_{n\nu}$ the probability that $\mu < \nu$, show that

$$P_{n\nu} = 1 - p_{1\nu} - \cdots - p_{n\nu},$$

and thus

$$\Psi(t) = \sum_{n=1}^{\infty} P_{n\nu} t^n = \frac{1 - \psi(t)}{1 - t} = \frac{1 - p^{\nu} t^{\nu}}{1 - t + p^{\nu} q t^{\nu+1}}.$$

Hence it can be shown (Cramér, Ref. 68) that $P_{n\nu} - e^{-np^\nu q}$ tends to zero as $n \to \infty$, uniformly for $1 \leqq \nu \leqq n$. It follows that for large n we have

$$\boldsymbol{E}(\mu) = \frac{\log n}{\log \frac{1}{p}} + O(1), \quad \boldsymbol{D}^2(\mu) = O(1).$$

14. The variable ξ is normal (m, σ). Show that the mean deviation is

$$\boldsymbol{E}(|\xi - m|) = \sigma \sqrt{\frac{2}{\pi}} = 0.79788\,\sigma.$$

15. In both cases of the Central Limit Theorem proved in 17.4, we have $\boldsymbol{E}\left|\frac{\xi - m}{\sigma}\right| \to \sqrt{\frac{2}{\pi}}$ as $n \to \infty$. — Use (7.5.9) and (9.5.1). (Cf Ex. 9.)

16. Let $\xi_1, \xi_2, \ldots$ be independent variables, such that ξ_ν has the possible values 0 and $\pm \nu^\alpha$, the respective probabilities being $1 - \nu^{-2\alpha}$, $\frac{1}{2}\nu^{-2\alpha}$, and $\frac{1}{2}\nu^{-2\alpha}$. Thus ξ_ν has the mean 0 and the s. d. 1. Show that the Liapounoff condition (17.4.3) is satisfied for $\alpha < \frac{1}{2}$, but not for $\alpha \geqq \frac{1}{2}$. Thus for $\alpha < \frac{1}{2}$ the sum $\xi = \sum_1^n \xi_\nu$ is asymptotically normal $(0, \sqrt{n})$. For $\alpha > \frac{1}{2}$, the probability that $\xi_1 = \cdots = \xi_n = 0$ does not tend to zero as $n \to \infty$, so that in this case the distribution of ξ does not tend to normality. The last result holds also for $\alpha = \frac{1}{2}$; cf Cramér, Ref. 11, p. 62.

17. If α_1 and α_2 are the two first moments of the logarithmico-normal distribution (17.5.3), and if η is the real root of the equation $\eta^3 + 3\eta - \gamma_1 = 0$, where γ_1 is the coefficient of skewness, the parameters a, m and σ of the distribution are given by

$$a = \alpha_1 - \frac{\sqrt{\alpha_2 - \alpha_1^2}}{\eta}, \quad \sigma^2 = \log(1 + \eta^2),$$

$$m = \log(\alpha_1 - a) - \tfrac{1}{2}\sigma^2.$$

18. Consider the expansion (17.6.3) of a fr. f. $f(x)$ in Gram-Charlier series, and take $f(x) = \frac{1}{\sigma\sqrt{2\pi}} e^{-\frac{x^2}{2\sigma^2}}$. For $x = 0$, we have $f(0) = \frac{1}{\sigma\sqrt{2\pi}}$, and the expansion becomes

$$\frac{1}{\sigma\sqrt{2\pi}} = \frac{1}{\sqrt{2\pi}} \sum_0^\infty \frac{(2\nu)!}{2^{2\nu}(\nu!)^2}(1 - \sigma^2)^\nu.$$

This is, however, only correct if $\sigma^2 \leqq 2$. For $\sigma^2 > 2$, the series is divergent. Find α and β such that $\alpha f(x) + \beta f(\sigma^2 x)$ is the fr. f. of a standardized variable, and show by means of this example that the coefficient $\frac{1}{4}$ in the convergence condition (17.6.6 a) cannot be replaced by any smaller number.

19. Calculate the coefficients γ_1 and γ_2 for the various distributions treated in Ch. 18.

20. If the variable η is uniformly distributed over $(a-h, a+h)$, the c. f. of η is $\frac{\sin ht}{ht} e^{ait}$. If ξ is an arbitrary variable independent of η, with the c. f. $\varphi(t)$, the sum $\xi + \eta$ has the c. f. $\frac{\sin ht}{ht} e^{ait} \varphi(t)$. Show that, by the aid of this result, the formula (10.3.3) may be directly deduced from (10.3.1).

21. Let n be a random variable having a Poisson distribution with the probabilities $\frac{x^\nu}{\nu!} e^{-x}$, where $\nu = 0, 1, \ldots$. If we consider here the parameter x as a random variable with the fr. f. $\frac{\alpha^\lambda}{\Gamma(\lambda)} x^{\lambda-1} e^{-\alpha x}$, $(x > 0)$, the probability that n takes any given value ν is

$$\int_0^\infty \frac{x^\nu}{\nu!} e^{-x} \cdot \frac{\alpha^\lambda}{\Gamma(\lambda)} x^{\lambda-1} e^{-\alpha x}\, dx = \left(\frac{\alpha}{1+\alpha}\right)^\lambda \cdot \binom{-\lambda}{\nu} \frac{(-1)^\nu}{(1+\alpha)^\nu}.$$

Find the c. f., the mean and the s. d. of this distribution, which is known as the *negative binomial distribution.*

22. $x_1, x_2, \ldots$ are independent variables having the same distribution with the mean 0 and the s. d. 1. Use the theorems 20.5 and 20.6 to show that the variables $y = \sqrt{n}\, \frac{x_1 + \cdots + x_n}{x_1^2 + \cdots + x_n^2}$ and $z = \frac{x_1 + \cdots + x_n}{\sqrt{x_1^2 + \cdots + x_n^2}}$ are both asymptotically normal (0, 1).

23. If x_n and y_n are asymptotically normal $(a, h/\sqrt{n})$ and $(b, k/\sqrt{n})$ respectively, where $b \neq 0$, then the variable $z_n = \sqrt{n}\,(x_n - a)/y_n$ is asymptotically normal $(0, h/b)$. — Note that there is no condition of independence in this case.

CHAPTER 21.

THE TWO-DIMENSIONAL CASE.

21.1. Two simple types of distributions. — Consider two one-dimensional random variables ξ and η. The joint probability distribution (cf 14.2) of ξ and η is a distribution in R_2, or a two-dimensional distribution. This case will be treated in the present chapter, before we proceed to the general case of variables and distributions in n dimensions.

According to 8.4, we are at liberty to define the joint distribution of ξ and η by the *probability function* $P(S)$, which represents the probability of the relation $(\xi, \eta) < S$, or by the *distribution function* $F(x, y)$ given by the relation

$$F(x, y) = P(\xi \leqq x, \eta \leqq y).$$

We shall often interpret the probability distribution by means of a distribution of a unit of mass over the (ξ, η)-plane. By projecting the mass in the two-dimensional distribution on one of the coordinate axes, we obtain (cf 8.4) the *marginal distribution* of the corresponding variable. Denoting by $F_1(x)$ the d. f. of the marginal distribution of ξ, and by $F_2(y)$ the corresponding function for η, we have

$$F_1(x) = P(\xi \leqq x) = F(x, \infty),$$
$$F_2(y) = P(\eta \leqq y) = F(\infty, y).$$

As in the one-dimensional case (cf 15.2), it will be convenient to introduce here two simple types of distributions: the *discrete* and the *continuous* type.

1. *The discrete type.* A two-dimensional distribution will be said to belong to the discrete type, if the corresponding marginal distributions both belong to the discrete type as defined in 15.2. In each

marginal distribution, the total mass is then concentrated in certain discrete mass points, of which at most a finite number are contained in any finite interval. Denote by $x_1, x_2, \ldots$ and by $y_1, y_2, \ldots$ the discrete mass points in the marginal distributions of ξ and η respectively. The total mass in the two-dimensional distribution will then be concentrated in the points of intersection of the straight lines $\xi = x_i$ and $\eta = y_k$, i. e. in the points (x_i, y_k), where i and k independently assume the values 1, 2, 3, ... If the mass situated in the point (x_i, y_k) is denoted by p_{ik}, we have

$$P(\xi = x_i, \eta = y_k) = p_{ik}, \tag{21.1.1}$$

while for every set S not containing any point (x_i, y_k) we have $P(S) = 0$. Since the total mass in the distribution must be unity, we always have

$$\sum_{i,k} p_{ik} = 1.$$

For certain combinations of indices i, k we may, of course, have $p_{ik} = 0$. The points (x_i, y_k) for which $p_{ik} > 0$ are the discrete mass points of the distribution.

Consider now the marginal distribution of ξ, the discrete mass points of which are $x_1, x_2, \ldots$ If $p_{i.}$ denotes the mass situated in the point x_i, we obviously have

$$p_{i.} = P(\xi = x_i) = \sum_k p_{ik}. \tag{21.1.2}$$

Similarly, in the marginal distribution of η, the point y_k carries the mass $p_{.k}$ given by

$$p_{.k} = P(\eta = y_k) = \sum_i p_{ik}. \tag{21.1.3}$$

By (15.11.2), a necessary and sufficient condition for the independence of the variables ξ and η is that we have for all i and k

$$p_{ik} = p_{i.}\, p_{.k}. \tag{21.1.4}$$

2. *The continuous type.* A two-dimensional distribution will be said to belong to the continuous type, if the d. f. $F(x, y)$ is everywhere continuous, and if the fr. f. (cf 8.4)

$$f(x, y) = \frac{\partial^2 F}{\partial x\, \partial y}$$

exists and is continuous everywhere, except possibly in certain points belonging to a finite number of curves. For any set S we then have

$$P(S) = \int_S f(x, y)\, dx\, dy,$$

and thus in particular for $S = \boldsymbol{R}_2$

$$\int_{-\infty}^{\infty} \int_{-\infty}^{\infty} f(x, y)\, dx\, dy = 1.$$

The marginal distribution of the variable ξ has the d. f.

$$P(\xi \leqq x) = \int_{-\infty}^{x} \int_{-\infty}^{\infty} f(t, u)\, dt\, du = \int_{-\infty}^{x} f_1(t)\, dt,$$

where

$$f_1(x) = \int_{-\infty}^{\infty} f(x, y)\, dy. \tag{21.1.5}$$

If, at a certain point $x = x_0$, the function $f(x, y)$ is continuous with respect to x for *almost all* (cf 5.3) values of y and if, in some neighbourhood of x_0, we have $f(x, y) < G(y)$, where $G(y)$ is integrable over $(-\infty, \infty)$, then it follows from (7.3.1) that $f_1(x)$ is continuous at $x = x_0$. In all cases that will occur in the applications, these conditions are satisfied for all x_0, except at most for a finite number of points. In such a case $f_1(x)$ has at most a finite number of discontinuities, so that the marginal distribution of ξ is of the continuous type and has the fr. f. $f_1(x)$. Similarly, we find that the marginal distribution of η has the fr. f.

$$f_2(y) = \int_{-\infty}^{\infty} f(x, y)\, dx. \tag{21.1.6}$$

By (15.11.3), a necessary and sufficient condition for the independence of the variables ξ and η is that we have for all x and y

$$f(x, y) = f_1(x) f_2(y). \tag{21.1.7}$$

21.2. Mean values, moments. — The mean value of a function $g(\xi, \eta)$ integrable over $\boldsymbol{R}_2$ with respect to the two-dimensional pr. f. $P(S)$ has been defined in (15.3.2) by the integral

$$\boldsymbol{E}(g(\xi, \eta)) = \int_{\boldsymbol{R}_2} g(x, y)\, dP(S). \tag{21.2.1}$$

For a distribution belonging to one of the two simple types, this reduces to a sum or an ordinary Lebesgue integral, as indicated in 15.3 for the one-dimensional case. The fundamental rules of calculation for mean values have already been deduced in 15.3 for any number of dimensions.

The *moments* of the distribution (cf 9.2) are the mean values

$$\alpha_{ik} = \boldsymbol{E}(\xi^i \eta^k) = \int_{\boldsymbol{R}_2} x^i y^k \, d P(S), \tag{21.2.2}$$

where i and k are non-negative integers. The sum $i + k$ of the indices is the *order* of the moment α_{ik}.

The moments $\alpha_{i0} = \boldsymbol{E}(\xi^i)$ and $\alpha_{0k} = \boldsymbol{E}(\eta^k)$ are identical with the moments of the one-dimensional marginal distributions of ξ and η respectively, as shown by the integral relation (9.2.2). In particular, we put

$$\alpha_{10} = \boldsymbol{E}(\xi) = m_1, \quad \alpha_{01} = \boldsymbol{E}(\eta) = m_2.$$

The point with the coordinates $\xi = m_1$, $\eta = m_2$ is the *centre of gravity* of the mass of the two-dimensional distribution. For the moments about the centre of gravity we shall use a particular notation, writing in generalization of (15.4.3)

$$\mu_{ik} = \boldsymbol{E}((\xi - m_1)^i (\eta - m_2)^k). \tag{21.2.3}$$

Thus in particular we have $\mu_{10} = \mu_{01} = 0$ and $\mu_{20} = \sigma_1^2$, $\mu_{02} = \sigma_2^2$, where σ_1 and σ_2 are the standard deviations of ξ and η.

Between the moments α_{ik} and the *central moments* μ_{ik} we have relations analogous to those given in 15.4 for the one-dimensional case. Thus for the second order moments we have

$$\mu_{20} = \alpha_{20} - m_1^2, \quad \mu_{11} = \alpha_{11} - m_1 m_2, \quad \mu_{02} = \alpha_{02} - m_2^2. \tag{21.2.4}$$

μ_{11} is often called the second order *product moment* or *mixed moment.* Further, while μ_{20} and μ_{02} are the *variances* of ξ and η, the product moment μ_{11} is also called the *covariance* of ξ and η.

In the particular case when the variables ξ and η are independent, we have by the multiplication theorem (15.3.4) $\alpha_{ik} = \alpha_{i0}\,\alpha_{0k}$ and $\mu_{ik} = \mu_{i0}\,\mu_{0k}$. Thus in particular we have in this case $\mu_{11} = \mu_{10}\,\mu_{01} = 0$.

For any real t and u we have

$$\boldsymbol{E}[(t(\xi - m_1) + u(\eta - m_2))^2] = \mu_{20} t^2 + 2\mu_{11} t u + \mu_{02} u^2. \tag{21.2.5}$$

The first member of this identity is the mean value of a square, and is thus non-negative. It follows that the second member is a non-negative quadratic form (cf 11.10) in t and u, so that the *moment matrix* $\boldsymbol{M} = \begin{Bmatrix} \mu_{20} & \mu_{11} \\ \mu_{11} & \mu_{02} \end{Bmatrix}$ is non-negative, and we have

$$\mu_{20}\,\mu_{02} - \mu_{11}^2 \geqq 0. \tag{21.2.6}$$

The rank r of $\boldsymbol{M}$ may (cf 11.6) have one of the values 0, 1 and 2. When $r = 2$, we have the sign $>$ in (21.2.6), while the sign $=$ holds for $r = 1$ and $r = 0$. We shall now show that certain simple properties of the distribution are directly connected with the value of r.

We have $r = 0$ when and only when the total mass of the distribution is situated in a single point.

We have $r = 1$ when and only when the total mass of the distribution is situated on a certain straight line, but not in a single point.

We have $r = 2$ when and only when there is no straight line that contains the total mass of the distribution.

It is obviously sufficient to prove the cases $r = 0$ and $r = 1$, as the case $r = 2$ then follows as a corollary. — When $r = 0$, we have $\mu_{20} = \mu_{02} = 0$, so that the marginal distribution of each variable has its total mass concentrated in one single point (cf 16.1). In the two-dimensional distribution, the whole mass must then be concentrated in the centre of gravity (m_1, m_2). Conversely, if we know that the whole mass of the distribution belongs to one single point, it follows immediately that $\mu_{20} = \mu_{02} = 0$, and hence by (21.2.6) $\mu_{11} = 0$, so that $\boldsymbol{M}$ is of rank zero.

Further, when $r = 1$, the form (21.2.5) is semi-definite (cf 11.10), an thus takes the value zero for some $t = t_0$ and $u = u_0$ not both equal to zero. This is only possible if the whole mass of the distribution is situated on the straight line

$$t_0(\xi - m_1) + u_0(\eta - m_2) = 0. \tag{21.2.7}$$

Conversely, if it is known that the total mass of the distribution is situated on a straight line, but not in a single point, it is evident that the line must pass through the centre of gravity, and thus have an equation of the form (21.2.7). The mean value in the first member of (21.2.5) then reduces to zero for $t = t_0$, $u = u_0$, so that the quadratic form in the second member is semi-definite, and it follows that $\boldsymbol{M}$ is of rank one. Thus our theorem is proved.

Let us now suppose that we have a distribution such that both variances μ_{20} and μ_{02} are positive. (This means i. a. that $\boldsymbol{M}$ is of rank 1 or 2.) We may then define a quantity ϱ by writing

$$\varrho = \frac{\mu_{11}}{\sqrt{\mu_{20}\,\mu_{02}}} = \frac{\mu_{11}}{\sigma_1\,\sigma_2}. \tag{21.2.8}$$

By (21.2.6) we then have $\varrho^2 \leqq 1$, or $-1 \leqq \varrho \leqq 1$. Further, the case $\varrho^2 = 1$ occurs when and only when $\boldsymbol{M}$ is of rank 1, i. e. when the whole mass of the distribution is situated on a straight line. — In the particular case when the variables ξ and η are independent, we have $\mu_{11} = 0$ and thus $\varrho = 0$.

The quantity ϱ is the *correlation coefficient* of the variables ξ and η; this will be further dealt with in 21.7.

Suppose that we are given any quantities m_1, m_2, and any μ_{20}, μ_{11}, μ_{02} subject to the restriction that the quadratic form $\mu_{20}\,t^2 + 2\,\mu_{11}\,t\,u + \mu_{02}\,u^2$ is non-negative. We can then always find a distribution having m_1, m_2 for its first order moments and μ_{20}, μ_{11}, μ_{02} for its second order central moments. The required conditions are, e. g., satisfied by the discrete distribution obtained by placing the mass $\frac{1+\varrho}{4}$ in each of the two points $(m_1 + \sigma_1,\ m_2 + \sigma_2)$ and $(m_1 - \sigma_1,\ m_2 - \sigma_2)$, and the mass $\frac{1-\varrho}{4}$ in each of the two points $(m_1 + \sigma_1,\ m_2 - \sigma_2)$ and $(m_1 - \sigma_1,\ m_2 + \sigma_2)$. The quantities σ_1, σ_2 and ϱ are here, of course, defined according to the above expressions.

21.3. Characteristic functions. — The mean value

$$\varphi(t, u) = \boldsymbol{E}\left(e^{i(t\xi + u\eta)}\right) = \int_{R_2} e^{i(tx + uy)}\,dP \tag{21.3.1}$$

is the *characteristic function* (c. f.) of the two-dimensional random variable (ξ, η), or of the corresponding distribution. We shall also often call $\varphi(t, u)$ the *joint c. f.* of the two one-dimensional variables ξ and η.

According to the theory of c. f:s given in Ch. 10, the one-to-one correspondence between one-dimensional distributions and their c. f:s (cf 15.9) extends itself to distributions in any number of dimensions. If two distributions are identical, so are their c. f:s, and conversely.

If the second order moments of the joint distribution of ξ and η are finite, we have in the neighbourhood of the point $t = u = 0$ the development analogous to (10.1.3)

$$(21.3.2) \quad \varphi(t, u) = 1 + \frac{i}{1!}(\alpha_{10}\, t + \alpha_{01}\, u) + \frac{i^2}{2!}(\alpha_{20}\, t^2 + 2\, \alpha_{11}\, t\, u + \alpha_{02}\, u^2) +$$

$$+ o(t^2 + u^2) = e^{i(m_1 t + m_2 u)} \left[1 + \frac{i^2}{2!}(\mu_{20}\, t + 2\, \mu_{11}\, t u + \mu_{02}\, u^2) + o(t^2 + u^2) \right].$$

In the particularly important case when the mean values m_1 and m_2 are both equal to zero, we thus have

$$(21.3.3) \qquad \varphi(t, u) = 1 - \tfrac{1}{2}(\mu_{20}\, t^2 + 2\, \mu_{11}\, t u + \mu_{02}\, u^2) + o(t^2 + u^2).$$

The c. f:s of the marginal distributions of ξ and η are

$$(21.3.4) \qquad \boldsymbol{E}(e^{it\xi}) = \varphi(t, 0), \text{ and } \boldsymbol{E}(e^{iu\eta}) = \varphi(0, u).$$

If the variables ξ and η are independent, we have

$$\varphi(t, u) = \boldsymbol{E}(e^{it\xi} \cdot e^{iu\eta}) = \boldsymbol{E}(e^{it\xi}) \cdot \boldsymbol{E}(e^{iu\eta}),$$

so that the joint c. f. $\varphi(t, u)$ is the product of the c. f:s of the marginal distributions corresponding to ξ and η respectively.

Conversely, suppose that it is known that the joint c. f. of ξ and η is of the form $\varphi_1(t) \cdot \varphi_2(u)$. Introducing, if necessary, a multiplicative constant into the factors, we may obviously assume $\varphi_1(0) = \varphi_2(0) = 1$, and then it follows from (21.3.4) that $\varphi_1(t)$ and $\varphi_2(u)$ are the c. f:s of ξ and η respectively. If the two-dimensional interval defined by $a_1 < \xi < b_1$, $a_2 < \eta < b_2$ is a continuity interval (cf 8.3) of the joint distribution of ξ and η, it further follows from the inversion formulae (10.3.1) and (10.6.2) that we have the multiplicative relation

$$P(a_1 < \xi < b_1,\ a_2 < \eta < b_2) = P(a_1 < \xi < b_1) \cdot P(a_2 < \eta < b_2).$$

Allowing here a_1 and a_2 to tend to $-\infty$, we obtain in particular, using the same notations as in 21.1, $F(x, y) = F_1(x) F_2(y)$ for all x and y that are continuity points of F_1 and F_2 respectively. By the general continuity properties of d. f:s, this relation is immediately extended to all x and y. From (14.4.5) it then follows that the variables ξ and η are independent, and we have thus proved the following theorem:

A necessary and sufficient condition for the independence of two one-dimensional random variables is that their joint c. f. is of the form

$$(21.3.5) \qquad \varphi(t, u) = \varphi_1(t)\, \varphi_2(u).$$

21.4. Conditional distributions. — The conditional distribution of a random variable η, relative to the hypothesis that another variable ξ belongs to some given set S, has been defined in 14.3. In the present paragraph, we shall consider this question somewhat more closely for distributions of the two simple types introduced in 21.1.

1. *The discrete type.* Consider the discrete distribution defined by (21.1.1), and let x_i be a value such that the marginal probability $P(\xi = x_i) = \sum_k p_{ik} = p_{i.}$ is positive. The *conditional probability* of the event $\eta = y_k$, relative to the hypothesis $\xi = x_i$, is then by (14.3.1)

$$P(\eta = y_k \mid \xi = x_i) = \frac{P(\xi = x_i,\ \eta = y_k)}{P(\xi = x_i)} = \frac{p_{ik}}{p_{i.}}. \tag{21.4.1}$$

For a fixed x_i, the conditional probabilities of the various possible values of y_k define the *conditional distribution* of η, relative to the hypothesis $\xi = x_i$. The sum of all these conditional probabilities is, of course, equal to 1.

If the (ξ, η)-distribution is interpreted in the usual way as a distribution of a unit of mass over the points (x_i, y_k), the conditional distribution is obtained by choosing a fixed x_i and multiplying each mass situated on the vertical through the point $\xi = x_i$ by the factor $1/p_{i.}$, so as to make the sum of all the multiplied masses equal to unity.

The *conditional mean value* of a function $g(\xi, \eta)$, relative to the hypothesis $\xi = x_i$, is defined as the mean value of $g(x_i, \eta)$ with respect to the conditional distribution of η defined by (21.4.1):

$$\boldsymbol{E}(g(\xi, \eta) \mid \xi = x_i) = \frac{\sum_k p_{ik}\, g(x_i, y_k)}{\sum_k p_{ik}}. \tag{21.4.2}$$

For $g(\xi, \eta) = \eta$, we obtain the *conditional mean* of η, which is the ordinate of the centre of gravity of the mass situated on the vertical $\xi = x_i$:

$$\boldsymbol{E}(\eta \mid \xi = x_i) = m_2^{(i)} = \frac{\sum_k p_{ik}\, y_k}{\sum_k p_{ik}}. \tag{21.4.3}$$

On the other hand, taking $g(\xi, \eta) = (\eta - m_2^{(i)})^2$, we obtain the *conditional variance* of η.

The conditional distribution of ξ, relative to the hypothesis $\eta = y_k$, and the corresponding conditional mean values, are defined by permutation of the variables in the expressions given above.

In the particular case when ξ and η are independent, (21.1.4) shows that we have $p_{ik} = p_{i.}p_{.k}$, and this gives us

$$(21.4.4) \qquad \begin{aligned} P(\xi = x_i \mid \eta = y_k) &= p_{i.} = P(\xi = x_i), \\ P(\eta = y_k \mid \xi = x_i) &= p_{.k} = P(\eta = y_k), \end{aligned}$$

in accordance with the general relations (14.4.2) and (14.4.3).

2. *The continuous type.* Let $f(x, y)$ be the joint fr. f. of the variables ξ and η. Consider an interval $(x, x+h)$ such that the mass situated in the vertical strip $x < \xi < x + h$, which represents the probability

$$P(x < \xi < x + h) = \int_x^{x+h} \int_{-\infty}^{\infty} f(x, y)\, dx\, dy,$$

is positive. The conditional probability of the event $\eta \leqq y$, relative to the hypothesis $x < \xi < x + h$, is then by (14.3.1)

$$P(\eta \leqq y \mid x < \xi < x + h) = \frac{P(x < \xi < x + h,\ \eta \leqq y)}{P(x < \xi < x + h)} = \frac{\int_x^{x+h} \int_{-\infty}^{y} f(x, y)\, dx\, dy}{\int_x^{x+h} \int_{-\infty}^{\infty} f(x, y)\, dx\, dy}.$$

This is the d. f. corresponding to the conditional distribution of η, relative to the hypothesis $x < \xi < x + h$. It is simply equal to the quantity of mass situated in the strip $x < \xi < x + h$ and below the line $\eta = y$, divided by the total mass in the strip. Let now h tend to zero. If the continuity conditions stated in connection with (21.1.5) are satisfied at the point x, and if the marginal fr. f. $f_1(x)$ takes a positive value at the point x, it follows from (5.1.4) that the conditional d. f. tends to the limit

$$(21.4.5) \qquad \lim_{h \to 0} P(\eta \leqq y \mid x < \xi < x + h) = \frac{\int_{-\infty}^{y} f(x, \eta)\, d\eta}{\int_{-\infty}^{\infty} f(x, \eta)\, d\eta} = \frac{\int_{-\infty}^{y} f(x, \eta)\, d\eta}{f_1(x)}.$$

For fixed x, the limit is evidently a d. f. in y, and this will be called the *conditional d.f. of η, relative to the hypothesis $\xi = x$.*

If $f(x, y)$ is continuous in y, the conditional d. f. may be differentiated with respect to y, and we obtain the corresponding *conditional fr.f.* of η:

$$f(y \mid x) = \frac{f(x, y)}{\int\limits_{-\infty}^{\infty} f(x, \eta)\, d\eta} = \frac{f(x, y)}{f_1(x)}. \tag{21.4.6}$$

The *conditional mean value* of a function $g(\xi, \eta)$, relative to the hypothesis $\xi = x$, is in this case

$$\mathbf{E}\,[g(\xi, \eta) \mid \xi = x] = \int\limits_{-\infty}^{\infty} g(x, y) f(y \mid x)\, dy = \frac{\int\limits_{-\infty}^{\infty} g(x, y) f(x, y)\, dy}{f_1(x)}.$$

Multiplying by $f_1(x)$ and integrating with respect to x, we obtain

$$\mathbf{E}\,g(\xi, \eta) = \int\limits_{-\infty}^{\infty}\int\limits_{-\infty}^{\infty} g(x, y) f(x, y)\, dx\, dy = \int\limits_{-\infty}^{\infty} \mathbf{E}\,[g(\xi, \eta) \mid \xi = x] f_1(x)\, dx. \tag{21.4.7}$$

The conditional mean and the conditional variance of η are

$$\mathbf{E}\,(\eta \mid \xi = x) = m_2(x) = \frac{\int\limits_{-\infty}^{\infty} y\, f(x, y)\, dy}{\int\limits_{-\infty}^{\infty} f(x, y)\, dy}, \tag{21.4.8}$$

$$\mathbf{D}^2\,(\eta \mid \xi = x) = \frac{\int\limits_{-\infty}^{\infty} (y - m_2(x))^2 f(x, y)\, dy}{\int\limits_{-\infty}^{\infty} f(x, y)\, dy}. \tag{21.4.9}$$

The point with the coordinates $\xi = x$, $\eta = m_2(x)$ is the limit, for $h \to 0$, of the centre of gravity of the mass in the strip $x < \xi < x + h$.

The conditional distribution of ξ for a given value of η, and the corresponding conditional mean values, are defined in a similar way. Thus e. g. the conditional fr. f. of ξ, relative to the hypothesis $\eta = y$, is

$$f(x \mid y) = \frac{f(x, y)}{\int\limits_{-\infty}^{\infty} f(\xi, y)\, d\xi} = \frac{f(x, y)}{f_2(y)} = \frac{f_1(x) f(y \mid x)}{f_2(y)}, \tag{21.4.10}$$

while the conditional mean $\mathbf{E}(\xi \mid \eta = y) = m_1(y)$ is the mean of ξ corresponding to the fr. f. $f(x \mid y)$.

If ξ and η are independent, we have $f(x, y) = f_1(x) f_2(y)$. It follows that in this case the conditional fr. f. of either variable is independent of the hypothesis made with respect to the other variable, and is identical with the fr. f. of the corresponding marginal distribution. Accordingly the conditional mean values for both variables agree with the mean values in the marginal distributions:

$$m_1(y) = m_1, \quad m_2(x) = m_2. \tag{21.4.11}$$

21.5. Regression, I. — Let ξ and η be random variables with a joint distribution of the continuous type, and suppose that the corresponding fr. f. $f(x, y)$ satisfies the continuity conditions stated in connection with (21.1.5) for every x such that the marginal fr. f. $f_1(x)$ is positive.

According to the preceding paragraph, the conditional fr. f. $f(y \mid x)$ given by (21.4.6) then represents the distribution of mass in an infinitely narrow vertical strip through the point $\xi = x$. We may here think of ξ as an *independent* variable; to a fixed value $\xi = x$ then corresponds a probability distribution of the *dependent* variable η, with the fr. f. $f(y \mid x)$.

Consider now some typical value of this conditional η-distribution, such as the mean, the mode, the median etc. Generally this value will depend on x, and may thus be denoted by y_x. As x varies, the point (x, y_x) will describe a certain curve. From the shape of this curve we obtain information with respect to the location of the conditional η-distribution for various values of ξ. (Cf fig. 22 a.)

A curve of this type will be called a *regression curve*, and will be said to represent the *regression of* η *on* ξ. In the sequel we shall always, unless explicitly stated otherwise, choose for y_x the conditional mean $m_2(x)$ of the variable η, as given by (21.4.8), and so obtain the *regression curve for the mean* of η as the locus of the point $(x, m_2(x))$ when x varies:

$$y = m_2(x) = \mathbf{E}(\eta \mid \xi = x). \tag{21.5.1}$$

If, instead of ξ, we consider η as our independent variable, the conditional fr. f. of the dependent variable ξ for a fixed value $\eta = y$ is given by (21.4.10). Any typical value x_y of the conditional distribution of ξ gives rise to a regression curve representing the *regression*

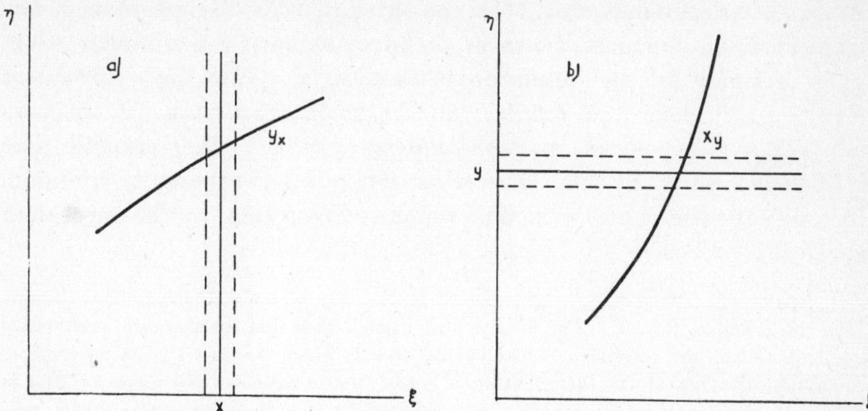

Fig. 22. a) Regression of η on ξ. b) Regression of ξ on η.

of ξ *on* η. (Cf fig. 22 b.) Thus the regression curve for the mean of ξ is the locus of the point $(m_1(y), y)$ when y varies, and has the equation

(21.5.2) $$x = m_1(y) = \boldsymbol{E}(\xi \mid \eta = y).$$

The two regression curves (21.5.1) and (21.5.2) will in general not coincide. In many important cases occurring in the applications, both regression curves are straight or at least approximately straight lines. Thus e. g. in the particular case when ξ and η are independent, it follows from (21.4.11) that the regression curves are straight lines parallel to the axes and passing through the centre of gravity (m_1, m_2). — When a regression curve is a straight line, we shall say that we are concerned with a case of *linear regression.*

The regression curves (21.5.1) and (21.5.2) possess an important minimum property. — Let us try to find, among all possible functions $g(\xi)$ of the single variable ξ, the particular function that gives the *best possible representation* or *estimation* of the other variable η. Interpreting the expression »best possible» in the sense of the least squares principle (cf 15.6), we then have to determine $g(\xi)$ so as to render the expression (cf 21.4.7)

(21.5.3)
$$\begin{aligned} \boldsymbol{E}[\eta - g(\xi)]^2 &= \int_{-\infty}^{\infty}\int_{-\infty}^{\infty} [y - g(x)]^2 f(x, y)\,dx\,dy \\ &= \int_{-\infty}^{\infty} f_1(x)\,dx \int_{-\infty}^{\infty} [y - g(x)]^2 f(y \mid x)\,dy \end{aligned}$$

as small as possible. By 15.4 the integral with respect to y in the last expression becomes, however, for every value of x a minimum when $g(x)$ is equal to the conditional mean $m_2(x)$. *Thus the minimum of* $\boldsymbol{E}[\eta - g(\xi)]^2$, *among all possible functions* $g(\xi)$, *is attained for the function* $g(\xi) = m_2(\xi)$, *which is graphically represented by the regression curve* (21.5.1). — Similarly, the expression $\boldsymbol{E}[\xi - h(\eta)]^2$ attains its minimum for the function $h(\eta) = m_1(\eta)$, which corresponds to the regression curve (21.5.2).

Similar definitions may be introduced in the case of a distribution of the discrete type, as given by (21.1.1). For every value x_i of ξ, such that the marginal probability $p_{i\,.}$ is positive, the conditional distribution of η is given by (21.4.1). Let us consider some typical value of this distribution, e. g. the conditional mean $m_2^{(i)}$ given by (21.4.3). When ξ assumes all possible values x_i, we thus obtain a sequence of points $(x_i, m_2^{(i)})$ representing the regression of η on ξ. Conversely, the regression of ξ on η is represented by the sequence of points $(m_1^{(k)}, y_k)$, where $m_1^{(k)}$ is the conditional mean of ξ, relative to the hypothesis $\eta = y_k$. In either case, we may connect the points corresponding to consecutive values of i or k by straight lines, and consider the curves thus formed as the regression curves of the discrete distribution.

21.6. Regression, II. — In the literature, we often find the name of regression curves applied also to another type of curves than that introduced in the preceding paragraph. We shall now proceed to a discussion of this other type of curves.

In the minimum problem considered in connection with (21.5.3), we tried to find, *among all possible functions* $g(\xi)$, one that renders the mean value of the square $(\eta - g(\xi))^2$ as small as possible, and we have seen that the solution of this problem is given by the regression curve (21.5.1). Instead of considering all possible functions $g(\xi)$ we may, however, restrict ourselves to *functions belonging to some given class*, such as the class of all linear functions, all polynomials of a given degree n, etc. Thus we require to find, among all functions $g(\xi)$ belonging to such a class, one that gives a best possible representation of η according to the principle of least squares. In such a case, the minimum problem may still have a definite solution, but this will generally correspond to a curve different from the regression curve (21.5.1). Curves obtained in this way will be denoted as *mean square regression curves*, or briefly *m. sq. regression curves.*[1])

The simplest case is that of the *linear m. sq. regression.* Here we propose to find the *best linear estimate of* η by means of ξ, i. e. the linear function $g(\xi) = \alpha + \beta\xi$ that renders the mean value of the square

[1]) When the meaning is clear from the context, we shall often drop the »m. sq.».

$(\eta - g(\xi))^2$ as small as possible. Now we may write, using the notations introduced in 21.2, and assuming $\mu_{20} > 0$, $\mu_{02} > 0$,

$$\text{(21.6.1)} \quad \begin{aligned} \boldsymbol{E}(\eta - \alpha - \beta\xi)^2 &= \boldsymbol{E}(\eta - m_2 - \beta(\xi - m_1) + m_2 - \alpha - \beta m_1)^2 \\ &= \mu_{20}\beta^2 - 2\mu_{11}\beta + \mu_{02} + (m_2 - \alpha - \beta m_1)^2. \end{aligned}$$

An easy calculation shows that the minimum problem has a unique solution given by

$$\text{(21.6.2)} \qquad \beta = \beta_{21} = \frac{\mu_{11}}{\mu_{20}} = \frac{\varrho\,\sigma_2}{\sigma_1}, \quad \alpha = m_2 - \beta_{21} m_1,$$

where ϱ is the correlation coefficient defined by (21.2.8). Thus the *m. sq. regression line of* η has the equation

$$\text{(21.6.3)} \qquad y = m_2 + \frac{\varrho\,\sigma_2}{\sigma_1}(x - m_1).$$

The line passes through (m_1, m_2), and the equation may also be written

$$\text{(21.6.4)} \qquad \frac{y - m_2}{\sigma_2} = \varrho \frac{x - m_1}{\sigma_1}.$$

We note that this line is defined for any distribution such that both variances are finite and positive, and not as the regression curves of the preceding paragraph for distributions of the two simple types only.

The quantity β_{21} defined by (21.6.2) is the *regression coefficient* of η on ξ. When the values of α and β given by (21.6.2) are introduced in (21.6.1), the latter expression assumes its minimum value

$$\text{(21.6.5)} \qquad \boldsymbol{E}_{\min}(\eta - \alpha - \beta\xi)^2 = \frac{\mu_{20}\mu_{02} - \mu_{11}^2}{\mu_{20}} = \sigma_2^2(1 - \varrho^2).$$

The expression $\boldsymbol{E}(\eta - \alpha - \beta\xi)^2 = \int\limits_{\boldsymbol{R}_2} (y - \alpha - \beta x)^2\, dP$ may be considered as a weighted mean of the square of the vertical distance $y - \alpha - \beta x$ between a mass particle dP with the coordinates (x, y) and the straight line $y = \alpha + \beta x$. Since this mean becomes a minimum for the regression line (21.6.4), this line may be called the *line of closest fit to the mass in the distribution*, when distances are measured along the axis of y, and the fit is judged according to the principle of least squares.

In the case of a distribution such that the regression curve $y = m_2(x)$ as defined by (21.5.1) exists, the expression $\boldsymbol{E}(\eta - \alpha - \beta\xi)^2$

may be written in the form

$$E(\eta - m_2(\xi))^2 + 2\,E[(\eta - m_2(\xi))(m_2(\xi) - \alpha - \beta\xi)] + E(m_2(\xi) - \alpha - \beta\xi)^2.$$

By (21.4.7) and (21.4.8) the second term of this expression is, however, equal to zero. Thus we obtain for any α and β

$$E(\eta - \alpha - \beta\xi)^2 = E(\eta - m_2(\xi))^2 + E(m_2(\xi) - \alpha - \beta\xi)^2. \tag{21.6.6}$$

Here, the first term in the second member is independent of α and β, so that the last term attains its minimum for the same values of α and β as the first member, i. e. for the values given by (21.6.2). Since $m_2(x) - \alpha - \beta x$ is the vertical distance between the regression curve $y = m_2(x)$ and the line $y = \alpha + \beta x$, it is thus seen that the m. sq. regression line (21.6.4) may also be considered as the *line of closest fit to the regression curve* $y = m_2(x)$, distances always being measured along the axis of y. *It immediately follows that, in a case when the regression curve* $y = m_2(x)$ *is a straight line, this is identical with the m. sq. regression line* (21.6.4).

So far we have been concerned with the linear m. sq. regression of η on ξ. In the converse case of the regression of ξ on η, we have to find the values of α and β that render the expression

$$E(\xi - \alpha - \beta\eta)^2 = \int_{R_2} (x - \alpha - \beta y)^2\, dP \tag{21.6.7}$$

as small as possible. In the same way as above, we find that the problem has a unique solution, and that the minimizing straight line $x = \alpha + \beta y$ may be considered as the line of closest fit to the mass in the distribution, or to the regression curve $x = m_1(y)$, when distances are measured *horizontally*, i. e. along the axis of x. The equation of this line, the *m. sq. regression line of* ξ, may be written

$$\frac{y - m_2}{\sigma_2} = \frac{1}{\varrho} \cdot \frac{x - m_1}{\sigma_1}, \tag{21.6.8}$$

and the regression coefficient has the expression

$$\beta = \beta_{12} = \frac{\mu_{11}}{\mu_{02}} = \frac{\varrho\,\sigma_1}{\sigma_2}, \tag{21.6.9}$$

while the corresponding minimum value of the expression (21.6.7) is

$$E_{\min}(\xi - \alpha - \beta\eta)^2 = \sigma_1^2(1 - \varrho^2). \tag{21.6.10}$$

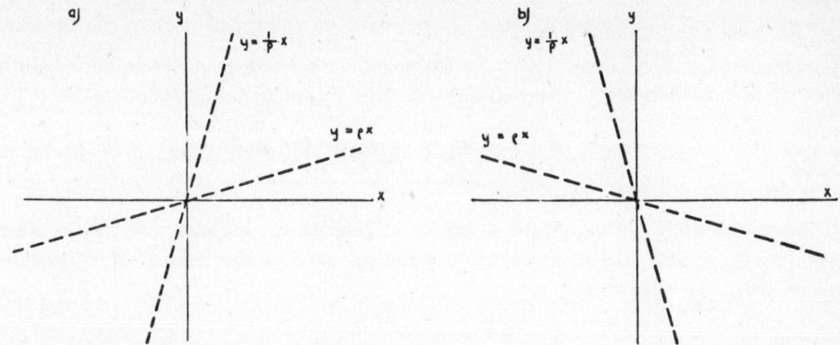

Fig. 23. M. sq. regression lines. $m_1 = m_2 = 0$, $\sigma_1 = \sigma_2 = 1$. a) $\varrho > 0$, b) $\varrho < 0$.

Both m. sq. regression lines (21.6.4) and (21.6.8) pass through the centre of gravity (m_1, m_2). The two lines can never coincide, except in the extreme cases $\varrho = \pm 1$, when the whole mass of the distribution is situated on a straight line (cf 21.2). Both regression lines then coincide with this line.

When $\varrho = 0$, the equations of the m. sq. regression lines reduce to $y = m_2$ and $x = m_1$, so that the lines are then parallel with the axes. This case occurs e. g. when the variables ξ and η are independent (cf 21.2 and 21.7).

If the variables are standardized by placing the origin in the centre of gravity and choosing σ_1 and σ_2 as units of measurement for ξ and η respectively, the equations of the m. sq. regression lines reduce to the simple form $y = \varrho x$ and $y = x/\varrho$. When ϱ is neither zero nor ± 1, these lines are disposed as shown by Fig. 23 a or 23 b, according as $\varrho > 0$ or $\varrho < 0$.

If, instead of measuring the distance between a point and a straight line in the direction of one of the coordinate axes, we consider the *shortest*, i. e. the orthogonal distance, we obtain a new type of regression lines. Let d denote the shortest distance between the point (ξ, η) and a straight line L. If L is determined such that $\boldsymbol{E}(d^2)$ becomes as small as possible, we obtain the *orthogonal m. sq. regression line*. This is the line of closest fit to the (ξ, η)-distribution, when distances are measured orthogonally.

Now $\boldsymbol{E}(d^2)$ may be considered as the *moment of inertia* of the mass in the distribution with respect to L. For a given direction of L, this always attains its minimum when L passes through the centre of gravity. We may thus write the equation of L in the form $(\xi - m_1) \sin \varphi - (\eta - m_2) \cos \varphi = 0$, where φ is the angle between L and the positive direction of the ξ-axis. The moment of inertia is then

$$\boldsymbol{E}(d^2) = \boldsymbol{E}((\xi - m_1) \sin \varphi - (\eta - m_2) \cos \varphi)^2$$
$$= \mu_{20} \sin^2 \varphi - 2\, \mu_{11} \sin \varphi \cos \varphi + \mu_{02} \cos^2 \varphi.$$

If, on each side of the centre of gravity, we mark on L a segment of length inversely proportional to $\sqrt{E(d^2)}$, the locus of the end-points when φ varies is an *ellipse of inertia* of the distribution. The equation of this ellipse is easily found to be

$$\frac{(\xi - m_1)^2}{\sigma_1^2} - \frac{2\varrho(\xi - m_1)(\eta - m_2)}{\sigma_1 \sigma_2} + \frac{(\eta - m_2)^2}{\sigma_2^2} = c^2.$$

For various values of c we obtain a family of homothetic ellipses with the common centre (m_1, m_2). The directions of the principal axes of this family of ellipses are obtained from the equation

$$\operatorname{tg} 2\varphi = \frac{2\mu_{11}}{\mu_{20} - \mu_{02}},$$

and the equations of the axes are

$$\eta - m_2 = \frac{2\mu_{11}}{\mu_{20} - \mu_{02} \pm \sqrt{(\mu_{20} - \mu_{02})^2 + 4\mu_{11}^2}}(\xi - m_1). \tag{21.6.11}$$

Here, the upper sign corresponds to the major axis of the ellipse and thus to the minimum of $E(d^2)$, i.e. to the orthogonal m. sq. regression line. In the case

$$\mu_{11} = \mu_{20} - \mu_{02} = 0$$

the problem is undetermined; in all other cases there is a unique solution.

The *parabolic m. sq. regression* of order $n > 1$ forms a generalization of the linear m. sq. regression. We here propose to determine a polynomial $g(\xi) = \beta_0 + \cdots + \beta_n \xi^n$ such that the mean value $M = E(\eta - g(\xi))^2$ becomes as small as possible. The curve $y = g(x)$ is then the n:th order parabola of closest fit to the mass in the distribution, or to the regression curve $y = m_2(x)$.

Assuming that all moments appearing in our formulae are finite, we obtain the conditions for a minimum:

$$\frac{1}{2}\frac{\partial M}{\partial \beta_\nu} = E[\xi^\nu(g(\xi) - \eta)] = \beta_0 \alpha_{\nu 0} + \cdots + \beta_n \alpha_{\nu+n, 0} - \alpha_{\nu 1} = 0$$

for $\nu = 0, 1, \ldots, n$. If the moments α_{ik} are known, we thus have $n + 1$ equations to determine the $n + 1$ unknowns $\beta_0, \ldots, \beta_n$.

The calculations involved in the determination of the unknown coefficients may be much simplified, if the regression polynomial $g(x)$ is considered as a linear aggregate of the *orthogonal polynomials* $p_\nu(x)$ associated with the marginal distribution of ξ. For all orders such that these polynomials are uniquely determined (cf 12.6), we have

$$E(p_m(\xi) p_n(\xi)) = \int_{-\infty}^{\infty} p_m(x) p_n(x)\, dF_1(x) = \begin{cases} 1 & \text{for } m = n, \\ 0 & \text{for } m \neq n, \end{cases} \tag{21.6.12}$$

where $p_n(x)$ is of the n:th degree, and $F_1(x)$ denotes the marginal d. f. of ξ. Any polynomial $g(x)$ of degree n may be written in the form

$$g(x) = c_0 p_0(x) + \cdots + c_n p_n(x)$$

with constant coefficients $c_0, \ldots, c_n$. The conditions for a minimum now become

$$\frac{1}{2}\frac{\partial M}{\partial c_\nu} = \boldsymbol{E}[p_\nu(\xi)(g(\xi) - \eta)] = c_\nu - \boldsymbol{E}(\eta\, p_\nu(\xi)) = 0. \tag{21.6.13}$$

Hence we obtain $c_\nu = \boldsymbol{E}(\eta\, p_\nu(\xi))$, so that the coefficients c_ν are obtained directly, without first having to solve a system of linear equations. It is further seen that the expression for c_ν is independent of the degree n. Thus if we know e. g. the regression polynomial of degree n, and require the corresponding polynomial of degree $n+1$, it is only necessary to calculate the additional term $c_{n+1} p_{n+1}(x)$. — Introducing the expressions of the c_ν into the mean value M, we find for the minimum value of M

$$\boldsymbol{E}_{\min}(\eta - g(\xi))^2 = \boldsymbol{E}(\eta^2) - c_0^2 - \cdots - c_n^2. \tag{21.6.14}$$

It should finally be observed that it is by no means essential for the validity of the above relations that the $p_\nu(x)$ are *polynomials*. Any sequence of functions satisfying the orthogonality conditions (21.6.12) may be used to form a m. sq. regression curve $y = g(x) = \sum c_\nu p_\nu(x)$, and the relations (21.6.13) and (21.6.14) then hold true irrespective of the form of the $p_\nu(x)$.

21.7. The correlation coefficient. According to (21.2.8), the *correlation coefficient* ϱ of ξ and η is defined by the expression

$$\varrho = \frac{\mu_{11}}{\sigma_1 \sigma_2} = \frac{\boldsymbol{E}[(\xi - m_1)(\eta - m_2)]}{\sqrt{\boldsymbol{E}(\xi - m_1)^2\, \boldsymbol{E}(\eta - m_2)^2}},$$

and we have seen in 21.2 that we always have $-1 \leqq \varrho \leqq 1$. The correlation coefficient is an important characteristic of the (ξ, η)-distribution. Its main properties are intimately connected with the two m. sq. regression lines

$$\begin{aligned} \frac{y - m_2}{\sigma_2} &= \varrho\, \frac{x - m_1}{\sigma_1}, \\ \frac{y - m_2}{\sigma_2} &= \frac{1}{\varrho} \cdot \frac{x - m_1}{\sigma_1}, \end{aligned} \tag{21.7.1}$$

which are the straight lines of closest fit to the mass in the (ξ, η)-distribution, in the sense defined in the preceding paragraph. The closeness of fit realized by these lines is measured by the expressions

$$
(21.7.2) \qquad \begin{aligned} E_{\min}(\eta - \alpha - \beta\,\xi)^2 &= \sigma_2^2\,(1-\varrho^2),\\ E_{\min}(\xi - \alpha - \beta\,\eta)^2 &= \sigma_1^2\,(1-\varrho^2), \end{aligned}
$$

respectively. Thus either variable has its variance reduced in the proportion $(1-\varrho^2):1$ by the subtraction of its best linear estimate in terms of the other variable. These expressions are sometimes called the *residual variances* of η and ξ respectively.

When $\varrho = 0$, no part of the variance of η can thus be removed by the subtraction of a linear function of ξ, and vice versa. In this case, we shall say that the variables are *uncorrelated.*

When $\varrho \neq 0$, a certain fraction of the variance of η may be removed by the subtraction of a linear function of ξ, and vice versa. The maximum amount of the reduction increases according to (21.7.2) in the same measure as ϱ differs from zero. In this case, we shall say that the variables are *correlated*, and that the correlation is *positive* or *negative* according as $\varrho > 0$ or $\varrho < 0$.

When ϱ reaches one of its extreme values ± 1, (21.7.2) shows that the residual variances are zero. We have shown in 21.2 that this case occurs when and only when the total mass of the (ξ, η)-distribution is situated on a straight line, which is then identical with both regression lines (21.7.1). In this extreme case, there is complete functional dependence between the variables: when ξ is known, there is only one possible value for η, and conversely. Either variable is a linear function of the other, and the two variables vary in the same sense, or in inverse senses, according as $\varrho = +1$ or $\varrho = -1$.

On account of these properties, the correlation coefficient ϱ may be regarded as a measure of the *degree of linearity* shown by the (ξ, η)-distribution. This degree reaches its maximum when $\varrho = \pm 1$ and the whole mass of the distribution is situated on a straight line. The opposite case occurs when $\varrho = 0$ and no reduction of the variance of either variable can be effected by the subtraction of a linear function of the other variable.

It has been shown in 21.2 that in the particular case when ξ and η are independent we have $\varrho = 0$. *Thus two independent variables are always uncorrelated.* It is most important to observe that the converse is not true. *Two uncorrelated variables are not necessarily independent.*

Consider, in fact, a one-dimensional fr. f. $g(x)$ which differs from zero only when $x > 0$, and has a finite second moment. Then

$$f(x, y) = \frac{g(\sqrt{x^2 + y^2})}{2\pi\sqrt{x^2 + y^2}}$$

is the fr. f. of a two-dimensional distribution, where the density of the mass is constant on every circle $x^2 + y^2 = c^2$. The centre of gravity is $m_1 = m_2 = 0$, and on account of the symmetry of the distribution we have $\mu_{11} = 0$, and hence $\varrho = 0$. Thus two variables with this distribution are *uncorrelated.* However, in order that the variables should be *independent*, it is by (15.11.3) necessary and sufficient that $f(x, y)$ should be of the form $f_1(x) f_2(y)$, and this condition is not always satisfied, as will be seen e. g. by taking $g(x) = e^{-x}$.

If ϱ is the correlation coefficient of ξ and η, it follows directly from the definition that the variables $\xi' = a\xi + b$ and $\eta' = c\eta + d$ have the correlation coefficient $\varrho' = \varrho \operatorname{sgn}(ac)$, where $\operatorname{sgn} x$ stands for ± 1, according as x is positive or negative.

In the particular case of a discrete distribution with only two possible values (x_1, x_2 and y_1, y_2 respectively) for each variable, we find after some reductions, using the notations of 21.1,

$$\varrho = \frac{p_{11}p_{22} - p_{12}p_{21}}{\sqrt{p_{1.}\, p_{2.}\, p_{.1}\, p_{.2}}} \operatorname{sgn}\left[(x_1 - x_2)(y_1 - y_2)\right]. \tag{21.7.3}$$

21.8. Linear transformation of variables. — Consider a linear transformation of the random variables ξ and η, corresponding to a rotation of axes about the centre of gravity. We then introduce new variables X and Y defined by

$$\begin{aligned} X &= \quad (\xi - m_1)\cos\varphi + (\eta - m_2)\sin\varphi, \\ Y &= -(\xi - m_1)\sin\varphi + (\eta - m_2)\cos\varphi, \end{aligned} \tag{21.8.1}$$

and conversely

$$\begin{aligned} \xi &= m_1 + X\cos\varphi - Y\sin\varphi, \\ \eta &= m_2 + X\sin\varphi + Y\cos\varphi. \end{aligned} \tag{21.8.2}$$

If the angle of rotation φ is determined by the equation $\operatorname{tg} 2\varphi = \frac{2\mu_{11}}{\mu_{20} - \mu_{02}}$, we find

$$E(XY) = \mu_{11}\cos 2\varphi - \tfrac{1}{2}(\mu_{20} - \mu_{02})\sin 2\varphi = 0,$$

so that X and Y are uncorrelated. In the particular case $\mu_{11} = \mu_{20} - \mu_{02} = 0$, when the equation for φ is undetermined, we have $E(XY) = 0$ for any φ. *Thus it is always possible to express ξ and η as linear functions of two uncorrelated variables.*

Consider in particular the case when the moment matrix $M = \begin{Bmatrix} \mu_{20} & \mu_{11} \\ \mu_{11} & \mu_{02} \end{Bmatrix}$ is of rank 1 (cf 21.2). We then have $\varrho = \pm 1$, and the whole mass of the distribution is situated on the line $\eta - m_2 = \frac{\varrho\sigma_2}{\sigma_1}(\xi - m_1)$. Let us now determine the angle of rotation φ from the equation $\operatorname{tg}\varphi = \frac{\varrho\sigma_2}{\sigma_1}$. From (21.8.1) we then find

$$\begin{aligned} E(Y^2) &= \sigma_1^2\sin^2\varphi - 2\varrho\sigma_1\sigma_2\sin\varphi\cos\varphi + \sigma_2^2\cos^2\varphi \\ &= (\sigma_1\sin\varphi - \varrho\sigma_2\cos\varphi)^2 = 0. \end{aligned}$$

Thus the variance of Y is equal to zero, so that Y is a variable which is almost always equal to zero (cf 16.1). If we then put $Y = 0$ in (21.8.2), the resulting equations between ξ, η and X will be satisfied with a probability equal to 1. *Thus two variables ξ and η with a moment matrix M of rank 1 may, with a probability equal to 1, be expressed as linear functions of one single variable.*

21.9. The correlation ratio and the mean square contingency. — Consider two variables ξ and η with a distribution of the *continuous* type, such that the conditional mean $m_2(x)$ is a continuous function of x. In the relation (21.6.6) we put $\alpha = m_2$, $\beta = 0$, and so obtain

$$(21.9.1) \qquad \sigma_2^2 = E(\eta - m_2)^2 = E(\eta - m_2(\xi))^2 + E(m_2(\xi) - m_2)^2.$$

We thus see that the variance of η may be represented as the sum of two components, viz. the mean square deviation of η from its conditional mean $m_2(\xi)$, and the mean square deviation of $m_2(\xi)$ from its mean m_2.

We now define a quantity $\theta_{\eta\xi}$ by putting

$$(21.9.2) \qquad \theta_{\eta\xi}^2 = \frac{1}{\sigma_2^2} E(m_2(\xi) - m_2)^2 = \frac{1}{\sigma_2^2}\int_{-\infty}^{\infty}(m_2(x) - m_2)^2 f_1(x)\,dx.$$

$\theta_{\eta\xi}$ is the *correlation ratio*[1]) of η on ξ introduced by K. Pearson. In the applications we are usually concerned with the square θ^2, and we may thus leave the sign of θ undetermined. From (21.9.1) we obtain

$$1 - \theta^2_{\eta\xi} = \frac{1}{\sigma_2^2} \boldsymbol{E} (\eta - m_2(\xi))^2, \tag{21.9.3}$$

and hence

$$0 \leqq \theta^2_{\eta\xi} \leqq 1. \tag{21.9.4}$$

We further write the equation of the first m. sq. regression line (21.7.1) in the form $y = \alpha + \beta x$, and insert these values of α and β in (21.6.6). Using (21.7.2) and (21.9.3), we then obtain after reduction

$$\theta^2_{\eta\xi} = \varrho^2 + \frac{1}{\sigma_2^2} \boldsymbol{E} (m_2(\xi) - \alpha - \beta\xi)^2. \tag{21.9.5}$$

It follows that $\theta^2_{\eta\xi} = 0$ when and only when $m_2(x)$ is independent of x. In fact, when $m_2(x)$ is constant, the regression curve $y = m_2(x)$ is a horizontal straight line, which implies $\varrho = \beta = 0$, and consequently $\theta^2_{\eta\xi} = 0$. The converse is shown in a similar way. — Further, (21.9.3) shows that $\theta^2_{\eta\xi} = 1$ when and only when the whole mass of the distribution is situated on the regression curve $y = m_2(x)$, so that there is complete functional dependence between the variables. For intermediate values of $\theta^2_{\eta\xi}$, (21.9.3) shows that the correlation ratio may be considered as a measure of the tendency of the mass to accumulate about the regression curve.

When the regression of η on ξ is linear, so that $y = m_2(x)$ is a straight line, (21.9.5) shows that we have $\theta^2_{\eta\xi} = \varrho^2$, and (21.9.3) reduces to the first relation (21.7.2). In such a case, the calculation of the correlation ratio does not give us any new information, if we already know the correlation coefficient ϱ.

In a case of non-linear regression, on the other hand, $\theta^2_{\eta\xi}$ always exceeds ϱ^2 by a quantity which measures the deviation of the curve $y = m_2(x)$ from the straight line of closest fit.

The correlation ratio $\theta_{\xi\eta}$ of ξ on η is, of course, defined by interchanging the variables in the above relations. The curve $y = m_2(x)$ is then replaced by the curve $x = m_1(y)$.

For a distribution of the *discrete* type, the correlation ratio may be similarly defined, replacing (21.9.2) and (21.9.3) by

[1]) In the literature, the correlation ratio is usually denoted by the letter η, which obviously cannot be used here, since η is a random variable.

$$(21.9.2\text{ a}) \qquad \theta^2_{\eta\xi} = \frac{1}{\sigma_2^2} \boldsymbol{E}\,(m_2^{(i)} - m_2)^2 = \frac{1}{\sigma_2^2} \sum_i p_{i\,.}\,(m_2^{(i)} - m_2)^2,$$

$$(21.9.3\text{ a}) \qquad 1 - \theta^2_{\eta\xi} = \frac{1}{\sigma_2^2} \boldsymbol{E}\,(\eta - m_2^{(i)})^2,$$

where $p_{i\,.}$ and $m_2^{(i)}$ are defined by (21.1.2) and (21.4.3) respectively. The relations (21.9.4), (21.9.5) and the above conclusions concerning the properties of the correlation ratio hold true with obvious modifications in this case.

The correlation coefficient and the correlation ratio both serve to characterize, in the sense explained above, the »degree of dependence» between two variables. Many other measures have been proposed for the same purpose. We shall here only mention the *mean square contingency* introduced by K. Pearson. Consider two variables ξ, η with a distribution of the discrete type as defined by (21.1.1), and suppose that the number of possible values is finite for both variables. The probabilities p_{ik} then form a matrix with, say, m rows and n columns. Since any row or column consisting exclusively of zeros may be discarded, we may suppose that every row and every column contains at least one positive element, so that the row sums $p_{i\,.}$ and the column sums $p_{.\,k}$ are all positive. The *mean square contingency* of the distribution is then

$$(21.9.6) \qquad \varphi^2 = \sum_{i,k} \frac{(p_{ik} - p_{i\,.}\,p_{.\,k})^2}{p_{i\,.}\,p_{.\,k}} = \sum_{i,k} \frac{p_{ik}^2}{p_{i\,.}\,p_{.\,k}} - 1.$$

By (21.1.4), $\varphi^2 = 0$ when and only when the variables are independent. On the other hand, by means of the inequalities $p_{ik} \leqq p_{i\,.}$ and $p_{ik} \leqq p_{.\,k}$ it follows from the last expression that $\varphi^2 \leqq q - 1$, where $q = \text{Min}\,(m, n)$ denotes the smaller of the numbers m and n, or their common value if both are equal. Further, the sign of equality holds in the last relation if and only if one of the variables is a uniquely determined function of the other. Thus $0 \leqq \dfrac{\varphi^2}{q-1} \leqq 1$, and the quantity $\dfrac{\varphi^2}{q-1}$ may be used as a measure, on a standardized scale, of the degree of dependence between the variables.

In the particular case $m = n = 2$, we obtain after reduction

$$(21.9.7) \qquad \varphi^2 = \frac{(p_{11}\,p_{22} - p_{12}\,p_{21})^2}{p_{1\,.}\,p_{2\,.}\,p_{.\,1}\,p_{.\,2}}.$$

Thus in this case φ^2 is the square of the correlation coefficient ϱ given by (21.7.3). We have here $q=2$, so that $\frac{\varphi^2}{q-1}$ is identical with φ^2. Further, φ^2 assumes its maximum value 1 only in the two cases $p_{12}=p_{21}=0$ or $p_{11}=p_{22}=0$.

21.10. The ellipse of concentration. — Consider a one-dimensional random variable ξ with the mean m and the s. d. σ. If ξ' is another variable which is uniformly distributed (cf 19.1) over the interval $(m-\sigma\sqrt{3},\ m+\sigma\sqrt{3})$, it is easily seen that ξ' has the same mean and s. d. as ξ. Thus the interval $(m-\sigma\sqrt{3},\ m+\sigma\sqrt{3})$ may be taken as a geometrical representation of the concentration of the ξ-distribution about its centre of gravity m (cf also 15.6).

We now propose to find an analogous geometrical representation of the concentration of a given *two-dimensional* distribution about its centre of gravity (m_1, m_2). For this purpose, we want to find a curve enclosing the point (m_1, m_2) such that, if a mass unit is uniformly distributed over the area bounded by the curve, this distribution will have the same first and second order moments as the given distribution. (By a »uniform distribution» we mean, of course, a distribution with a constant fr. f.)

In this general form, the problem is obviously undetermined, and we shall restrict ourselves to finding an *ellipse* having the required property. In order to simplify the writing, we may suppose $m_1=m_2=0$. Let the second order central moments of the given distribution be μ_{20}, μ_{11} and μ_{02}. We shall suppose that we have $\varrho^2<1$, so that our distribution does not belong to the extreme type that has its total mass situated on a straight line.

Consider the non-negative quadratic form

$$q(\xi,\eta)=a_{11}\,\xi^2+2\,a_{12}\,\xi\,\eta+a_{22}\,\eta^2.$$

By (11.12.3) the area enclosed by the ellipse $q=c^2$ is $\pi\,c^2/\sqrt{A}$, where $A=a_{11}\,a_{22}-a_{12}^2$. If a mass unit is uniformly distributed over this area, the first order moments of the distribution will evidently be zero, while the second order moments are according to (11.12.4)

$$\frac{c^2}{4}\cdot\frac{a_{22}}{A},\quad -\frac{c^2}{4}\cdot\frac{a_{12}}{A}\quad\text{and}\quad\frac{c^2}{4}\cdot\frac{a_{11}}{A}.$$

It is required to determine c and the a_{ik} such that these moments

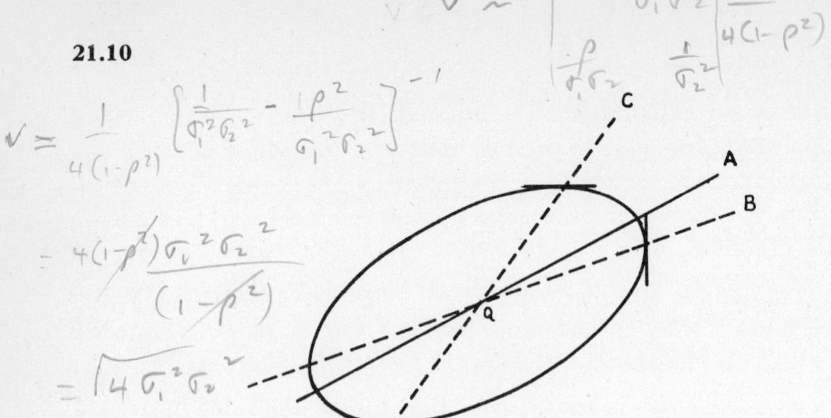

Fig. 24. Concentration ellipse and regression lines, $\varrho > 0$.
Q = centre of gravity. QA = orthogonal m. sq. regression line. QB = m. sq. regression line, η on ξ. QC = m. sq. regression line, ξ on η.

coincide with μ_{20}, μ_{11} and μ_{02} respectively. It is readily seen that this is effected by taking $c^2 = 4$, and

$$a_{11} = \frac{\mu_{02}}{M}, \quad a_{12} = -\frac{\mu_{11}}{M}, \quad a_{22} = \frac{\mu_{20}}{M},$$

where $M = \mu_{20}\,\mu_{02} - \mu_{11}^2$. It will be seen that the form $q(\xi, \eta)$ thus obtained is the reciprocal (cf 11.7) of the form

$$Q(\xi, \eta) = \mu_{20}\,\xi^2 + 2\,\mu_{11}\,\xi\,\eta + \mu_{02}\,\eta^2.$$

Returning to the general case of an arbitrary centre of gravity (m_1, m_2), and replacing the μ_{ik} by their expressions in terms of σ_1, σ_2 and ϱ, it thus follows that *a uniform distribution of a mass unit over the area enclosed by the ellipse*

$$\text{(21.10.1)} \qquad \frac{1}{1-\varrho^2}\left(\frac{(\xi - m_1)^2}{\sigma_1^2} - \frac{2\,\varrho\,(\xi - m_1)\,(\eta - m_2)}{\sigma_1\,\sigma_2} + \frac{(\eta - m_2)^2}{\sigma_2^2}\right) = 4$$

has the same first and second order moments as the given distribution. — This ellipse will be called the ellipse of concentration corresponding to the given distribution.

The domain enclosed by the ellipse (21.10.1) may thus be regarded as a two-dimensional analogue of the interval $(m - \sigma\sqrt{3},\ m + \sigma\sqrt{3})$. When two distributions in $\boldsymbol{R}_2$ with the same centre of gravity are such that one of the concentration ellipses lies wholly within the other, the former distribution will be said to have a *greater concentration* than the latter. This concept will find an important use in the theory of estimation (cf 32.7).

If we replace the constant 4 in the equation (21.10.1) by an arbitrary constant c^2, we obtain for various values of c^2 a family of homothetic ellipses with the common centre (m_1, m_2), which is identical with the family of ellipses of inertia considered in 21.6. The common major axis of the ellipses coincides with the orthogonal m. sq. regression line of the distribution (cf 21.6). The ordinary m. sq. regression lines are diameters of the ellipses, each of which is conjugate to one of the coordinate axes. The situation is illustrated by Fig. 24.

21.11. Addition of independent variables. — Consider the two-dimensional random variables $\boldsymbol{x}_1 = (\xi_1, \eta_1)$ and $\boldsymbol{x}_2 = (\xi_2, \eta_2)$. We define the sum $\boldsymbol{x} = \boldsymbol{x}_1 + \boldsymbol{x}_2$ according to the rules of vector addition:

$$\boldsymbol{x} = (\xi, \eta) = (\xi_1 + \xi_2, \eta_1 + \eta_2).$$

By 14.5, $\boldsymbol{x}$ is a two-dimensional random variable with a distribution uniquely determined by the simultaneous distribution of $\boldsymbol{x}_1$ and $\boldsymbol{x}_2$.

Let us now suppose that $\boldsymbol{x}_1$ and $\boldsymbol{x}_2$ are *independent* variables according to the definition of 14.4, and denote by $\varphi(t, u)$, $\varphi_1(t, u)$ and $\varphi_2(t, u)$ the c. f:s of $\boldsymbol{x}$, $\boldsymbol{x}_1$ and $\boldsymbol{x}_2$ respectively. By the theorem (15.3.4) on the mean value of a product of independent variables we then have

$$(21.11.1) \qquad \begin{aligned} \varphi(t, u) &= \boldsymbol{E}\left(e^{i(t\xi + u\eta)}\right) \\ &= \boldsymbol{E}\left(e^{i(t\xi_1 + u\eta_1)} \cdot e^{i(t\xi_2 + u\eta_2)}\right) = \varphi_1(t, u)\,\varphi_2(t, u). \end{aligned}$$

The generalization to an arbitrary number of terms is evident, and we thus obtain the same theorem as for one-dimensional variables (cf 15.12): *The c.f. of a sum of independent variables is the product of the c.f:s of the terms.*

We shall now consider the case of a sum $\boldsymbol{x} = \boldsymbol{x}_1 + \boldsymbol{x}_2 + \cdots + \boldsymbol{x}_n$, where the $\boldsymbol{x}_\nu = (\xi_\nu, \eta_\nu)$ are independent variables all having the same two-dimensional distribution. We shall suppose that this latter distribution has finite moments of the second order $\mu_{20}, \mu_{11}, \mu_{02}$, and that the first order moments are zero: $m_1 = m_2 = 0$. If $\varphi(t, u)$ is the c. f. of this common distribution of the $\boldsymbol{x}_\nu$, we have by (21.3.3)

$$(21.11.2) \qquad \varphi(t, u) = 1 - \tfrac{1}{2}(\mu_{20} t^2 + 2\mu_{11} t u + \mu_{02} u^2) + o(t^2 + u^2).$$

On the other hand, we have $\boldsymbol{x} = (\xi_1 + \cdots + \xi_n, \eta_1 + \cdots + \eta_n)$ and

$$\frac{\boldsymbol{x}}{\sqrt{n}} = \left(\frac{\xi_1 + \cdots + \xi_n}{\sqrt{n}}, \frac{\eta_1 + \cdots + \eta_n}{\sqrt{n}}\right).$$

If $\varphi_n(t, u)$ is the c. f. of $\boldsymbol{x}/\sqrt{n}$, it thus follows from the above that we have

$$\varphi_n(t, u) = \left[\varphi\left(\frac{t}{\sqrt{n}}, \frac{u}{\sqrt{n}}\right)\right]^n.$$

Substituting in (21.11.2) $t/\sqrt{n}$ and $u/\sqrt{n}$ for t and u, we obtain

$$\varphi_n(t, u) = \left[1 - \frac{\mu_{20} t^2 + 2 \mu_{11} t u + \mu_{02} u^2}{2 n} + \frac{\delta(n, t, u)}{n}\right]^n$$

where, for any fixed t and u, the quantity $\delta(n, t, u)$ tends to zero as $n \to \infty$. Hence we obtain, in the same way as in the proof of the Lindeberg-Lévy theorem in 17.4,

$$\lim_{n \to \infty} \varphi_n(t, u) = e^{-\frac{1}{2}(\mu_{20} t^2 + 2 \mu_{11} t u + \mu_{02} u^2)}. \tag{21.11.3}$$

Thus $\varphi_n(t, u)$ tends for all t and u to a limit which is obviously continuous for $(t, u) = (0, 0)$. By the continuity theorem for c. f:s proved in 10.7, we may then assert that this limit is the c. f. of a certain distribution which in its turn is the limit, for $n \to \infty$, of the distribution of the variable $\boldsymbol{x}/\sqrt{n}$.

Thus if $\boldsymbol{x}_1, \boldsymbol{x}_2, \ldots$ *are independent two-dimensional variables, all having the same distribution with finite second order moments and first order moments equal to zero, the distribution of the variable* $\dfrac{\boldsymbol{x}_1 + \cdots + \boldsymbol{x}_n}{\sqrt{n}}$ *always tends to a limiting distribution as* $n \to \infty$, *and the c.f. of the limiting distribution is given by the second member of* (21.11.3). — Except the trivial restriction $m_1 = m_2 = 0$, this is the two-dimensional generalization of the Lindeberg-Lévy theorem of 17.4.

It should be observed that, with respect to the second order moments, we have here only assumed that these are finite. Now, given any quantities μ_{20}, μ_{11} and μ_{02} such that the quadratic form

$$\mu_{20} t^2 + 2 \mu_{11} t u + \mu_{02} u^2$$

is non-negative, it is possible (cf 21.2) to find a distribution with $m_1 = m_2 = 0$ and the given quantities for their second order moments. Taking this distribution as the common distribution of the $\boldsymbol{x}_\nu$ in the above theorem, it follows that the expression in the second member of (21.11.3) is always the c. f. of a certain distribution, as soon as the quadratic form within the brackets is non-negative. If $\boldsymbol{x}$ is a variable having this c. f., and if $\boldsymbol{m} = (m_1, m_2)$ is a constant vector, the variable $\boldsymbol{m} + \boldsymbol{x}$ has the c. f.

$$e^{i(m_1 t + m_2 u) - \frac{1}{2}(\mu_{20} t^2 + 2\mu_{11} t u + \mu_{02} u^2)}. \tag{21.11.4}$$

The distribution corresponding to this c. f. is the *two-dimensional normal distribution*, which will be further discussed in the following paragraph.

21.12. The normal distribution. — We now proceed to study the distribution corresponding to the c. f. (21.11.4). We shall have to distinguish two cases according as the non-negative quadratic form

$$Q(t, u) = \mu_{20} t^2 + 2\mu_{11} t u + \mu_{02} u^2$$

is definite or semi-definite positive (cf 11.10). In the former case, we shall say that we are concerned with a *non-singular normal distribution*, whereas in the latter case we have a *singular normal distribution*. When we use the expression *normal distribution* without specification, it will always be understood that we include both kinds of distributions.

We shall first consider the case of a *definite positive* form $Q(t, u)$. Then the reciprocal form $Q^{-1}(x, y)$ exists and has the expression (cf 21.10)

$$Q^{-1}(x, y) = \frac{\mu_{02} x^2 - 2\mu_{11} x y + \mu_{20} y^2}{M}$$

$$= \frac{1}{1 - \varrho^2}\left(\frac{x^2}{\sigma_1^2} - \frac{2\varrho x y}{\sigma_1 \sigma_2} + \frac{y^2}{\sigma_2^2}\right),$$

where $M = \mu_{20}\mu_{02} - \mu_{11}^2 = \sigma_1^2 \sigma_2^2 (1 - \varrho^2)$. From (11.12.1 b) we now obtain

$$\int_{-\infty}^{\infty}\int_{-\infty}^{\infty} e^{i(tx + uy) - \frac{1}{2} Q^{-1}(x, y)}\, dx\, dy = 2\pi\sqrt{M}\, e^{-\frac{1}{2} Q(t, u)},$$

or, substituting $x - m_1$ for x and $y - m_2$ for y,

$$\frac{1}{2\pi\sigma_1\sigma_2\sqrt{1 - \varrho^2}} \int_{-\infty}^{\infty}\int_{-\infty}^{\infty} e^{i(tx + uy) - \frac{1}{2} Q^{-1}(x - m_1, y - m_2)}\, dx\, dy = e^{i(m_1 t + m_2 u) - \frac{1}{2} Q(t, u)}.$$

The last relation shows that the function

$$f(x, y) = \frac{1}{2\pi\sigma_1\sigma_2\sqrt{1 - \varrho^2}}\, e^{-\frac{1}{2} Q^{-1}(x - m_1, y - m_2)} \tag{21.12.1}$$

is a two-dimensional fr. f. with the c. f.

$$\varphi(t, u) = e^{i(m_1 t + m_2 u) - \frac{1}{2} Q(t, u)}. \tag{21.12.2}$$

The development (21.3.2) for the c. f. shows that the quantities m_i and μ_{ik} have, for this distribution, their usual signification as mean values and second order central moments. The function $f(x, y)$ defined by (21.12.1) is the *normal fr. f.* in two variables. It has a maximum point at the centre of gravity (m_1, m_2). The homothetic ellipses

$$\frac{1}{2(1-\varrho^2)}\left(\frac{(x-m_1)^2}{\sigma_1^2} - \frac{2\varrho(x-m_1)(y-m_2)}{\sigma_1\sigma_2} + \frac{(y-m_2)^2}{\sigma_2^2}\right) = c^2, \tag{21.12.3}$$

that have already appeared in 21.6 and 21.10 in connection with the ellipses of inertia and of concentration of an arbitrary distribution, play in the case of a normal distribution the further rôle of *equiprobability curves.* For any point belonging to (21.12.3) we have, in fact, $f(x, y) = \frac{1}{2\pi\sigma_1\sigma_2\sqrt{1-\varrho^2}} e^{-c^2}$. Since by (11.12.3) the area of the ring between the ellipses corresponding to c and $c + dc$ is

$$4\pi\sigma_1\sigma_2\sqrt{1-\varrho^2}\, c\, dc,$$

the mass situated in this ring is $2ce^{-c^2}dc$, and thus the mass in the whole plane outside the ellipse (21.12.3) is (cf Ex. 15, p. 319)

$$\int_c^\infty 2ce^{-c^2}dc = e^{-c^2}.$$

The form of the equiprobability ellipses (21.12.3) gives a good idea of the shape of the normal frequency surface $z = f(x, y)$. For $\varrho = 0$, $\sigma_1 = \sigma_2$, the ellipses are circles. As ϱ approaches $+1$ or -1, the ellipses become thin and needle-shaped, thus showing the tendency of the mass to accumulate towards the common major axis of the ellipses, which is the orthogonal m. sq. regression line (cf 21.6) of the distribution.

A variable (ξ, η) with the fr. f. (21.12.1) is said to possess a *non-singular normal distribution.* The c. f. of the marginal distribution of ξ is then by (21.3.4)

$$\varphi(t, 0) = e^{i m_1 t - \frac{1}{2}\sigma_1^2 t^2}$$

Thus by 17.2 ξ is normal (m_1, σ_1), with the marginal fr. f.

$$f_1(x) = \frac{1}{\sigma_1 \sqrt{2\pi}} e^{-\frac{(x-m_1)^2}{2\sigma_1^2}}$$

By index permutation we obtain the corresponding expression for the marginal fr. f. $f_2(y)$ of η.

In the particular case when $\varrho = 0$, it is seen that we have $f(x, y) = f_1(x) f_2(y)$, which implies that the variables are independent. For the normal distribution, it is thus legitimate to assert that two non-correlated variables are independent, though we have seen in 21.7 that for a general distribution this may be untrue.

The conditional fr. f. of η, relative to the hypothesis $\xi = x$, is by (21.4.6)

$$(21.12.4) \quad f(y \mid x) = \frac{f(x, y)}{f_1(x)} = \frac{1}{\sigma_2 \sqrt{2\pi(1-\varrho^2)}} e^{-\frac{1}{2\sigma_2^2(1-\varrho^2)}\left(y - m_2 - \frac{\varrho\sigma_2}{\sigma_1}(x - m_1)\right)^2}.$$

This is a normal fr. f. in y, with the mean

$$m_2(x) = m_2 + \frac{\varrho\,\sigma_2}{\sigma_1}(x - m_1)$$

and the s. d. $\sigma_2 \sqrt{1 - \varrho^2}$. Thus the regression of η on ξ is linear, and the conditional variance of η is independent of the value assumed by ξ. — The analogous properties of the conditional distribution of ξ for a given value of η are deduced in the same way.

When the non-negative form $Q(t, u)$ is *semi-definite*, the determinant M is zero, and no reciprocal form exists (cf 11.7 and 11.10). It follows, however, from the preceding paragraph that the expression (21.12.2) is still the c. f. of a certain distribution, and this will be called a *singular normal distribution*. By 21.2, the total mass of this distribution is situated in a single point or on a straight line, according as the rank of the moment matrix $\boldsymbol{M}$ is 0 or 1.

In such a case, it is evident that no finite two-dimensional fr. f. exists. Still, a singular normal distribution may always be regarded as the *limit* of a sequence of non-singular normal distributions. In order to see this, we may consider the sequence of non-singular normal distributions corresponding to the given values of m_1 and m_2, and the sequence of definite positive forms $Q_\nu(t, u) = Q(t, u) + \varepsilon_\nu^2(t^2 + u^2)$, where $\varepsilon_\nu \to 0$. The corresponding c. f:s tend, of course, to the limit (21.12.2), and by the continuity theorem 10.7 the non-singular distributions then tend to the given singular distribution.

Consider a singular normal distribution with a moment matrix $\boldsymbol{M}$ of rank 1. By 21.8, the corresponding variables ξ and η may, with a probability equal to 1, be represented as linear functions of a single variable X. Conversely, X is a linear function of ξ and η, and the c. f. of X is then of the form $e^{mit-\frac{1}{2}\sigma^2 t^2}$, so that X is normally distributed. The case when $\boldsymbol{M}$ is of rank 0 may be regarded as the limiting case $\sigma = 0$, and we thus have the following result:

A two-dimensional singular normal distribution may be regarded as an ordinary one-dimensional normal distribution on a certain straight line in the plane.

When $m_1 = m_2 = 0$, we obtain from (12.6.8) the following expansion of the normal fr. f. in powers of ϱ:

$$f(x, y) = \frac{1}{2\pi\sigma_1\sigma_2\sqrt{1-\varrho^2}} e^{-\frac{1}{2(1-\varrho^2)}\left(\frac{x^2}{\sigma_1^2} - \frac{2\varrho x y}{\sigma_1\sigma_2} + \frac{y^2}{\sigma_2^2}\right)} = \tag{21.12.5}$$

$$= \frac{1}{\sigma_1\sigma_2}\sum_0^\infty \frac{\Phi^{(\nu+1)}\left(\frac{x}{\sigma_1}\right)\Phi^{(\nu+1)}\left(\frac{y}{\sigma_2}\right)}{\nu!}\varrho^\nu.$$

The series may be integrated term by term, and we deduce a corresponding expression for the normal d. f.

$$\int_{-\infty}^{x}\int_{-\infty}^{y} f(u, v)\,du\,dv = \sum_0^\infty \frac{\Phi^{(\nu)}\left(\frac{x}{\sigma_1}\right)\Phi^{(\nu)}\left(\frac{y}{\sigma_2}\right)}{\nu!}\varrho^\nu. \tag{21.12.6}$$

For $x = y = 0$ we obtain from (21.12.5)

$$\sum_0^\infty \frac{[\Phi^{(\nu+1)}(0)]^2}{\nu!}\varrho^\nu = \frac{1}{2\pi\sqrt{1-\varrho^2}},$$

and hence by integration with respect to ϱ

$$\sum_1^\infty \frac{[\Phi^{(\nu)}(0)]^2}{\nu!}\varrho^\nu = \frac{1}{2\pi}\int_0^\varrho \frac{dr}{\sqrt{1-r^2}} = \frac{1}{2\pi}\arcsin\varrho.$$

Now (21.12.6) gives

$$\int_{-\infty}^{0}\int_{-\infty}^{0} f(u, v)\,du\,dv = \tfrac{1}{4} + \frac{1}{2\pi}\arcsin\varrho.$$

By the symmetry properties of the fr. f. $f(x, y)$, it then follows that in each of the first and third quadrants of the (x, y)-plane we have the mass $\frac{1}{4} + \frac{1}{2\pi}\arcsin\varrho$, while each of the second and fourth quadrants contains the mass $\frac{1}{4} - \frac{1}{2\pi}\arcsin\varrho$. These relations are due to Stieltjes, Ref. 220, and Sheppard, Ref. 211.

CHAPTER 22.

General Properties of Distributions in $\boldsymbol{R}_n$.

22.1. Two simple types of distributions. Conditional distributions. — The joint probability distribution (cf 14.2) of n one-dimensional random variables $\xi_1, \ldots, \xi_n$ is a distribution in the n-dimensional space $\boldsymbol{R}_n$, with the variable point $\boldsymbol{x} = (\xi_1, \ldots, \xi_n)$.

The *probability function* (cf 8.4) of the distribution is a set function $P(S) = P(\boldsymbol{x} < S)$, which for any set S in $\boldsymbol{R}_n$ represents the probability of the relation $\boldsymbol{x} < S$. The *distribution function*, on the other hand, is a function of n real variables defined by the relation (8.3.1):

$$F(x_1, \ldots, x_n) = P(\xi_1 \leqq x_1, \ldots, \xi_n \leqq x_n).$$

The distribution is uniquely defined by either function P or F.

As before, we shall make a frequent use of our mechanical illustration, interpreting the probability distribution by means of a distribution of a unit of mass over $\boldsymbol{R}_n$. If we pick out a group of k variables $\xi_{\nu_1}, \ldots, \xi_{\nu_k}$, and project the mass in the original n-dimensional distribution on the k-dimensional subspace of these variables, we obtain (cf 8.4) the *k-dimensional marginal distribution* of $\xi_{\nu_1}, \ldots, \xi_{\nu_k}$. The corresponding marginal d. f. is obtained, as in the two-dimensional case, by putting the $n-k$ remaining variables in F equal to $+\infty$. Thus in particular the marginal d. f. of the single variable ξ_1 is $F_1(x) = F(x, \infty, \ldots, \infty)$, and similarly for any ξ_ν.

As in the cases $n = 1$ and $n = 2$ (cf 15.2 and 21.1), we now introduce the two simple types of distributions: the *discrete* and the *continuous* type. The definitions and properties of these are directly analogous to those given in 21.1, and we shall here only add some brief comments.

For a distribution of the *discrete* type, we have on the axis of each ξ_ν a finite or enumerable set of points $x_{\nu 1}, x_{\nu 2}, \ldots$, which are the discrete mass points of the marginal distribution of ξ_ν. The total mass of the n-dimensional distribution of $\boldsymbol{x} = (\xi_1, \ldots, \xi_n)$ is then concentrated in the discrete points $(x_{1 i_1}, \ldots, x_{n i_n})$, each of these points carrying a mass $p_{i_1 \ldots i_n} \geqq 0$, so that

$$P(\xi_1 = x_{1 i_1}, \ldots, \xi_n = x_{n i_n}) = p_{i_1 \ldots i_n},$$

$$\sum_{i_1, \ldots, i_n} p_{i_1 \ldots i_n} = 1.$$

The marginal distribution of any group of k variables is also of the discrete type, and the corresponding p:s are obtained in a similar way as in (21.1.2) and (21.1.3), by summing $p_{i_1 \ldots i_n}$ over all values of the $n - k$ remaining variables.

For a distribution of the *continuous* type, the d. f. F is everywhere continuous, and the *probability density* or *frequency function* (cf 8.4)

$$f(x_1, \ldots, x_n) = \frac{\partial^n F}{\partial x_1 \ldots \partial x_n}$$

exists and is continuous everywhere, except possibly in certain points belonging to a finite number of hypersurfaces in $\boldsymbol{R}_n$. The differential $f(x_1, \ldots, x_n)\, d x_1 \ldots d x_n$ will be called the *probability element* (cf 15.1) of the distribution. The fr. f. of the marginal distribution of any group of k variables is obtained by integrating $f(x_1, \ldots, x_n)$ with respect to the $n - k$ remaining variables, as shown for the two-dimensional case by (21.1.5) and (21.1.6).

When $\xi_1, \ldots, \xi_n$ have a distribution of the continuous type, the *conditional fr. f.* of $\xi_1, \ldots, \xi_k$, relative to the hypothesis $\xi_{k+1} = x_{k+1}, \ldots, \xi_n = x_n$, is given by the expression generalizing (21.4.10):

$$f(x_1, \ldots, x_k \mid x_{k+1}, \ldots, x_n) =$$

$$(22.1.1) \qquad = \frac{f(x_1, \ldots, x_n)}{\int\limits_{-\infty}^{\infty} \cdots \int\limits_{-\infty}^{\infty} f(\xi_1, \ldots, \xi_k, x_{k+1}, \ldots, x_n)\, d\xi_1 \ldots d\xi_k}.$$

Finally, let us consider two variables $\boldsymbol{x} = (\xi_1, \ldots, \xi_m)$ and $\boldsymbol{y} = (\eta_1, \ldots, \eta_n)$ such that the $(m + n)$-dimensional combined variable $(\boldsymbol{x}, \boldsymbol{y})$ has a distribution of the continuous type. In generalization of (21.1.7) we then find that a necessary and sufficient condition for the independence of $\boldsymbol{x}$ and $\boldsymbol{y}$ is

$$(22.1.2) \qquad f(x_1, \ldots, x_m, y_1, \ldots, y_n) = f_1(x_1, \ldots, x_m) f_2(y_1, \ldots, y_n),$$

where f, f_1 and f_2 are the fr. f:s of $(\boldsymbol{x}, \boldsymbol{y})$, $\boldsymbol{x}$ and $\boldsymbol{y}$ respectively. The generalization to any number of variables $\boldsymbol{x}, \boldsymbol{y}, \ldots$ is immediate.

22.2. Change of variables in a continuous distribution. — Let $\boldsymbol{x} = (\xi_1, \ldots, \xi_n)$ be a random variable in $\boldsymbol{R}_n$, and consider the m functions

$$(22.2.1) \qquad \eta_i = g_i(\xi_1, \ldots, \xi_n), \qquad (i = 1, 2, \ldots, m),$$

where m is not necessarily equal to n. According to 14.5, the vector $\boldsymbol{y} = (\eta_1, \ldots, \eta_m)$ then constitutes a random variable in a space $\boldsymbol{R}_m$ of m dimensions, with a probability distribution uniquely determined by the distribution of $\boldsymbol{x}$.

We shall here only consider the particular case when $m = n$, and the $\boldsymbol{x}$-distribution belongs to the continuous type. If the functions g_i satisfy certain conditions, the $\boldsymbol{y}$-distribution may then be explicitly determined, as we are now going to show.

Let us assume that the following conditions A) and B) are satisfied for all $\boldsymbol{x}$ such that the fr. f. $f(x_1, \ldots, x_n)$ is different from zero:

A) The functions g_i are everywhere unique and continuous, and have continuous partial derivatives $\frac{\partial \eta_i}{\partial \xi_k}$ in all points $\boldsymbol{x}$, except possibly in certain points belonging to a finite number of hypersurfaces.

B) The relations (22.2.1), where we now take $m = n$, define a one-to-one correspondence between the points $\boldsymbol{x} = (\xi_1, \ldots, \xi_n)$ and $\boldsymbol{y} = (\eta_1, \ldots, \eta_n)$, so that we have conversely $\xi_i = h_i(\eta_1, \ldots, \eta_n)$ for $i = 1, \ldots, n$, where the h_i are unique.

Consider a point $\boldsymbol{x}$ which does not belong to any of the exceptional hypersurfaces, and is such that the Jacobian $\frac{\partial(\eta_1, \ldots, \eta_n)}{\partial(\xi_1, \ldots, \xi_n)} = \left|\frac{\partial \eta_i}{\partial \xi_k}\right|$ is different from zero. The Jacobian of the inverse transformation, $J = \frac{\partial(\xi_1, \ldots, \xi_n)}{\partial(\eta_1, \ldots, \eta_n)} = \left|\frac{\partial \xi_i}{\partial \eta_k}\right|$ is then finite in the point $\boldsymbol{y}$ corresponding to $\boldsymbol{x}$, since we have

$$\frac{\partial(\eta_1, \ldots, \eta_n)}{\partial(\xi_1, \ldots, \xi_n)} \cdot \frac{\partial(\xi_1, \ldots, \xi_n)}{\partial(\eta_1, \ldots, \eta_n)} = 1.$$

When S is a sufficiently small neighbourhood of $\boldsymbol{x}$, and T is the corresponding set in the $\boldsymbol{y}$-space, J is finite for all points of T, and we have

$$P(S) = \int_S f(x_1, \ldots, x_n)\, d x_1 \ldots d x_n = \int_T f(x_1, \ldots, x_n) |J|\, d y_1 \ldots d y_n \tag{22.2.2}$$

where in the last integral the x_i should be replaced by their expressions $x_i = h_i(y_1, \ldots, y_n)$ in terms of the y_i.

The probability element of the $\boldsymbol{x}$-distribution is thus transformed according to the relation

$$f(x_1, \ldots, x_n)\, d x_1 \ldots d x_n = f(x_1, \ldots, x_n) |J|\, d y_1 \ldots d y_n, \tag{22.2.3}$$

where in the second member $x_i = h_i(y_1, \ldots, y_n)$. The fr. f. of the new variable $\boldsymbol{y} = (\eta_1, \ldots, \eta_n)$ is thus $f(x_1, \ldots, x_n)\,|J|$.

When $n = 1$, and the transformation $\eta = g(\xi)$ or $\xi = h(\eta)$ is unique in both senses, (22.2.3) reduces to

$$f(x)\,d\,x = f[h(y)]\,|\,h'(y)\,|\,d\,y,$$

where the coefficient of $d\,y$ is the fr. f. of the variable η. An example of this relation is given by the expression (15.1.2), which is related to the linear transformation $\eta = a\,\xi + b$, or $\xi = \frac{\eta - b}{a}$.

Suppose now that the condition B is not satisfied. To each point $\boldsymbol{x}$, there still corresponds one and only one point $\boldsymbol{y}$, but the converse transformation is not unique: to a given $\boldsymbol{y}$ there may correspond more than one $\boldsymbol{x}$. We then have to divide the $\boldsymbol{x}$-space in several parts, so that in each part the correspondence is unique in both senses. The mass carried by a set T in the $\boldsymbol{y}$-space will then be equal to the sum of the contributions arising from the corresponding sets in the various parts of the $\boldsymbol{x}$-space. Each contribution is represented by a multiple integral that may be transformed according to (22.2.2), and it thus follows that the fr. f. of $\boldsymbol{y}$ now assumes the form $\Sigma f_\nu\,|\,J_\nu\,|$, where the sum is extended over the various points $\boldsymbol{x}$ corresponding to a given $\boldsymbol{y}$, and f_ν and J_ν are the corresponding values of $f(x_1, \ldots, x_n)$ and J.

In the case $n = 1$, an example of this type is afforded by the transformation $\eta = \xi^2$ considered in 15.1. The expression (15.1.4) for the fr. f. is evidently a special case of the general expression $\Sigma f_\nu\,|\,J_\nu\,|$. — A more complicated example will occur in 29.3.

22.3. Mean values, moments. — The mean value of a function $g(\xi_1, \ldots, \xi_n)$ integrable over $\boldsymbol{R}_n$ with respect to the n-dimensional pr. f. $P(S)$ has been defined in (15.3.2) by the integral

$$\boldsymbol{E}\,g(\xi_1, \ldots, \xi_n) = \int_{\boldsymbol{R}_n} g(x_1, \ldots, x_n)\,d\,P.$$

The *moments* of the distribution (cf 9.2 and 21.2) are the mean values

$$\alpha_{\nu_1 \ldots \nu_n} = \boldsymbol{E}\,(\xi_1^{\nu_1} \ldots \xi_n^{\nu_n}) = \int_{\boldsymbol{R}_n} x_1^{\nu_1} \ldots x_n^{\nu_n}\,d\,P, \tag{22.3.1}$$

where $\nu_1 + \cdots + \nu_n$ is the *order* of the moment. For the first order moments we shall use the notation

$$m_i = \boldsymbol{E}\,(\xi_i) = \int_{\boldsymbol{R}_n} x_i\,d\,P.$$

The point $\boldsymbol{m} = (m_1, \ldots, m_n)$ is the *centre of gravity* of the mass in the n-dimensional distribution.

The *central moments* $\mu_{\nu_1 \ldots \nu_n}$, or the moments about the point $\boldsymbol{m}$, are obtained by replacing in (22.3.1) each power $\xi_i^{\nu_i}$ by $(\xi_i - m_i)^{\nu_i}$. The *second order central moments* play an important part in the sequel, and whenever nothing is explicitly said to the contrary, we shall always assume that these are finite. The use of the μ-notation for these moments would be somewhat awkward when $n > 2$, owing to the large number of subscripts required. In order to simplify the writing, we shall find it convenient to introduce a particular notation, putting

$$\lambda_{ii} = \sigma_i^2 = \boldsymbol{E}(\xi_i - m_i)^2, \tag{22.3.2}$$
$$\lambda_{ik} = \varrho_{ik}\,\sigma_i\,\sigma_k = \boldsymbol{E}((\xi_i - m_i)(\xi_k - m_k)).$$

Thus λ_{ii} denotes the variance and σ_i the s. d. of the variable ξ_i, while λ_{ik} denotes the covariance of ξ_i and ξ_k. The correlation coefficient $\varrho_{ik} = \dfrac{\lambda_{ik}}{\sigma_i\,\sigma_k}$ is, of course, defined only when σ_i and σ_k are both positive.

Obviously we have $\lambda_{ki} = \lambda_{ik}$, $\varrho_{ki} = \varrho_{ik}$ and $\varrho_{ii} = 1$. — In the particular case $n = 2$, we have $\lambda_{11} = \mu_{20}$, $\lambda_{12} = \mu_{11}$, $\lambda_{22} = \mu_{02}$.

In generalization of (21.2.5), we find that the mean value

$$\boldsymbol{E}\left(\sum_1^n t_i(\xi_i - m_i)\right)^2 = \sum_{i,\,k=1}^n \lambda_{ik}\,t_i\,t_k \tag{22.3.3}$$

is never negative, so that the second member is a non-negative quadratic form in $t_1, \ldots, t_n$. The matrix of this form is the *moment matrix*

$$\boldsymbol{\Lambda} = \begin{Bmatrix} \lambda_{11} & \ldots & \lambda_{1n} \\ \cdot & \cdot & \cdot \\ \lambda_{n1} & \ldots & \lambda_{nn} \end{Bmatrix},$$

while the form obtained by the substitution $t_i = \dfrac{u_i}{\sigma_i}$ corresponds to the *correlation matrix*

$$\boldsymbol{P} = \begin{Bmatrix} \varrho_{11} & \ldots & \varrho_{1n} \\ \cdot & \cdot & \cdot \\ \varrho_{n1} & \ldots & \varrho_{nn} \end{Bmatrix},$$

which is defined as soon as all the σ_i are positive.

Thus the symmetric matrices $\boldsymbol{\Lambda}$ and $\boldsymbol{P}$ are both non-negative (cf 11.10). Between $\boldsymbol{\Lambda}$ and $\boldsymbol{P}$, we have the relation

$$\boldsymbol{\Lambda} = \boldsymbol{\Sigma} \boldsymbol{P} \boldsymbol{\Sigma}$$

where $\boldsymbol{\Sigma}$ denotes the diagonal matrix formed with $\sigma_1, \ldots, \sigma_n$ as its diagonal elements. By 11.6, it then follows that $\boldsymbol{\Lambda}$ and $\boldsymbol{P}$ have the same rank. For the corresponding determinants $\Lambda = |\lambda_{ik}|$ and $P = |\varrho_{ik}|$, we have $\Lambda = \sigma_1^2 \ldots \sigma_n^2 P$. From (11.10.3) we obtain

$$(22.3.4) \qquad 0 \leqq \Lambda \leqq \lambda_{11} \ldots \lambda_{nn}, \qquad 0 \leqq P \leqq \varrho_{11} \ldots \varrho_{nn} = 1.$$

In the particular case when $\lambda_{ik} = 0$ for $i \neq k$, we shall say that the variables $\xi_1, \ldots, \xi_n$ are *uncorrelated*. The moment matrix $\boldsymbol{\Lambda}$ is then a diagonal matrix, and $\Lambda = \lambda_{11} \ldots \lambda_{nn}$. If, in addition, all the σ_i are positive, the correlation matrix $\boldsymbol{P}$ exists and is identical with the unit matrix $\boldsymbol{I}$, so that $P = 1$. Moreover, it is *only* in the uncorrelated case that we have $\Lambda = \lambda_{11} \ldots \lambda_{nn}$ and $P = 1$.

22.4. Characteristic functions. — The c. f. of the n-dimensional random variable $\boldsymbol{x} = (\xi_1, \ldots, \xi_n)$ is a function of the vector $\boldsymbol{t} = (t_1, \ldots, t_n)$, defined by the mean value (cf 10.6)

$$\varphi(\boldsymbol{t}) = \boldsymbol{E}(e^{i \boldsymbol{t}' \boldsymbol{x}}) = \int_{\boldsymbol{R}_n} e^{i \boldsymbol{t}' \boldsymbol{x}} \, dP,$$

where, in accordance with (11.2.1), $\boldsymbol{t}' \boldsymbol{x} = t_1 \xi_1 + \cdots + t_n \xi_n$. The properties of the c. f. of a two-dimensional variable (cf 21.3) directly extend themselves to the case of a general n. In particular we have in the neighbourhood of $\boldsymbol{t} = 0$ a development generalizing (21.3.2)

$$(22.4.1) \qquad \varphi(\boldsymbol{t}) = e^{i \boldsymbol{t}' \boldsymbol{m}} \left(1 + \frac{i^2}{2!} \sum_{j,k} \lambda_{jk} t_j t_k + o\left(\sum_j t_j^2\right)\right).$$

If $\boldsymbol{m} = 0$, this reduces to

$$(22.4.2) \qquad \varphi(\boldsymbol{t}) = 1 - \tfrac{1}{2} \sum_{j,k} \lambda_{jk} t_j t_k + o\left(\sum_j t_j^2\right).$$

The *semi-invariants* of a distribution in n dimensions are defined by means of the expansion of $\log \varphi$ in the same way as in 15.10 for the case $n = 1$.

As in 21.3, it is shown that a necessary and sufficient condition for the independence of the variables $\boldsymbol{x}$ and $\boldsymbol{y}$ is that their joint c. f. is of the form $\varphi(\boldsymbol{t}, \boldsymbol{u}) = \varphi_1(\boldsymbol{t}) \varphi_2(\boldsymbol{u})$.

The c. f. of the marginal distribution of any group of k variables picked out from $\xi_1, \ldots, \xi_n$ is obtained from $\varphi(\boldsymbol{t})$ by putting $t_i = 0$ for all the $n - k$ remaining variables. Thus the joint c. f. of $\xi_1, \ldots, \xi_k$ is

$$\boldsymbol{E}\left(e^{i(t_1 \xi_1 + \cdots + t_k \xi_k)}\right) = \varphi(t_1, \ldots, t_k, 0, \ldots, 0). \tag{22.4.3}$$

22.5. Rank of a distribution. — The *rank* of a distribution in $\boldsymbol{R}_n$ (Frisch, Ref. 113; cf also Lukomski, Ref. 151) will be defined as the common rank r of the moment matrix $\boldsymbol{\Lambda}$ and the correlation matrix $\boldsymbol{P}$ introduced in 22.3. The distribution will be called *singular* or *non-singular*, according as $r < n$ or $r = n$.

In the particular case $n = 2$, $\boldsymbol{\Lambda}$ is identical with the matrix $\boldsymbol{M}$ considered in 21.2. It was there shown that the rank of $\boldsymbol{M}$ is directly connected with certain linear degeneration properties of the distribution. We shall now prove that a similar connection exists in the case of a general n.

A distribution in $\boldsymbol{R}_n$ is non-singular when and only when there is no hyperplane in $\boldsymbol{R}_n$ that contains the total mass of the distribution.

In order that a distribution in $\boldsymbol{R}_n$ should be of rank r, where $r < n$, it is necessary and sufficient that the total mass of the distribution should belong to a linear set L_r of r dimensions, but not to any linear set of less than r dimensions.

Obviously it is sufficient to prove the second part of this theorem, since the first part then follows as a corollary. We recall that, by 3.4, a linear set of r dimensions in $\boldsymbol{R}_n$ is defined by $n - r$ independent linear relations between the coordinates.

Suppose first that we are given a distribution of rank $r < n$. The quadratic form of matrix $\boldsymbol{\Lambda}$

$$Q(\boldsymbol{t}) = \sum_{i,k} \lambda_{ik} t_i t_k = \boldsymbol{E}\left(\sum_i t_i (\xi_i - m_i)\right)^2 \tag{22.5.1}$$

is then of rank r, and accordingly (cf 11.10) there are exactly $n - r$ linearly independent vectors $\boldsymbol{t}_p = (t_1^{(p)}, \ldots, t_n^{(p)})$ such that $Q(\boldsymbol{t}_p) = 0$. For each vector $\boldsymbol{t}_p$, (22.5.1) shows that the relation

$$\sum_i t_i^{(p)} (\xi_i - m_i) = 0 \tag{22.5.2}$$

must be satisfied with the probability 1. The $n - r$ relations corresponding to the $n - r$ vectors $\boldsymbol{t}_p$ then determine a linear set L_r containing the total mass of the distribution, and since any vector $\boldsymbol{t}$

such that $Q(\boldsymbol{t}) = 0$ must be a linear combination of the $\boldsymbol{t}_p$, there can be no linear set of lower dimensionality with the same property.

Conversely, if it is known that the total mass of the distribution belongs to a linear set L_r, but not to any linear set of lower dimensionality, it is in the first place obvious that L_r passes through the centre of gravity $\boldsymbol{m}$, so that each of the $n-r$ independent relations that define L_r must be of the form (22.5.2). The corresponding set of coefficients $t_i^{(p)}$ then by (22.5.1) defines a vector $\boldsymbol{t}_p$ such that $Q(\boldsymbol{t}_p) = 0$, and since there are exactly $n-r$ independent relations of this kind, $Q(\boldsymbol{t})$ is by 11.10 of rank r, and our theorem is proved.

Thus for a distribution of rank $r < n$, there are exactly $n-r$ independent linear relations between the variables that are satisfied with a probability equal to one. As an example we may consider the case $n = 3$. A singular distribution in $\boldsymbol{R}_3$ is of rank 2, 1 or 0, according as the total mass is confined to a plane, a straight line or a point, and accordingly there are 1, 2 or 3 independent linear relations between the variables that are satisfied with a probability equal to one.

22.6. Linear transformation of variables. — Let $\xi_1, \ldots, \xi_n$ be random variables with a given distribution in $\boldsymbol{R}_n$, such that $\boldsymbol{m} = 0$. Consider a linear transformation

$$\eta_i = \sum_{k=1}^{n} c_{ik} \xi_k \qquad (i = 1, 2, \ldots, m), \tag{22.6.1}$$

with the matrix $\boldsymbol{C} = \boldsymbol{C}_{mn} = \{c_{ik}\}$, where m is not necessarily equal to n. In matrix notation (cf 11.3), the transformation (22.6.1) is simply $\boldsymbol{y} = \boldsymbol{C}\boldsymbol{x}$. This transformation defines a new random variable $\boldsymbol{y} = (\eta_1, \ldots, \eta_m)$ with an m-dimensional distribution uniquely defined by the given n-dimensional distribution of $\boldsymbol{x}$ (cf 14.5 and 22.2).

Obviously every η_i has the mean value zero. Writing $\lambda_{ik} = \boldsymbol{E}(\xi_i \xi_k)$, $\mu_{ik} = \boldsymbol{E}(\eta_i \eta_k)$, we further obtain from (22.6.1)

$$\mu_{ik} = \sum_{r, s=1}^{n} c_{ir} \lambda_{rs} c_{ks}.$$

This holds even when $\boldsymbol{m} \neq 0$, and shows that the moment matrices $\boldsymbol{\Lambda} = \boldsymbol{\Lambda}_{nn} = \{\lambda_{ik}\}$ and $\boldsymbol{M} = \boldsymbol{M}_{mm} = \{\mu_{ik}\}$ satisfy the relation

$$\boldsymbol{M} = \boldsymbol{C} \boldsymbol{\Lambda} \boldsymbol{C}'. \tag{22.6.2}$$

If, in the c. f. $\varphi(\boldsymbol{t})$ of the variable $\boldsymbol{x}$, we replace $t_1, \ldots, t_n$ by new variables $u_1, \ldots, u_m$ by means of the contragredient transformation (cf 11.7.5) $\boldsymbol{t} = \boldsymbol{C}'\boldsymbol{u}$, we have by (11.7.6) $\boldsymbol{t}'\boldsymbol{x} = \boldsymbol{u}'\boldsymbol{y}$, and thus

$$\varphi(\boldsymbol{t}) = \boldsymbol{E}(e^{i\boldsymbol{t}'\boldsymbol{x}}) = \boldsymbol{E}(e^{i\boldsymbol{u}'\boldsymbol{y}}) = \psi(\boldsymbol{u}), \tag{22.6.3}$$

where $\psi(\boldsymbol{u}) = \psi(u_1, \ldots, u_m)$ is the c. f. of the new variable $\boldsymbol{y}$.

From (22.6.2) we infer, by means of the properties of the rank of a product matrix (cf 11.6), that *the rank of the $\boldsymbol{y}$-distribution never exceeds the rank of the $\boldsymbol{x}$-distribution.*

Consider now the particular case $m = n$, and suppose that the transformation matrix $\boldsymbol{C} = \boldsymbol{C}_{nn}$ is non-singular. Then by 11.6 the matrices $\boldsymbol{\Lambda}$ and $\boldsymbol{M}$ have the same rank, so that in this case *the transformation* (22.6.1) *does not affect the rank of the distribution.* — Let us, in particular, choose for $\boldsymbol{C}$ an orthogonal matrix such that the transformed matrix $\boldsymbol{M}$ is a diagonal matrix (cf 11.9). This implies $\mu_{ik} = 0$ for $i \neq k$, so that $\eta_1, \ldots, \eta_n$ are uncorrelated variables (cf the discussion of the case $n = 2$ in 21.8). In this case, the reciprocal matrix $\boldsymbol{C}^{-1}$ exists (cf 11.7), and the reciprocal transformation $\boldsymbol{x} = \boldsymbol{C}^{-1}\boldsymbol{y}$ shows that the ξ_i may be expressed as linear functions of the η_i. If the $\boldsymbol{x}$-distribution is of rank r, the diagonal matrix $\boldsymbol{M}$ contains exactly r positive diagonal elements, while all other elements of $\boldsymbol{M}$ are zeros. If $r < n$, we can always suppose the η_i so arranged that the positive elements are $\mu_{11}, \ldots, \mu_{rr}$. For $i = r + 1, \ldots, n$, we then have $\mu_{ii} = \boldsymbol{E}(\eta_i^2) = 0$, which shows that η_i is almost always equal to zero. Thus we have the following generalization of 21.8:

If the distribution of n variables $\xi_1, \ldots, \xi_n$ is of rank r, the ξ_i may with a probability equal to 1 be expressed as linear functions of r uncorrelated variables $\eta_1, \ldots, \eta_r$.

The concept of *convergence in probability* (cf 20.3) immediately extends itself to multi-dimensional variables. A variable $\boldsymbol{x} = (\xi_1, \ldots, \xi_n)$ is said to converge in probability to the constant vector $\boldsymbol{a} = (a_1, \ldots, a_n)$ if ξ_i converges in probability to a_i for $i = 1, \ldots, n$. We shall require the following analogue of the convergence theorem of 20.6, which may be proved by a straightforward generalization of the proof for the one-dimensional case:

Suppose that we have for every $\nu = 1, 2, \ldots$.

$$\boldsymbol{y}_\nu = \boldsymbol{A}\boldsymbol{x}_\nu + \boldsymbol{z}_\nu,$$

where $\boldsymbol{x}_\nu$, $\boldsymbol{y}_\nu$ and $\boldsymbol{z}_\nu$ are n-dimensional random variables, while $\boldsymbol{A}$ is a matrix of order $n \cdot n$ with constant elements. Suppose further that, as

$n \to \infty$, the n-dimensional distribution of $\boldsymbol{x}_\nu$ tends to a certain limiting distribution, while $\boldsymbol{z}_\nu$ converges in probability to zero. Then $\boldsymbol{y}_\nu$ has the limiting distribution defined by the linear transformation $\boldsymbol{y} = \boldsymbol{A}\,\boldsymbol{x}$, where $\boldsymbol{x}$ has the limiting distribution of the $\boldsymbol{x}_\nu$.

22.7. The ellipsoid of concentration. — The definition of the ellipse of concentration given in 21.10 may be generalized to any number of dimensions. Let the variables $\xi_1, \ldots, \xi_n$ have a non-singular distribution in $\boldsymbol{R}_n$ with $\boldsymbol{m} = 0$ and the second order central moments λ_{ik}, and consider the non-negative quadratic form

$$q(\xi_1, \ldots, \xi_n) = \sum_{i,k} a_{ik}\, \xi_i\, \xi_k.$$

If a mass unit is uniformly distributed (i. e. such that the fr. f. is constant) over the domain bounded by the n-dimensional ellipsoid $q = c^2$, the first order moments of this distribution will evidently be zero, while the second order moments are according to (11.12.4)

$$\frac{c^2}{n+2} \cdot \frac{A_{ik}}{A} \qquad (i, k = 1, 2, \ldots, n).$$

It is now required to determine c and the a_{ik} such that these moments coincide with the given moments λ_{ik}. It is readily seen that this is effected by choosing, in generalization of 21.10, $c^2 = n + 2$ and

$$a_{ik} = \frac{\Lambda_{ki}}{\Lambda} = \frac{\Lambda_{ik}}{\Lambda}.$$

Thus the ellipsoid

$$q(\xi_1, \ldots, \xi_n) = \sum_{i,k} \frac{\Lambda_{ik}}{\Lambda}\, \xi_i\, \xi_k = n + 2 \tag{22.7.1}$$

has the required property. This will be called the *ellipsoid of concentration* corresponding to the given distribution, and will serve as a geometrical illustration of the mode of concentration of the distribution about the origin. The modification of the definition to be made in the case of a general $\boldsymbol{m}$ is obvious. When two distributions with the same centre of gravity are such that one of the concentration ellipsoids lies wholly within the other, the former distribution will be said to have a greater concentration than the latter.

The quadratic form q appearing in (22.7.1) is the reciprocal of the form

$$Q(\xi_1, \ldots, \xi_n) = \sum_{i,k} \lambda_{ik} \xi_i \xi_k.$$

(Since Λ is a symmetric matrix, we may replace Λ_{ki} by Λ_{ik} in the elements of the reciprocal matrix as defined in 11.7.)

The n-dimensional volume of the ellipsoid (22.7.1) has by (11.12.3) the expression

$$\frac{(n+2)^{\frac{n}{2}}\, \pi^{\frac{n}{2}}}{\Gamma\left(\frac{n}{2}+1\right)} \sqrt{\Lambda} = \frac{(n+2)^{\frac{n}{2}}\, \pi^{\frac{n}{2}}}{\Gamma\left(\frac{n}{2}+1\right)} \sigma_1 \ldots \sigma_n \sqrt{P},$$

where the determinants $\Lambda = |\lambda_{ik}|$ and $P = |\varrho_{ik}|$ are both positive, since the distribution is non-singular. When $\sigma_1, \ldots, \sigma_n$ are given, it follows from (22.3.4) that the volume reaches its maximum when the variables are uncorrelated ($P = 1$), while on the other hand the volume tends to zero when the ϱ_{ik} tend to the correlation coefficients of a singular distribution. The ratio between the volume and its maximum value is equal to $\sqrt{P}$; this quantity has been called the *scatter coefficient* of the distribution (Frisch, Ref. 113). It may be regarded as a measure of the degree of »non-singularity» of the distribution. — For $n = 2$, we have $\sqrt{P} = \sqrt{1 - \varrho^2}$.

On the other hand, the square of the volume of the ellipsoid is proportional to the determinant $\Lambda = \sigma_1^2 \ldots \sigma_n^2 P$, and this expression has been called the *generalized variance* of the distribution (Wilks, Ref. 232). For $n = 1$, Λ reduces to the ordinary variance σ^2, and for $n = 2$ we have $\Lambda = \sigma_1^2 \sigma_2^2 (1 - \varrho^2)$.

We finally remark that the identity between the homothetic families generated by the ellipses of concentration and of inertia, which has been pointed out in 21.10 for the two-dimensional case, breaks down for $n > 2$.

CHAPTER 23.

Regression and Correlation in n Variables.

23.1. Regression surfaces. — The regression curves introduced in 21.5 may be generalized to any number of variables, when the distribution belongs to one of the two simple types. Consider e. g. n variables $\xi_1, \ldots, \xi_n$ with a distribution of the continuous type. The *con-*

ditional mean value of ξ_1, relative to the hypothesis $\xi_i = x_i$ for $i = 2, \ldots, n$, is

$$E(\xi_1 \mid \xi_2 = x_2, \ldots, \xi_n = x_n) = m_1(x_2, \ldots, x_n) = \frac{\int\limits_{-\infty}^{\infty} x_1 f(x_1, \ldots, x_n)\, dx_1}{\int\limits_{-\infty}^{\infty} f(x_1, \ldots, x_n)\, dx_1}.$$

The locus of the point $(m_1, x_2, \ldots, x_n)$ for all possible values of $x_2, \ldots, x_n$ is the *regression surface for the mean* of ξ_1, and has the equation

$$x_1 = m_1(x_2, \ldots, x_n),$$

which is a straightforward generalization of (21.5.2).

23.2. Linear mean square regression. — We now consider n variables $\xi_1, \ldots, \xi_n$ with a perfectly general distribution, such that the second order moments are finite. In order to simplify the writing, we shall further in this chapter always suppose $\boldsymbol{m} = 0$. The formulae corresponding to an arbitrary centre of gravity will then be obtained simply by substituting $\xi_i - m_i$ for ξ_i in the relations given below.

The *mean square regression plane* for ξ_1 with respect to $\xi_2, \ldots, \xi_n$ will be defined as that hyperplane

$$\xi_1 = \beta_{12 \cdot 34 \ldots n}\, \xi_2 + \beta_{13 \cdot 24 \ldots n}\, \xi_3 + \cdots + \beta_{1n \cdot 23 \ldots n-1}\, \xi_n \tag{23.2.1}$$

which gives the closest fit to the mass in the n-dimensional distribution in the sense that the mean value

$$E(\xi_1 - \beta_{12 \cdot 34 \ldots n}\, \xi_2 - \cdots - \beta_{1n \cdot 23 \ldots n-1}\, \xi_n)^2 \tag{23.2.2}$$

is as small as possible. Thus the expression on the right hand side of (23.2.1) is the *best linear estimate of* ξ_1 in terms of $\xi_2, \ldots, \xi_n$, in the sense of minimizing (23.2.2). We may here regard $\xi_2, \ldots, \xi_n$ as independent variables, and ξ_1 as a dependent variable which is approximately represented, or estimated, by a linear combination of the independent variables.

In a similar way we define the m. sq. regression plane for any other variable ξ_i, in which case of course ξ_i takes the place of the dependent variable, while all the remaining variables $\xi_1, \ldots, \xi_{i-1}, \xi_{i+1}, \ldots, \xi_n$ are regarded as independent.

For the *regression coefficients*[1]) β, we have here used a notation

[1]) Often also called *partial regression coefficients*.

introduced by Yule (Ref. 251). Each β has two *primary subscripts* followed by a point, and then $n-2$ *secondary subscripts*. The first of the primary subscripts refers to the dependent variable, and the second to that independent variable to which the coefficient is attached. Thus the *order* of the two primary subscripts is essential. The secondary subscripts indicate, in an arbitrary order, the remaining independent variables. — Sometimes, when no misunderstanding seems possible, we may omit the secondary subscripts.

In order to determine the regression coefficients, we differentiate the expression (23.2.2) with respect to each of the $n-1$ unknown coefficients β, and then obtain the $n-1$ equations

$$\begin{aligned}
\lambda_{22}\,\beta_{12} + \lambda_{23}\,\beta_{13} + \cdots + \lambda_{2n}\,\beta_{1n} &= \lambda_{21},\\
\lambda_{32}\,\beta_{12} + \lambda_{33}\,\beta_{13} + \cdots + \lambda_{3n}\,\beta_{1n} &= \lambda_{31},\\
\cdots\cdots\cdots\cdots\cdots\cdots\cdots\cdots\cdots\cdots\\
\lambda_{n2}\,\beta_{12} + \lambda_{n3}\,\beta_{13} + \cdots + \lambda_{nn}\,\beta_{1n} &= \lambda_{n1},
\end{aligned}$$

where we have omitted the secondary subscripts, thus writing β_{1k} instead of the complete expression $\beta_{1k\cdot 23\ldots k-1,\,k+1\ldots n}$. The determinant of this system of equations is Λ_{11}, the cofactor of λ_{11} in the determinant $\Lambda = |\lambda_{ik}|$.

Let us first suppose that the $\boldsymbol{x}$-distribution is non-singular (cf 22.5). The moment matrix $\boldsymbol{\Lambda}$ and the correlation matrix $\boldsymbol{P}$ are then definite positive, so that $\Lambda_{11} > 0$, and by (11.8.2) our equations have a unique solution

$$\beta_{1k} = -\frac{\Lambda_{1k}}{\Lambda_{11}} = -\frac{\sigma_1}{\sigma_k}\cdot\frac{P_{1k}}{P_{11}}. \tag{23.2.3}$$

By simple permutation of indices we obtain the corresponding expression

$$\beta_{ik} = -\frac{\Lambda_{ik}}{\Lambda_{ii}} = -\frac{\sigma_i}{\sigma_k}\cdot\frac{P_{ik}}{P_{ii}} \tag{23.2.4}$$

for the coefficient β_{ik} in the regression plane for ξ_i. The omitted secondary subscripts are here, of course, all the numbers $1, 2, \ldots, n$ with the exception of i and k, while the Λ_{ik} and P_{ik} are cofactors in Λ and P.

In a non-singular distribution, the regression plane for each variable with respect to all the others is thus uniquely determined, and the regression coefficients are given by (23.2.4). — *In the particular case of* n

uncorrelated variables, it follows that all regression coefficients are zero, since we have $\Lambda_{ik} = 0$ for $i \neq k$.

Suppose now that the x-distribution is singular, with a rank $r < n$. We then *may* have $\Lambda_{ii} = 0$, and accordingly some regression coefficients may be infinite or undetermined. As an example, we may consider the case $n = 3$. For a distribution of rank 2, the total mass is situated in a certain plane. As long as this plane is not parallel to one of the axes, it is then obvious that all three regression planes will coincide with this plane, so that all regression coefficients are finite and uniquely determined. If, on the other hand, the plane is parallel to one of the axes, e. g. the axis of ξ_1, the two-dimensional marginal distribution of ξ_2 and ξ_3 will have its total mass confined to a straight line. Now the moment matrix of this marginal distribution has the determinant Λ_{11}, and thus we have $\Lambda_{11} = 0$. In this case, we may say that the regression plane for ξ_1 is parallel to the axis of ξ_1, so that at least one of the regression coefficients $\beta_{12\cdot 3}$ and $\beta_{13\cdot 2}$ is infinite. — For a distribution of rank 1 or 0, on the other hand, the total mass belongs to a certain straight line or to a certain point. Each regression plane must then contain this line or point, but is otherwise undetermined.

As in 21.6, we can show that the m.sq. regression plane (23.2.1) is also the plane of closest fit to the regression surface $x_1 = m_1(x_2, \ldots, x_n)$, for all distributions such that the latter exists. If it is known that the regression surface is a plane, this plane must thus be identical with the m. sq. regression plane.

Consider next a group of any number $h < n$ of the variables ξ, say $\xi_i, \xi_j, \ldots, \xi_q$. The h-dimensional marginal distribution of these variables has a moment matrix which is a certain submatrix $\boldsymbol{\Lambda}^*$ of $\boldsymbol{\Lambda}$. We can then form the regression plane of ξ_i with respect to $\xi_j, \ldots, \xi_q$, and the regression coefficients will be given by expressions analogous to (23.2.4), where Λ_{ii} and Λ_{ik} are replaced by the corresponding cofactors from the determinant $\Lambda^* = |\boldsymbol{\Lambda}^*|$. — If, in particular, we consider the group of the $n-1$ variables $\xi_1, \ldots, \xi_{j-1}, \xi_{j+1}, \ldots, \xi_n$, we obtain

$$\beta_{ik} = -\frac{\Lambda_{jj\cdot ik}}{\Lambda_{jj\cdot ii}} \tag{23.2.5}$$

where the omitted secondary subscripts are the numbers $1, 2, \ldots, n$, with the exception of i, j and k, while $\Lambda_{jj\cdot ik}$ is the cofactor of λ_{ik} in Λ_{jj} (cf 11.5.3).

23.3. Residuals. — Suppose $\Lambda_{11} \neq 0$. The difference

$$(23.3.1) \qquad \eta_{1\cdot 23\ldots n} = \xi_1 - \beta_{12}\xi_2 - \cdots - \beta_{1n}\xi_n,$$

where the regression coefficients β_{1k} are given by (23.2.3), may be considered as that part of the variable ξ_1, which remains after subtraction of the best linear estimate of ξ_1 in terms of $\xi_2, \ldots, \xi_n$. This is known as the *residual* of ξ_1 with respect to $\xi_2, \ldots, \xi_n$.

The residual is uncorrelated with any of the »subtracted» variables We have, in fact, introducing the expressions of the β:s,

$$(23.3.2) \qquad \eta_{1\cdot 23\ldots n} = \frac{1}{\Lambda_{11}} \sum_{1}^{n} \Lambda_{1k}\xi_k.$$

Hence $\boldsymbol{E}(\eta_{1\cdot 23\ldots n}) = 0$, and

$$(23.3.3) \qquad \boldsymbol{E}(\xi_i \eta_{1\cdot 23\ldots n}) = \frac{1}{\Lambda_{11}} \sum_{k=1}^{n} \lambda_{ik}\Lambda_{1k} = \begin{cases} \dfrac{\Lambda}{\Lambda_{11}} & \text{for } i = 1, \\ 0 & \text{for } i = 2, 3, \ldots, n. \end{cases}$$

It follows that the *residual variance* $\sigma^2_{1\cdot 23\ldots n} = \boldsymbol{E}(\eta^2_{1\cdot 23\ldots n})$ is given by

$$(23.3.4) \qquad \sigma^2_{1\cdot 23\ldots n} = \boldsymbol{E}(\xi_1 \eta_{1\cdot 23\ldots n}) = \frac{\Lambda}{\Lambda_{11}} = \sigma_1^2 \frac{P}{P_{11}},$$

and further that the two residuals $\eta_{1\cdot 23\ldots n}$ and $\eta_{i\cdot jk\ldots q}$ are uncorrelated, provided that all subscripts $i, j, \ldots, q$ of the latter occur among the secondary subscripts of the former.

The residual variance $\sigma^2_{1\cdot 23\ldots n}$ may, of course, be regarded as a measure of the greatest closeness of fit that may be obtained when we try to represent ξ_1 by a linear combination of $\xi_2, \ldots, \xi_n$. — In the case $n = 2$, the expression (23.3.4) reduces to $\sigma^2_{1\cdot 2} = \sigma_1^2(1 - \varrho^2)$, in accordance with (21.7.2).

23.4. Partial correlation. — The correlation between the variables ξ_1 and ξ_2 is measured by the correlation coefficient ϱ_{12}, which is sometimes also called the *total correlation coefficient* of ξ_1 and ξ_2. If ξ_1 and ξ_2 are considered in conjunction with $n-2$ further variables $\xi_3, \ldots, \xi_n$ we may, however, regard the variation of ξ_1 and ξ_2 as to a certain extent due to the variation of these other variables. Now the residuals $\eta_{1\cdot 34\ldots n}$ and $\eta_{2\cdot 34\ldots n}$ represent, according to the preceding paragraph, those parts of the variables ξ_1 and ξ_2 respectively, which remain after subtraction of the best linear estimates in terms of $\xi_3, \ldots, \xi_n$. Thus we may regard the correlation coefficient between these two residuals as a measure of the correlation between ξ_1 and ξ_2 *after removal of any part of the variation due to the influence of* $\xi_3, \ldots, \xi_n$. This will be called the *partial correlation coefficient* of ξ_1 and ξ_2, with respect to $\xi_3, \ldots, \xi_n$, and will be denoted by $\varrho_{12 \cdot 34 \ldots n}$. Here the order of the subscripts is, of course, immaterial for primary as well as for secondary subscripts. — We thus have

$$\varrho_{12 \cdot 34 \ldots n} = \frac{\boldsymbol{E}(\eta_{1 \cdot 34 \ldots n}\, \eta_{2 \cdot 34 \ldots n})}{\sqrt{\boldsymbol{E}(\eta_{1 \cdot 34 \ldots n}^2)\, \boldsymbol{E}(\eta_{2 \cdot 34 \ldots n}^2)}}. \tag{23.4.1}$$

This expression being an ordinary correlation coefficient between two random variables, we must have $-1 \leqq \varrho_{12 \cdot 34 \ldots n} \leqq 1$.

The residuals $\eta_{1 \cdot 34 \ldots n}$ and $\eta_{2 \cdot 34 \ldots n}$ may be expressed in a form analogous to (23.3.2), if we make use of the expression (23.2.5) for the regression coefficients in a group of $n-1$ variables. We then obtain the two following relations analogous to (23.3.4)

$$\boldsymbol{E}(\eta_{1 \cdot 34 \ldots, n}^2) = \boldsymbol{E}(\xi_1\, \eta_{1 \cdot 34 \ldots n}) = \frac{\Lambda_{22}}{\Lambda_{22 \cdot 11}} = \frac{\Lambda_{22}}{\Lambda_{11 \cdot 22}},$$

$$\boldsymbol{E}(\eta_{2 \cdot 34 \ldots n}^2) = \boldsymbol{E}(\xi_2\, \eta_{2 \cdot 34 \ldots n}) = \frac{\Lambda_{11}}{\Lambda_{11 \cdot 22}},$$

and further

$$\boldsymbol{E}(\eta_{1 \cdot 34 \ldots n}\, \eta_{2 \cdot 34 \ldots n}) = \boldsymbol{E}(\xi_1\, \eta_{2 \cdot 34 \ldots n}) = \frac{1}{\Lambda_{11 \cdot 22}} \sum_{2}^{n} \lambda_{1k}\, \Lambda_{11 \cdot 2k} = -\frac{\Lambda_{12}}{\Lambda_{11 \cdot 22}}.$$

Inserting these expressions in (23.4.1) we obtain the simple formula

$$\varrho_{12 \cdot 34 \ldots n} = -\frac{\Lambda_{12}}{\sqrt{\Lambda_{11}\, \Lambda_{22}}} = -\frac{P_{12}}{\sqrt{P_{11}\, P_{22}}}. \tag{23.4.2}$$

By index permutation we obtain an analogous expression for the partial correlation coefficient of any two variables ξ_i and ξ_k, with respect to the $n-2$ remaining variables.

It is thus seen that any partial correlation coefficient may be expressed in terms of the central moments λ_{ik}, or the total correlation coefficients ϱ_{ik} of the variables concerned. Thus we obtain, e. g., in the case $n = 3$

$$\varrho_{12 \cdot 3} = \frac{\varrho_{12} - \varrho_{13}\, \varrho_{23}}{\sqrt{(1-\varrho_{13}^2)(1-\varrho_{23}^2)}}. \tag{23.4.3}$$

In the particular case of n uncorrelated variables, it follows from (23.4.2) that all partial correlation coefficients are, like the corresponding total correlation coefficients, equal to zero. We thus have, e. g., $\varrho_{12 \cdot 34 \ldots n} = \varrho_{12} = 0$. As soon as there is correlation between the variables, however, $\varrho_{12 \cdot 34 \ldots n}$ is in general different from ϱ_{12}. It is, e. g., easily seen from (23.4.3) that ϱ_{12} and $\varrho_{12 \cdot 3}$ may have different signs, and that either of these coefficients may be equal to zero, while the other is different from zero.

When all total correlation coefficients ϱ_{ik} are known, the partial correlation coefficients may be directly calculated from (23.4.2) and the analogous explicit expressions obtained by index permutation. The numerical calculations may be simplified by the use of certain recurrence relations, such as

$$\varrho_{12 \cdot 34 \ldots n} = \frac{\varrho_{12 \cdot 34 \ldots n-1} - \varrho_{1n \cdot 34 \ldots n-1}\,\varrho_{2n \cdot 34 \ldots n-1}}{\sqrt{(1 - \varrho^2_{1n \cdot 34 \ldots n-1})(1 - \varrho^2_{2n \cdot 34 \ldots n-1})}}, \tag{23.4.4}$$

(cf Ex. 11, p. 319), which shows an obvious analogy to (23.4.3). By this relation, any partial correlation coefficient may be expressed in terms of similar coefficients, where the number of secondary subscripts is reduced by one. Starting from the total coefficients ϱ_{ik}, we may thus first calculate all partial coefficients $\varrho_{ij \cdot k}$ with one secondary subscript, then the coefficients $\varrho_{ij \cdot kl}$ with two secondary subscripts, etc.

Further, when the total and partial correlation coefficients are known, any desired residual variances and partial regression coefficients may be calculated by means of the relations (cf Ex. 12—13, p. 319)

$$\begin{aligned} \sigma^2_{1 \cdot 23 \ldots n} &= \sigma^2_1 (1 - \varrho^2_{12})(1 - \varrho^2_{13 \cdot 2})(1 - \varrho^2_{14 \cdot 23}) \ldots (1 - \varrho^2_{1n \cdot 23 \ldots n-1}), \\ \beta_{12 \cdot 34 \ldots n} &= \varrho_{12 \cdot 34 \ldots n} \frac{\sigma_{1 \cdot 34 \ldots n}}{\sigma_{2 \cdot 34 \ldots n}}, \end{aligned} \tag{23.4.5}$$

and the analogous relations obtained by index permutation. It will be seen that these relations are direct generalizations of (21.6.9) and (21.6.10). — From the last relation we obtain

$$\varrho^2_{12 \cdot 34 \ldots n} = \beta_{12 \cdot 34 \ldots n}\, \beta_{21 \cdot 34 \ldots n}. \tag{23.4.6}$$

23.5. The multiple correlation coefficient. — Consider the residual defined by (23.3.1)

$$\eta_{1 \cdot 23 \ldots n} = \xi_1 - \beta_{12}\,\xi_2 - \cdots - \beta_{1n}\,\xi_n = \xi_1 - \xi_1^*,$$

where $\xi_1^* = \beta_{12}\,\xi_2 + \cdots + \beta_{1n}\,\xi_n$ is the best linear estimate of ξ_1 in terms of $\xi_2, \ldots, \xi_n$. It is easily shown that, among all linear combinations of $\xi_2, \ldots, \xi_n$, it is ξ_1^* that has the *maximum correlation* with ξ_1, as measured by the ordinary correlation coefficient. The correlation coefficient of the variables ξ_1 and ξ_1^* may thus be regarded as a measure of the correlation between ξ_1 on the one side, and the *totality of all variables* $\xi_2, \ldots, \xi_n$ on the other. We shall call this the *multiple correlation coefficient* between ξ_1 and $(\xi_2, \ldots, \xi_n)$, and write

$$\varrho_{1(23\ldots n)} = \frac{\boldsymbol{E}(\xi_1 \xi_1^*)}{\sqrt{\boldsymbol{E}(\xi_1^2)\,\boldsymbol{E}(\xi_1^{*2})}}. \tag{23.5.1}$$

By (23.3.3) and (23.3.4) we have, however, writing for simplicity η_1 instead of $\eta_{1\cdot 23\ldots n}$

$$\boldsymbol{E}(\xi_1 \xi_1^*) = \boldsymbol{E}(\xi_1(\xi_1 - \eta_1)) = \lambda_{11} - \frac{\Lambda}{\Lambda_{11}},$$

$$\boldsymbol{E}(\xi_1^{*2}) = \boldsymbol{E}(\xi_1^2 - 2\,\xi_1\eta_1 + \eta_1^2) = \lambda_{11} - \frac{\Lambda}{\Lambda_{11}},$$

and thus

$$\varrho_{1(23\ldots n)} = \sqrt{1 - \frac{\Lambda}{\lambda_{11}\Lambda_{11}}} = \sqrt{1 - \frac{P}{P_{11}}}. \tag{23.5.2}$$

By (11.10.2) we have $\Lambda \leqq \lambda_{11}\Lambda_{11}$, so that $\boldsymbol{E}(\xi_1 \xi_1^*) \geqq 0$, and

$$0 \leqq \varrho_{1(23\ldots n)} \leqq 1.$$

When $\varrho_{1(23\ldots n)} = 1$, the variable ξ_1 is »almost certainly» equal to a linear combination of $\xi_2, \ldots, \xi_n$. This means that the total mass of the joint distribution of all n variables is confined to a certain hyperplane in $\boldsymbol{R}_n$, so that the distribution is singular, and we have $\Lambda = P = 0$, in accordance with (23.5.2). On the other hand, for a non-singular distribution it follows from the development (11.5.3) that we have

$$\varrho_{1(23\ldots n)}^2 = \frac{1}{P_{11}} \sum_{i,k=2}^{n} P_{11\cdot ik}\,\varrho_{1i}\,\varrho_{1k},$$

where the sum in the second member is, by 11.10, a definite positive quadratic form in the variables $\varrho_{12}, \ldots, \varrho_{1n}$. Thus $\varrho_{1(23\ldots n)} = 0$ when and only when $\varrho_{12} = \cdots = \varrho_{1n} = 0$ i. e. when ξ_1 is uncorrelated with every ξ_i for $i = 2, 3, \ldots, n$.

For the numerical calculation, it is convenient to use the relation (cf Ex. 13, p. 319)

$$\varrho_{1(23\ldots n)}^2 = 1 - \frac{\sigma_{1\cdot 23\ldots n}^2}{\sigma_1^2}. \tag{23.5.3}$$

23.6. Orthogonal mean square regression. — The orthogonal m. sq. regression line introduced in 21.6 may be generalized to any number of variables. A hyperplane H passing through the centre of gravity $\boldsymbol{m} = 0$ of our n-dimensional distribution has the equation

$$\beta_1 \xi_1 + \beta_2 \xi_2 + \cdots + \beta_n \xi_n = 0,$$

where $\beta_1, \ldots, \beta_n$ denote the generalized direction cosines of the normal to the plane, so that $\sum \beta_i^2 = 1$. The square of the distance between H and the point $\boldsymbol{x} = (\xi_1, \ldots, \xi_n)$ is $d^2 = (\sum \beta_i \xi_i)^2$. Let us try to find H such that the mean value $\boldsymbol{E}(d^2)$ becomes as small as possible. If such a hyperplane H exists, it will be called an *orthogonal m. sq. regression plane* of the distribution (cf K. Pearson, Ref. 183 a).

For a distribution of rank less than n, the problem is trivial, since the whole mass belongs to a certain hyperplane H, which must then yield the value $\boldsymbol{E}(d^2) = 0$. We may thus suppose that the $\boldsymbol{x}$-distribution is non-singular, which by 11.9 implies that the characteristic numbers $\varkappa_i$ of the moment matrix $\boldsymbol{\Lambda}$ are all positive. Let $\varkappa_0$ denote the *smallest* of the characteristic numbers, and let $\alpha_1, \ldots, \alpha_n$ be a solution of the homogeneous system

$$\begin{aligned}
(\lambda_{11} - \varkappa_0)\alpha_1 + \lambda_{12}\alpha_2 + \cdots + \lambda_{1n}\alpha_n &= 0, \\
\lambda_{21}\alpha_1 + (\lambda_{22} - \varkappa_0)\alpha_2 + \cdots + \lambda_{2n}\alpha_n &= 0, \\
\cdots\cdots\cdots\cdots\cdots\cdots\cdots\cdots\cdots\cdots& \\
\lambda_{n1}\alpha_1 + \lambda_{n2}\alpha_2 + \cdots + (\lambda_{nn} - \varkappa_0)\alpha_n &= 0,
\end{aligned}$$

where the α_i are not all equal to zero. By 11.8, such a solution certainly exists, since $|\boldsymbol{\Lambda} - \varkappa_0 \boldsymbol{I}| = 0$. Further, we may obviously suppose $\sum \alpha_i^2 = 1$. *Then the hyperplane H_0 with the equation $\sum \alpha_i \xi_i = 0$ has the required properties.* Let, in fact, d_0 denote the distance from the point $\boldsymbol{x}$ to H_0, while d is the distance to any other hyperplane $\sum \beta_i \xi_i = 0$. We then have, writing $z_i = \beta_i - \alpha_i$ and bearing in mind that $\sum \alpha_i^2 = \sum \beta_i^2 = 1$,

$$\begin{aligned}
\boldsymbol{E}(d^2) &= \sum_{i,k} \lambda_{ik}(\alpha_i + z_i)(\alpha_k + z_k) \\
&= \sum_{i,k} \lambda_{ik}\alpha_i\alpha_k + 2\sum_i z_i \sum_k \lambda_{ik}\alpha_k + \sum_{i,k}\lambda_{ik} z_i z_k \\
&= \boldsymbol{E}(d_0^2) + 2\varkappa_0 \sum_i \alpha_i z_i + \sum_{i,k} \lambda_{ik} z_i z_k \\
&= \boldsymbol{E}(d_0^2) + \sum_{i,k} (\lambda_{ik} - \varkappa_0 \varepsilon_{ik}) z_i z_k,
\end{aligned}$$

where the ε_{ik} are the elements of the unit matrix $\boldsymbol{I}$. Since $\varkappa_0$ is the smallest characteristic number of $\boldsymbol{\Lambda}$, the matrix $\boldsymbol{\Lambda} - \varkappa_0 \boldsymbol{I}$ is by 11.10 non-negative, and thus we have $\boldsymbol{E}(d^2) \geqq \boldsymbol{E}(d_0^2)$.

It can further be shown that, if $\varkappa_0$ is a *simple* root of the secular equation of $\boldsymbol{\Lambda}$, the orthogonal regression plane H_0 found in this way is unique, whereas if $\varkappa_0$ is a *multiple* root, there are an infinity of planes with the required properties.

These results become intuitive, if we remember that, by (11.9.6), the reciprocal matrix Λ^{-1} has the characteristic numbers $\frac{1}{\varkappa_i}$, so that the squares of the principal axes of the concentration ellipsoid (22.7.1) are proportional to the numbers $\varkappa_i$. This shows that the orthogonal m. sq. regression plane is orthogonal to the *smallest* axis of the concentration ellipsoid, and is thus determinate or indeterminate, according as this smallest axis is unique or not.

We can also define a *straight line L of closest fit* to the distribution, by the condition that $E(\delta^2)$ should be a minimum, where δ denotes the shortest distance between L and a point $\boldsymbol{x}$. It can be shown that this line coincides with the *greatest* axis of the concentration ellipsoid.

CHAPTER 24.

The Normal Distribution.

24.1. The characteristic function. — As in the two-variable case (21.11 and 21.12), we introduce first the c. f. of the normal distribution. Let

$$Q(\boldsymbol{t}) = Q(t_1, \ldots, t_n) = \sum_{j,k} \lambda_{jk} t_j t_k$$

denote a non-negative quadratic form in $\boldsymbol{t} = (t_1, \ldots, t_n)$, while $\boldsymbol{m} = (m_1, \ldots, m_n)$ is a real vector. *We shall then show that the function*

$$\varphi(\boldsymbol{t}) = \varphi(t_1, \ldots, t_n) = e^{i \sum_j m_j t_j - \frac{1}{2} Q(t_1, \ldots, t_n)} \tag{24.1.1}$$

is the c.f. of a certain distribution in $\boldsymbol{R}_n$. This distribution will be called a normal distribution.

Before proceeding to the proof of this statement, which will be given in the two following paragraphs, we shall make some introductory remarks. — In matrix notation (cf 11.2 and 11.4), the expression (24.1.1) of the c. f. may be written

$$\varphi(\boldsymbol{t}) = e^{i \boldsymbol{m}' \boldsymbol{t} - \frac{1}{2} \boldsymbol{t}' \boldsymbol{\Lambda} \boldsymbol{t}}. \tag{24.1.2}$$

The development (22.4.1) shows that the quantities m_j and λ_{jk} have here their usual signification as mean values and second order central moments. By (22.4.3), it further follows that *any marginal distribution of a normal distribution is itself normal.*

If the moment matrix $\boldsymbol{\Lambda} = \{\lambda_{jk}\}$ is a diagonal matrix, the c. f. (24.1.1) breaks up into a product $\varphi_1(t_1) \ldots \varphi_n(t_n)$, where each factor is the c. f. of a one-dimensional normal distribution. *Thus n uncorrelated and normally distributed variables are always independent.*

As in the two-variable case, we shall have to distinguish two cases, according as the non-negative form Q is definite or semi-definite. Obviously we may suppose throughout that $\boldsymbol{m} = 0$, since this only involves the addition of a constant vector to the variable $\boldsymbol{x} = (\xi_1, \ldots, \xi_n)$. We use the same notations for moments, correlation coefficients etc. as in the preceding chapters.

24.2. The non-singular normal distribution. — If the quadratic form Q is definite positive, the reciprocal form Q^{-1} exists, and we have (cf. 11.7)

$$Q(\boldsymbol{t}) = Q(t_1, \ldots, t_n) = \sum_{j,k} \lambda_{jk} t_j t_k,$$

$$Q^{-1}(\boldsymbol{x}) = Q^{-1}(x_1, \ldots, x_n) = \sum_{j,k} \frac{\Lambda_{jk}}{\Lambda} x_j x_k.$$

(Since the moment matrix $\boldsymbol{\Lambda}$ is symmetric, we are entitled to write Λ_{jk} instead of Λ_{kj}.) By (11.12.1 b) we then have

$$\frac{1}{(2\pi)^{\frac{n}{2}} \sqrt{\Lambda}} \int\limits_{\mathbf{R}_n} e^{i \sum\limits_j t_j x_j - \frac{1}{2} Q^{-1}(x_1, \ldots, x_n)} \, dx_1 \ldots dx_n = e^{-\frac{1}{2} Q(t_1, \ldots, t_n)}.$$

This shows that the function

$$(24.2.1) \qquad \begin{aligned} f(\boldsymbol{x}) &= \frac{1}{(2\pi)^{\frac{n}{2}} \sqrt{\Lambda}} e^{-\frac{1}{2\Lambda} \sum\limits_{j,k} \Lambda_{jk} x_j x_k} \\ &= \frac{1}{(2\pi)^{\frac{n}{2}} \sigma_1 \ldots \sigma_n \sqrt{P}} e^{-\frac{1}{2P} \sum\limits_{j,k} P_{jk} \frac{x_j}{\sigma_j} \cdot \frac{x_k}{\sigma_k}} \end{aligned}$$

is a probability density in $\mathbf{R}_n$, *with the c.f.*

$$(24.2.2) \qquad \varphi(\boldsymbol{t}) = e^{-\frac{1}{2} \sum\limits_{j,k} \lambda_{jk} t_j t_k}.$$

Substituting in (24.2.1) $x_j - m_j$ for x_j, we obtain the fr. f. of the general *non-singular normal distribution* in $\mathbf{R}_n$, the c. f. of which is given by (24.1.1). For this distribution, the family of homothetic ellipsoids $\frac{1}{2\Lambda}\sum_{j,k} \Lambda_{jk}(x_j - m_j)(x_k - m_k) = c^2$ generated by the concentration ellipsoid (22.7.1) are *equiprobability surfaces*, the fr. f. being on one of these surfaces proportional to e^{-c^2} (cf Ex. 15, p. 319).

24.3. The singular normal distribution. — When the non-negative form Q is semi-definite, no reciprocal form exists, and the expression (24.2.1) for the fr. f. becomes indeterminate. As in the two-dimensional case (cf 21.12) we find, however, that the function $\varphi(\boldsymbol{t}) = e^{-\frac{1}{2}Q(\boldsymbol{t})}$ may be represented as the limit of a sequence of functions of the same type, but with definite forms Q_ν. (We may, e. g., take $Q_\nu = Q + \varepsilon_\nu^2 \sum_1 t_j^2$, where $\varepsilon_\nu \to 0$.) By the continuity theorem of 10.7, it then follows that the corresponding non-singular normal distributions tend to a limiting distribution, and that $\varphi(\boldsymbol{t})$ is the c. f. of this limiting distribution, which will be called a *singular normal distribution.*

If the rank of the semi-definite form Q is denoted by r, we have $r < n$, and the moment matrix $\boldsymbol{\Lambda}$ of the variables $\xi_1, \ldots, \xi_n$ has the same rank r. It then follows from 22.5 that the total mass of the distribution is confined to a certain linear set L_r of r dimensions. Further by 22.6 the variables $\xi_1, \ldots, \xi_n$ may with a probability equal to 1 be expressed as linear functions of r uncorrelated variables $\eta_1, \ldots, \eta_r$, which are themselves linear functions of the ξ_j. Now it will be shown in the following paragraph that any linear functions of normally distributed variables are themselves normally distributed, and by 24.1 we know that uncorrelated normally distributed variables are always independent. Hence we deduce the following theorem:

If the n variables $\xi_1, \ldots, \xi_n$ are distributed in a normal distribution of rank r, they can with a probability equal to 1 be expressed as linear functions of r independent and normally distributed variables. — Obviously this theorem holds true also for $r = n$.

24.4. Linear transformation of normally distributed variables. — The expressions *normal distribution* and *normally distributed variables* will in the sequel always be understood so as to include singular as well as non-singular distributions.

Let the variable $\boldsymbol{x} = (\xi_1, \ldots, \xi_n)$ have a normal distribution in $\boldsymbol{R}_n$, such that $\boldsymbol{m} = 0$. By the linear transformation (22.6.1), we introduce a new variable $\boldsymbol{y} = (\eta_1, \ldots, \eta_m)$, where m is not necessarily equal to n.

In matrix notation we then have $\boldsymbol{y} = \boldsymbol{C}\boldsymbol{x}$, where $\boldsymbol{C} = \boldsymbol{C}_{mn}$. Between the moment matrices $\boldsymbol{\Lambda}$ and $\boldsymbol{M}$ of $\boldsymbol{x}$ and $\boldsymbol{y}$, we have by (22.6.2) the relation $\boldsymbol{M} = \boldsymbol{C}\boldsymbol{\Lambda}\boldsymbol{C}'$, which holds even when $\boldsymbol{m} \neq 0$.

We shall now try to find the c. f. of $\boldsymbol{y}$. By (24.1.2), the c. f. of $\boldsymbol{x}$ is in matrix notation

$$\varphi(\boldsymbol{t}) = \boldsymbol{E}\left(e^{i\,\boldsymbol{t}'\boldsymbol{x}}\right) = e^{-\frac{1}{2}\boldsymbol{t}'\boldsymbol{\Lambda}\,\boldsymbol{t}}.$$

If we replace here $\boldsymbol{t}$ by a new variable $\boldsymbol{u}$ by means of the contragredient substitution $\boldsymbol{t} = \boldsymbol{C}'\boldsymbol{u}$, we obtain according to (22.6.3) the c. f. $\psi(\boldsymbol{u})$ of $\boldsymbol{y}$. We thus have

$$\psi(\boldsymbol{u}) = \boldsymbol{E}\left(e^{i\,\boldsymbol{u}'\boldsymbol{y}}\right) = e^{-\frac{1}{2}\boldsymbol{u}'\boldsymbol{C}\boldsymbol{\Lambda}\boldsymbol{C}'\boldsymbol{u}} = e^{-\frac{1}{2}\boldsymbol{u}'\boldsymbol{M}\boldsymbol{u}}.$$

The last expression is, however, the c. f. of a normal distribution in $\boldsymbol{R}_m$, with the moment matrix $\boldsymbol{M}$. *Thus any number of linear functions of normally distributed variables are themselves normally distributed.* — The remark of 24.1 that any marginal distribution of a normal distribution is itself normal, is included as a particular case in this proposition.

24.5. Distribution of a sum of squares. — In 18.1, we have studied the distribution of the sum $\sum_{1}^{n} \xi_\nu^2$, where the ξ_ν are independent and normal (0, 1). This is the χ^2 distribution with n degrees of freedom, and the fr. f. of $\sum \xi_\nu^2$ is the function $k_n(x)$ defined by (18.1.3).

On a later occasion (cf 30.1—30.3), we shall require the distribution of $\sum \xi_\nu^2$ in the more general case when $\xi_1, \ldots, \xi_n$ are normally distributed with zero means and a moment matrix $\boldsymbol{\Lambda}$, the characteristic numbers (cf 11.9) of which are all equal to 0 or 1. Suppose that p of the characteristic numbers are 0, while the $n-p$ others are 1. Then we may find an orthogonal transformation $\boldsymbol{y} = \boldsymbol{C}\boldsymbol{x}$ replacing the old variables $\boldsymbol{x} = (\xi_1, \ldots, \xi_n)$ by new variables $\boldsymbol{y} = (\eta_1, \ldots, \eta_n)$, such that the transformed moment matrix $\boldsymbol{M} = \boldsymbol{C}\boldsymbol{\Lambda}\boldsymbol{C}'$ is a diagonal matrix with its $n-p$ first diagonal elements equal to 1, while the p others are 0. This implies, however, that the new variables $\eta_1, \ldots, \eta_{n-p}$ are independent and normal (0, 1), while $\eta_{n-p+1}, \ldots, \eta_n$ have zero means and zero variances, and are thus with the probability 1 equal to zero. Hence we have with the probability 1

$$\sum_1^n \xi_\nu^2 = \sum_1^n \eta_\nu^2 = \sum_1^{n-p} \eta_\nu^2.$$

Thus $\sum_1^n \xi_\nu^2$ *is distributed as the sum of the squares of* $n-p$ *independent variables that are normal* (0, 1), *i. e.* $\sum_1^n \xi_\nu^2$ *has the* χ^2 *distribution with* $n-p$ *degrees of freedom, and the fr. f.* $k_{n-p}(x)$.

We finally consider the still more general case of a *sequence of variables* $\boldsymbol{x}', \boldsymbol{x}'', \ldots$, such that the distribution of the general term $\boldsymbol{x} = (\xi_1, \ldots, \xi_n)$ tends to a normal distribution of the type considered above. Applying 10.7 and the multi-dimensional form of (7.5.9) to the c. f. of $\sum_1^n \xi_\nu^2$, it then follows that, *in the limit, the sum of squares* $\sum_1^n \xi_\nu^2$ *has a* χ^2 *distribution with* $n-p$ *degrees of freedom.*

24.6. Conditional distributions. — Let $\xi_1, \ldots, \xi_n$ be n variables having a non-singular normal distribution with $\boldsymbol{m} = 0$, the fr. f. of which is given by (24.2.1). The conditional fr. f. of a certain number of the variables, when the remaining variables assume prescribed values, is given by an expression of the form (22.1.1), and it is easily seen that in the present case this is always a non-singular normal fr. f. We shall treat as examples the conditional distributions for one and two variables.

One variable. — The conditional fr. f. of ξ_1, relative to the hypothesis $\xi_i = x_i$ for $i = 2, \ldots, n$, is by (22.1.1)

$$f(x_1 \mid x_2, \ldots, x_n) = \frac{e^{-\frac{1}{2\Lambda}\sum \Lambda_{jk} x_j x_k}}{\int\limits_{-\infty}^{\infty} e^{-\frac{1}{2\Lambda}\sum \Lambda_{jk} x_j x_k}\, d x_1}$$

$$= A\, e^{-\frac{1}{2\Lambda}\left(\Lambda_{11} x_1^2 + 2\sum_2^n \Lambda_{1k} x_1 x_k\right)}$$

$$= B\, e^{-\frac{\Lambda_{11}}{2\Lambda}\left(x_1 + \sum_2^n \frac{\Lambda_{1k}}{\Lambda_{11}} x_k\right)^2},$$

where A and B are independent of x_1, but may depend on $x_2, \ldots, x_n$. Now we know that the last expression is a fr. f. in x_1, and it follows that we must have $B = \sqrt{\frac{\Lambda_{11}}{2\pi\Lambda}}$, so that the conditional distribution of ξ_1 is a normal distribution with the variance $\frac{\Lambda}{\Lambda_{11}}$ and the mean

$$\begin{aligned} m_1(x_2, \ldots, x_n) &= -\frac{\Lambda_{12}}{\Lambda_{11}} x_2 - \cdots - \frac{\Lambda_{1n}}{\Lambda_{11}} x_n \\ &= \beta_{12} x_2 + \cdots + \beta_{1n} x_n, \end{aligned}$$

where the β:s are the regression coefficients given by (23.2.3). Thus the regression is linear, and accordingly (cf 23.2) we find that the regression surface for the mean of ξ_1 coincides with the m. sq. regression plane. We further observe that the conditional variance $\frac{\Lambda}{\Lambda_{11}}$ is independent of $x_2, \ldots, x_n$, and is equal to the residual variance $\boldsymbol{E}(\eta_{1 \cdot 23 \ldots n}^2)$ as given by (23.3.4).

Two variables. — The conditional fr. f. of ξ_1 and ξ_2 is

$$\begin{aligned} f(x_1, x_2 \mid x_3, \ldots, x_n) &= \frac{e^{-\frac{1}{2\Lambda}\sum \Lambda_{jk} x_j x_k}}{\int\limits_{-\infty}^{\infty}\int\limits_{-\infty}^{\infty} e^{-\frac{1}{2\Lambda}\sum \Lambda_{jk} x_j x_k}\, dx_1\, dx_2} \\ &= C e^{-\frac{1}{2\Lambda}(\Lambda_{11} x_1^2 + 2\Lambda_{12} x_1 x_2 + \Lambda_{22} x_2^2) + D x_1 + E x_2} \end{aligned}$$

where C, D and E are independent of x_1 and x_2. We now introduce three quantities s_1, s_2 and r defined by the expressions

$$s_1^2 = \frac{\Lambda_{22}}{\Lambda_{11 \cdot 22}}, \quad s_2^2 = \frac{\Lambda_{11}}{\Lambda_{11 \cdot 22}}, \quad r = -\frac{\Lambda_{12}}{\sqrt{\Lambda_{11}\Lambda_{22}}}.$$

We then obtain by (11.7.3)

$$\frac{1}{(1-r^2)s_1^2} = \frac{\Lambda_{11}\Lambda_{11 \cdot 22}}{\Lambda_{11}\Lambda_{22} - \Lambda_{12}^2} = \frac{\Lambda_{11}}{\Lambda},$$

and in a similar way

$$\frac{1}{(1-r^2)s_2^2} = \frac{\Lambda_{22}}{\Lambda}, \qquad -\frac{r}{(1-r^2)s_1 s_2} = \frac{\Lambda_{12}}{\Lambda},$$

so that

$$\frac{1}{\Lambda}(\Lambda_{11}x_1^2 + 2\Lambda_{12}x_1x_2 + \Lambda_{22}x_2^2) = \frac{1}{1-r^2}\left(\frac{x_1^2}{s_1^2} - \frac{2\,r\,x_1x_2}{s_1s_2} + \frac{x_2^2}{s_2^2}\right).$$

Comparing this with the expression of the two-dimensional normal fr. f. given in 21.12, we find that the conditional distribution of ξ_1 and ξ_2 is a non-singular normal distribution with the conditional variances $\frac{\Lambda_{22}}{\Lambda_{11\cdot 22}}$ and $\frac{\Lambda_{11}}{\Lambda_{11\cdot 22}}$, and the conditional correlation coefficient $-\frac{\Lambda_{12}}{\sqrt{\Lambda_{11}\Lambda_{22}}}$. We observe that all these three quantities are independent of $x_3, \ldots, x_n$. The variances are identical with the variances of the residuals $\eta_{1\cdot 34\ldots n}$ and $\eta_{2\cdot 34\ldots n}$ studied in 23.4, while the conditional correlation coefficient is identical with the correlation coefficient of these two residuals, or the partial correlation coefficient $\varrho_{12\cdot 34\ldots n}$ as given by (23.4.2). For the normal distribution, the latter coefficient has thus the important property of showing not only the correlation between the residuals but, moreover, the correlation between ξ_1 and ξ_2 for any fixed values of $\xi_3, \ldots, \xi_n$.

24.7. Addition of independent variables. The central limit theorem. — The sum of two n-dimensional random variables $\boldsymbol{x} = (\xi_1, \ldots, \xi_n)$ and $\boldsymbol{y} = (\eta_1, \ldots, \eta_n)$ is defined as in the two-dimensional case (cf 21.11), by writing $\boldsymbol{x} + \boldsymbol{y} = (\xi_1 + \eta_1, \ldots, \xi_n + \eta_n)$. As in 21.11, it is proved that *the c. f. of a sum of independent variables is the product of the c. f:s of the terms.*

The expression (24.1.1) for the c. f. of the normal distribution further immediately shows that *the sum of any number of normally distributed and independent variables is itself normally distributed*, as proved for the one-dimensional case in 17.3.

In 21.11, we have considered a sum of a large number of independent two-dimensional variables, all having the same distribution. We have proved that, if the sum is divided by the square root of the number of terms, the distribution of this standardized sum tends to a certain normal distribution, as the number of terms tends to infinity. A straightforward generalization of the proof of this theorem shows that the theorem holds for variables in any number of dimensions. — This is the generalization to n dimensions of the Lindeberg-Lévy theorem of 17.4, and thus forms the simplest case of the *Central Limit Theorem* for variables in $\boldsymbol{R}_n$. The general form of this theorem asserts that, subject to certain conditions, *the sum of a large number of independent n-dimensional random variables is asymptotically normally distributed.* — The exact conditions for the validity of the theorem, in the general case when the terms may have unequal distributions, are rather complicated, and we shall not go further into the matter here. A fairly general statement will be found in Cramér, Ref. 11, p. 113.

Exercises to Chapters 21—24.

1. ξ and η are two variables with finite second order moments. Show that $D^2(\xi+\eta) = D^2(\xi) + D^2(\eta)$ when and only when the variables are uncorrelated.

2. Let $\varphi_1(t)$, $\varphi_2(t)$ and $\varphi(t)$ denote the c. f:s of ξ, η, and $\xi+\eta$ respectively. It has been shown in 15.12 that $\varphi(t) = \varphi_1(t)\,\varphi_2(t)$ when ξ and η are independent. Conversely, if we know that $\varphi(t) = \varphi_1(t)\,\varphi_2(t)$ for all t, does it follow that ξ and η are independent? — Consider the fr. f. $f(x, y) = \frac{1}{4}[1 + xy(x^2 - y^2)]$, $(|x| < 1,\ |y| < 1)$, and show by means of this example that the answer is negative.

3. Consider the expansion (21.3.2) for the c. f. of a two-dimensional distribution. Show that, if the distribution has finite moments of all orders, this expansion may be extended to terms of any degree in t and u. Use this expansion to show that, for the normal distribution, any central moment μ_{ik} of even order $i + k = 2n$ is equal to the coefficient of $t^i u^k$ in the polynomial $\dfrac{i!\,k!}{2^n\,n!}(\mu_{20} t^2 + 2\mu_{11} tu + \mu_{02} u^2)^n$.

4. The joint distribution of ξ and η is normal, with zero mean values and the correlation coefficient ϱ. Show that the correlation coefficient of ξ^2 and η^2 is ϱ^2.

5. Consider two variables ξ and η with a joint distribution of the continuous type, and let $\varphi(t, u)$ denote the joint c. f. Using the notations of 21.4, we then have

$$\left(\frac{\partial^n \varphi}{\partial u^n}\right)_{u=0} = i^n \int_{-\infty}^{\infty} e^{itx}\,dx \int_{-\infty}^{\infty} y^n f(x, y)\,dy = i^n \int_{-\infty}^{\infty} e^{itx}\,\boldsymbol{E}(\eta^n \mid \xi = x) f_1(x)\,dx.$$

Conversely, there is a reciprocal formula analogous to (10.3.2):

$$\boldsymbol{E}(\eta^n \mid \xi = x) = \frac{1}{2\pi\, i^n f_1(x)} \int_{-\infty}^{\infty} e^{-itx} \left(\frac{\partial^n \varphi}{\partial u^n}\right)_{u=0} dt,$$

if the last integral is absolutely convergent. Use this result to deduce the properties given in 21.12 of the conditional mean and the conditional variance of the normal distribution.

6. We use the same notations as in the preceding exercise, and suppose that η is never negative. If the integral

$$g(x) = \frac{1}{2\pi i} \int_{-\infty}^{\infty} \left(\frac{\partial \varphi}{\partial u}\right)_{u=-tx} dt$$

is uniformly convergent with respect to x, it represents the fr. f. $g(x)$ of the variable $\frac{\xi}{\eta}$. (Generalization of Cramér, Ref. 11, p. 46, who gives the proof for the particular case when ξ and η are independent.) Use this result to deduce the distributions of 18.2 and 18.3, and generalize Student's distribution to the case when the variable ξ in (18.2.1) is normal (m, σ), where $m \neq 0$ (the »non-central» t-distribution).

7. Find the necessary and sufficient conditions that three given numbers ϱ_{12}, ϱ_{13} and ϱ_{23} may be the correlation coefficients of some three-dimensional distribution. Find the possible values of c in the particular case when $\varrho_{12} = \varrho_{13} = \varrho_{23} = c$.

8. Each of the variables x, y and z has the mean 0 and the s. d. 1. The variables satisfy the relation $ax + by + cz = 0$. Find the moment matrix $\boldsymbol{\Lambda}$, and show that we must have $a^4 + b^4 + c^4 \leqq 2(a^2 b^2 + a^2 c^2 + b^2 c^2)$.

9. A certain random experiment may produce any of n mutually exclusive events $E_1, \ldots, E_n$, the probability of E_j being $p_j > 0$, where $\sum_1^n p_j = 1$. In a series of N repetitions, E_j occurs ν_j times, where $\sum_1^n \nu_j = N$. Show that the probability of this result is $\frac{N!}{\nu_1! \ldots \nu_n!} p_1^{\nu_1} \ldots p_n^{\nu_n}$. The joint distribution of $\nu_1, \ldots, \nu_n$ defined by these probabilities is a generalization of the binomial distribution, known as the *multinomial distribution.* Show that for this distribution $m_j = \boldsymbol{E}(\nu_j) = Np_j$, $\lambda_{jj} = \boldsymbol{E}(\nu_j - Np_j)^2 = Np_j(1 - p_j)$, $\lambda_{jk} = \boldsymbol{E}\left((\nu_j - Np_j)(\nu_k - Np_k)\right) = -Np_j p_k$. For the moment matrix $\boldsymbol{\Lambda}$, we have $\Lambda = 0$ and $\Lambda_{jj} = N^{n-1} p_1 p_2 \ldots p_n \neq 0$, so that the rank of the distribution is $n - 1$, in accordance with the relation $\sum_1^n \nu_j = N$ between the variables.

Show that $\varrho_{12} = -\sqrt{\frac{p_1 p_2}{(1 - p_1)(1 - p_2)}}$ and

$$\varrho_{12 \cdot 34 \ldots j} = -\sqrt{\frac{p_1 p_2}{(1 - p_1 - p_3 - \ldots - p_j)(1 - p_2 - p_3 - \ldots - p_j)}}$$

for $j = 3, \ldots, n$.

Show further that the joint c. f. of the variables $x_j = \frac{\nu_j - Np_j}{\sqrt{Np_j}}$ is $\varphi(t_1, \ldots, t_n) = e^{-i\sqrt{N}\sum_1^n t_j \sqrt{p_j}} \left(\sum_1^n p_j e^{\frac{it_j}{\sqrt{Np_j}}}\right)^N$. As $N \to \infty$, φ tends to the limit

$$e^{-\frac{1}{2}\left(\sum_1^n t_j^2 - \left(\sum_1^n t_j \sqrt{p_j}\right)^2\right)}.$$

This is the c. f. of a normal distribution in $\boldsymbol{R}_n$. Show that this distribution is of rank $n - 1$, and that the variables satisfy the relation $\sum_1^n x_j \sqrt{p_j} = 0$. Find ϱ_{12} and $\varrho_{12 \cdot 34 \ldots j}$.

10. Take in the multinomial distribution $p_j = \frac{\lambda_j}{N}$ for $j = 1, \ldots, n-1$, and $p_n = 1 - \frac{\lambda_1 + \cdots + \lambda_{n-1}}{N}$. Investigate the limiting distribution as $N \to \infty$ (multidimensional Poisson distribution).

11. Show that the residual $\eta_{1\cdot 23\ldots n}$ defined by (23.3.1) may also be interpreted as the residual of the variable $\eta_{1\cdot 23\ldots n-1}$ with respect to the single variable $\eta_{n\cdot 23\ldots n-1}$. Show that, by means of this result, the formula (23.4.4) for the partial correlation coefficient may be deduced from (23.4.3).

12. Use the result of the preceding exercise to prove the relation

$$\boldsymbol{E}\left(\eta_{1\cdot 23\ldots n}^2\right) = \boldsymbol{E}\left(\eta_{1\cdot 23\ldots n-1}^2\right)\left(1 - \varrho_{1n\cdot 23\ldots n-1}^2\right).$$

This shows that the representation of ξ_1 by means of a linear combination of $\xi_2, \ldots, \xi_{n-1}$ will be improved by including also the further variable ξ_n when and only when $\varrho_{1n\cdot 23\ldots n-1} \neq 0$.

13. Prove the relations (23.4.5) and (23.5.3).

14. Use the continuity theorem 10.7 to prove the following proposition: If a sequence of normal distributions in $\boldsymbol{R}_n$ converges to a distribution, the limiting distribution is normal. (Note that, in accordance with 24.4, the expression »normal distribution» includes singular as well as non-singular distributions.)

15. The variables $\xi_1, \ldots, \xi_n$ have a non-singular normal distribution, with the mean values $m_1, \ldots, m_n$ and the moment matrix $\boldsymbol{\Lambda}$. Use (11.12.3) and the final remark of 24.2 to show that the variable

$$\eta = \sum_{j,k=1}^{n} \frac{\Lambda_{jk}}{\Lambda}(\xi_j - m_j)(\xi_k - m_k)$$

has a χ^2-distribution with n degrees of freedom, the fr. f. being given by (18.1.3).

16. $\xi_1, \ldots, \xi_n$ are independent and normally distributed variables, all having the same s. d. σ, while the mean values may be different. New variables $\eta_1, \ldots, \eta_n$ are introduced by an orthogonal transformation. Show by means of 24.4 that the η_i are independent and normally distributed, all having the same s. d. σ as the ξ_i.

THIRD PART

STATISTICAL INFERENCE

Chapters 25–26. Generalities.

CHAPTER 25.

Preliminary Notions on Sampling.

25.1. Introductory remarks. — In accordance with our general discussion of principles in Chs 13—14, the whole theory of random variables and probability distributions developed in Part II should be considered as a system of mathematical propositions designed to form a model of the statistical regularities observed in connection with sequences of random experiments.

As already pointed out in 14.6, it will now be our task to work out methods for testing the mathematical theory by experience, and to show how the theory may be applied to problems of statistical inference. — These questions will form the subject-matter of Part III.

Among the sets of statistical data occurring in practical applications, we may distinguish certain general classes which, in some ways, require different types of theoretical treatment. In the present chapter, we shall give a few brief indications concerning some of the most important of these classes. — The following chapter will be devoted to a preliminary survey of questions of principle connected with the testing and applications of the theory.

25.2. Simple random sampling. — Consider a random experiment $\mathfrak{E}$, connected with a one-dimensional random variable ξ. If we make n independent repetitions of $\mathfrak{E}$, we shall obtain a sequence of n observed values of the variable, say $x_1, x_2, \ldots, x_n$.

A sequence of this type, forming the result of n independent repetitions of a certain random experiment, is representative of a simple but fundamentally important class of statistical data. With respect to data belonging to this class, we shall often use a current terminology derived from certain particular fields of application, as we are now going to explain.

Consider a random experiment $\mathfrak{E}$ of the following type: A certain set containing a finite number of elements is given, and our experiment consists in choosing at random an element from the set, observing the value of some characteristic ξ of the element, and then replacing the element in the set. It is assumed that the experiment is so arranged that the probability of being chosen is the same for all elements. — Using expressions borrowed from the statistical study of human and other biological populations, we shall talk of the given set as the *parent population*, and of its elements as *members* or *individuals* (cf 13.3). The group of individuals observed in the course of n repetitions of the experiment $\mathfrak{E}$ will be called a *random sample* from the population, and the sampling process thus described will be denoted as *simple random sampling.*

Often we are not interested in the individuals as such, but only in the values of the variable characteristic ξ and their distribution among the members. In such cases we shall find it advantageous to consider the parent populations as composed, not of individuals, but of *values of* ξ. A sequence of n observed values $x_1, \ldots, x_n$ will then be conceived as a random sample from this population of ξ-values. Talking from this point of view, we may replace the parent population by an urn containing one ticket for each member of the population, with the corresponding value of ξ inscribed on it. The experiment $\mathfrak{E}$ will then consist in drawing at random a ticket, noting the value inscribed, and replacing the ticket in the urn.

As there are only a finite number of tickets in the urn, the random variable ξ will only have a finite number of possible values, so that its distribution will be of the discrete type (cf 15.2). By taking the number N of tickets very large, this distribution may, however, be made to approximate as closely as we please to any distribution given in advance, and when N tends to infinity the error involved in the approximation may be made to tend to zero. *As a matter of illustration*, we may thus interpret any type of random experiment $\mathfrak{E}$ as the random selection of an individual from an *infinite parent population* (cf 13.3). We then imagine an urn containing an infinite number of tickets, on each of which a certain number is written, in such a way that the distribution of these numbers is identical with the distribution of the random variable ξ associated with $\mathfrak{E}$. Each performance of $\mathfrak{E}$ is now interpreted as the drawing of a ticket from this urn, and a sequence $x_1, \ldots, x_n$ of observed values of ξ is regarded as a random sample from the infinite population of numbers inscribed on the tickets. The values $x_1, \ldots, x_n$ will accordingly be called the *sample values.*

It must be expressly observed that this extension of the idea of sampling to the case of an *infinite* population should be regarded as a mere illustration for the purpose of introducing a convenient terminology, and should by no means be taken to imply that conceptions such as the random selection of individuals from an infinite population form part of our theory.

Bearing this reservation in mind we shall, however, often find it convenient to use the sampling terminology in the extended sense suggested above. A set of observed values of a random variable with a certain d. f. $F(x)$ will thus often be regarded as a *random sample from a population having the d. f.* $F(x)$ or, as we shall sometimes briefly say, a *random sample from the distribution corresponding to* $F(x)$.

Whenever in the sequel expressions such as »sample» or »sampling» are used without further specification, it will always be understood that we are concerned with simple random sampling.

All the above may be directly extended to the case of a random variable in any number k of dimensions. Every individual in our imaginary infinite population will then be characterized by a set of k numbers, and any sequence of observed values of the k-dimensional random variable may be interpreted as a random sample from such an infinite k-dimensional population.

25.3. The distribution of the sample. — Consider a sequence of n observed values $x_1, \ldots, x_n$ of a one-dimensional random variable ξ with the d. f. $F(x)$. According to the preceding paragraph, we may regard $x_1, \ldots, x_n$ as a set of sample values, »drawn» from a population with the d. f. $F(x)$. The sample may be geometrically represented by the set of n points $x_1, \ldots, x_n$ on the x-axis.

The *distribution of the sample* will then be defined as the distribution obtained by placing a mass equal to $1/n$ in each of the points $x_1, \ldots, x_n$. This is a distribution of the discrete type, having n discrete mass points (some of which may, of course, coincide). The corresponding d. f., which will be denoted by $F^*(x)$, is a step-function with a step of the height $1/n$ in each x_i. If we denote by ν the number of sample values that are $\leqq x$, we evidently have

$$F^*(x) = \frac{\nu}{n}, \tag{25.3.1}$$

so that $F^*(x)$ represents the frequency ratio of the event $\xi \leqq x$ in our sequence of n observations.

Obviously this distribution is uniquely determined by the sample. On the other hand, two samples consisting of the same values in different arrangements will give the same distribution. The distribution determines, in fact, only the positions of the sample values on the x-axis, but not their mutual order in the sample.

For the distribution thus defined, with the d. f. $F^*(x)$, we may calculate various characteristics such as moments, semi-invariants, coefficients of skewness and excess etc., according to the general rules for one-dimensional distributions given in Ch. 15. These characteristics will be called the moments etc. *of the sample*, as distinct from the corresponding characteristics *of the distribution* associated with the random variable ξ and the d. f. $F(x)$. The latter characteristics will also be called the moments etc. *of the population.*

Thus e. g. by 15.4 the ν:th moment *of the sample* is

$$\int_{-\infty}^{\infty} x^\nu \, d F^*(x) = \frac{1}{n} \sum_{1}^{n} x_i^\nu,$$

i. e. the arithmetic mean of the ν:th powers of the sample values, while the corresponding moment *of the population* is $\alpha_\nu = \int_{-\infty}^{\infty} x^\nu \, d F(x)$.

The above definitions directly extend themselves to samples from multi-dimensional populations. Suppose e. g. that we have a sample of n pairs of values $(x_1, y_1), \ldots, (x_n, y_n)$ of a two-dimensional random variable. This sample may be geometrically represented by the set of n points $(x_1, y_1), \ldots, (x_n, y_n)$ in a plane, and the *distribution of the sample* is the discrete distribution obtained by placing a mass equal to $1/n$ in each of these n points. For this distribution, we may calculate moments, coefficients of regression and correlation, and other characteristics according to the general rules for two-dimensional distributions given in Ch. 21. These are the moments etc. *of the sample* as distinct from the corresponding characteristics *of the distribution* (or of the population). — The extension to samples from populations of more than two dimensions is obvious.

The distribution of a sample, as well as the moments and other characteristics of such a distribution, will play an important part in the sequel. In this connection, we shall use a particular system of notations that will be explained in 27.1.

25.4. The sample values as random variables. Sampling distributions. — In order to obtain a sample of n values of a one-dimensional random variable with the d. f. $F(x)$, we have to perform a sequence of n independent repetitions of the random experiment $\mathfrak{E}$ to which the variable is attached. This sequence of n repetitions forms a combined experiment, bearing on n independent variables $x_1, \ldots, x_n$, where x_i is associated with the i:th repetition of $\mathfrak{E}$. The sample values $x_1, \ldots, x_n$ that express the result of such a combined experiment thus give rise to a combined random variable $(x_1, \ldots, x_n)$ in n dimensions, where the x_i are independent variables, all of which have the same d. f. $F(x)$. The values of $x_1, \ldots, x_n$ observed in an actual sample form an observed »value» of the n-dimensional random variable $(x_1, \ldots, x_n)$.

When the sample values are thus conceived as random variables, any function of $x_1, \ldots, x_n$ is by 14.5 a random variable with a distribution uniquely determined by the joint distribution of the x_i, i. e. by the d. f. $F(x)$. Now any moment or other characteristic of the sample is a certain function $g(x_1, \ldots, x_n)$ of the sample values. *Consequently any sample characteristic gives rise to a random variable with a distribution uniquely determined by $F(x)$.*

If samples of n values are repeatedly drawn from the same population, and if for each sample the characteristic $g(x_1, \ldots, x_n)$ is calculated, the sequence of values obtained in this way will constitute a sequence of observed values of the random variable $g(x_1, \ldots, x_n)$. The probability distribution of this variable will be called the *sampling distribution* of the corresponding characteristic.

These remarks are immediately extended to the case of samples from multi-dimensional populations. In the same sense as above, the sample values will here be conceived as random variables. Further, any moment, correlation coefficient or other characteristic of such a sample is a function of the sample values, and thus gives rise to a certain random variable, the distribution of which is uniquely determined by the distribution of the population. This is the *sampling distribution* of the characteristic.

Thus we may talk of the sampling distribution of the mean of a sample, of the variance, the correlation coefficient etc. The properties of sampling distributions of various important sample characteristics will be studied in Chs 27—29.

25.5. Statistical image of a distribution. — As an example of the concepts introduced in the preceding paragraph, we consider the d. f.

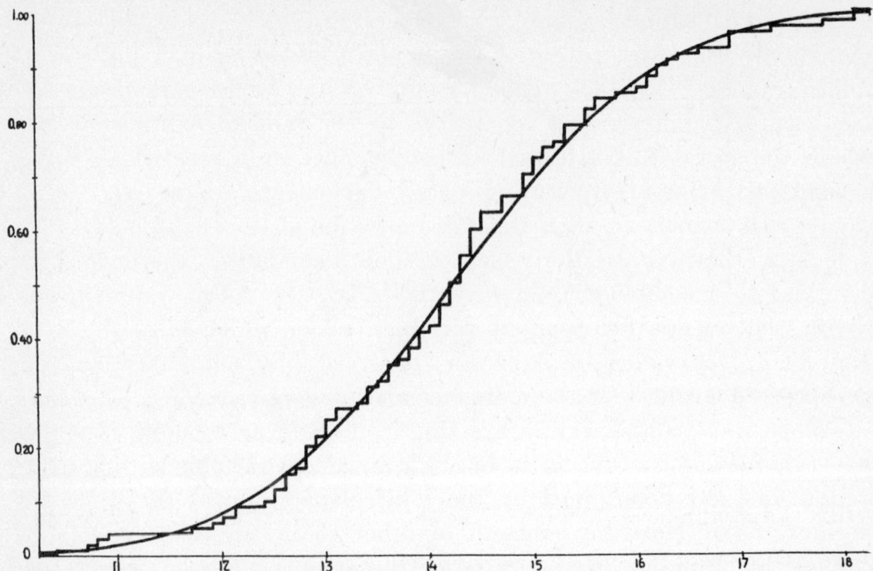

Fig. 25. Sum polygon for 100 mean temperatures (Celsius) in Stockholm, June 1841—1940, and normal distribution function.

$F^*(x)$ of a one-dimensional sample, which by (25.3.1) is a function of the sample values, containing a variable parameter x. As observed in 25.3, $F^*(x)$ is equal to the frequency of the event $\xi \leqq x$ in a sequence of n repetitions of $\mathfrak{E}$. Now, by the definition of the d. f. $F(x)$ of the variable ξ, the event $\xi \leqq x$ has the probability $F(x)$. Thus it follows from the Bernoulli theorem, as interpreted in 20.3, that $F^*(x)$ converges in probability to $F(x)$, as $n \to \infty$.

When n is large, it is thus practically certain that the d. f. $F^*(x)$ of the sample will be approximately equal to the d. f. $F(x)$ of the population. Consequently we may regard the distribution of the sample as a kind of *statistical image* of the distribution of the population. The graph $y = F^*(x)$ of the step-function $F^*(x)$ is known as the *sum polygon* of the sample. For large values of n, this will thus be expected to give a good approximation to the curve $y = F(x)$. As an example, we show in Fig. 25 the sum polygon for a sample of 100 mean temperatures in Stockholm for the month of June (cf Table 30.4.2), together with the (hypothetical) normal d. f. of the corresponding population.

In practice, samples from continuous distributions are often *grouped*. This means that we are not given the individual sample values, but only the number of sample values falling into certain specified *class*

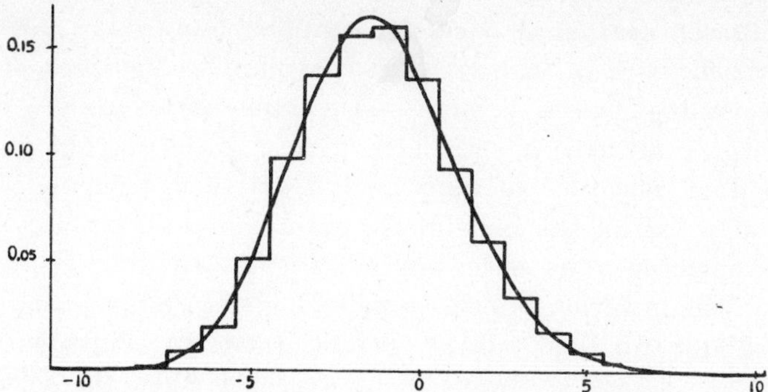

Fig. 26. Histogram for the breadths of 12 000 beans, and frequency curve according to Edgeworth's series. The scale on the horizontal axis refers to a conventional numeration of the class intervals.

intervals. We then take every class interval as the basis of a rectangle with the height $\frac{\nu}{n h}$, where h is the length of the interval, while ν denotes the number of sample values in the class. The figure obtained in this way is the *histogram* of the sample. The area of any rectangle in the histogram is equal to the corresponding class frequency $\frac{\nu}{n}\cdot$ For large n this may be expected to be approximately equal to the probability that an observed value of the variable will belong to the corresponding class interval, which is identical with the integral of the fr. f. $f(x)$ over the interval. Thus the upper contour of the histogram will form a statistical image of the fr. f., in the same way as the sum polygon does so for the d. f. As an example, we show in Fig. 26 the histogram of the sample of 12 000 breadths of beans given in Table 30.4.3, together with the (hypothetical) fr. f. of the corresponding population, according to the Edgeworth expansion (17.7.5).

Analogous remarks apply to the distribution of a sample in any number of dimensions. Later on, we shall find that the same kind of relationship also exists between the various characteristics of the distributions of the sample and of the population. It will, in fact, be shown in 27.3 and 27.8 that, under fairly general conditions, a characteristic of the sample converges in probability to the corresponding characteristic of the population, as the size of the sample tends to infinity. In such cases, the sample characteristics may be regarded as *estimates* of the corresponding population characteristics. The systematic investigation of such estimates and their probabilitity distributions will, in the sequel, provide some of the most powerful tools of statistical inference.

25.6. Biased sampling. Random sampling numbers. — When we are concerned with a *finite* parent population, the idea of simple random sampling has a precise and concrete significance. We may always imagine an experimental arrangement satisfying the conditions for a random selection of individuals from such a population, with equal chances for all the individuals, even though its practical realization may sometimes be exceedingly difficult. In practice there will often be a bias in favour of certain individuals or groups of individuals, and accordingly we then talk of a *biased sampling.* Experience shows e. g. that such a bias is always to be expected when the selection of individuals from a population is more or less dependent on human choice.

It does not enter into the plan of this book to give an account of questions belonging to the *technique of random sampling*, such as the arrangements by which bias may be as far as possible eliminated. We shall only remark that in many cases it is possible to use with advantage some of the published tables of *random sampling numbers.* (Ref. 262, 263, 267.) Such a table consists of a sequence of digits intended to represent the result of a simple random sampling from a population consisting of the ten digits 0, 1, . . ., 9. By joining two columns of the table we may obtain a sequence of numbers formed in the same way from the population consisting of the 10^2 numbers 00, . . ., 99, and similarly for three, four or any larger number of columns.

Suppose that we want to use such a table to draw a random sample of 100 individuals from a population consisting of, say, 8183 members. The members are first numbered from 0000 to 8182. We then read a sequence of four-figure numbers from the table, disregarding numbers above 8182, and go on until we have obtained 100 numbers. Our sample will then consist of the members corresponding to these numbers. If the sampling is to be made without replacement (cf 25.7), we must also during the course of reading the numbers from the table disregard any number that has already appeared.

The tables may also be used to obtain a sample of observed values of a random variable with any given d. f. $F(x)$. Suppose that we dispose of a table of values of $F(x)$ that enables us, for every m-figure number r, to solve the equation $F(a_r) = r \cdot 10^{-m}$ with respect to a_r. From our table of random numbers, we now read a sequence of m-figure numbers r, and determine the sample values x such that the x corresponding to any r falls in the interval $a_r < x \leqq a_{r+1}$. Thus we obtain in this way a *grouped sample:* the sample values are not exactly determined, but the process yields the number of sample values belonging to any interval (a_r, a_{r+1}), and it is seen that the probability for any sample value to fall in this interval has the correct value

$$F(a_{r+1}) - F(a_r) = 10^{-m}.$$

The larger we take m, the finer is the grouping and the more accurate the determination of the sample values. — Further discussion of the tables of random sampling numbers and their use will be found in the introductions to the tables and in two papers by Kendall and Babington Smith (Ref. 137).

25.7. Sampling without replacement. The representative method. — In practice, a sample from a finite population is often taken in such a way that a drawn individual is not replaced in the population before the next drawing. A sequence of drawings of this type has obviously not the character of repetitions of a random experiment under uniform conditions, since the composition of the population changes from one drawing to another. We talk here of *sampling without replacement*, as distinct from simple random sampling, which is a *sampling with replacement*. When the population is very large, and the sample only contains a small fraction of the total population, it is obvious that the difference between these modes of sampling is unimportant, and in the limiting case when the population becomes infinite, while the size of the sample remains finite, the difference disappears.

Sampling without replacement plays an important part in applied statistics. When it is desired to obtain information as to the characteristics of some large population, such as the inhabitants of a country, the fir-trees of a district, a consignment of articles delivered by a factory etc., it is often practically impossible to observe or measure every individual in the whole population. The method generally used in such situations is known as the *representative method:* a sample of individuals is selected for observation, and it is endeavoured to make the sample as representative as possible of the total population. The observed characteristics of the sample are then used to form estimates of the unknown characteristics of the total population. Usually in such cases samples are taken without replacement. The method of selection may be *random* or *purposive*; in the latter case we deliberately choose the individuals entering into our sample in order to obtain a representative sample. Often also *mixed* methods are used. — For the theory of the representative method, we refer to Neyman, Ref. 161. Some simple cases will be considered in 34.2 and 34.4.

CHAPTER 26.

Statistical Inference.

26.1. Introductory remarks. — It has been strongly emphasized in 13.4 that no mathematical theory deals directly with the things of which we have immediate experience. The mathematical theory belongs entirely to the conceptual sphere, and deals with purely abstract objects. The theory is, however, designed to form a model of a certain group of phenomena in the physical world, and the abstract objects and propositions of the theory have their counterparts in certain observable things, and relations between things. If the model is to be practically useful, there must be some kind of general agreement between the theoretical propositions and their empirical counterparts. When a certain proposition has its counterpart in some directly observable relation, we must require that our observations should, in fact, show that this relation holds. If, in repeated tests, an agreement of this character has been found, and if we regard this agreement as sufficiently accurate and permanent, the theory may be accepted for practical use.

In the present chapter, we shall discuss some points that arise when these general principles are applied to the mathematical theory of probability. We shall first consider the testing of the agreement between theory and facts, and then proceed to give a brief survey of the applications of the theory for purposes of statistical inference.

26.2. Agreement between theory and facts. Tests of significance. — The concept of mathematical probability as defined in 13.5 has its empirical counterpart in certain directly observable frequency ratios. The proposition: »The probability of the event E in connection with the random experiment $\mathfrak{E}$ is equal to P» has, by 13.5, its counterpart in the statement denoted as the *frequency interpretation* of the probability P, which runs as follows: »In a long sequence of repetitions of $\mathfrak{E}$, it is practically certain that the frequency of E will be approximately equal to P».

Accordingly we must require that, whenever a theoretical deduction leads to a definite numerical value for the probability of a certain observable event, the truth of the corresponding frequency interpretation should be borne out by our observations.

Thus e. g. when the probability of an event is very small, we must require that in the long run the event should occur at most in a very small percentage of all repetitions of the corresponding experiment. Consequently we must be able to regard it as practically certain that, in one single performance of the experiment, the event will not occur (cf 13.5). — Similarly, when the probability of an event differs from unity by a very small amount, we must require that it should be practically certain that, in one single performance of the corresponding experiment, the event will occur.

In a great number of cases, the problem of testing the agreement between theory and facts presents itself in the following form. We have at our disposal a sample of n observed values of some variable, and we want to know if this variable can be reasonably regarded as a random variable having a probability distribution with certain given properties. In some cases, the hypothetical distribution will be completely specified: we may, e. g., ask if it is reasonable to suppose that our sample has been drawn by simple random sampling from a population having a normal distribution with $m = 0$ and $\sigma = 1$ (cf 17.2). In other cases, we are given a certain *class of distributions*, and we ask if our sample might have been drawn from a population having *some* distribution belonging to the given class.

Consider the simple case when the hypothetical distribution is completely specified, say by means of its d. f. $F(x)$. We then have to *test* the *statistical hypothesis* that our sample has been drawn from a population with this distribution.

We begin by assuming that the hypothesis to be tested is true. It then follows from 25.5 that the d. f. $F^*(x)$ of the sample may be expected to form an approximation to the given d. f. $F(x)$, when n is large. Let us define some non-negative *measure of the deviation of* F^* *from* F. This may, of course, be made in various ways, but any deviation measure D will be some function of the sample values, and will thus according to 25.4 have a determined sampling distribution. By means of this sampling distribution, we may calculate the probability $P(D > D_0)$ that the deviation D will exceed any given quantity D_0. This probability may be made as small as we please by taking D_0 sufficiently large. Let us choose D_0 such that $P(D > D_0) = \varepsilon$, where ε is so small that we are prepared to regard it as practically certain that an event of probability ε will not occur in one single trial.

Suppose now that we are given an actual sample of n values, and let us calculate the quantity D from these values. Then if we find a value $D > D_0$, this means that an event of probability ε has presented itself. However, on our hypothesis such an event ought to be practically impossible in one single trial, and thus we must come to the conclusion that in this case our hypothesis has been *disproved by experience.* On the other hand, if we find a value $D \leqq D_0$, we shall be willing to accept the hypothesis as a reasonable interpretation of our data, at least until further experience has been gained in the matter.

This is our first instance of a type of argument which is of a very frequent occurrence in statistical inference. We shall often encounter situations where we are concerned with some more or less complicated hypothesis regarding the properties of the probability distributions of certain variables, and it is required to test whether available statistical data agree with this hypothesis or not. A first approach to the problem is obtained by proceeding as in the simple case considered above. If the hypothesis is true, our sample values should form a statistical image (cf 25.5) of the hypothetical distribution, and we accordingly introduce some convenient measure D of the deviation of the sample from the distribution. By means of the sampling distribution of D, we then find a quantity D_0 such that $P(D > D_0) = \varepsilon$, where ε is determined as above. If, in an actual case, we find a value $D > D_0$, we then say that the deviation is *significant*, and we consider the hypothesis as disproved. On the other hand, when $D \leqq D_0$, the deviation is regarded as possibly due to random fluctuations, and the data are regarded as consistent with the hypothesis.

A test of this general character will be called a *test of significance* relative to the hypothesis in question. In the simple case when the test is concerned with the agreement between the distribution of a set of sample values and a theoretical distribution, we talk more specifically of a *test of goodness of fit.* The probability ε, which may be arbitrarily fixed, is called the *level of significance* of the test.

In a case when our deviation measure D exceeds the *significance limit* D_0, we thus regard the hypothesis as disproved by experience. This is, of course, by no means equivalent to a *logical* disproof. Even if the hypothesis is true, the event $D > D_0$ with the probability ε *may* occur in an exceptional case. However, when ε is sufficiently small, we feel *practically* justified in disregarding this possibility.

On the other hand, the occurrence of a single value $D \leqq D_0$ does not provide a *proof* of the truth of the hypothesis. It only shows that, from the point of view of the particular test applied, the agreement between theory and observations is satisfactory. Before a statistical hypothesis can be regarded as practically established, it will have to pass repeated tests of different kinds.

In Chs 30—31, we shall discuss various simple tests of significance, and give numerical examples of their application. In Ch. 35, the general foundations of tests of this character will be submitted to a critical analysis.

26.3. Description. — In 13.4, the applications of a mathematical theory were roughly classified under the headings: *Description, Analysis* and *Prediction*. There are, of course, no sharp distinctions between the three classes, and the whole classification is only introduced as a matter of convenience. We shall now briefly comment upon some important groups of applications belonging to the three classes.

In the first place, the theory may be used for purely *descriptive* purposes. When a large set of statistical data has been collected, we are often interested in some particular properties of the phenomenon under investigation. It is then desirable to be able to condense the information with respect to these properties, which may be contained in the mass of original data, in a small number of descriptive characteristics. The ordinary characteristics of the distribution of the sample values, such as moments, semi-invariants, coefficients of regression and correlation etc., may generally be used with advantage for such purposes. The use of frequency-curves for the graduation of data, which plays an important part in the early literature of the subject, also belongs primarily to this group of applications.

When we replace the mass of original data by a small number of descriptive characteristics, we perform a *reduction of the data*, according to the terminology of R. A. Fisher (Ref. 13, 89). It is obviously important that this reduction will be so arranged that as much as possible of the relevant information contained in the original data is extracted by the set of descriptive characteristics chosen. Now the essential properties of any sample characteristic are expressed by its sampling distribution, and thus the systematic investigation of such distributions in Chs 27—29 will be a necessary preliminary to the working out of useful methods of reduction.

In most cases, however, the final object of a statistical investigation will not be of a purely descriptive nature. The descriptive characteristics will, in fact, usually be required for some definite purpose. We may, e.g., want to compare various sets of data with the aid of the characteristics of each set, or we may want to form estimates of the values of the characteristics that we expect to find in future sets of data. In such cases, the description of the actual data forms only a preliminary stage of the inquiry, and we are in reality concerned with an application belonging to one of the two following classes.

26.4. Analysis. — When a mathematical theory has been tested and approved, it may be used to provide tools for a scientific *analysis* of observational data. In the present case we may characterize this type of applications by saying that we are trying to *argue from the sample to the population.* We are given certain sets of statistical data, which are conceived to be samples from certain populations, and we try to use the data to learn something about the distributions of the populations. A great variety of problems of this class occur in statistical practice. In this preliminary survey, we shall only mention some of the main types which, in later chapters, will be more thoroughly discussed.

In 26.2, we have already met with the following type of problems: We are given a sample of observed values of a variable, and we ask if it is reasonable to assume that the sample may have been drawn from a distribution belonging to some given class. Are we, e. g., justified in saying that the errors in a certain kind of physical measurements are normally distributed? Or that the distribution of incomes among the citizens of a certain state follows the law of Pareto (cf 19.3)? — In neither case the distribution of an actual sample will coincide *exactly* with the hypothetical distribution, since the former is of the discrete, and the latter of the continuous type. But are we entitled to ascribe the deviation of the observed distribution from the hypothetical to random fluctuations, or should we conclude that the deviation is *significant*, i. e. indicative of a real difference between the unknown distribution of the population and the hypothetical distribution?

We have seen in 26.2 how this question may be attacked by means of the introduction of a *test of significance.* We then have to calculate a certain measure of deviation D, and in an actual case the deviation is regarded as significant, if D exceeds a certain given value D_0, while otherwise the deviation will be ascribed to random fluctuations.

In other cases, we assume that the general character of the distributions is known from earlier experience, and we require information as to the values of some particular characteristics of the distributions.

Suppose, e. g., that we want to compare the effects of two different methods of treatment of the same disease, and let us assume that for each method there is a constant probability of recovery. Are the two probabilities different? In order to throw light upon the problem, we collect one sample of cases for each method, and compare the two frequencies of recovery. In general these will be different, and we are facing the same question as in the previous case: Is the difference due to random fluctuations, or is it significant, i. e. indicative of a real difference between the probabilities?

Similar, though often more complicated problems arise in many cases, e. g. in agricultural, industrial or medical statistics, when we want to compare the effects of various methods of treatment or of production. We are then concerned with the means or some other characteristics of our samples, and we ask whether the differences between the observed values of these characteristics should be ascribed to random fluctuations or judged to be significant.

In such cases, it is often useful to begin by considering the hypothesis that there is *no* difference between the effects of the methods, so that in reality all our samples come from the same population. (This is sometimes called the *null hypothesis.*) This being assumed, it will often be possible to work out a test of significance for the differences between the means or other characteristics in which we are interested. If the differences exceed certain limits, they will be regarded as significant, and we shall conclude that there is a real difference between the methods; otherwise we shall ascribe the differences to random fluctuations.

This type of applications belongs to the realm of the statistical *analysis of causes.* Suppose, more generally, that we want to know whether there exists any appreciable causal relationship between two variables x and y that we are investigating. As a first approach to the problem, we may then set up the null hypothesis, which in this case implies that the variables are independent, and proceed to work out a test of significance for this hypothesis on the general lines indicated above. Suppose, e. g., that we are interested in tracing a possible connection between the annual quantities x and y of two commodities consumed in a given group of households. From a sample of observed values of the two-dimensional variable (x, y), we may then calculate e. g. the sample correlation coefficient r. In general this coefficient will be different from zero, whereas on the null hypothesis the correlation coefficient ϱ of the corresponding distribution is equal to zero. Is the difference significant, or should it be ascribed to random fluctuations? In order to answer this question, we shall have to work out a test of significance, based on the properties of the sampling distribution of r. If r differs significantly from zero, this may be taken as an indication of some kind of dependence between the variables. The converse conclusion is, however, not legitimate. Even if the population value ϱ is equal to zero, the variables may be dependent (cf 21.7).

Various tests of significance adapted to problems of the general character indicated above will be treated in Chs 30—31. The test of significance to be applied to a given problem may always be chosen in many different ways. It thus becomes an important problem to examine the principles underlying the choice of a test, to compare the properties of various alternative tests and, if possible, to show how to find the test that will be most efficient for a given purpose. Questions belonging to this order of ideas will be considered in Ch. 35.

In a further type of problems of statistical analysis it is required to use a set of sample values to form *estimates* of various characteristics of the population from which the sample is supposed to be drawn, and to form an idea of the *precision* of such estimates. The simplest problem of this type is the classical problem of *inverse probability*: given the frequency of an event E in a sequence of repetitions of a random experiment, what kind of conclusions can be drawn with respect to the unknown value of the probability p of E? It is fairly obvious that in this case the observed frequency ratio may be taken as an estimate of p, but will it be possible to measure the precision of this estimate, and even to make some valid probability statement concerning the difference between the estimate and the unknown »true value» of p? — A more complicated problem of the same character arises in the *theory of errors*, where we have at our disposal a set of measurements on quantities connected with a certain number of unknown constants, and it is required to form estimates of the values of these constants, and to appreciate the precision of the estimates. Similar problems occur in connection with the method of *multiple regression*, which is of great importance in many fields of application. In certain economic problems, e. g., economic theory leads us to assume that there exist certain linear or approximately linear relations between variables connected with consumers' incomes, prices and quantities of various commodities produced or consumed in a given market. When a set of observed values of these variables are available, it is then required to form estimates of the »elasticities» or similar quantities that appear as coefficients in the relations between the variables.

A general form of the estimation problem may be stated in the following way. We consider a random variable (in any number of dimensions), the distribution of which has a known mathematical form, but contains a certain number of unknown constant parameters. We are given a sample of observed values of the variable, and it is required to use the sample values to form estimates of the parameters, and to appreciate the precision of the estimates. In general, there will be an infinite number of different functions of the sample values that may be used as estimates, and it will then be important to compare the properties of various possible estimates for the same parameter, and in particular to find the functions (if any) that yield estimates *of maximum precision.* Further, when a system of estimates has been computed, it will be natural to ask if it is possible to make some valid probability statements concerning the deviations of the estimates from the unknown »true values» of the parameters. Problems of this type form the object of the *theory of estimation*, which will be treated in Chs 32—34. — Finally, some applications of the preceding theories will be given in Chs 36—37.

26.5. Prediction. — The word prediction should here be understood in a very wide sense, as related to the ability to answer questions such as: What is going to happen under given conditions? — What consequences are we likely to encounter if we take this or that possible course of action? — What course of action should we take in order to produce some given event? — Prediction, in this wide sense of the word, is the *practical* aim of any form of science.

Questions of the type indicated often arise in connection with random variables. We shall quote some examples:

What numbers of marriages, births and deaths are we likely to find in a given country during the next year? — What distribution of colours should we expect in the offspring of a pair of mice of known genetical constitution? — What effects are likely to occur, if the price of a certain commodity is raised or lowered by a given amount? — Given the results of certain routine tests on a sample from a batch of manufactured articles, should the batch be a) destroyed, or b) placed on the market under a guarantee? — How should the premiums and funds of an insurance office be calculated in order to produce a stable business? — What margin of security should be applied in the planning of a new telephone exchange in order to reduce the risk of a temporary overloading within reasonable limits?

If we suppose that we know the probability distributions of the variables that enter into a question of this type, it will be seen that we shall often be in a position to give at least a tentative answer to the question. A full discussion of a question of this type, however, usually requires an intimate knowledge of the particular field of application concerned. In a work on general statistical theory, such as the present one, it is obviously not possible to enter upon such discussions.

Chapters 27–29. Sampling Distributions.

CHAPTER 27.

Characteristics of Sampling Distributions.

27.1 Notations. — Consider a one-dimensional random variable ξ with the d. f. $F(x)$. For the moments and other characteristics of the distribution of ξ we shall use the notations introduced in Ch. 15. Thus m and σ denote the mean and the variance of the variable, while α_ν, μ_ν and $\varkappa_\nu$ denote respectively the moment, central moment and semi-invariant of order ν. We shall suppose throughout, and without further notice, that these quantities are finite, as far as they are required for the deduction of our formulae.

By n repetitions of the random experiment to which the variable ξ is attached, we obtain a sequence of n observed values of the variable: $x_1, x_2, \ldots, x_n$. As explained in 25.2, we shall in this connection use a terminology derived from the process of simple random sampling, thus regarding the set of values $x_1, \ldots, x_n$ as a sample from a population specified by the d. f. $F(x)$. The *distribution of the sample* is obtained (cf 25.3) by placing a mass equal to $1/n$ in each point x_i, and the moments and other *characteristics of the sample* are defined as the characteristics of this distribution.

In all investigations dealing with sample characteristics, it is most important to use a clear and consistent system of notations. In this respect, we shall as far as possible apply the following three rules throughout the rest of the book:

1. *The arithmetic mean of any number of quantities such as* $x_1, \ldots, x_n$ *or* $y_1, \ldots y_k$ *will be denoted by the corresponding letter with a bar:* $\bar{x}$ *or* $\bar{y}$.

2. *When a certain characteristic of the population (i. e. of the distribution of the variable* ξ*) is ordinarily denoted by a Greek letter, the corresponding characteristic of the sample will be denoted by the corresponding italic letter:* s^2 *for* σ^2, a_ν *for* α_ν, *etc.*

3. *In cases not covered by the two preceding rules we shall usually denote sample characteristics by placing an asterisk on the letter denoting* *the corresponding population characteristic, thus writing e. g. $F^*(x)$ for the d. f. of the sample, which corresponds to the population d. f. $F(x)$.*

Thus the mean and the variance of the sample are (cf 25.3)

$$\bar{x} = \frac{1}{n} \sum_i x_i, \quad s^2 = \frac{1}{n} \sum_i (x_i - \bar{x})^2, \tag{27.1.1}$$

where the summation is extended over all sample values: $i = 1, 2, \ldots n$. The moments a_ν and the central moments m_ν of the sample are

$$a_\nu = \frac{1}{n} \sum_i x_i^\nu, \quad m_\nu = \frac{1}{n} \sum_i (x_i - \bar{x})^\nu. \tag{27.1.2}$$

The coefficients of skewness and excess of the sample are, in accordance with (15.8.1) and (15.8.2),

$$g_1 = \frac{m_3}{m_2^{3/2}}, \quad g_2 = \frac{m_4}{m_2^2} - 3. \tag{27.1.3}$$

The relations (15.4.4) between the moments and the central moments hold true for any distribution; thus in particular they remain valid if m, α_ν and μ_ν are replaced by the corresponding sample characteristics $\bar{x}$, a_ν and m_ν.

For the d. f. of the sample, we have already in (25.3.1) introduced the notation $F^*(x)$. Similarly the c. f. of the sample is[1])

$$\varphi^*(t) = \int_{-\infty}^{\infty} e^{itx}\, d F^*(x) = \frac{1}{n} \sum_i e^{itx_i}, \tag{27.1.4}$$

and the semi-invariants of the sample are thus according to (15.10.2) defined by the development[2])

$$\log \varphi^*(t) = \sum_1^\infty \frac{k_\nu}{\nu!} (\boldsymbol{i}\, t)^\nu. \tag{27.1.5}$$

All moments and semi-invariants of the sample are finite, and the relations (15.10.3) — (15.10.5) between moments and semi-invariants

[1]) When there is a possibility of confusion, we shall use a heavy-faced $\boldsymbol{i}$ to denote the imaginary unit.

[2]) At this point our notation differs from the notation of R. A. Fisher (Ref. 13), who uses the symbol k_ν to denote the unbiased estimate of $\varkappa_\nu$ which, in our notation, is denoted by K_ν (cf 27.6).

hold true when the population characteristics are replaced by sample characteristics.

The same rules will be applied to samples from multi-dimensional populations. Thus e. g. if we are given n pairs of observed values $(x_1, y_1), \ldots, (x_n, y_n)$ from a two-dimensional distribution, we write (cf 21.2)

$$\bar{x} = \frac{1}{n} \sum_i x_i, \qquad \bar{y} = \frac{1}{n} \sum_i y_i,$$

$$(27.1.6) \qquad \begin{aligned} m_{20} &= s_1^2 = \frac{1}{n} \sum_i (x_i - \bar{x})^2, \\ m_{11} &= r s_1 s_2 = \frac{1}{n} \sum_i (x_i - \bar{x})(y_i - \bar{y}), \\ m_{02} &= s_2^2 = \frac{1}{n} \sum_i (y_i - \bar{y})^2. \end{aligned}$$

In particular, the quantity r defined by the relation

$$(27.1.7) \qquad r = \frac{m_{11}}{s_1 s_2}$$

is the correlation coefficient of the sample, which corresponds to the correlation coefficient ϱ of the population. Since r is the correlation coefficient of an actual distribution (viz. the distribution of the sample), it follows from 21.2 that we have $-1 \leqq r \leqq 1$. The extreme values $r = \pm 1$ can only occur when all the sample points (x_i, y_i) are situated on a single straight line.

For a sample in more than two dimensions, we use notations derived according to the above rules from the notations introduced in Chs 22—23. Thus e. g. we denote by s_i the s. d. of the sample values of the i:th variable, while r_{ij} is the correlation coefficient between the sample values of the i:th and the j:th variable. We further write R for the determinant $|r_{ij}|$, and denote the regression coefficients, the partial correlation coefficients etc. of the sample by symbols such as (cf 23.2.3 and 23.4.2)

$$b_{12 \cdot 34 \ldots k} = -\frac{s_1}{s_2} \cdot \frac{R_{12}}{R_{11}},$$

$$r_{12 \cdot 34 \ldots k} = -\frac{R_{12}}{\sqrt{R_{11} R_{22}}},$$

where k is the number of dimensions, while the R_{ij} are the cofactors of R. As before, all relations between the characteristics deduced in Part II hold true when the population characteristics are replaced by sample characteristics.

We now come back for one moment to the one-dimensional case. According to 25.4, any characteristic $g(x_1, \ldots, x_n)$ of an actual sample may be regarded as an observed value of a random variable $g(x_1, \ldots, x_n)$, where $x_1, \ldots, x_n$ are independent variables, all having the same distribution as the original variable ξ. The distribution of the random variable $g(x_1, \ldots, x_n)$ is called the *sampling distribution* of the characteristic $g(x_1, \ldots, x_n)$. Thus we may talk of the sampling distribution of the mean $\bar{x}$, of the variance s^2, etc.

The same remarks apply to samples in any number of dimensions. Any sample characteristic may be regarded as an observed value of a certain random variable, the distribution of which is called the sampling distribution of the characteristic. Thus we may talk of the sampling distribution of the correlation coefficient r, of the correlation determinant R, etc.

For any sample characteristic g, we may thus consider its sampling distribution, and calculate the moments, semi-invariants etc. of this distribution. As usual (cf 15.3 and 15.6) we employ in such cases the symbols $\boldsymbol{E}(g)$ and $\boldsymbol{D}(g)$ to denote the mean and the s. d. of the random variable $g = g(x_1, \ldots, x_n)$. Further, when we are concerned with some characteristic of the g-distribution (such as a central moment, a semi-invariant etc.), which has been given a standard notation (such as μ_ν or $\varkappa_\nu$) in Ch. 15, we shall sometimes use the standard symbol of this characteristic, followed by the corresponding random variable within brackets. Thus we shall write e. g. for the central moment of order ν of the sample characteristic $g = g(x_1, \ldots, x_n)$

$$\mu_\nu(g) = \boldsymbol{E}(g - \boldsymbol{E}(g))^\nu.$$

Similarly, when two sample characteristics $f(x_1, \ldots, x_n)$ and $g(x_1, \ldots, x_n)$ are considered simultaneously, the correlation coefficient of their joint sampling distribution will be denoted by

$$\varrho(f, g) = \frac{\mu_{11}(f, g)}{\sqrt{\mu_2(f)\,\mu_2(g)}}.$$

Whenever we are concerned with sampling distributions connected with a given population, it should always be borne in mind that the sample characteristics ($\bar{x}$, s, m_ν, k_ν, r *etc.*) *are conceived as random variables, while the population characteristics* (m, σ, μ_ν, $\varkappa_\nu$, ϱ *etc.*) *are fixed* (*though sometimes unknown*) *constants.*

27.2. The sample mean $\bar{x}$. — Consider a one-dimensional sample with the values $x_1, \ldots, x_n$. Regarding the x_i as independent random variables, each having the d. f. $F(x)$, we obtain

$$(27.2.1) \qquad \begin{aligned} \boldsymbol{E}(\bar{x}) &= \frac{1}{n}\sum_i \boldsymbol{E}(x_i) = m, \\ \boldsymbol{D}^2(\bar{x}) &= \frac{1}{n^2}\sum_i \boldsymbol{D}^2(x_i) = \frac{\mu_2}{n}. \end{aligned}$$

Thus the random variable $\bar{x} = \frac{1}{n}\Sigma\, x_i$ has the mean m and the variance μ_2/n, i. e. the s. d. $\sigma/\sqrt{n}$. It then immediately follows from Tchebycheff's theorem 20.4 that the sample mean $\bar{x}$ converges in probability to the population mean m, as n tends to infinity.[1])

Writing $\bar{x} - m = \frac{1}{n}\Sigma(x_i - m)$, and bearing in mind that the x_i are independent, and that any difference $x_i - m$ has the mean value zero, we further obtain

$$\begin{aligned} \mu_3(\bar{x}) &= \boldsymbol{E}(\bar{x} - m)^3 = \frac{1}{n^3}\boldsymbol{E}\left(\sum_i (x_i - m)\right)^3 \\ &= \frac{1}{n^3}\sum_i \boldsymbol{E}(x_i - m)^3 = \frac{\mu_3}{n^2}, \end{aligned}$$

$$(27.2.2) \qquad \begin{aligned} \mu_4(\bar{x}) &= \boldsymbol{E}(\bar{x} - m)^4 = \frac{1}{n^4}\boldsymbol{E}\left(\sum_i (x_i - m)\right)^4 \\ &= \frac{1}{n^4}\sum_i \boldsymbol{E}(x_i - m)^4 + \frac{6}{n^4}\sum_{i<j}\boldsymbol{E}\left((x_i - m)^2(x_j - m)^2\right) \\ &= \frac{\mu_4}{n^3} + \frac{3(n-1)}{n^3}\mu_2^2 = \frac{3\mu_2^2}{n^2} + \frac{\mu_4 - 3\mu_2^2}{n^3}. \end{aligned}$$

The higher central moments of $\bar{x}$ may be found by similar, though somewhat more tedious, calculations. Thus we find

[1]) By the less elementary Khintchine's theorem 20.5, it follows that this property holds as soon as the population mean m exists, even when μ_2 is not finite.

$$\mu_5(\bar{x}) = \mathbf{E}(\bar{x} - m)^5 = \frac{10\,\mu_2\,\mu_3}{n^3} + O\left(\frac{1}{n^4}\right),$$

$$\mu_6(\bar{x}) = \mathbf{E}(\bar{x} - m)^6 = \frac{15\,\mu_2^3}{n^3} + O\left(\frac{1}{n^4}\right),$$

and generally

$$\mathbf{E}(\bar{x} - m)^{2k-1} = O\left(\frac{1}{n^k}\right), \quad \mathbf{E}(\bar{x} - m)^{2k} = O\left(\frac{1}{n^k}\right). \tag{27.2.3}$$

In the important particular case when the distribution of the population is normal (m, σ), it has been pointed out in 17.3 that $\bar{x}$ is also normal, with mean m and s. d. $\sigma/\sqrt{n}$. It follows that in this case any $\mu_\nu(\bar{x})$ of odd order is zero, while the three first central moments of even order reduce to

$$\mu_2(\bar{x}) = \mathbf{D}^2(\bar{x}) = \frac{\sigma^2}{n}, \quad \mu_4(\bar{x}) = \frac{3\,\sigma^4}{n^2}, \quad \mu_6(\bar{x}) = \frac{15\,\sigma^6}{n^3}.$$

27.3. The moments a_ν. — For any sample moment $a_\nu = \frac{1}{n}\sum x_i^\nu$ we obtain in direct generalization of (27.2.1) and (27.2.3),

$$\begin{aligned}
\mathbf{E}(a_\nu) &= \frac{1}{n}\sum_i \mathbf{E}(x_i^\nu) = \alpha_\nu,\\
\mathbf{D}^2(a_\nu) &= \frac{1}{n^2}\sum_i \mathbf{D}^2(x_i^\nu)\\
&= \frac{1}{n^2}\sum_i \left(\mathbf{E}(x_i^{2\nu}) - \mathbf{E}^2(x_i^\nu)\right) = \frac{\alpha_{2\nu} - \alpha_\nu^2}{n},\\
\mathbf{E}(a_\nu - \alpha_\nu)^{2k-1} &= O\left(\frac{1}{n^k}\right), \quad \mathbf{E}(a_\nu - \alpha_\nu)^{2k} = O\left(\frac{1}{n^k}\right).
\end{aligned} \tag{27.3.1}$$

By Khintchine's theorem 20.5 it follows from the first of these relations that, as soon as the population moment α_ν exists, the sample moment a_ν converges in probability to α_ν, as $n \to \infty$.

It now follows from the corollary to theorem 20.6 that any rational function, or power of a rational function, of the sample moments a_ν converges in probability to the constant obtained by substituting throughout α_ν for a_ν, provided that all the α_ν occurring in the resulting expression exist, and that the constant thus obtained is finite.

Hence in particular the central moments m_ν, the semi-invariants k_ν

and the coefficients g_1 and g_2 defined by (27.1.3) all converge in probability to the corresponding population characteristics, as $n \to \infty$. In large samples, any of these sample characteristics may thus be regarded as an *estimate* of the corresponding population characteristic. We shall, however, later find that the estimates obtained in this way are not always the best that we can obtain (cf 27.6 and 33.1).

Any mean value of the type

$$\text{(27.3.2)} \qquad \boldsymbol{E}(a_\mu^p a_\nu^q \ldots) = \frac{1}{n^{p+q+\cdots}} \boldsymbol{E}\left(\left(\sum_i x_i^\mu\right)^p \left(\sum_i x_i^\nu\right)^q \cdots\right),$$

where $p, q, \ldots$ are integers, can be obtained by straightforward, though often tedious, algebraical calculation. We have only to use the fact that the x_i are independent variables such that $\boldsymbol{E}(x_i^\nu) = \alpha_\nu$. — In the particular case when the population mean m is equal to zero, α_ν coincides with the central moment μ_ν. If the sample mean $a_1 = \bar{x}$ occurs among the factors in (27.3.2), the calculations are in this case simplified, since any term containing one of the x_i in the first degree has then the mean value zero.

27.4. The variance m_2. — Any central sample moment $m_\nu = \frac{1}{n}\sum_i (x_i - \bar{x})^\nu$ is independent of the position of the origin on the scale of the variable. Placing the origin in the mean of the population, we have $m = 0$. When we are concerned with the sampling distributions of the m_ν, we may thus always suppose $m = 0$, and so introduce the simplification mentioned at the end of the preceding paragraph. The formulae thus obtained will hold true irrespective of the value of m.

We accordingly suppose $m = 0$, and consider the sample variance $m_2 = s^2 = \frac{1}{n}\Sigma(x_i - \bar{x})^2 = a_2 - \bar{x}^2$. By (27.2.1) and (27.3.1) we have, since $m = 0$,

$$\text{(27.4.1)} \qquad \boldsymbol{E}(m_2) = \boldsymbol{E}(a_2) - \boldsymbol{E}(\bar{x}^2) = \mu_2 - \frac{\mu_2}{n} = \frac{n-1}{n}\mu_2.$$

We further have $m_2^2 = a_2^2 - 2\bar{x}^2 a_2 + \bar{x}^4$. Assuming always $m = 0$, we find

$$E(a_2^2) = \frac{1}{n^2} E\left(\sum_i x_i^2\right)^2 = \frac{\mu_4 + (n-1)\mu_2^2}{n},$$

$$E(\bar{x}^2 a_2) = \frac{1}{n^3} E\left[\left(\sum_i x_i\right)^2 \sum_i x_i^2\right] = \frac{\mu_4 + (n-1)\mu_2^2}{n^2},$$

$$E(\bar{x}^4) = \frac{1}{n^4} E\left(\sum_i x_i\right)^4 = \frac{\mu_4 + 3(n-1)\mu_2^2}{n^3},$$

and hence after reduction

$$E(m_2^2) = \mu_2^2 + \frac{\mu_4 - 3\mu_2^2}{n} - \frac{2\mu_4 - 5\mu_2^2}{n^2} + \frac{\mu_4 - 3\mu_2^2}{n^3},$$

(27.4.2) $$D^2(m_2) = E(m_2^2) - E^2(m_2) = \frac{\mu_4 - \mu_2^2}{n} - \frac{2(\mu_4 - 2\mu_2^2)}{n^2} + \frac{\mu_4 - 3\mu_2^2}{n^3}.$$

The higher central moments of m_2 may be obtained in the same way. The calculations are long and uninteresting, but no difficulty of principle is involved. We give only the leading terms of the third and fourth moments:

(27.4.3)
$$\mu_3(m_2) = E\left(m_2 - \frac{n-1}{n}\mu_2\right)^3 = \frac{\mu_6 - 3\mu_2\mu_4 - 6\mu_3^2 + 2\mu_2^3}{n^2} + O\left(\frac{1}{n^3}\right),$$
$$\mu_4(m_2) = E\left(m_2 - \frac{n-1}{n}\mu_2\right)^4 = \frac{3(\mu_4 - \mu_2^2)^2}{n^2} + O\left(\frac{1}{n^3}\right).$$

We shall finally consider the covariance (cf 21.2) between the mean $\bar{x}$ and the variance m_2 of the sample. For an arbitrary value of m, this is

$$\mu_{11}(\bar{x}, m_2) = E\left((\bar{x} - m)\left(m_2 - \frac{n-1}{n}\mu_2\right)\right) = E((\bar{x} - m)\, m_2).$$

Since the last expression is clearly independent of the position of the origin, we may again assume $m = 0$, and thus obtain by calculations of the same kind as above

(27.4.4)
$$\mu_{11}(\bar{x}, m_2) = E(\bar{x} m_2) = E(\bar{x} a_2) - E(\bar{x}^3) = \frac{\mu_3}{n} - \frac{\mu_3}{n^2} = \frac{n-1}{n^2}\mu_3.$$

For any *symmetric* distribution, we have $\mu_3 = 0$, and thus $\bar{x}$ and m_2 are uncorrelated. We shall see later (cf 29.3) that, in the particular case of a *normal* population, $\bar{x}$ and m_2 are not only uncorrelated, but even *independent.* For a normal population, (27.4.1) and (27.4.2) give

$$E(m_2) = \frac{n-1}{n}\sigma^2, \quad D^2(m_2) = \frac{2(n-1)}{n^2}\sigma^4. \tag{27.4.5}$$

27.5. Higher central moments and semi-invariants. — The expressions for the characteristics of the sampling distributions of m_ν and k_ν are of rapidly increasing complexity when ν becomes greater than 2, and we shall only mention a few comparatively simple cases, omitting details of calculation. For further information, the reader may be referred e. g. to papers by Tschuprow (Ref. 227) and Craig (Ref. 67).

By calculations of the same kind as in the preceding paragraphs, we obtain the expressions

$$\begin{aligned} E(m_3) &= \frac{(n-1)(n-2)}{n^2}\mu_3, \\ E(m_4) &= \frac{(n-1)(n^2-3n+3)}{n^3}\mu_4 + \frac{3(n-1)(2n-3)}{n^3}\mu_2^2. \end{aligned} \tag{27.5.1}$$

For any m_ν we have

$$m_\nu = \frac{1}{n}\sum_i (x_i - \bar{x})^\nu = a_\nu - \binom{\nu}{1}\bar{x}\,a_{\nu-1} + \binom{\nu}{2}\bar{x}^2 a_{\nu-2} - \cdots. \tag{27.5.2}$$

As before, we may suppose $m = 0$, so that $E(a_\nu) = \mu_\nu$, and

$$E(\bar{x}\,a_{\nu-1}) = \frac{1}{n^2}E\left(\sum_i x_i \sum_i x_i^{\nu-1}\right) = \frac{\mu_\nu}{n}.$$

For $1 < i \leqq \nu$, we have by (27.2.3) and (27.3.1), using the Schwarz inequality (9.5.1),

$$E^2(\bar{x}^i a_{\nu-i}) \leqq E(\bar{x}^{2i})\,E(a_{\nu-i}^2) = O\left(\frac{1}{n^i}\right),$$

so that $E(\bar{x}^i a_{\nu-i}) = O\left(n^{-\frac{i}{2}}\right)$, and (27.5.2) gives

$$(27.5.3) \qquad \boldsymbol{E}(m_\nu) = \mu_\nu + O\left(\frac{1}{n}\right).$$

Further, by (27.5.2) any power of $m_\nu - \mu_\nu$ is composed of terms of the form $\bar{x}^i (a_\nu - \mu_\nu)^j a_{k_1} a_{k_2} \ldots$, and it is shown in the same way as above that the mean value of such a term is of the order $n^{-\frac{i+j}{2}}$. Thus in order to calculate the leading term of $\boldsymbol{E}(m_\nu - \mu_\nu)^k$, it is sufficient to retain the terms

$$m_\nu - \mu_\nu = a_\nu - \mu_\nu - \binom{\nu}{1} \bar{x}\, a_{\nu-1},$$

while all the following terms of (27.5.2) give a contribution of lower order. For $k = 2$ we obtain in this way, since by (27.5.3) the difference $\boldsymbol{E}(m_\nu) - \mu_\nu$ is of order n^{-1},

$$(27.5.4) \qquad \boldsymbol{D}^2(m_\nu) = \frac{\mu_{2\nu} - 2\nu\,\mu_{\nu-1}\,\mu_{\nu+1} - \mu_\nu^2 + \nu^2\,\mu_2\,\mu_{\nu-1}^2}{n} + O\left(\frac{1}{n^2}\right).$$

Generally we obtain for any even power of $m_\nu - \mu_\nu$

$$(27.5.5) \qquad \boldsymbol{E}(m_\nu - \mu_\nu)^{2k} = O\left(\frac{1}{n^k}\right).$$

The mean value of a product $(m_\nu - \mu_\nu)(m_\varrho - \mu_\varrho)$ may be calculated in the same way, and we thus obtain, using again (27.5.3), the following expression for the covariance between m_ν and m_ϱ:

$$(27.5.6) \qquad \mu_{11}(m_\nu, m_\varrho) =$$

$$= \frac{\mu_{\nu+\varrho} - \nu\,\mu_{\nu-1}\,\mu_{\varrho+1} - \varrho\,\mu_{\nu+1}\,\mu_{\varrho-1} - \mu_\nu\,\mu_\varrho + \nu\,\varrho\,\mu_2\,\mu_{\nu-1}\,\mu_{\varrho-1}}{n} + O\left(\frac{1}{n^2}\right).$$

The expressions of the first semi-invariants k_ν of the sample are obtained by substituting in (15.10.5) the sample moments m_ν for the population moments μ_ν. We obtain

$$k_1 = \bar{x}, \qquad k_2 = m_2, \qquad k_3 = m_3, \qquad k_4 = m_4 - 3\,m_2^2.$$

We may then deduce expressions for the means and variances of the k_ν by means of the formulae for the m_ν given above. In particular we obtain in this way, expressing $\boldsymbol{E}(k_\nu)$ in terms of the population semi-invariants $\varkappa_\nu$

$$\begin{aligned} \mathbf{E}(k_1) &= \varkappa_1, \\ \mathbf{E}(k_2) &= \frac{n-1}{n}\varkappa_2, \\ \mathbf{E}(k_3) &= \frac{(n-1)(n-2)}{n^2}\varkappa_3, \\ \mathbf{E}(k_4) &= \frac{(n-1)(n^2-6n+6)}{n^3}\varkappa_4 - \frac{6(n-1)}{n^2}\varkappa_2^2. \end{aligned} \tag{27.5.7}$$

27.6. Unbiased estimates. — Consider the sample variance $m_2 = \frac{1}{n}\Sigma(x_i - \bar{x})^2$. According to 27.3, m_2 converges in probability to the population variance μ_2 as $n \to \infty$, and for large values of n we may thus use m_2 as an estimate of μ_2. In the terminology introduced by R. A. Fisher (Ref. 89, 96), an estimate which converges in probability to the estimated value, as the size of the sample tends to infinity, is called a *consistent* estimate. Thus m_2 is a consistent estimate of μ_2.

On the other hand, it is shown by (27.4.1) that the mean value of m_2 is not μ_2 but $\frac{n-1}{n}\mu_2$. Thus if we repeatedly draw samples of a fixed size n from the given population, and calculate the variance m_2 for each sample, the arithmetic mean of all the observed m_2-values will *not* converge in probability to the »true value» μ_2, but to the smaller value $\frac{n-1}{n}\mu_2$. As an estimate of μ_2, the quantity m_2 is thus affected with a certain negative *bias*, which may be removed if we replace m_2 by the quantity

$$M_2 = \frac{n}{n-1}m_2 = \frac{n}{n-1}s^2 = \frac{1}{n-1}\sum(x_i - \bar{x})^2.$$

We have, in fact, $\mathbf{E}(M_2) = \frac{n}{n-1}\mathbf{E}(m_2) = \mu_2$, and accordingly M_2 is called an *unbiased* estimate of μ_2. Since the factor $\frac{n}{n-1}$ tends to unity as $n \to \infty$, both M_2 and m_2 converge in probability to μ_2, so that M_2 is consistent as well as unbiased, while m_2 is consistent, but not unbiased.

Similarly, by 27.3, any central moment m_ν or semi-invariant k_ν of the sample is a consistent estimate of the corresponding μ_ν or $\varkappa_\nu$, but it follows from (27.5.1) and (27.5.7) that for $\nu > 1$ these estimates are not unbiased. As in the case of m_2 we may, however, by simple corrections form estimates which are both consistent and unbiased. Thus we obtain for $\nu = 2, 3$ and 4 the following corrected estimates of μ_ν and $\varkappa_\nu$:

$$M_2 = \frac{n}{n-1} m_2,$$

$$M_3 = \frac{n^2}{(n-1)(n-2)} m_3,$$

$$M_4 = \frac{n(n^2 - 2n + 3)}{(n-1)(n-2)(n-3)} m_4 - \frac{3n(2n-3)}{(n-1)(n-2)(n-3)} m_2^2,$$

and

$$K_2 = \frac{n}{n-1} m_2,$$

$$K_3 = \frac{n^2}{(n-1)(n-2)} m_3,$$

$$K_4 = \frac{n^2}{(n-1)(n-2)(n-3)} [(n+1) m_4 - 3(n-1) m_2^2].$$

By means of the formulae given in the two preceding paragraphs, it is easily verified that in all these cases we have $\boldsymbol{E}(M_\nu) = \mu_\nu$ and $\boldsymbol{E}(K_\nu) = \varkappa_\nu$. For large values of n, it is often indifferent whether we use M_ν and K_ν, or m_ν and k_ν, but for small n the bias involved in the latter quantities may be considerable. — We shall return to questions connected with the properties of estimates in Ch. 32.

We have seen in the preceding paragraphs that the algebraical process of working out formulae for the sampling characteristics of the quantities m_ν and k_ν becomes very laborious, as soon as we leave the simplest cases. It has been discovered by R. A. Fisher (Ref. 99), who has introduced the quantities K_ν (which he denotes by k_ν, cf footnote p. 342), that the corresponding calculations for the K_ν may be considerably simplified by means of combinatorial methods. These methods have been further developed by Fisher himself, Wishart and others. A good account of the subject has been given by Kendall (Ref. 19), who gives numerous references to the literature.

27.7. Functions of moments. — It often occurs that the mean and the variance of some function of the sample moments are required.

When the function is a polynomial in $\bar{x}$ and the central moments m_ν, the problem can be solved by the method developed in 27.3—27.5. Even when fractional powers are involved, we may often use a similar direct method. Consider e. g. the simple example of the standard deviation $s = \sqrt{m_2}$ of the sample. We have identically

$$\sqrt{m_2} - \sqrt{\mu_2} = \frac{m_2 - \mu_2}{2\sqrt{\mu_2}} - \frac{(m_2 - \mu_2)^2}{2\sqrt{\mu_2}\,(\sqrt{m_2} + \sqrt{\mu_2})^2}.$$

By (27.4.1), the first term in the second member has a mean value of order n^{-1}. The last term is smaller in absolute value than $\dfrac{(m_2 - \mu_2)^2}{2\,\mu_2^{3/2}}$, and thus by (27.4.2) and (27.4.1) its mean value is also of order n^{-1}. Thus we obtain

$$E(\sqrt{m_2}) = \sqrt{\mu_2} + O\left(\frac{1}{n}\right). \tag{27.7.1}$$

By a similar calculation we obtain

$$D^2(\sqrt{m_2}) = \frac{\mu_4 - \mu_2^2}{4\,\mu_2\,n} + O\left(\frac{1}{n^2}\right). \tag{27.7.2}$$

In many cases, however, we are concerned with functions involving ratios between powers of certain moments, such as the coefficients g_1 and g_2, the coefficient of correlation etc. We shall give a theorem that covers the most important of these cases. The theorem will be stated and proved for the case of a function $H(m_\nu, m_\varrho)$ of two central moments m_ν and m_ϱ, but is immediately extended to any number of arguments, including also the mean $\bar{x}$. The case of a function of one single argument is, of course, included as the particular case when the function is independent of one of the two arguments. The theorem also holds, with the same proof, for functions of moments of multi-dimensional samples (cf 27.8).

Consider a function $H(m_\nu, m_\varrho)$ which does not contain n explicitly. We may regard H either as a function of the two arguments m_ν and m_ϱ or, replacing m_ν and m_ϱ by their expressions in terms of the sample values, as a function of the n variables $x_1, \ldots, x_n$. In the latter case the function may, of course, contain n explicitly. — We shall now prove the following theorem:

Suppose that the two following conditions are satisfied:

1) *In some neighbourhood of the point $m_\nu = \mu_\nu$, $m_\varrho = \mu_\varrho$, the function H is continuous and has continuous derivatives of the first and second order with respect to the arguments m_ν and m_ϱ.*

2) *For all possible values of the* x_i, *we have* $|H| < C n^p$, *where* C *and* p *are non-negative constants.*

Denoting by H_0, H_1 *and* H_2 *the values assumed by the function* $H(m_\nu, m_\varrho)$ *and its first order partial derivatives in the point* $m_\nu = \mu_\nu$, $m_\varrho = \mu_\varrho$, *the mean and the variance of the random variable* $H(m_\nu, m_\varrho)$ *are then given by*

$$(27.7.3)\qquad \begin{aligned} \mathbf{E}(H) &= H_0 + O\left(\frac{1}{n}\right),\\ \mathbf{D}^2(H) &= \mu_2(m_\nu) H_1^2 + 2\mu_{11}(m_\nu, m_\varrho) H_1 H_2 + \mu_2(m_\varrho) H_2^2 + O\left(\frac{1}{n^{3/2}}\right). \end{aligned}$$

By (27.5.4) and (27.5.6), the variance of H is thus of the form $c/n + O(n^{-3/2})$, where c is constant. — The proofs of these relations found in the literature are often unsatisfactory. The condition 2) as given above may be considerably generalized, but *some* condition of this type is necessary for the truth of the theorem. In fact, if we altogether omit condition 2), it would e. g. follow that, for any population with $\mu_2 > 0$, the function $1/m_2$ would have a mean value of the form $1/\mu_2 + O(n^{-1})$. This is, however, evidently false. The mean of $1/m_2$ cannot be finite for any population with a distribution of the discrete type, since we have then a positive probability that $m_2 = 0$. It is easy to show that similar contradictions may arise even for continuous distributions.

In 28.4, it will be proved that the function $H(m_\nu, m_\varrho)$ is asymptotically normally distributed for large values of n. It is interesting to observe that, in this proof, no condition corresponding to the present condition 2) will be required.

Let $P(S)$ denote the pr. f. of the joint distribution of $x_1, x_2, \ldots, x_n$. $P(S)$ is a set function in the space $\mathbf{R}_n$ of the x_i. If, in Tchebycheff's theorem (15.7.1), we take $g(\xi) = (m_\nu - \mu_\nu)^{2k}$, it follows from (27.5.5) that we have for any $\varepsilon > 0$

$$P[(m_\nu - \mu_\nu)^{2k} \geqq \varepsilon^{2k}] < \frac{A}{\varepsilon^{2k} n^k},$$

or

$$P[|m_\nu - \mu_\nu| \geqq \varepsilon] < \frac{A}{\varepsilon^{2k} n^k},$$

where A is a constant independent of n and ε. The corresponding result holds, of course, for m_ϱ. Denote by Z the set of all points in $\mathbf{R}_n$ such that the inequalities $|m_\nu - \mu_\nu| < \varepsilon$ and $|m_\varrho - \mu_\varrho| < \varepsilon$ are both satisfied, while Z^* is the complementary set. We then have, according to the above,

$$(27.7.4)\qquad P(Z^*) < \frac{2A}{\varepsilon^{2k} n^k}, \quad P(Z) > 1 - \frac{2A}{\varepsilon^{2k} n^k}.$$

Now

$$\mathbf{E}(H) = \int_Z H\,dP + \int_{Z^*} H\,dP,$$

and by condition 2) the modulus of the last integral is smaller than $\frac{2\,A\,C\,n^p}{\varepsilon^{2k}\,n^k}$. Choosing $k > p + 1$, it follows that

$$\mathbf{E}(H) = \int_Z H\,dP + O\left(\frac{1}{n}\right). \tag{27.7.5}$$

If ε is sufficiently small, we have by condition 1) for any point in the set Z

$$\begin{aligned} H(m_\nu, m_\varrho) &= H_0 + H_1(m_\nu - \mu_\nu) + H_2(m_\varrho - \mu_\varrho) + R, \\ R &= \tfrac{1}{2}[H'_{11}(m_\nu - \mu_\nu)^2 + 2\,H'_{12}(m_\nu - \mu_\nu)(m_\varrho - \mu_\varrho) + H'_{22}(m_\varrho - \mu_\varrho)^2], \end{aligned} \tag{27.7.6}$$

where the H'_{ij} denote the values of the second order derivatives in some intermediate point between (μ_ν, μ_ϱ) and (m_ν, m_ϱ). Hence

$$\begin{aligned} \int_Z H\,dP = H_0\,P(Z) &+ H_1\int_Z (m_\nu - \mu_\nu)\,dP + \\ &+ H_2\int_Z (m_\varrho - \mu_\varrho)\,dP + \int_Z R\,dP. \end{aligned} \tag{27.7.7}$$

Consider now the terms in the second member of the last relation. By (27.7.4), the first term differs from H_0 by a quantity of order n^{-k}, which is smaller than n^{-1}, since $k > p + 1 \geqq 1$. The two following terms are at most of order n^{-1}, since H_1 and H_2 are independent of n, and we have by (27.5.3) and (27.5.5), using the Schwarz inequality (9.5.1),

$$\begin{aligned} \int_Z (m_\nu - \mu_\nu)\,dP &= \mathbf{E}(m_\nu - \mu_\nu) - \int_{Z^*} (m_\nu - \mu_\nu)\,dP \\ &= O\left(\frac{1}{n}\right) - \int_{Z^*} (m_\nu - \mu_\nu)\,dP, \end{aligned}$$

$$\left|\int_{Z^*}(m_\nu - \mu_\nu)\,dP\right| \leqq \left[\int_{Z^*}(m_\nu - \mu_\nu)^2\,dP \cdot \int_{Z^*} dP\right]^{\frac{1}{2}}$$

$$\leqq [\boldsymbol{E}(m_\nu - \mu_\nu)^2 \cdot P(Z^*)]^{\frac{1}{2}} = O\left(n^{-\frac{1+k}{2}}\right),$$

and similarly for the term containing m_ϱ. Finally, by condition 1) the derivatives H'_{ij} are bounded for all sufficiently small ε, and it then follows in the same way that the last term in (27.7.7) is also of order n^{-1}. Hence the first member of (27.7.7) differs from H_0 by a quantity of order n^{-1}, and according to (27.7.5) we have thus proved the first relation (27.7.3).

In order to prove also the second relation (27.7.3), we write

$$\boldsymbol{E}(H - H_0)^2 = \int_Z (H - H_0)^2\,dP + \int_{Z^*}(H - H_0)^2\,dP.$$

Choosing now $k > 2p + \frac{3}{2}$, we obtain by means of condition 2) and the first relation (27.7.3) just proved

$$\boldsymbol{D}^2(H) = \int_Z (H - H_0)^2\,dP + O\left(n^{-\frac{3}{2}}\right).$$

We then express $(H - H_0)^2$ by means of the development (27.7.6), and proceed in the same way as before. The calculations are quite similar to those made above, except with respect to the terms of the type $\int_Z (m_\nu - \mu_\nu)\,R\,dP$, where we have, e. g., using (15.4.6) and (27.5.5),

$$\left|\int_Z H'_{11}(m_\nu - \mu_\nu)^3\,dP\right| < K\boldsymbol{E}(|m_\nu - \mu_\nu|^3) \leqq K(\boldsymbol{E}(m_\nu - \mu_\nu)^4)^{\frac{3}{4}} = O\left(n^{-\frac{3}{2}}\right).$$

This completes the proof of the theorem.

We shall now apply the relations (27.7.3) to some examples. Consider first the coefficients of skewness and excess of the sample:

$$g_1 = \frac{m_3}{m_2^{3/2}}, \quad g_2 = \frac{m_4}{m_2^2} - 3.$$

As soon as $\mu_2 > 0$, these functions satisfy condition 1). In order to show that condition 2) is also satisfied, we write

$$g_1 = \sqrt{n}\,\frac{\Sigma (x_i - \bar{x})^3}{(\Sigma (x_i - \bar{x})^2)^{3/2}} = \sqrt{n} \sum_i \frac{(x_i - \bar{x})^3}{(\sum_j (x_j - \bar{x})^2)^{3/2}},$$

and hence infer

$$|g_1| \leq \sqrt{n} \sum_i \left(\frac{(x_i - \bar{x})^2}{\sum_j (x_j - \bar{x})^2} \right)^{3/2} \leq \sqrt{n} \sum_i \frac{(x_i - \bar{x})^2}{\sum_j (x_j - \bar{x})^2} = \sqrt{n}\,.$$

In a similar way it is shown that $|g_2| < n$ for all $n > 3$. — Thus we may apply (27.7.3) to find the means and the variances of g_1 and g_2. From (27.5.4) and (27.5.6) we find, to the order of approximation given by (27.7.3),

$$\boldsymbol{E}(g_1) = \gamma_1, \qquad \boldsymbol{E}(g_2) = \gamma_2,$$

(27.7.8)
$$\boldsymbol{D}^2(g_1) = \frac{4\,\mu_2^2\,\mu_6 - 12\,\mu_2\,\mu_3\,\mu_5 - 24\,\mu_2^3\,\mu_4 + 9\,\mu_3^2\,\mu_4 + 35\,\mu_2^2\,\mu_3^2 + 36\,\mu_2^5}{4\,\mu_2^5\,n},$$

$$\boldsymbol{D}^2(g_2) = \frac{\mu_2^2\,\mu_8 - 4\,\mu_2\,\mu_4\,\mu_6 - 8\,\mu_2^2\,\mu_3\,\mu_5 + 4\,\mu_4^3 - \mu_2^2\,\mu_4^2 + 16\,\mu_2\,\mu_3^2\,\mu_4 + 16\,\mu_2^3\,\mu_3^2}{\mu_2^6\,n}.$$

When the parent population is normal, these approximate expressions reduce to

(27.7.9)
$$\boldsymbol{E}(g_1) = \boldsymbol{E}(g_2) = 0,$$
$$\boldsymbol{D}^2(g_1) = \frac{6}{n}, \quad \boldsymbol{D}^2(g_2) = \frac{24}{n}.$$

The *exact* expressions for the normal case will be given in (29.3.7).

As our next example we consider the ratio

$$V = \frac{s}{\bar{x}} = \frac{\sqrt{m_2}}{\bar{x}},$$

which is known as the *coefficient of variation* of the sample. When the population distribution is such that the variable takes *only positive values*, we have

$$V^2 = \frac{\Sigma (x_i - \bar{x})^2}{n\,\bar{x}^2} = n\,\frac{\Sigma x_i^2}{(\Sigma x_i)^2} - 1$$

$$= n \sum_i \left(\frac{x_i}{\sum_j x_j} \right)^2 - 1 < n \sum_i \frac{x_i}{\sum_j x_j} = n,$$

so that we may apply (27.7.3), replacing, in accordance with the remark made in connection with the theorem, m_ν by $\bar{x}$. By (27.2.1),

(27.4.2) and (27.4.4) we then obtain, to the order of approximation given by (27.7.3),

$$\text{(27.7.10)} \qquad \begin{aligned} \mathbf{E}(V) &= \frac{\sigma}{m}, \\ \mathbf{D}^2(V) &= \frac{m^2(\mu_4 - \mu_2^2) - 4\,m\,\mu_2\,\mu_3 + 4\,\mu_2^3}{4\,m^4\,\mu_2\,n}. \end{aligned}$$

A normal population does not satisfy the condition that the variable takes only positive values, and it is easily seen that for such a population V is not bounded, so that condition 2) is not satisfied. We may, however, consider a normal distribution truncated at $x = 0$ (cf 19.3), and when $\frac{\sigma}{m}$ is fairly small, the central moments of such a distribution will be approximately equal to the corresponding moments of a complete normal distribution. In this case, the approximate expression for the variance of V reduces to

$$\text{(27.7.11)} \qquad \mathbf{D}^2(V) = \frac{\sigma^2}{2\,m^2\,n}\left(1 + 2\,\frac{\sigma^2}{m^2}\right).$$

27.8. Characteristics of multi-dimensional distributions. — The formulae for sample characteristics deduced in 27.2—27.6, as well as the theorem proved in 27.7, may be directly extended to the characteristics of multi-dimensional samples. The calculations are quite similar to those given above, and we shall here only quote some formulae relating to the two-dimensional case. The definitions of the symbols used below have been given in 27.1, and we assume throughout that all the requisite moments are finite. — We have

$$\mathbf{E}(m_{ik}) = \mu_{ik} + O\left(\frac{1}{n}\right),$$

$$\mathbf{E}(m_{11}) = \frac{n-1}{n}\,\mu_{11}, \quad \mathbf{D}^2(m_{11}) = \frac{\mu_{22} - \mu_{11}^2}{n} + O\left(\frac{1}{n^2}\right),$$

$$\mu_{11}(m_{20}, m_{02}) = \frac{\mu_{22} - \mu_{20}\,\mu_{02}}{n} + O\left(\frac{1}{n^2}\right),$$

$$\mu_{11}(m_{11}, m_{20}) = \frac{\mu_{31} - \mu_{11}\,\mu_{20}}{n} + O\left(\frac{1}{n^2}\right).$$

The sample correlation coefficient

$$r = \frac{m_{11}}{\sqrt{m_{20}\, m_{02}}}$$

obviously satisfies the conditions of the theorem of 27.7, since we have $|r| \leqq 1$. Denoting by ϱ the population value of the correlation coefficient, we then obtain by means of the relations given above, to the order of approximation given by (27.7.3),

$$\boldsymbol{E}(r) = \varrho,$$

(27.8.1)
$$\boldsymbol{D}^2(r) = \frac{\varrho^2}{4n}\left(\frac{\mu_{40}}{\mu_{20}^2} + \frac{\mu_{04}}{\mu_{02}^2} + \frac{2\,\mu_{22}}{\mu_{20}\,\mu_{02}} + \frac{4\,\mu_{22}}{\mu_{11}^2} - \frac{4\,\mu_{31}}{\mu_{11}\,\mu_{20}} - \frac{4\,\mu_{13}}{\mu_{11}\,\mu_{02}}\right).$$

For a normal population, the expression for the variance reduces (cf Ex. 3, p. 317) to the following expression, which is correct to the order $n^{-3/2}$,

(27.8.2)
$$\boldsymbol{D}^2(r) = \frac{(1-\varrho^2)^2}{n}.$$

We finally observe that the theorem of 27.3 on the convergence in probability of sample characteristics holds true without modification in the multi-dimensional case. Thus e. g. r converges in probability to ϱ, while the partial correlation coefficient $r_{12\cdot34\ldots k}$ of the sample converges in probability to $\varrho_{12\cdot34\ldots k}$, etc.

27.9. Corrections for grouping. — In practice samples are very often *grouped* (cf 25.5). Suppose that we draw a sample of n from a one-dimensional distribution of the continuous type, with the fr. f. $f(x)$, and let the sample values be grouped into intervals of length h, with the mid-points $\xi_i = \xi_0 + ih$, where $i = 0, \pm 1, \pm 2, \ldots.$ In such cases it is usual to assume, in calculating the moments and other sample characteristics, that all sample values belonging to a certain interval fall in the mid-point of that interval. We are then in reality sampling from a distribution of the discrete type, where the variable may take any value $\xi_i = \xi_0 + ih$ with the probability

$$p_i = \int_{\xi_i - \frac{1}{2}h}^{\xi_i + \frac{1}{2}h} f(x)\, dx.$$

The moments etc. that we are estimating from our sample characteristics according to the formulae previously given in this chapter, are thus the moments of this »grouped distribution»:

$$\bar{\alpha}_\nu = \sum_{-\infty}^{\infty} p_i \xi_i^\nu.$$

However, in many cases it is not these moments that we really want to know, but the moments of the given continuous distribution:

$$\alpha_\nu = \int_{-\infty}^{\infty} x^\nu f(x)\, dx.$$

Consequently it becomes important to investigate the relations between the two sets of moments. It will be shown that, subject to certain conditions, approximate values of the moments α_ν may be obtained by applying certain corrections to the *raw* or *grouped* moments $\bar{\alpha}_\nu$.

The raw moments may be written

$$\bar{\alpha}_\nu = \sum_{-\infty}^{\infty} \xi_i^\nu \int_{\xi_i - \frac{1}{2}h}^{\xi_i + \frac{1}{2}h} f(x)\, dx = \sum_{-\infty}^{\infty} g(\xi_i),$$

where $\xi_i = \xi_0 + i h$, and

$$g(\xi) = \xi^\nu \int_{\xi - \frac{1}{2}h}^{\xi + \frac{1}{2}h} f(x)\, dx. \tag{27.9.1}$$

From the Euler-MacLaurin sum formula (12.2.5) we then obtain, assuming $f(x)$ continuous for all x,

$$\begin{aligned} \bar{\alpha}_\nu &= \int_{-\infty}^{\infty} (\xi_0 + h y)^\nu\, dy \int_{\xi_0 + hy - \frac{1}{2}h}^{\xi_0 + hy + \frac{1}{2}h} f(x)\, dx + R, \\ R &= -h \int_{-\infty}^{\infty} P_1(y)\, g'(\xi_0 + h y)\, dy. \end{aligned} \tag{27.9.2}$$

Let us assume for the moment that the remainder R may be neglected. We then obtain, reverting the order of integration,

$$\bar{\alpha}_\nu = \int\limits_{-\infty}^{\infty} f(x)\,dx \int\limits_{\frac{x-\xi_0}{h}-\frac{1}{2}}^{\frac{x-\xi_0}{h}+\frac{1}{2}} (\xi_0 + h y)^\nu \, dy$$

$$= \int\limits_{-\infty}^{\infty} \frac{\left(x+\frac{h}{2}\right)^{\nu+1} - \left(x-\frac{h}{2}\right)^{\nu+1}}{h(\nu+1)} f(x)\,dx$$

$$= \frac{1}{\nu+1} \sum_{i=0}^{\left[\frac{\nu}{2}\right]} \binom{\nu+1}{2i+1} \left(\frac{h}{2}\right)^{2i} \alpha_{\nu-2i}.$$

Thus the grouped moments $\bar{\alpha}_\nu$ may be expressed as linear functions of the »true» moments α_ν. Solving the equations successively with respect to the α_ν, we obtain

(27.9.3)
$$\begin{aligned}
\alpha_1 &= \bar{\alpha}_1, \\
\alpha_2 &= \bar{\alpha}_2 - \tfrac{1}{12} h^2, \\
\alpha_3 &= \bar{\alpha}_3 - \tfrac{1}{4} \bar{\alpha}_1 h^2, \\
\alpha_4 &= \bar{\alpha}_4 - \tfrac{1}{2} \bar{\alpha}_2 h^2 + \tfrac{7}{240} h^4, \\
\alpha_5 &= \bar{\alpha}_5 - \tfrac{5}{6} \bar{\alpha}_3 h^2 + \tfrac{7}{48} \bar{\alpha}_1 h^4, \\
\alpha_6 &= \bar{\alpha}_6 - \tfrac{5}{4} \bar{\alpha}_4 h^2 + \tfrac{7}{16} \bar{\alpha}_2 h^4 - \tfrac{31}{1344} h^6, \\
&\cdots\cdots\cdots\cdots
\end{aligned}$$

These are the formulae known as *Sheppard's corrections* (Ref. 212). The general expression is (cf Wold, Ref. 245)

$$\alpha_\nu = \sum_{i=0}^{\nu} \binom{\nu}{i} (2^{1-i} - 1) B_i \bar{\alpha}_{\nu-i} h^i,$$

where the B_i are the Bernoulli numbers defined by (12.2.2).

If we place the origin in the mean of the distribution, we have $\alpha_1 = \bar{\alpha}_1 = 0$, and so obtain the corrections for the central moments:

(27.9.4)
$$\begin{aligned}
\mu_2 &= \bar{\mu}_2 - \tfrac{1}{12} h^2, \\
\mu_3 &= \bar{\mu}_3, \\
\mu_4 &= \bar{\mu}_4 - \tfrac{1}{2} \bar{\mu}_2 h^2 + \tfrac{7}{240} h^4, \\
&\cdots\cdots\cdots\cdots
\end{aligned}$$

These relations hold under the assumption that the remainder R in (27.9.2) may be neglected. Suppose now that we are given two positive integers s and k such that:

1) $f(x)$ and its first $2s$ derivatives are continuous for all x.

2) The product $x^{k+2} f^{(i)}(x)$ is bounded for all x and for $i = 0, 1, \ldots, 2s$. — The function $g(\xi)$ given by (27.9.1) will then be continuous for all ξ together with its first $2s+1$ derivatives, and it is easily seen that for $\nu = 1, 2, \ldots, k$ and $i = 0, 1, \ldots, 2s+1$ we have

$$g^{(i)}(\xi) = O(\xi^{-2}) \tag{27.9.5}$$

as $\xi \to \pm \infty$. Consequently we may apply the Euler-MacLaurin formula in the form (12.2.6), and thus find that the remainder R may be written in the form

$$R = (-1)^{s+1} h^{2s+1} \int_{-\infty}^{\infty} P_{2s+1}(y)\, g^{(2s+1)}(\xi_0 + h y)\, dy.$$

It then follows from (12.2.1) and (27.9.5) that we have

$$|R| < A h^{2s+1} \int_{-\infty}^{\infty} \frac{dy}{1 + (\xi_0 + h y)^2} < B h^{2s},$$

where A and B are constants not depending on h. Thus if h, the width of the class interval, is sufficiently small, R may be neglected and the corrections (27.9.3) or (27.9.4) applied to moments of any order $\nu \leqq k$, the error involved being of the order h^{2s}.

Whenever the frequency curve $y = f(x)$ has a contact of high order with the x-axis at both ends of the range, the above conditions 1) and 2) are satisfied for moderate values of s and k. In such cases, it has been found in practice that the result of applying Sheppard's corrections to the moments is usually good even when h is not very small. It is, however, always advisable to compare the amount of the correction to be applied to a certain moment with the standard deviation of the sampling distribution of that moment. If, as is often the case, the correction only amounts to a small fraction of the s. d., it does not really matter whether the correction is applied or not.

In cases where the frequency curve has not a high order terminal contact, it is usually better not to apply Sheppard's corrections. Other correction formulae have been proposed for use in such cases, but they do not seem to be of sufficiently general validity (cf Elderton, Ref. 12, p. 231).

Langdon and Ore (Ref. 144) and Wold (Ref. 245, 246) have given corrections for the semi-invariants which are valid under the same conditions as Sheppard's. These have the simple form

$$\varkappa_1 = \bar{\varkappa}_1, \quad \text{and} \quad \varkappa_\nu = \bar{\varkappa}_\nu - \frac{B_\nu}{\nu} h^\nu \qquad (\nu > 1).$$

The deduction of Sheppard's corrections may be extended to moments of multi-dimensional samples. In particular we have for a two-dimensional distribution with class intervals of the length h_1 for x and h_2 for y

$$\begin{aligned} &\mu_{11} = \bar{\mu}_{11}, \quad \mu_{21} = \bar{\mu}_{21}, \quad \mu_{31} = \bar{\mu}_{31} - \tfrac{1}{4}\bar{\mu}_{11} h_1^2, \\ &\mu_{22} = \bar{\mu}_{22} - \tfrac{1}{12}\bar{\mu}_{20} h_2^2 - \tfrac{1}{12}\bar{\mu}_{02} h_1^2 + \tfrac{1}{144} h_1^2 h_2^2. \end{aligned} \qquad (27.9.6)$$

The corrections for μ_{12} and μ_{13} are, of course, obtained by permutation of indices, and the corrections for the marginal moments μ_{i0} and μ_{0j} follow directly from (27.9.4), so that by these formulae we are able to find the corrections for all moments of orders not exceeding four.

It should finally be remarked that the problem of corrections for grouping has been treated also from various other points of view. The reader may be referred e. g. to Fisher (Ref. 89) and Kendall (Ref. 136).

CHAPTER 28.

Asymptotic Properties of Sampling Distributions.

28.1. Introductory remarks. — In 27.3 and 27.8, we have seen that all ordinary sample characteristics that are functions of the moments converge in probability to the corresponding population characteristics, as the size n of the sample tends to infinity. In the present chapter, the asymptotic behaviour for large n of the sampling distributions of these and certain other characteristics will be considered somewhat more closely. Following up a remark made in 17.5, we shall first show that, under very general conditions, characteristics based on the sample moments are *asymptotically normally distributed* for large n. We shall then consider certain other classes of sample characteristics, some of which are, like the moment characteristics, asymptotically normal, while others show a totally different asymptotic behaviour.

28.2. The moments. — Consider n sample values $x_1, \ldots, x_n$ from a one-dimensional distribution. The quantity $n a_\nu = \sum_i x_i^\nu$ is a sum of n independent random variables x_i^ν, all having the same distribution, with the mean $E(x_i^\nu) = \alpha_\nu$ and the variance $D^2(x_i^\nu) = \alpha_{2\nu} - \alpha_\nu^2$. We may then apply the Lindeberg-Lévy case of the Central Limit Theorem (cf 17.4) and find that, as $n \to \infty$, the d. f. of the standardized sum

$$\frac{\Sigma x_i^\nu - n\alpha_\nu}{\sqrt{n(\alpha_{2\nu} - \alpha_\nu^2)}} = \sqrt{n}\frac{a_\nu - \alpha_\nu}{\sqrt{\alpha_{2\nu} - \alpha_\nu^2}}$$

tends to the normal d. f. $\Phi(x)$. According to the terminology introduced in 17.4, any sample moment a_ν is thus *asymptotically normal* $\left(\alpha_\nu, \sqrt{(\alpha_{2\nu} - \alpha_\nu^2)/n}\right)$. We observe that the parameters of the limiting normal distribution are identical with the mean and the s. d. of a_ν, as given by (27.3.1). — In particular, the mean $a_1 = \bar{x}$ of the sample is asymptotically normal $(m, \sigma/\sqrt{n})$, as already pointed out in 17.4.

Similarly, when we consider simultaneously the two random variables $n a_\nu = \Sigma x_i^\nu$ and $n a_\varrho = \Sigma x_i^\varrho$, an application of the two-dimensional form of the Lindeberg-Lévy theorem (cf 21.11) shows that the joint distribution of the two variables $\sqrt{n}(a_\nu - \alpha_\nu)$ and $\sqrt{n}(a_\varrho - \alpha_\varrho)$ tends to a certain two-dimensional normal distribution. The argument is evidently general, and by means of the multi-dimensional form of the Lindeberg-Lévy theorem (cf 24.7) we obtain the following result:

The joint distribution of any number of the quantities $\sqrt{n}(a_\nu - \alpha_\nu)$ *tends to a normal distribution with zero mean values and the second order moments*

$$\begin{aligned} \lambda_{\nu\nu} &= \sigma_\nu^2 = E\left(n(a_\nu - \alpha_\nu)^2\right) = \alpha_{2\nu} - \alpha_\nu^2, \\ \lambda_{\nu\varrho} &= E\left(n(a_\nu - \alpha_\nu)(a_\varrho - \alpha_\varrho)\right) = \alpha_{\nu+\varrho} - \alpha_\nu\alpha_\varrho. \end{aligned} \tag{28.2.1}$$

Thus if we introduce standardized variables z_ν defined by

$$a_\nu = \alpha_\nu + \frac{\sigma_\nu}{\sqrt{n}} z_\nu, \tag{28.2.2}$$

every z_ν will have zero mean and unit s. d., and the joint distribution of the z_ν will be asymptotically normal, with the covariances

$$E(z_\nu z_\varrho) = \frac{\lambda_{\nu\varrho}}{\sigma_\nu \sigma_\varrho}.$$

The extension of the above considerations to moments of multi-dimensional samples is immediate.

28.3. The central moments. — By the remarks made in connection with (27.5.2), any central moment m_ν may be written in the form

$$m_\nu = a_\nu - \nu \bar{x} a_{\nu-1} + \frac{w}{n},$$

where w is a random variable such that $E(w^2)$ is smaller than a quantity independent of n. According to 27.4, we may without loss of generality assume $m = 0$, so that $\alpha_\nu = \mu_\nu$, and

$$m_\nu - \mu_\nu = a_\nu - \alpha_\nu - \nu \bar{x} a_{\nu-1} + \frac{w}{n}.$$

Introducing the standardized variables z_ν defined by (28.2.2), we then have

$$\text{(28.3.1)} \qquad \sqrt{n}\,(m_\nu - \mu_\nu) = \sigma_\nu z_\nu - \nu \sigma_1 \mu_{\nu-1} z_1 + \frac{R}{\sqrt{n}},$$

where $R = w - \nu \sigma_1 \sigma_{\nu-1} z_1 z_{\nu-1}$. Now by (9.5.1)

$$\begin{aligned} E(|R|) &\leqq E(|w|) + \nu \sigma_1 \sigma_{\nu-1} E(|z_1 z_{\nu-1}|) \\ &\leqq \sqrt{E(w^2)} + \nu \sigma_1 \sigma_{\nu-1} \sqrt{E(z_1^2) E(z_{\nu-1}^2)}, \end{aligned}$$

so that $E(|R|)$ is smaller than a quantity independent of n, and it then follows by an application of Tchebycheff's theorem (15.7.1) that $R/\sqrt{n}$ converges in probability to zero. Applying the theorem 20.6 to the expression (28.3.1) we thus find that the variable $\sqrt{n}\,(m_\nu - \mu_\nu)$ has, in the limit as $n \to \infty$, the same distribution as the linear expression $\sigma_\nu z_\nu - \nu \sigma_1 \mu_{\nu-1} z_1$. The joint distribution of z_ν and z_1 is, however, asymptotically normal, and any linear combination of normally distributed variables is, by 24.4, itself normally distributed.

Thus any central moment m_ν of the sample is asymptotically normally distributed, with the mean μ_ν and the variance

$$\frac{\sigma_\nu^2 - 2\nu \mu_{\nu-1} \lambda_{\nu 1} + \nu^2 \sigma_1^2 \mu_{\nu-1}^2}{n} = \frac{\mu_{2\nu} - 2\nu \mu_{\nu-1} \mu_{\nu+1} - \mu_\nu^2 + \nu^2 \mu_2 \mu_{\nu-1}^2}{n}.$$

We observe that the variance of the limiting normal distribution is identical with the leading term of $D^2(m_\nu)$ as given by (27.5.4). — If we consider simultaneously any number of the m_ν, we find in the same way, using the last theorem of 22.6, that the joint distribution of the m_ν is asymptotically normal, with the means μ_ν, and variances and covariances given by the leading terms of (27.5.4) and (27.5.6). — As in the preceding paragraph, the extension to moments of multi-dimensional samples is immediate.

28.4. Functions of moments. — As in 27.7, we shall confine our attention to the case of a function $H(m_\nu, m_\varrho)$ of two central moments from a one-dimensional sample. However, the extension to any number of arguments, to multi-dimensional samples and to the joint distribution of any number of functions is immediate. We shall prove the following theorem.

If, in some neighbourhood of the point $m_\nu = \mu_\nu$, $m_\varrho = \mu_\varrho$, the function $H(m_\nu, m_\varrho)$ is continuous and has continuous derivatives of the first and second order with respect to the arguments m_ν and m_ϱ, the random variable $H(m_\nu, m_\varrho)$ is asymptotically normal, the mean and the variance of the limiting normal distribution being given by the leading terms of (27.7.3).

It will be observed that in this theorem there is nothing corresponding to condition 2) of the theorem of 27.7. Thus we may e. g. assert that the function $\frac{1}{m_2}$ is asymptotically normal $\left(\frac{1}{\mu_2}, \frac{\sqrt{\mu_4-\mu_2^2}}{\mu_2^2\sqrt{n}}\right)$, though for certain populations (cf 27.7) neither the mean nor the variance of $\frac{1}{m_2}$ is finite. We remind in this connection of a remark made in 17.4 to the effect that a variable may be asymptotically normal even though its mean and variance do not exist, or do not tend to the mean and variance of the limiting normal distribution.

As in 27.7, we consider the set Z of all points $(x_1, \ldots, x_n)$ such that $|m_\nu - \mu_\nu| < \varepsilon$ and $|m_\varrho - \mu_\varrho| < \varepsilon$. In the present case we shall, however, allow ε to depend on n, and shall in fact choose $\varepsilon = n^{-\frac{3}{8}}$. We then have, using the notations of 27.7 and choosing $k = 1$,

$$P(Z) > 1 - \frac{2A}{\varepsilon^2 n} = 1 - 2An^{-\frac{1}{4}}.$$

If n is sufficiently large, we have for any point of Z the development (27.7.6), which may be written

$$\sqrt{n}(H - H_0) = H_1\sqrt{n}(m_\nu - \mu_\nu) + H_2\sqrt{n}(m_\varrho - \mu_\varrho) + R\sqrt{n},$$

where $|R\sqrt{n}| < K\varepsilon^2\sqrt{n} = K n^{-\frac{1}{4}}$. Thus the inequality $|R\sqrt{n}| < K n^{-\frac{1}{4}}$ is satisfied with a probability $\geqq P(Z) > 1 - 2 A n^{-\frac{1}{4}}$, so that $R\sqrt{n}$ converges in probability to zero. By theorem 20.6, we then find that the variables $\sqrt{n}(H - H_0)$ and $H_1\sqrt{n}(m_\nu - \mu_\nu) + H_2\sqrt{n}(m_\varrho - \mu_\varrho)$ have, in the limit as $n \to \infty$, the same distribution. By the preceding paragraph, the latter variable is, however, asymptotically normal with the mean and the variance required by our theorem, which is thus proved.

It follows from this theorem that any sample characteristic based on moments is, for large values of n, *approximately normally distributed about the corresponding population characteristic, with a variance of the form* c/n, *provided only that the leading terms of* (27.7.3) *yield finite values for the mean and the variance of the limiting distribution.*

This is true for samples in any number of dimensions. Thus e. g. the coefficients of skewness and excess (15.8), the coefficients of regression (21.6 and 23.2), the generalized variance (22.7), and the coefficients of total, partial and multiple correlation (21.7, 23.4 and 23.5) are all asymptotically normally distributed about the corresponding coefficients of the population.

One important remark should, however, be made in this connection. In general, the constant c in the expression of the variance will have a positive value. However, in exceptional cases c may be zero, which implies that the variance is of a smaller order than n^{-1}. Looking back on the proof of the theorem, it is readily seen that in such a case the proof shows that the variable $\sqrt{n}(H - H_0)$ converges in probability to zero, which may be expressed by saying that H is asymptotically normal *with zero variance*, as far as terms of order n^{-1} are concerned. It may, however, then occur that some expression of the form $n^p(H - H_0)$ with $p > \frac{1}{2}$ may have a definite limiting distribution, but this is *not necessarily normal.* We shall encounter an example of this phenomenon in 29.12, in connection with the distribution of the multiple correlation coefficient in the particular case when the corresponding population value is zero.

28.5. The quantiles. — Consider a sample of n values from a one-dimensional distribution of the continuous type, with the d. f. $F(x)$ and the fr. f. $f(x) = F'(x)$. Let $\zeta = \zeta_p$ denote the quantile (cf 15.6) of order p of the distribution, i. e. the root (assumed unique) of the equation $F(\zeta) = p$, where $0 < p < 1$. We shall suppose that, in some neighbourhood of $x = \zeta_p$, the fr. f. $f(x)$ is continuous and has a continuous derivative $f'(x)$.

We further denote by z_p the corresponding quantile of the sample. If np is not an integer, and if we arrange the sample values in ascending order of magnitude: $x_1 \leqq x_2 \leqq \cdots \leqq x_n$, there is a unique quantile z_p equal to the sample value $x_{\mu+1}$, where $\mu = [np]$ denotes the greatest integer $\leqq np$. If np is an integer, we are in the indeterminate case (cf 15.5—15.6), and z_p may be any value in the interval (x_{np}, x_{np+1}). In order to avoid trivial complications, we assume in the sequel that np is not an integer.

Let $g(x)$ denote the fr. f. of the random variable $z = z_p$. The probability $g(x)\,dx$ that z is situated in an infinitesimal interval $(x, x + dx)$ is identical with the probability that, among the n sample values, $\mu = [np]$ are $< x$, and $n - \mu - 1$ are $> x + dx$, while the remaining value falls between x and $x + dx$. Hence

$$g(x)\,dx = \binom{n}{\mu}(n-\mu)(F(x))^{\mu}(1 - F(x))^{n-\mu-1} f(x)\,dx.$$

In order to study the behaviour of the distribution of z for large n, we consider the random variable $y = \sqrt{n/pq}\, f(\zeta)(z - \zeta)$, where $q = 1 - p$. By (15.1.2) y has the fr. f.

$$\frac{1}{f(\zeta)}\sqrt{\frac{pq}{n}}\, g\left(\zeta + \sqrt{\frac{pq}{n}} \cdot \frac{x}{f(\zeta)}\right) = A_1 A_2 A_3,$$

where we have for any fixed x as $n \to \infty$ (cf 16.4.8)

$$A_1 = \sqrt{\frac{pq}{n}}\binom{n}{\mu} p^{\mu} q^{n-\mu} \cdot \frac{n-\mu}{q} \to \frac{1}{\sqrt{2\pi}},$$

$$A_2 = \frac{f\left(\zeta + \sqrt{\frac{pq}{n}} \cdot \frac{x}{f(\zeta)}\right)}{f(\zeta)} \to 1,$$

$$A_3 = \left(\frac{F(t)}{p}\right)^{\mu}\left(\frac{1 - F(t)}{q}\right)^{n-\mu-1},$$

where $t = \zeta + \sqrt{\frac{pq}{n}} \cdot \frac{x}{f(\zeta)}$. Now $F(\zeta) = p$, and thus

$$F(t) = p + x\sqrt{\frac{pq}{n}} + \tfrac{1}{2} x^2 \frac{pq}{n} \cdot \frac{f'(\zeta)}{f^2(\zeta)} + o\left(\frac{1}{n}\right).$$

Substituting this in the expression of A_3, we find after some calculation

$$A_3 \to e^{-\frac{x^2}{2}},$$

so that the fr. f. of y tends to the normal fr. f. $\frac{1}{\sqrt{2\pi}} e^{-\frac{x^2}{2}}$. It is also seen that A_1, A_2 and A_3 are uniformly bounded in any interval $a < x < b$, so that by (5.3.6) the probability of the inequality $a<y<b$ tends to the limit $\frac{1}{\sqrt{2\pi}} \int_a^b e^{-\frac{x^2}{2}} dx$.

It follows that the sample quantile z_p *is asymptotically normal* $\left(\zeta, \frac{1}{f(\zeta)} \cdot \sqrt{\frac{pq}{n}}\right)$, *where* $\zeta = \zeta_p$ *is the corresponding quantile of the population. — In particular the median of the sample is asymptotically normal* $\left(\zeta, \frac{1}{2 f(\zeta) \sqrt{n}}\right)$, *where* $\zeta = \zeta_{\frac{1}{2}}$ *is the median of the population.*

For a normal distribution, with the parameters m and σ, the median is m, and we have $f(m) = \frac{1}{\sigma\sqrt{2\pi}}$. Thus the median z of a sample of n from this distribution is asymptotically normal $\left(m, \sigma\sqrt{\frac{\pi}{2n}}\right)$.

On the other hand, we know that the mean $\bar{x}$ of such a sample is *exactly* normal $\left(m, \frac{\sigma}{\sqrt{n}}\right)$. — As $n \to \infty$, z and $\bar{x}$ both converge in probability to m, and for large values of n we may use either z or $\bar{x}$ as an estimate of m. The latter estimate should, however, be considered as having the *greater precision*, since the s. d. $\frac{\sigma}{\sqrt{n}}$ corresponding to $\bar{x}$ is smaller than the s. d. $\sigma \sqrt{\frac{\pi}{2n}} = 1.2533 \frac{\sigma}{\sqrt{n}}$ corresponding to z. — A systematic comparison of the precision of various estimates of a population characteristic will be given in the theory of estimation (cf. Ch. 32).

Consider now the joint distribution of two quantiles z' and z'', of orders p_1 and p_2, where $p_1 < p_2$. By a calculation of the same kind as above, it can be shown that this distribution is asymptotically normal. The means of the limiting normal distribution are the corresponding quantiles ζ' and ζ'' of the population, while the asymptotic expressions of the second order moments $\mu_2(z')$, $\mu_{11}(z', z'')$, $\mu_2(z'')$ are

$$\frac{p_1 q_1}{n f^2(\zeta')}, \quad \frac{p_1 q_2}{n f(\zeta') f(\zeta'')}, \quad \frac{p_2 q_2}{n f^2(\zeta'')}.$$

Choosing in particular $p_1 = \frac{1}{4}$, $p_2 = \frac{3}{4}$, ζ' and ζ'' are the lower and upper quartiles of the population, and we find that the semi-interquartile range (cf 15.6) of the sample, $\frac{1}{2}(z'' - z')$, is asymptotically distributed in a normal distribution with the mean $\frac{1}{2}(\zeta'' - \zeta')$ and the s. d.

$$\frac{1}{8\sqrt{n}}\sqrt{\frac{3}{f^2(\zeta')} - \frac{2}{f(\zeta')f(\zeta'')} + \frac{3}{f^2(\zeta'')}}.$$

— For a normal (m, σ) population, the mean of the semi-interquartile range becomes $0.6745\,\sigma$, and the s. d. $0.7867\,\frac{\sigma}{\sqrt{n}}\cdot$

28.6. The extreme values and the range. — So far, we have only considered sample characteristics which, in large samples, tend to be normally distributed. We now turn to a group of characteristics showing a totally different behaviour.

In a one-dimensional sample of n values, there are always two finite and uniquely determined *extreme values*,[1] and also a finite *range*, which is the difference between the extremes. More generally, we may arrange the n sample values in order of magnitude, and consider the ν:th value from the top or from the bottom. For $\nu = 1$ we obtain, of course, the extreme values.

It is often important to know the sampling distributions of the extreme values, the ν:th values, the range, and other similar characteristics of the sample. We shall now consider some properties of these distributions.

We restrict ourselves to the case when the population has a distribution of the continuous type, with the d. f. F and the fr. f. $f = F'$. Let x denote the ν:th value from the top in a sample of n from this population. The probability element $g_\nu(x)\,dx$ in the sampling distribution of x is identical with the probability that, among the n sample values, $n - \nu$ are $< x$, and $\nu - 1$ are $> x + dx$, while the remaining value falls between x and $x + dx$. Hence

$$(28.6.1) \qquad g_\nu(x)\,dx = n\binom{n-1}{\nu-1}(F(x))^{n-\nu}(1 - F(x))^{\nu-1} f(x)\,dx.$$

If we introduce a new variable ξ by the substitution

[1]) If, e.g., the two uppermost values are equal, any of them will be considered as the upper extreme value, and similarly in other cases.

(28.6.2) $$\xi = n(1 - F(x)),$$

we shall have $0 \leqq \xi \leqq n$, and the fr. f. $h_\nu(\xi)$ of the new variable will be

(28.6.3) $$h_\nu(\xi) = \binom{n-1}{\nu-1}\left(\frac{\xi}{n}\right)^{\nu-1}\left(1-\frac{\xi}{n}\right)^{n-\nu}$$

for $0 \leqq \xi \leqq n$, and $h_\nu(\xi) = 0$ outside $(0, n)$. As $n \to \infty$, $h_\nu(\xi)$ converges for any $\xi \geqq 0$ to the limit

(28.6.4) $$\lim_{n\to\infty} h_\nu(\xi) = \frac{\xi^{\nu-1}}{\Gamma(\nu)} e^{-\xi}.$$

Further, $h_\nu(\xi)$ is uniformly bounded for all n in every finite ξ-interval, and thus by (5.3.6) ξ is, in the limit as $n \to \infty$, distributed according to the fr. f. (28.6.4), which is a particular case of (12.3.3).

Similarly, if y denotes the ν:th value from the bottom in our sample, and if we introduce a new variable η by the substitution

(28.6.5) $$\eta = n F(y),$$

we find that η has the fr. f. $h_\nu(\eta)$ and thus, in the limit, the fr. f. $\frac{\eta^{\nu-1}}{\Gamma(\nu)} e^{-\eta}$.

We may also consider the joint distribution of the ν:th value x from the top and the ν:th value y from the bottom. Introducing the variables ξ and η by the substitutions (28.6.2) and (28.6.5), it is then proved in the same way as above that the joint fr. f. of ξ and η is

(28.6.6) $$\frac{1}{n^2}\cdot\frac{n!}{[(\nu-1)!]^2(n-2\nu)!}\left(\frac{\xi}{n}\right)^{\nu-1}\left(\frac{\eta}{n}\right)^{\nu-1}\left(1-\frac{\xi}{n}-\frac{\eta}{n}\right)^{n-2\nu},$$

where $\xi > 0$, $\eta > 0$, $\xi + \eta < n$, and $2\nu < n$. As $n \to \infty$, this tends to

(28.6.7) $$\frac{\xi^{\nu-1}}{\Gamma(\nu)} e^{-\xi}\cdot\frac{\eta^{\nu-1}}{\Gamma(\nu)} e^{-\eta},$$

so that ξ and η are, in the limit, independent.

When the d. f. F is given, it is sometimes possible to solve the equations (28.6.2) and (28.6.5) explicitly with respect to x and y. We then obtain the ν:th values x and y expressed in terms of the auxiliary variables ξ and η of known distributions. When an explicit solution cannot be given, it is often possible to obtain an asymptotic solution for large values of n. In such cases, the known distributions of ξ

and η may be used to find the limiting forms of the distributions of the ν:th values, the range etc. We now proceed to consider some examples of this method, omitting certain details of calculation.

1. *The rectangular distribution.* — Let the sampled variable be uniformly distributed (cf 19.1) over the interval (a, b). If, in a sample of n from this distribution, x and y are the ν:th values from the top and from the bottom, (28.6.2) and (28.6.5) give

$$x = b - \frac{b-a}{n}\xi, \qquad y = a + \frac{b-a}{n}\eta,$$

where ξ and η have the joint fr. f. (28.6.6), with the limiting form (28.6.7). Hence we obtain

$$\mathbf{E}(x) = b - \frac{\nu}{n+1}(b-a), \quad \mathbf{D}^2(x) = \frac{\nu(n-\nu+1)}{(n+1)^2(n+2)}(b-a)^2,$$

and similar expressions for y. We further have

$$\text{(28.6.8)} \qquad \mathbf{E}\left(\frac{x+y}{2}\right) = \frac{a+b}{2}, \quad \mathbf{D}^2\left(\frac{x+y}{2}\right) = \frac{\nu}{2(n+1)(n+2)}(b-a)^2,$$

which shows that the arithmetic mean of the ν:th values x and y provides a consistent and unbiased estimate (cf 27.6) of the mean $(a+b)/2$ of the distribution. Finally, we have for the difference $x-y$

$$\text{(28.6.9)} \quad \mathbf{E}(x-y) = \left(1 - \frac{2\nu}{n+1}\right)(b-a), \quad \mathbf{D}^2(x-y) = \frac{2\nu(n-2\nu+1)}{(n+1)^2(n+2)}(b-a)^2.$$

For $\nu = 1$ the difference $x - y$ is, of course, the range of the sample.

2. *The triangular distribution.* — In the case of a triangular distribution (cf 19.1) over the range (a, b), the equations (28.6.2) and (28.6.5) give, when $x > \frac{a+b}{2}$ and $y < \frac{a+b}{2}$,

$$x = b - (b-a)\sqrt{\frac{\xi}{2n}}, \quad y = a + (b-a)\sqrt{\frac{\eta}{2n}}.$$

We consider only the particular case $\nu = 1$, when x and y are the extreme values of the sample, and then obtain

$$\mathbf{E}\left(\frac{x+y}{2}\right)=\frac{a+b}{2}, \quad \mathbf{D}^2\left(\frac{x+y}{2}\right)=\frac{4-\pi}{16\,n}(b-a)^2+O\left(\frac{1}{n^2}\right),$$

(28.6.10)

$$\mathbf{E}(x-y)=\left(1-\sqrt{\frac{\pi}{2\,n}}\right)(b-a)+O\left(\frac{1}{n^{3/2}}\right), \quad \mathbf{D}^2(x-y)=\frac{4-\pi}{4\,n}(b-a)^2+O\left(\frac{1}{n^2}\right).$$

3. *Cauchy's distribution.* — For the distribution given by the fr. f. (19.2.1), the substitution (28.6.2) gives

$$\xi=\frac{n\lambda}{\pi}\int_x^\infty\frac{dt}{\lambda^2+(t-\mu)^2}=\frac{n}{\pi}\operatorname{arc\,cot}\frac{x-\mu}{\lambda},$$

or

$$x=\mu+\lambda\cot\frac{\pi\xi}{n}=\mu+\frac{\lambda n}{\pi\xi}+O\left(\frac{\xi}{n}\right)$$

where ξ has the limiting distribution (28.6.4). The remainder converges in probability to zero, and it then follows from 20.6 that the ν:th value x from the top is, in the limit, distributed as $\mu+\frac{\lambda n}{\pi}v$, where $v=\frac{1}{\xi}$ has the fr. f. $\frac{1}{\Gamma(\nu)}v^{-\nu-1}e^{-\frac{1}{v}}$. Similarly the ν:th value from the bottom, y, is distributed as $\mu-\frac{\lambda n}{\pi}w$, where w is, in the limit, independent of v and has a distribution of the same form. In the case $\nu=1$, the mean values of x and y are not finite. For $\nu>2$ we have

$$\mathbf{E}\left(\frac{x+y}{2}\right)=\mu, \quad \mathbf{D}^2\left(\frac{x+y}{2}\right)=\frac{1}{2(\nu-1)^2(\nu-2)}\left(\frac{\lambda n}{\pi}\right)^2+O(n) \tag{28.6.11}$$

We observe that the variance does not tend to zero as $n\to\infty$. Accordingly $\frac{x+y}{2}$ does not converge in probability to μ, so that $\frac{x+y}{2}$ is not a consistent estimate (cf 27.6) of μ.

4. *Laplace's distribution.* — For the fr. f. (19.2.4) we obtain for the ν:th value x from the top, when $x>\mu$,

$$x=\mu+\lambda\log\frac{n}{2}-\lambda\log\xi,$$

where ξ has the limiting distribution (28.6.4). Substituting v for $-\log\xi$, we thus have

$$x = \mu + \lambda \log \frac{n}{2} + \lambda v,$$

where $v = -\log \xi$ has, in the limit, the fr. f.

$$j_\nu(v) = \frac{1}{\Gamma(\nu)} e^{-\nu v - e^{-v}}.$$

Similarly, the ν:th value from the bottom is

$$y = \mu - \lambda \log \frac{n}{2} - \lambda w,$$

where w is, in the limit, independent of v and has the fr. f. $j_\nu(w)$. In the particular case $\nu = 1$ we have (cf the following example)

$$\text{(28.6.12)} \qquad \boldsymbol{E}\left(\frac{x+y}{2}\right) = \mu, \quad \boldsymbol{D}^2\left(\frac{x+y}{2}\right) = \frac{\lambda^2 \pi^2}{12} + O\left(\frac{1}{n}\right),$$

and we observe that, as in the preceding case, $\frac{x+y}{2}$ is not a consistent estimate of μ.

5. *The normal distribution.* — Consider first a normal distribution with the standardized parameters $m = 0$ and $\sigma = 1$. If x is the ν:th value from the top in a sample of n from this distribution, (28.6.2) gives

$$\xi = \frac{n}{\sqrt{2\pi}} \int_x^\infty e^{-\frac{t^2}{2}} dt.$$

It is required to find an asymptotic solution of this equation with respect to x, when n is large. By partial integration, the equation may be put in the form

$$\frac{\xi\sqrt{2\pi}}{n} = \frac{1}{x} e^{-\frac{x^2}{2}} \left(1 + O\left(\frac{1}{x^2}\right)\right).$$

Assuming ξ bounded, we obtain after some calculation

$$x = \sqrt{2 \log n} - \frac{\log \log n + \log 4\pi}{2\sqrt{2 \log n}} - \frac{\log \xi}{\sqrt{2 \log n}} + O\left(\frac{1}{\log n}\right),$$

and it follows that the remainder converges in probability to zero.

Proceeding to the general case of a normal distribution with arbitrary parameters m and σ, we need only replace x by $\frac{x-m}{\sigma}$. Substituting at the same time v for $-\log \xi$, we thus find that the ν:th value x from the top has the expression

$$(28.6.13) \qquad x = m + \sigma \sqrt{2 \log n} - \sigma \frac{\log \log n + \log 4\pi}{2\sqrt{2 \log n}} + \frac{\sigma}{\sqrt{2 \log n}} v,$$

where $v = -\log \xi$ is a variable which, in the limit as $n \to \infty$, has the fr. f.

$$(28.6.14) \qquad j_\nu(v) = \frac{1}{\Gamma(\nu)} e^{-\nu v - e^{-v}}$$

already encountered in the preceding example. Similarly we have, for the ν:th value y from the bottom, the expression

$$(28.6.15) \qquad y = m - \sigma \sqrt{2 \log n} + \sigma \frac{\log \log n + \log 4\pi}{2\sqrt{2 \log n}} - \frac{\sigma}{\sqrt{2 \log n}} w,$$

where w is, in the limit, independent of v and has the fr. f. $j_\nu(w)$.

Thus for large values of n the ν:th values x and y are related by simple linear transformations to variables having the limiting distribution defined by the fr. f. (28.6.14). The frequency curves $u = j_\nu(v)$ are shown for some values of ν in Fig. 27.

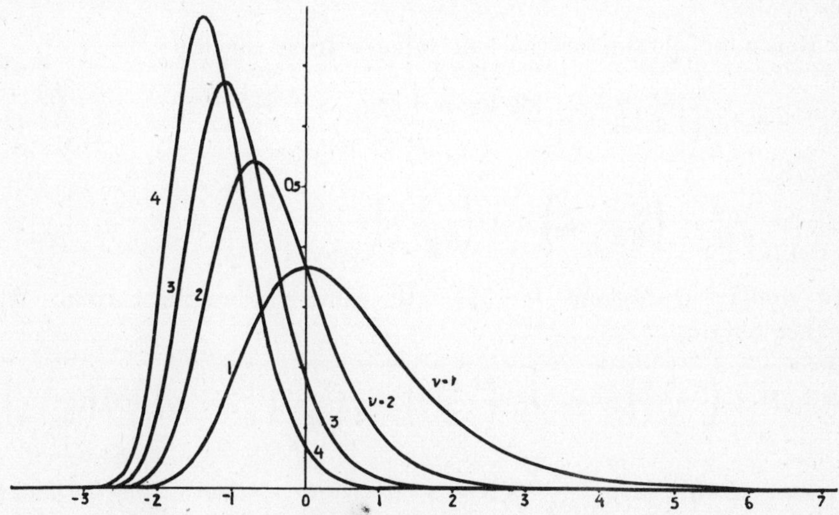

Fig. 27. The frequency curve $u = j_\nu(v)$ for $\nu = 1, 2, 3, 4$.

We observe that the limiting distribution has, except for different normalization, the same form as in the preceding example. A straightforward generalization of the above argument shows that the same limiting fr. f. $j_\nu(v)$ appears in all cases where the fr. f. of the parent distribution is, for large values of $|x|$, asymptotically expressed by

$$f(x) \sim A\, e^{-B|x|^p},$$

where A, B and p are positive constants.

The mode of a variable which has the fr. f. $j_\nu(v)$ is $-\log \nu$, while the mean and the variance are given by the relations

$$\boldsymbol{E}(v) = \int_{-\infty}^{\infty} v\, j_\nu(v)\, dv = -\frac{1}{\Gamma(\nu)} \int_0^\infty \xi^{\nu-1} \log \xi\, e^{-\xi}\, d\xi = C - S_1,$$

$$\boldsymbol{D}^2(v) = \int_{-\infty}^{\infty} v^2 j_\nu(v)\, dv - (C - S_1)^2 =$$

$$= \frac{1}{\Gamma(\nu)} \int_0^\infty \xi^{\nu-1} \log^2 \xi\, e^{-\xi}\, d\xi - (C - S_1)^2 = \frac{\pi^2}{6} - S_2,$$

obtained by means of (12.5.6) and (12.5.7). Here C denotes Euler's constant defined by (12.2.7), while

$$S_1 = \frac{1}{1} + \frac{1}{2} + \cdots + \frac{1}{\nu - 1}, \quad S_2 = \frac{1}{1^2} + \frac{1}{2^2} + \cdots + \frac{1}{(\nu - 1)^2}.$$

Hence we obtain for the ν:th value x from the top:

$$\boldsymbol{E}(x) = m + \sigma\left(\sqrt{2 \log n} - \frac{\log\log n + \log 4\pi + 2(S_1 - C)}{2\sqrt{2\log n}} + O\left(\frac{1}{\log n}\right)\right),$$

(28.6.16)

$$\boldsymbol{D}^2(x) = \frac{\sigma^2}{2\log n}\left(\frac{\pi^2}{6} - S_2\right) + O\left(\frac{1}{\log^2 n}\right),$$

and similar expressions for the ν:th value y from the bottom. We further obtain

$$(28.6.17) \quad \boldsymbol{E}\left(\frac{x+y}{2}\right) = m, \quad \boldsymbol{D}^2\left(\frac{x+y}{2}\right) = \frac{\sigma^2}{4\log n}\left(\frac{\pi^2}{6} - S_2\right) + O\left(\frac{1}{\log^2 n}\right),$$

so that in this case $\frac{x+y}{2}$ gives a consistent estimate for m, though the variance only tends to zero as $(\log n)^{-1}$, which is not nearly so rapidly as n^{-1}. — For the difference $x - y$ between the ν:th values we have

$$\mathbf{E}(x-y) = \sigma\left(\frac{4\log n - \log\log n - \log 4\pi - 2(S_1 - C)}{\sqrt{2\log n}} + O\left(\frac{1}{\log n}\right)\right),$$

(28.6.18)

$$\mathbf{D}^2(x-y) = \frac{\sigma^2}{\log n}\left(\frac{\pi^2}{6} - S_2\right) + O\left(\frac{1}{\log^2 n}\right).$$

We may thus obtain a consistent estimate for σ by multiplying $x - y$ with an appropriate constant, and the variance of this estimate will, for a given large value of n, be approximately proportional to

$$\frac{\pi^2}{6} - S_2 = \sum_{\nu}^{\infty} \frac{1}{r^2}.$$

The limiting forms discussed above in connection with the normal distribution and Laplace's distribution are due partly to R. A. Fisher and Tippet (Ref. 110), and partly to Gumbel (Ref. 120), in whose papers further information concerning the properties of these distributions and their statistical applications will be found.

In the limiting expressions for the case of the normal distribution, the remainder terms are of the same order as a negative power of $\log n$. Now $\log n$ tends to infinity less rapidly than any power of n, and accordingly it has been found that the approach to the limiting forms is here considerably slower than e.g. in the case of the approach to normality of the distribution of some moment characteristic. The *exact* distributions of the extreme values and the range of a sample

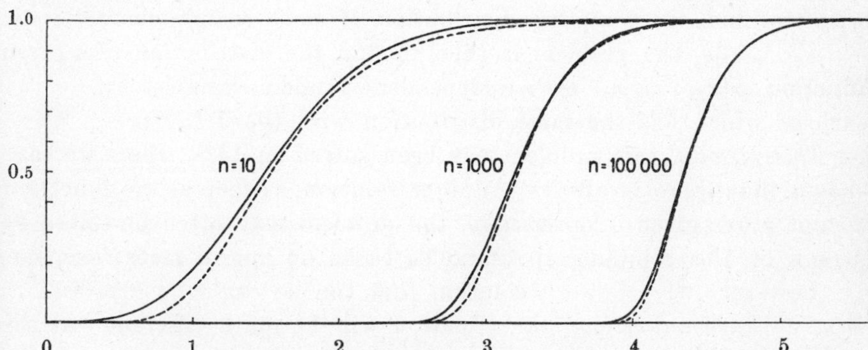

Fig. 28. Distribution function for the upper extreme of a sample of n values from a normal population with $m = 0$ and $\sigma = 1$.
Exact: ———. Approximate formula: ··········.

from a normal distribution have been investigated by various authors, and certain tables are available. The reader is referred to K. Pearson's tables, and to papers by Irwin, Tippet, E. S. Pearson and Davies, E. S. Pearson and Hartley (Ref. 264, 131, 226, 196, 197). We give in Fig. 28 some comparisons between the exact distribution of the largest member of a sample and the corresponding distributions calculated from the limiting expressions (28.6.13)—(28.6.14).

CHAPTER 29.

Exact Sampling Distributions.

29.1. The problem. In the two preceding chapters, we have shown how to calculate moments and various other characteristics of sampling distributions, and we have investigated the asymptotic behaviour of the distributions for samples of infinitely increasing size. However, it is clear that a knowledge of the *exact* form of a sampling distribution would be of a far greater value than the knowledge of a number of moment characteristics and of a limiting expression for large values of n. Especially when we are dealing with *small samples*, as is often the case in the applications, the asymptotic expressions are sometimes grossly inadequate, and a knowledge of the exact form of the distribution would then be highly desirable.

Suppose that we are concerned with a sample of n observed values from a one-dimensional distribution with the d. f. $F(x)$, and that we wish to find the sampling distribution of some sample characteristic $g(x_1, \ldots, x_n)$. The problem is then to find the distribution of a given function $g(x_1, \ldots, x_n)$ of n independent random variables $x_1, \ldots, x_n$, each of which has the same distribution with the d. f. $F(x)$.

Theoretically, this problem has been solved in 14.5, where we have shown that there is always a unique solution, as soon as the functions F and g are given. *Numerically*, the problem may often be solved by means of the computation of tables based on approximate formulae. If, however, we require a solution that can be *explicitly expressed in terms of known functions*, the situation will be quite different. At the present state of our knowledge such a solution can, in fact, only be reached in a comparatively small number of cases.

One case where a result of a certain generality can be given, is the simple case of the *mean* $\bar{x} = \frac{1}{n}\sum_i x_i$ of a one-dimensional sample. In Chs 16—19 we have seen (cf 16.2, 16.5, 17.3, 18.1, 19.2) that many distributions possess what we have called an *addition theorem*, i. e. a theorem that gives an explicit expression for the d. f. $G_n(x)$ of the sum $x_1 + \cdots + x_n$, where the x_i are independent, each having the given d. f. $F(x)$. The d. f. of the mean $\bar{x}$ is then $G_n(nx)$, and thus *we can find the exact sampling distribution of the mean, whenever the parent distribution possesses an addition theorem.* — We shall give some examples:

When the parent $F(x)$ is normal (m, σ), we have seen in 17.3 that the mean $\bar{x}$ is normal $(m, \sigma/\sqrt{n})$.

When $F(x)$ corresponds to a Cauchy distribution, we have seen in 19.2 that $\bar{x}$ has the same d. f. $F(x)$ as the parent population.

When the parent has a Poisson distribution with the parameter λ, the mean $\bar{x}$ has the possible values $0, \frac{1}{n}, \frac{2}{n}, \ldots$, and it follows from (16.5.4) that we have $P\left(\bar{x} = \frac{\nu}{n}\right) = \frac{(n\lambda)^\nu}{\nu!} e^{-n\lambda}$.

Apart from the case of the mean (with respect to this case, cf Irwin, Ref. 132), very few results of a general character are known about the exact form of sampling distributions. Only in one particular case, viz. the case of *sampling from a normal parent distribution* (in any number of dimensions), has it so far been possible to investigate the subject systematically and reach results of a certain completeness. In the present chapter, we shall be concerned with this case.

Some isolated results belonging to this order of ideas were discovered at an early stage by Helmert, K. Pearson and Student. The first systematic investigations of the subject were, however, made by R. A. Fisher, who gave rigorous proofs of the earlier results and discovered the exact forms of the distributions in fundamentally important new cases. In his work on these problems, Fisher generally uses methods of analytical geometry in a multi-dimensional space. Other methods, involving the use of characteristic functions, or of certain transformations of variables etc., have later been applied to this type of problems. In the sequel, we shall give examples of the use of various methods.

29.2. Fisher's lemma. Degrees of freedom. — In the study of sampling distributions connected with normally distributed variables, the following transformation due to R. A. Fisher (Ref. 97) is often useful. Suppose that $x_1, \ldots, x_n$ are independent random variables, each of which is normal $(0, \sigma)$. Consider an *orthogonal* transformation (cf 11.9)

$$y_i = c_{i1} x_1 + c_{i2} x_2 + \cdots + c_{in} x_n, \qquad (i = 1, 2, \ldots, n), \tag{29.2.1}$$

replacing the variables $x_1, \ldots, x_n$ by new variables $y_1, \ldots, y_n$. By 24.4, the joint distribution of the y_i is normal, and we obtain (cf Ex. 16, p. 319) $\boldsymbol{E}(y_i) = 0$, and

$$\boldsymbol{E}(y_i y_k) = \sigma^2 \sum_{j=1}^{n} c_{ij} c_{kj} = \begin{cases} \sigma^2 & \text{for } i = k, \\ 0 & \text{for } i \neq k, \end{cases}$$

so that the new variables y_i are uncorrelated. It then follows from 24.1 that they are even independent. *Thus the transformed variables* y_i *are independent and normal* $(0, \sigma)$.

The geometrical signification of this result is evident. The transformation (29.2.1) corresponds (cf 11.9) to a rotation of the system of coordinates about the origin, and our result shows that the particular normal distribution in $\boldsymbol{R}_n$ considered here is invariant under this rotation.

Suppose now that, at first, only a certain number $p < n$ of linear functions $y_1, y_2, \ldots, y_p$ are given, where $y_i = c_{i1} x_1 + \cdots + c_{in} x_n$, and the c_{ij} satisfy the orthogonality conditions

$$\sum_{j=1}^{n} c_{ij} c_{kj} = \begin{cases} 1 & \text{for } i = k, \\ 0 & \text{for } i \neq k, \end{cases}$$

for $i = 1, 2, \ldots, p$ and $k = 1, 2, \ldots, p$. By 11.9 we can then always find $n - p$ further rows $c_{i1}, \ldots, c_{in}$, where $i = p + 1, \ldots, n$, such that the complete matrix $\boldsymbol{C}_{nn} = \{c_{ik}\}$ is orthogonal. — Consider the quadratic form in $x_1, \ldots, x_n$

$$Q(x_1, \ldots, x_n) = \sum_{1}^{n} x_i^2 - y_1^2 - \cdots - y_p^2. \tag{29.2.2}$$

If we apply here the orthogonal transformation (29.2.1), $\sum_{1}^{n} x_i^2$ is by 11.9 transformed into $\sum_{1}^{n} y_i^2$, and thus we obtain

$$Q = y_{p+1}^2 + \cdots + y_n^2.$$

Thus Q is equal to the sum of the squares of $n-p$ independent normal $(0, \sigma)$ variables which are, moreover, independent of $y_1, \ldots, y_p$. Using (18.1.8), we obtain the following lemma due to R. A. Fisher (Ref. 97):

The variable Q *defined by* (29.2.2) *is independent of* $y_1, \ldots, y_p$ *and has the fr.f.*

$$\frac{1}{\sigma^2} k_{n-p}\left(\frac{x}{\sigma^2}\right) = \frac{1}{2^{\frac{n-p}{2}} \sigma^{n-p} \Gamma\left(\frac{n-p}{2}\right)} x^{\frac{n-p}{2}-1} e^{-\frac{x}{2\sigma^2}},$$

where $k_n(x)$ *is the fr.f.* (18.1.3) *of the* χ^2*-distribution.*

The number $n-p$ is the *rank* of the form Q (cf 11.6), i.e. the smallest number of independent variables on which the form may be brought by a non-singular linear transformation. In statistical applications, this number of free variables entering into a problem is usually, in accordance with the terminology introduced by R. A. Fisher, denoted as the number of *degrees of freedom* (abbreviated *d. of fr.*) of the problem, or of the distribution of the random variables attached to the problem.

Thus e.g. the variable $\chi^2 = \sum_1^n \xi_\nu^2$ and its fr. f. $k_n(x)$ considered in 18.1 are said to possess n degrees of freedom, since the quadratic form χ^2 is of rank n. The corresponding distribution will accordingly be called the *χ^2-distribution with n degrees of freedom.*

Similarly the form $Q = \sum_1^n x_i^2 - y_1^2 - \cdots - y_p^2$ of rank $n-p$ considered above will be said to possess $n-p$ degrees of freedom, and the result proved above thus implies that *the variable* Q/σ^2 *is distributed in a* χ^2*-distribution with* $n-p$ *degrees of freedom.*

The same terminology will often be applied also to other distributions. In the case of Student's distribution, it is customary to say that the fr. f. $s_n(x)$ defined by (18.2.4) is attached to *Student's distribution with* n *degrees of freedom*, since the quadratic form in the denominator of the variable t as defined by (18.2.1) has the rank n. For Fisher's z-distribution (cf. 18.3), we have to distinguish between the m d. of fr. in the *numerator* of (18.3.1), and the n d. of fr. in the *denominator*.

29.3. The joint distribution of $\bar{x}$ and s^2 in samples from a normal distribution. — We have already pointed out in 29.1 that the mean

$\bar{x}$ of a sample of n from a parent distribution which is normal (m, σ) is itself normal $(m, \sigma/\sqrt{n})$. We now proceed to consider the distribution of the sample variance $s^2 = m_2 = \frac{1}{n}\sum (x_i - \bar{x})^2$ and, at the same time, the joint distribution of $\bar{x}$ and s^2. Without loss of generality, we may then assume that the population mean m is zero, since this does not affect s^2, and is equivalent to the addition of a constant to $\bar{x}$.

We thus assume that every x_i is normal $(0, \sigma)$, and consider the identity (cf 11.11.2)

$$ns^2 = \sum_1^n (x_i - \bar{x})^2 = \sum_1^n x_i^2 - n\bar{x}^2. \tag{29.3.1}$$

Now $n\bar{x}^2 = \left(\frac{x_1}{\sqrt{n}} + \cdots + \frac{x_n}{\sqrt{n}}\right)^2$ is the square of a linear form $c_1 x_1 + \cdots + c_n x_n$ such that $c_1^2 + \cdots + c_n^2 = 1$. We may thus apply the lemma of the preceding paragraph, taking in (29.2.2) $p = 1$ and $y_1 = \sqrt{n}\,\bar{x}$. Returning to the case of a general population mean m, we then have the following theorem first rigorously proved by R. A. Fisher (Ref. 97):

The mean $\bar{x}$ and the variance s^2 of a normal sample are independent, and $\bar{x}$ is normal $(m, \sigma/\sqrt{n})$, while ns^2/σ^2 is distributed in a χ^2-distribution with $n-1$ degrees of freedom.

It can be shown that the independence of $\bar{x}$ and s^2 holds *only* when the parent distribution is normal (cf Geary, Ref. 115, and Lukacs, Ref. 150). On the other hand, we have seen in 27.4 that $\bar{x}$ and s^2 are *uncorrelated* whenever the third central moment μ_3 of the parent distribution is zero.

It follows from the theorem that the unbiased estimate (cf 27.6) of the variance, $\frac{n}{n-1}s^2$, has the fr. f. $\frac{n-1}{\sigma^2}k_{n-1}\left(\frac{(n-1)x}{\sigma^2}\right)$. Comparing with the fr. f. of $\frac{1}{n}\sum_1^n x_i^2$ given in the table at the end of 18.1, it is seen that the variable $\frac{n}{n-1}s^2 = \frac{1}{n-1}\sum_1^n (x_i - \bar{x})^2$ is distributed as the arithmetic mean of $n-1$ squares of independent normal $(0, \sigma)$ variables, in accordance with the fact that there are $n-1$ d. of fr. in the distribution.

The mean and the variance of $s^2 = m_2$ have already been given in (27.4.5). By means of (18.1.5) we obtain the following general expression of the moments

$$(29.3.2) \qquad \boldsymbol{E}(m_2^\nu) = \frac{(n-1)(n+1)(n+3)\cdots(n+2\nu-3)}{n^\nu}\sigma^{2\nu}.$$

Hence we deduce the expressions for the coefficients of skewness and excess:

$$\gamma_1(m_2) = \frac{2\sqrt{2}}{\sqrt{n-1}}, \quad \gamma_2(m_2) = \frac{12}{n-1}.$$

For the s. d. $s = \sqrt{m_2}$ of the sample we obtain from the theorem, using Stirling's formula (12.5.3)

$$(29.3.3) \qquad \begin{aligned} \boldsymbol{E}(s) &= \frac{\Gamma\left(\frac{n}{2}\right)}{\Gamma\left(\frac{n-1}{2}\right)}\sqrt{\frac{2}{n}}\,\sigma = \sigma + O\left(\frac{1}{n}\right), \\ \boldsymbol{D}^2(s) &= \left(\frac{n-1}{n} - \frac{\Gamma^2\left(\frac{n}{2}\right)}{\Gamma^2\left(\frac{n-1}{2}\right)}\cdot\frac{2}{n}\right)\sigma^2 = \frac{\sigma^2}{2n} + O\left(\frac{1}{n^2}\right), \end{aligned}$$

in accordance with the general expressions (27.7.1) and (27.7.2).

In view of the great importance of the theorem on the joint distribution of $\bar{x}$ and s^2, we shall now give another proof of the same result, using certain transformations of variables, combined with geometrical arguments. As before, we suppose in the proof that $m = 0$.

Consider the n-dimensional *sample space* $\boldsymbol{R}_n$ of the variables $x_1, \ldots, x_n$. Our sample is represented by a variable point in this space, the *sample point* $X = X(x_1, \ldots, x_n)$. Let XR be the perpendicular from X to the line $x_1 = x_2 = \cdots = x_n$. Then R has the coordinates $(\bar{x}, \ldots, \bar{x})$ so that the square of the distance OR from the origin O to R is $n\bar{x}^2$, and consequently $\overline{XR}^2 = \overline{OX}^2 - \overline{OR}^2 = \sum_1^n x_i^2 - n\bar{x}^2 = n s^2$.

The joint distribution of the variables x_i is conceived in the usual way as a distribution of a mass unit over $\boldsymbol{R}_n$, and the probability element of this distribution is

$$dP = \frac{1}{(2\pi)^{\frac{n}{2}}\sigma^n} e^{-\frac{1}{2\sigma^2}\sum_1^n x_i^2} dx_1 \ldots dx_n.$$

We now perform a rotation of the coordinate axes, such that one of the axes is brought to coincide with the line OR. This rotation is expressed by an orthogonal substitution $y_i = \sum_1^n c_{ij} x_j$, where one of the y_i, say y_n, is equal to $\sqrt{n}\,\bar{x} = \frac{x_1}{\sqrt{n}} + \cdots + \frac{x_n}{\sqrt{n}}$. We then obtain $\sum_1^n x_i^2 = \sum_1^n y_i^2 = n\bar{x}^2 + \sum_1^{n-1} y_i^2$, and hence $\sum_1^{n-1} y_i^2 = n s^2$. The determinant of the substitution being ± 1, we have by (22.2.3)

$$\begin{aligned} dP &= \frac{1}{(2\pi)^{\frac{n}{2}}\sigma^n} e^{-\frac{n}{2\sigma^2}(\bar{x}^2+s^2)} dy_1 \ldots dy_{n-1}\, dy_n \\ &= \frac{\sqrt{n}}{(2\pi)^{\frac{n}{2}}\sigma^n} e^{-\frac{n}{2\sigma^2}(\bar{x}^2+s^2)} dy_1 \ldots dy_{n-1}\, d\bar{x}. \end{aligned}$$

We further introduce the substitution

$$y_i = \sqrt{n}\, s\, z_i, \qquad (i = 1, 2, \ldots, n-1), \tag{29.3.4}$$

which signifies that we take the length $XR = \sqrt{n}\, s$ as unit. However, by the last substitution we have replaced the $n-1$ variables y_i by n new variables s and $z_1, \ldots, z_{n-1}$. Accordingly there is a relation between the new variables, which is found by squaring and adding the $n-1$ equations (29.3.4). We then obtain

$$\sum_1^{n-1} z_i^2 = 1, \tag{29.3.5}$$

and thus one of the z_i, say z_{n-1}, may be expressed as a function of the $n-2$ others, so that in (29.3.4) the old variables $y_1, \ldots, y_{n-1}$ are replaced by the new variables s and $z_1, \ldots, z_{n-2}$. For the Jacobian J of the transformation we have, since $\frac{\partial z_{n-1}}{\partial z_i} = -\frac{z_i}{z_{n-1}}$,

$$= \begin{vmatrix} \sqrt{n}\, z_1 & \sqrt{n}\, s & 0 & \ldots & 0 \\ \sqrt{n}\, z_2 & 0 & \sqrt{n}\, s & \ldots & 0 \\ \cdot & \cdot & \cdot & \cdot & \cdot \\ \sqrt{n}\, z_{n-2} & 0 & 0 & \ldots & \sqrt{n}\, s \\ \sqrt{n}\, z_{n-1} & -\sqrt{n}\, s \dfrac{z_1}{z_{n-1}} & \ldots & & -\sqrt{n}\, s \dfrac{z_{n-2}}{z_{n-1}} \end{vmatrix} = \frac{n^{\frac{n-1}{2}} s^{n-2}}{z_{n-1}} \begin{vmatrix} z_1 & 1 & 0 & \ldots & 0 \\ z_2 & 0 & 1 & \ldots & 0 \\ \cdot & \cdot & \cdot & \cdot & \cdot \\ z_{n-2} & 0 & 0 & \ldots & 1 \\ z_{n-1}^2 & -z_1 & -z_2 & \ldots & -z_{n-2} \end{vmatrix}$$

$$= (-1)^{n-1} \frac{n^{\frac{n-1}{2}} s^{n-2}}{z_{n-1}} = \pm \frac{n^{\frac{n-1}{2}} s^{n-2}}{\sqrt{1 - z_1^2 - \cdots - z_{n-2}^2}}.$$

To any system of values $(y_1, \ldots, y_{n-1}) \neq (0, \ldots, 0)$ we obtain from (29.3.4) and (29.3.5) a uniquely determined system of values of $z_1, \ldots, z_{n-2}$ and s, such that $s > 0$. On the other hand, to any given system of values of $z_1, \ldots, z_{n-2}$ and s, such that $\sum_1^{n-2} z_i^2 < 1$ and $s > 0$, there correspond *two* values of z_{n-1} with opposite signs determined by (29.3.5), viz. $z_{n-1} = \pm \sqrt{1 - z_1^2 - \cdots - z_{n-2}^2}$, and thus two systems of values of the y_i, say $y_1, \ldots, y_{n-2}, \pm y_{n-1}$. Both these systems yield the same value of the probability element dP and the modulus $|J|$ of the Jacobian, and thus we obtain by means of a remark in 22.2 the expression

$$dP = \frac{2\, n^{\frac{n}{2}}}{(2\pi)^{\frac{n}{2}} \sigma^n} e^{-\frac{n}{2\sigma^2}(\bar{x}^2 + s^2)} \frac{s^{n-2}}{\sqrt{1 - z_1^2 - \cdots - z_{n-2}^2}} d\bar{x}\, ds\, dz_1 \ldots dz_{n-2}$$

$$\frac{\sqrt{n}}{\sigma\sqrt{2\pi}} e^{-\frac{\bar{x}^2}{2\sigma^2}} d\bar{x} \cdot \frac{2\left(\frac{n}{2}\right)^{\frac{n-1}{2}}}{\sigma^{n-1}\, \Gamma\left(\frac{n-1}{2}\right)} s^{n-2} e^{-\frac{n}{2\sigma^2} s^2} ds \cdot \frac{\Gamma\left(\frac{n-1}{2}\right)}{\pi^{\frac{n-1}{2}}} \frac{dz_1 \ldots dz_{n-2}}{\sqrt{1 - z_1^2 - \cdots - z_{n-2}^2}}.$$

The probability element dP appears here as a product of three factors, viz. the probability elements of $\bar{x}$ and s, and the joint probability element of $z_1, \ldots, z_{n-2}$. We thus see (cf 22.1.2) that $\bar{x}$ and s are independent not only of one another, but also of the combined variable $(z_1, \ldots, z_{n-2})$, and that the distributions of $\bar{x}$ and s are those given by the above theorem.[1]

[1] The same result can be obtained by means of the transformation $x_i = \bar{x} + s\, z_i$, which has been used for this and other purposes e. g. by Behrens, Steffensen, Rasch and Hald (Ref. 60, 218, 206).

For a later purpose we finally observe that, in the general case when the population mean m is not zero, the above transformation of the probability element may be written

$$dP = \frac{1}{(2\pi)^{\frac{n}{2}}\sigma^n} e^{-\frac{1}{2\sigma^2}\sum_1^n (x_i-m)^2} dx_1 \ldots dx_n$$

(29.3.6)

$$= \frac{\sqrt{n}}{\sigma\sqrt{2\pi}} e^{-\frac{n}{2\sigma^2}(\bar{x}-m)^2} d\bar{x} \cdot \frac{2\left(\frac{n}{2}\right)^{\frac{n-1}{2}}}{\sigma^{n-1}\Gamma\left(\frac{n-1}{2}\right)} s^{n-2} e^{-\frac{n}{2\sigma^2}s^2} ds \cdot \frac{\Gamma\left(\frac{n-1}{2}\right)}{\pi^{\frac{n-1}{2}}} \frac{dz_1 \ldots dz_{n-2}}{\sqrt{1-z_1^2-\cdots-z_{n-2}^2}}$$

Consider the effect of the above transformation on the expression

$$\frac{m_\nu}{m_2^{\nu/2}} = \frac{1}{n}\sum_1^n \left(\frac{x_i-\bar{x}}{s}\right)^\nu, \qquad (\nu > 2).$$

By means of the identity (29.3.1), it is easily shown that every $x_i - \bar{x}$ is transformed into a linear combination of $y_1, \ldots, y_{n-1}$. It then follows from (29.3.4) and (29.3.5) that $m_\nu m_2^{-\nu/2}$ is a function of $z_1, \ldots, z_{n-2}$ only. Thus the three variables $\bar{x}$, s *and* $m_\nu m_2^{-\nu/2}$ *are independent.* (Cf Geary, Ref. 116).

Following Geary, we can use this observation to obtain *exact* expressions (first given by Fisher, Ref. 101) for the mean and the variance of the coefficients $g_1 = m_3 m_2^{-3/2}$ and $g_2 = m_4 m_2^{-2} - 3$, instead of the asymptotic expressions (27.7.9). It follows, in fact, from the independence theorem that

$$\mathbf{E}\left(m_\nu^p m_2^{-\frac{\nu p}{2}}\right) \cdot \mathbf{E}\left(m_2^{\frac{\nu p}{2}}\right) = \mathbf{E}\left(m_\nu^p\right),$$

so that the mean value of $(m_\nu m_2^{-\nu/2})^p$ can be calculated from $\mathbf{E}(m_\nu^p)$ and $\mathbf{E}\left(m_2^{\frac{\nu p}{2}}\right)$. In this way we obtain

$$\mathbf{E}(g_1) = 0, \quad \mathbf{E}(g_2) = -\frac{6}{n+1},$$

(29.3.7)

$$\mathbf{D}^2(g_1) = \frac{6(n-2)}{(n+1)(n+3)},$$

$$\mathbf{D}^2(g_2) = \frac{24n(n-2)(n-3)}{(n+1)^2(n+3)(n+5)}.$$

Thus g_2 is affected with a negative bias of order n^{-1}, while g_1 is unbiased. If, instead of g_1 and g_2, we consider the analogous quantities

$$G_1 = \frac{K_3}{K_2^{3/2}} = \frac{\sqrt{n(n-1)}}{n-2} g_1,$$

(29.3.8)

$$G_2 = \frac{K_4}{K_2^2} = \frac{n-1}{(n-2)(n-3)}[(n+1)g_2 + 6],$$

where the K_ν are the unbiased semi-invariant estimates of Fisher (cf 27.6), the bias disappears, and we obtain

$$\begin{aligned} &E(G_1) = E(G_2) = 0, \\ (29.3.9) \qquad &D^2(G_1) = \frac{6\,n(n-1)}{(n-2)(n+1)(n+3)}, \\ &D^2(G_2) = \frac{24\,n(n-1)^2}{(n-3)(n-2)(n+3)(n+5)}. \end{aligned}$$

29.4. Student's ratio. — Consider the variables $\sqrt{n}(\bar{x} - m)$ and $\frac{n}{n-1}s^2$, when the parent distribution is normal (m, σ). According to the preceding paragraph, these two variables are independent, and $\sqrt{n}(\bar{x} - m)$ is normal $(0, \sigma)$, while $\frac{n}{n-1}s^2$ is distributed as the arithmetic mean of $n-1$ squares of independent normal $(0, \sigma)$ variables. By the definition of Student's distribution in 18.2, the ratio

$$t = \frac{\sqrt{n}(\bar{x} - m)}{\sqrt{\frac{n}{n-1}s^2}} = \sqrt{n-1}\,\frac{\bar{x} - m}{s} \tag{29.4.1}$$

is then distributed in *Student's distribution with* $n-1$ *degrees of freedom.* Thus t has the fr. f.

$$s_{n-1}(x) = \frac{1}{\sqrt{(n-1)\pi}} \frac{\Gamma\left(\frac{n}{2}\right)}{\Gamma\left(\frac{n-1}{2}\right)} \left(1 + \frac{x^2}{n-1}\right)^{-\frac{n}{2}}.$$

This can, of course, also be shown more directly. Assuming for simplicity $m = 0$, we replace the sample variables $x_1, \ldots, x_n$ by new variables $y_1, \ldots, y_n$ by means of an orthogonal transformation such that $y_1 = \sqrt{n}\,\bar{x} = \frac{x_1}{\sqrt{n}} + \cdots + \frac{x_n}{\sqrt{n}}$. Then $n s^2 = \sum_1^n x_i^2 - n\bar{x}^2 = \sum_2^n y_i^2$ and thus

$$t = \frac{y_1}{\sqrt{\frac{1}{n-1}\sum_2^n y_i^2}},$$

where by 29.2 the y_i are independent and normal $(0, \sigma)$. We can then directly apply the argument of (18.2.1)—(18.2.4).

If, in the first expression of t in (29.4.1), we replace $\frac{n}{n-1} s^2$ by its mean σ^2, we obtain the variable $\sqrt{n} \frac{\bar{x} - m}{\sigma}$, which is obviously normal (0, 1). It follows from 20.6 that the difference $t - \sqrt{n} \frac{\bar{x} - m}{\sigma}$ converges in probability to zero as $n \to \infty$. Accordingly by (20.2.2) the fr. f. of t tends to $\frac{1}{\sqrt{2\pi}} e^{-x^2/2}$ as $n \to \infty$.

The variable t defined by (29.4.1) is known as *Student's ratio.*[1] Its distribution was first discovered by Student (Ref. 221), whose results were then rigorously proved by R. A. Fisher (Ref. 97).

As already pointed out in 18.2, the fr. f. s_{n-1}, as well as the variable t itself, does not contain σ. As soon as we know m, we may thus calculate t from the sample values, and compare the observed value of t with the theoretical distribution. In this way we obtain a practically important test of significance for the *deviation of the sample mean* $\bar{x}$ *from some hypothetical value of the population mean* m (cf 31.2 and 31.3, Ex. 4).

Of even greater practical importance is the application of Student's distribution to test the significance of the *difference between two mean values* (R. A. Fisher, Ref. 97; cf 31.2). The sampling distribution relevant to this problem is obtained as follows.

Suppose that we have two independent samples $x_1, \ldots, x_{n_1}$ and $y_1, \ldots, y_{n_2}$, drawn from the same normal population. Without loss of generality, we may assume $m = 0$. Let the mean and the variance of the first sample be denoted by $\bar{x} = \frac{1}{n_1} \sum_1^{n_1} x_i$ and $s_1^2 = \frac{1}{n_1} \sum_1^{n_1} (x_i - \bar{x})^2$, while $\bar{y}$ and s_2^2 are the corresponding characteristics of the second sample. We now replace all the $n_1 + n_2$ variables $x_1, \ldots, x_{n_1}, y_1, \ldots, y_{n_2}$ by new variables $z_1, \ldots, z_{n_1+n_2}$, by means of an orthogonal transformation such that $z_1 = \sqrt{n_1}\, \bar{x}$ and $z_2 = \sqrt{n_2}\, \bar{y}$. The quadratic form

$$Q = n_1 s_1^2 + n_2 s_2^2 = \sum_1^{n_1} x_i^2 + \sum_1^{n_2} y_i^2 - n_1 \bar{x}^2 - n_2 \bar{y}^2$$

is then transformed into $Q = \sum_3^{n_1+n_2} z_i^2$, which shows that the rank, or

[1]) Student actually considered the ratio $z = t/\sqrt{n-1} = (\bar{x} - m)/s$.

the number of d. of fr., of Q is $n_1 + n_2 - 2$. If we define a random variable u by the relation

$$u = \sqrt{\frac{n_1 n_2 (n_1 + n_2 - 2)}{n_1 + n_2}} \cdot \frac{\bar{x} - \bar{y}}{\sqrt{Q}} \tag{29.4.2}$$

$$= \sqrt{\frac{n_1 n_2 (n_1 + n_2 - 2)}{n_1 + n_2}} \cdot \frac{\bar{x} - \bar{y}}{\sqrt{n_1 s_1^2 + n_2 s_2^2}},$$

u is then transformed into

$$u = \frac{\sqrt{\frac{n_2}{n_1 + n_2}}\, z_1 - \sqrt{\frac{n_1}{n_1 + n_2}}\, z_2}{\sqrt{\frac{1}{n_1 + n_2 - 2} \sum_{3}^{n_1+n_2} z_i^2}} = \frac{w}{\sqrt{\frac{1}{n_1 + n_2 - 2} \sum_{3}^{n_1+n_2} z_i^2}},$$

where w and $z_3, \ldots, z_{n_1+n_2}$ are independent and normal $(0, \sigma)$. We can now once more apply the argument of 18.2, and it follows that *the variable u is distributed in Student's distribution with $n_1 + n_2 - 2$ d. of fr.*, so that u has the fr. f. $s_{n_1+n_2-2}(x)$. This result evidently holds true irrespective of the value of m. — It will be observed that in this case neither the variable u nor the corresponding fr. f. contains any of the parameters m and σ of the parent distribution. Thus we can calculate u directly from the sample values, and compare the observed value of u with the theoretical distribution (cf 31.2 and 31.3, Ex. 4).

Consider the quadratic form $n s^2 = \sum_1^n (x_i - \bar{x})^2 = \sum_1^n x_i^2 - n \bar{x}^2$ in the n sample variables $x_1, \ldots, x_n$, assuming that the population mean m is zero. Replacing the x_i by new variables y_i by means of an orthogonal transformation such that the two first variables are

$$y_1 = \sqrt{n}\, \bar{x} = \frac{x_1}{\sqrt{n}} + \frac{x_2}{\sqrt{n}} + \cdots + \frac{x_n}{\sqrt{n}},$$

$$y_2 = \sqrt{\frac{n}{n-1}}\,(x_1 - \bar{x}) = \sqrt{\frac{n-1}{n}}\, x_1 - \frac{x_2}{\sqrt{n(n-1)}} - \cdots - \frac{x_n}{\sqrt{n(n-1)}},$$

the form $n s^2$ is transformed into $\sum_2^n y_i^2$. Consequently the variable

$$\tau = \frac{x_1 - \bar{x}}{s}, \tag{29.4.3}$$

which expresses the deviation of the sample value x_1 from the sample mean $\bar{x}$, measured in units of the s. d. s of the sample, becomes

$$\tau = \frac{y_2}{\sqrt{\frac{1}{n-1}\sum_{2}^{n} y_i^2}}.$$

Now $y_2, \ldots y_n$ are independent and normal $(0, \sigma)$, and thus by (18.2.6) and (18.2.7) the variable τ has the fr. f. (cf Thompson, Ref. 225, and Arley, Ref. 53)

$$\text{(29.4.4)} \qquad \frac{1}{\sqrt{(n-1)\pi}} \frac{\Gamma\left(\frac{n-1}{2}\right)}{\Gamma\left(\frac{n-2}{2}\right)} \left(1 - \frac{x^2}{n-1}\right)^{\frac{n-4}{2}}, \qquad (|x| < \sqrt{n-1}).$$

The variable $\frac{\tau\sqrt{n-2}}{\sqrt{n-1-\tau^2}}$ is then, by 18.2, distributed in Student's distribution with $n-2$ d. of fr. — It follows from the definition of τ that these results hold irrespective of the value of m. Any relative deviation $\frac{x_i - \bar{x}}{s}$ has, of course, the same distribution as τ. These results are of importance in connection with the question of criteria for the rejection of outlying observations.

More generally, if we consider the arithmetic mean $\bar{x}_k = \frac{x_1 + \cdots + x_k}{k}$, where $1 \leq k < n$, and write $\tau_k = \frac{\bar{x}_k - \bar{x}}{s}$, the variable $\tau_k \sqrt{\frac{k(n-1)}{n-k}}$ has the fr. f. (29.4.4), and consequently the variable

$$\text{(29.4.5)} \qquad t = \frac{\tau_k \sqrt{k(n-2)}}{\sqrt{n-k-k\tau_k^2}}$$

has Student's distribution with $n-2$ d. of fr. (Thompson, Ref. 225). This may be used for testing the significance of the difference between the mean of a sub-group and a general mean (cf 31.3, Ex. 5).

29.5. A lemma. — We now proceed to the study of sampling distributions connected with a *multi-dimensional normal parent distribution.* In this preliminary paragraph, we shall prove certain results due to Wishart and Bartlett (Ref. 240, 241) that will be required in the sequel. Let $A = \begin{Bmatrix} a_{11} & \ldots & a_{1k} \\ \cdot & \cdot & \cdot \\ a_{k1} & \ldots & a_{kk} \end{Bmatrix}$, where $a_{ji} = a_{ij}$, be a definite positive matrix (cf 11.10) with constant elements, while $X = \begin{Bmatrix} x_{11} & \ldots & x_{1k} \\ \cdot & \cdot & \cdot \\ x_{k1} & \ldots & x_{kk} \end{Bmatrix}$, where $x_{ji} = x_{ij}$, is a variable matrix. Owing to the symmetry $\boldsymbol{X}$ contains, of course, only $\frac{1}{2}k(k+1)$ distinct variables x_{ij}. The determinants of the matrices are denoted by $A = |a_{ij}|$ and $X = |x_{ij}|$.

Consider now the $\frac{1}{2}k(k+1)$-dimensional space $\boldsymbol{R}_{\frac{1}{2}k(k+1)}$ of the variables x_{ij}, where $k \geqq 1$. Let S denote the set of all points of this space such that the corresponding matrix $\boldsymbol{X}$ is definite positive, while S^* is the complementary set. For any $n > k$, we now define a function of the variables x_{ij} by writing

$$f_n(x_{11}, \ldots, x_{kk}) = \begin{cases} C_{kn} A^{\frac{n-1}{2}} X^{\frac{n-k-2}{2}} e^{-\sum\limits_{i,j} a_{ij} x_{ij}} & \text{in } S, \\ 0 & \text{in } S^*, \end{cases} \tag{29.5.1}$$

where C_{kn} is a constant depending on k and n, but not on the a_{ij} or the x_{ij}. The sum is extended over $i = 1, \ldots, k$ and $j = 1, \ldots, k$.

We shall now show that the constant C_{kn} may be so determined that $f_n(x_{11}, \ldots, x_{kk})$ is the fr.f. of a distribution in $\boldsymbol{R}_{\frac{1}{2}k(k+1)}$. — The complete expression of C_{kn} is, in fact,

$$C_{kn} = \frac{1}{\pi^{\frac{k(k-1)}{4}} \Gamma\left(\frac{n-1}{2}\right) \Gamma\left(\frac{n-2}{2}\right) \cdots \Gamma\left(\frac{n-k}{2}\right)}. \tag{29.5.2}$$

For $k = 1$, (29.5.1)—(29.5.2) reduce to $f_n(x) = \dfrac{a^{\frac{n-1}{2}}}{\Gamma\left(\frac{n-1}{2}\right)} x^{\frac{n-3}{2}} e^{-a x}$, $(x > 0,\ a > 0)$, which is evidently a fr. f. in $\boldsymbol{R}_1$.

For $k > 1$, we have to show that C_{kn} may be determined such that the integral of f_n over the whole space $\boldsymbol{R}_{\frac{1}{2}k(k+1)}$ is equal to 1. We shall first consider the particular case when $\boldsymbol{A}$ is a diagonal matrix (cf 11.1), so that $a_{ij} = 0$ for $i \neq j$. Since $\boldsymbol{A}$ is definite positive, we then have $a_{ii} > 0$ for $i = 1, \ldots, k$. — In any point of the set S, we have $x_{ii} > 0$ for $i = 1, \ldots, k$. Introducing, for every x_{ij} with $i \neq j$, the substitution

$$x_{ij} = y_{ij} \sqrt{x_{ii} x_{jj}}, \tag{29.5.3}$$

we have $y_{ji} = y_{ij}$, and $\boldsymbol{X} = \boldsymbol{DYD}$, where $\boldsymbol{D}$ denotes the diagonal matrix with the elements $\sqrt{x_{11}}, \sqrt{x_{22}}, \ldots, \sqrt{x_{kk}}$, while

$$\mathbf{Y} = \begin{Bmatrix} 1 & y_{12} & \dots & y_{1k} \\ y_{21} & 1 & \dots & y_{2k} \\ \cdot & \cdot & \cdot & \cdot \\ y_{k1} & y_{k2} & \dots & 1 \end{Bmatrix}.$$

Denoting by Y the determinant of $\mathbf{Y}$ we thus have $X = x_{11} x_{22} \dots x_{kk} Y$. When $\mathbf{X}$ is definite positive, so is $\mathbf{Y}$, and conversely. The Jacobian of the transformation (29.5.3) being $(x_{11} x_{12} \dots x_{kk})^{\frac{k-1}{2}}$, we thus have

$$\int\limits_S X^{\frac{n-k-2}{2}} e^{-\sum\limits_1^k a_{ii} x_{ii}} d x_{11} d x_{12} \dots d x_{kk}$$

$$= \int\limits_0^\infty \cdots \int\limits_0^\infty (x_{11} x_{22} \dots x_{kk})^{\frac{n-3}{2}} e^{-\sum\limits_1^k a_{ii} x_{ii}} d x_{11} d x_{22} \dots d x_{kk} \cdot$$

$$\cdot \int\limits_{S'} Y^{\frac{n-k-2}{2}} d y_{12} \dots d y_{k-1,k},$$

the integral with respect to the y_{ij} being extended over the set S' of all y_{ij} such that $\mathbf{Y}$ is definite positive. Obviously the integral with respect to the y_{ij}, say J_k, depends only on k and n, so that the whole integral reduces to

$$\frac{\left[\Gamma\left(\frac{n-1}{2}\right)\right]^k J_k}{(a_{11} a_{22} \dots a_{kk})^{\frac{n-1}{2}}} = \frac{H_{kn}}{A^{\frac{n-1}{2}}},$$

where H_{kn} depends only on k and n. Taking in (29.5.1) $C_{kn} = H_{kn}^{-1}$, it follows that the integral of $f_n(x_{11}, \dots, x_{kk})$ over the whole space $\mathbf{R}_{\frac{1}{2}k(k+1)}$ is equal to 1, so that f_n (being obviously non-negative) is the fr. f. of a distribution in $\mathbf{R}_{\frac{1}{2}k(k+1)}$.

In order to complete the proof in the case when $a_{ij} = 0$ for $i \neq j$, it remains to verify the expression (29.5.2) for C_{kn}. It follows from the above that we have to prove

$$J_k = \int\limits_{S'} Y^{\frac{n-k-2}{2}} d y_{12} \dots d y_{k-1,k} = \pi^{\frac{k(k-1)}{4}} \prod_{i=1}^k \frac{\Gamma\left(\frac{n-i}{2}\right)}{\Gamma\left(\frac{n-1}{2}\right)},$$

for $2 \leq k < n$. This may be proved by induction, and we shall indicate the general lines of the proof. For $k = 2$, our relation reduces to

$$J_2 = \int_{-1}^{1} (1-y^2)^{\frac{n-4}{2}}\, dy = \sqrt{\pi}\, \frac{\Gamma\left(\frac{n-2}{2}\right)}{\Gamma\left(\frac{n-1}{2}\right)},$$

which may be directly verified, since the substitution $y^2 = z$ changes the integral into a Beta-function (cf. 12.4). Suppose now that our relation has been proved for a certain value of k, and consider J_{k+1}. Expanding the determinant under the integral according to (11.5.3), we obtain for J_{k+1} the expression

$$\int_{S'} dy_{12} \ldots dy_{k-1,k} \int \Big(Y - \sum_{i,j=1}^{k} Y_{ij}\, y_{i,k+1}\, y_{j,k+1}\Big)^{\frac{n-k-3}{2}} dy_{1,k+1} \ldots dy_{k,k+1}$$

where the integral with respect to the $y_{i,k+1}$ has to be extended over all values of the variables such that $\sum_{i,j=1}^{k} Y_{ij}\, y_{i,k+1}\, y_{j,k+1} < Y$. The latter integral may be evaluated by the same methods as the integrals (11.12.3)—(11.12.4), and we obtain

$$J_{k+1} = J_k \frac{\Gamma\left(\frac{n-k-1}{2}\right)}{\Gamma\left(\frac{n-1}{2}\right)} \pi^{\frac{k}{2}} = \pi^{\frac{k(k+1)}{4}} \prod_{i=1}^{k+1} \frac{\Gamma\left(\frac{n-i}{2}\right)}{\Gamma\left(\frac{n-1}{2}\right)}.$$

Thus the relation holds for $k+1$, and the proof is completed.

In the general case when $\boldsymbol{A}$ is any definite positive matrix, we consider the transformation

$$C'AC = B, \qquad C'XC = Y, \tag{29.5.4}$$

where $\boldsymbol{C}$ is an orthogonal matrix such that $\boldsymbol{B}$ is a diagonal matrix (cf 11.9). The set S in the x-space is transformed into the analogous set S_1 in the y-space. From the proof given above, it then follows that the function

$$g_n(y_{11}, \ldots, y_{kk}) = \begin{cases} C_{kn}\, B^{\frac{n-1}{2}}\, Y^{\frac{n-k-2}{2}}\, e^{-\sum_{i,j} b_{ij} y_{ij}} & \text{in } S_1, \\ 0 & \text{in } S_1^*, \end{cases} \tag{29.5.5}$$

is a fr. f. in the y-space. (Note that we have $b_{ij} = 0$ for $i \neq j$.) Now, since the determinant of $\boldsymbol{C}$ is equal to ± 1, we have $A = B$ and $X = Y$, and it is further verified by direct substitution that we have $\sum_{i,j} a_{ij} x_{ij} = \sum_{i,j} b_{ij} y_{ij}$. Thus if, in the distribution (29.5.5), we introduce the transformation of random variables defined by (29.5.4), we obtain according to 22.2 a transformed distribution with the fr. f. $f_n(x_{11}, \ldots, x_{kk})$. Thus f_n is a fr. f., and our assertion is proved.

In the particular case $k = 2$, there are three variables x_{11}, x_{22} and $x_{12} = x_{21}$. The set S is the domain defined by the inequalities $x_{11} > 0$, $x_{22} > 0$, $x_{12}^2 < x_{11} x_{22}$. In S we have

$$(29.5.6) \quad f_n(x_{11}, x_{12}, x_{22}) = C_{2n} (a_{11} a_{22} - a_{12}^2)^{\frac{n-1}{2}} (x_{11} x_{22} - x_{12}^2)^{\frac{n-4}{2}} e^{-a_{11} x_{11} - a_{22} x_{22} - 2 a_{12} x_{12}},$$

where (cf 12.4.4)

$$C_{2n} = \frac{1}{\sqrt{\pi}\, \Gamma\left(\frac{n-1}{2}\right) \Gamma\left(\frac{n-2}{2}\right)} = \frac{2^{n-3}}{\pi\, \Gamma(n-2)}.$$

Outside S the fr. f. is zero.

We shall also consider the c. f. $\varphi_n(t_{11}, \ldots, t_{kk})$ corresponding to the fr. f. $f_n(x_{11}, \ldots, x_{kk})$ defined by (29.5.1). Let $\boldsymbol{T} = \{t_{ij}\}$ denote the symmetric matrix of the variables t_{ij}, and put

$$\varepsilon_{ij} = \begin{cases} 1 & \text{for } i = j, \\ \frac{1}{2} & \text{for } i \neq j. \end{cases}$$

Since $f_n = 0$ in S^*, the c. f. corresponding to the fr. f. f_n is

$$\varphi_n(t_{11}, \ldots, t_{kk}) = \int_S e^{\boldsymbol{i} \sum_{i,j} \varepsilon_{ij} t_{ij} x_{ij}} f_n(x_{11}, \ldots, x_{kk})\, d x_{11}\, d x_{12} \ldots d x_{kk}.$$

(In order to avoid confusion, we use here a heavy-faced $\boldsymbol{i}$ to denote the imaginary unit, as already mentioned in 27.1.) For $t_{ij} = 0$, the integral is equal to 1, so that we have

$$\int_S X^{\frac{n-k-2}{2}} e^{-\sum_{i,j} a_{ij} x_{ij}}\, d x_{11}\, d x_{12} \ldots d x_{kk} = \frac{1}{C_{kn} A^{\frac{n-1}{2}}}.$$

Replacing here a_{ij} by $a_{ij} - \boldsymbol{i} \varepsilon_{ij} t_{ij}$, and denoting by A^* the determinant $A^* = |a_{ij} - \boldsymbol{i} \varepsilon_{ij} t_{ij}|$, we obtain finally the expression

$$(29.5.7) \qquad \varphi_n(t_{11}, \ldots, t_{kk}) = \left(\frac{A}{A^*}\right)^{\frac{n-1}{2}}$$

for the c. f. corresponding to the distribution (29.5.1).[1])

29.6. Sampling from a two-dimensional normal distribution. — In a basic paper of 1915, R. A. Fisher (Ref. 88) gave exact expressions

[1]) Ingham (Ref. 130) has shown directly that the c. f. (29.5.7) gives, according to the inversion formula (10.6.3), the fr. f. (29.5.1).

for certain sampling distributions connected with a two-dimensional normal parent distribution. We shall now prove some of Fisher's results, using the method of characteristic functions first applied to these problems by Romanovsky (Ref. 208, 209). It will be found that the distributions obtained are particular cases of the distributions considered in the preceding paragraph.

Consider a non-singular normal distribution in two variables (cf 21.12). Without loss of generality, we may assume the first order moments equal to zero, so that the fr. f. is in the usual notation

$$\frac{1}{2\pi\sigma_1\sigma_2\sqrt{1-\varrho^2}} e^{-\frac{1}{2(1-\varrho^2)}\left(\frac{x^2}{\sigma_1^2}-\frac{2\varrho x y}{\sigma_1\sigma_2}+\frac{y^2}{\sigma_2^2}\right)} = \frac{1}{2\pi\sqrt{M}} e^{-\frac{1}{2M}(\mu_{02}x^2-2\mu_{11}xy+\mu_{20}y^2)},$$

where $M = \mu_{20}\mu_{02} - \mu_{11}^2 = \sigma_1^2\sigma_2^2(1-\varrho^2)$ is the determinant of the moment matrix $\boldsymbol{M} = \begin{Bmatrix} \mu_{20} & \mu_{11} \\ \mu_{11} & \mu_{02} \end{Bmatrix}$. From a sample of n observed pairs of values $(x_1, y_1), \ldots, (x_n, y_n)$, we calculate the moment characteristics of the first and second orders (cf 27.1.6)

$$\bar{x} = \frac{1}{n}\sum_i x_i, \qquad \bar{y} = \frac{1}{n}\sum_i y_i,$$

$$(29.6.1) \qquad \begin{aligned} m_{20} &= s_1^2 = \frac{1}{n}\sum_i (x_i-\bar{x})^2 = \frac{1}{n}\sum_i x_i^2 - \bar{x}^2, \\ m_{11} &= r s_1 s_2 = \frac{1}{n}\sum_i (x_i-\bar{x})(y_i-\bar{y}) = \frac{1}{n}\sum_i x_i y_i - \bar{x}\bar{y}, \\ m_{02} &= s_2^2 = \frac{1}{n}\sum_i (y_i-\bar{y})^2 = \frac{1}{n}\sum_i y_i^2 - \bar{y}^2. \end{aligned}$$

We now propose to find the joint distribution of the five random variables $\bar{x}$, $\bar{y}$, m_{20}, m_{11} and m_{02}. The c. f. of this distribution is a function of five variables t_1, t_2, t_{20}, t_{11} and t_{02}, viz.

$$(29.6.2) \qquad \begin{aligned} &\boldsymbol{E}\left(e^{\boldsymbol{i}(t_1\bar{x}+t_2\bar{y}+t_{20}m_{20}+t_{11}m_{11}+t_{02}m_{02})}\right) = \\ &\qquad = \frac{1}{(2\pi)^n M^{\frac{n}{2}}}\int e^{\Omega}\,dx_1\ldots dx_n\,dy_1\ldots dy_n, \end{aligned}$$

where

$$\Omega = \boldsymbol{i}(t_1\bar{x}+\cdots+t_{02}m_{02}) - \frac{1}{2M}\sum_1^n(\mu_{02}x_i^2 - 2\mu_{11}x_i y_i + \mu_{20}y_i^2).$$

and the integral is extended over the $2n$-dimensional space of the variables $x_1, \ldots, x_n, y_1, \ldots, y_n$.

We now replace $x_1, \ldots, x_n$ by new variables $\xi_1, \ldots, \xi_n$ by means of an orthogonal transformation such that $\xi_1 = \sqrt{n}\,\bar{x}$, and apply a transformation with the same matrix to $y_1, \ldots, y_n$, which are thus replaced by new variables $\eta_1, \ldots, \eta_n$ such that $\eta_1 = \sqrt{n}\,\bar{y}$. We then have

$$\sum_1^n x_i^2 = \sum_1^n \xi_i^2, \qquad \sum_1^n x_i y_i = \sum_1^n \xi_i \eta_i, \qquad \sum_1^n y_i^2 = \sum_1^n \eta_i^2,$$

$$n\, m_{20} = \sum_2^n \xi_i^2, \qquad n\, m_{11} = \sum_2^n \xi_i \eta_i, \qquad n\, m_{02} = \sum_2^n \eta_i^2,$$

and hence

$$\Omega = i\,\frac{t_1 \xi_1 + t_2 \eta_1}{\sqrt{n}} - \frac{1}{2M}(\mu_{02}\, \xi_1^2 - 2\,\mu_{11}\, \xi_1 \eta_1 + \mu_{20}\, \eta_1^2) -$$

$$- \frac{1}{n} \sum_2^n \left[\left(\frac{n\,\mu_{02}}{2M} - i\,t_{20} \right) \xi_i^2 + 2 \left(-\frac{n\,\mu_{11}}{2M} - \tfrac{1}{2}\, i\, t_{11} \right) \xi_i \eta_i + \right.$$

$$\left. + \left(\frac{n\,\mu_{20}}{2M} - i\, t_{02} \right) \eta_i^2 \right].$$

Introducing this expression of Ω in (29.6.2), the transformed $2n$-fold integral reduces to a product of n double integrals, which may be directly evaluated by means of (11.12.1) and (11.12.2). The joint c. f. (29.6.2) then takes the form

$$e^{-\frac{1}{2n}(\mu_{20} t_1^2 + 2\,\mu_{11} t_1 t_2 + \mu_{02} t_2^2)} \cdot \left(\frac{A}{A^*} \right)^{\frac{n-1}{2}}, \tag{29.6.3}$$

where

$$A = \begin{vmatrix} \dfrac{n\,\mu_{02}}{2M} & -\dfrac{n\,\mu_{11}}{2M} \\[2ex] -\dfrac{n\,\mu_{11}}{2M} & \dfrac{n\,\mu_{20}}{2M} \end{vmatrix} = \frac{n^2}{4M},$$

$$A^* = \begin{vmatrix} \dfrac{n\,\mu_{02}}{2M} - i\,t_{20} & -\dfrac{n\,\mu_{11}}{2M} - \tfrac{1}{2}\, i\, t_{11} \\[2ex] -\dfrac{n\,\mu_{11}}{2M} - \tfrac{1}{2}\, i\, t_{11} & \dfrac{n\,\mu_{20}}{2M} - i\, t_{02} \end{vmatrix}.$$

The joint c. f. (29.6.3) is a product of two factors, the first of which contains only the variables t_1 and t_2, while the second factor contains only t_{20}, t_{11} and t_{02}. The first factor is, by (21.12.2), the c. f. of a normal distribution with zero mean values[1]) and the moment matrix $n^{-1}\boldsymbol{M}$. The second factor, on the other hand, is a particular case of the c. f. (29.5.7). In fact, if we take in the preceding paragraph $k=2$ and

$$\boldsymbol{A}=\begin{Bmatrix} \frac{n\,\mu_{02}}{2\,M} & -\frac{n\,\mu_{11}}{2\,M} \\ -\frac{n\,\mu_{11}}{2\,M} & \frac{n\,\mu_{20}}{2\,M} \end{Bmatrix}=\frac{n}{2}\boldsymbol{M}^{-1},$$

$$\boldsymbol{T}=\begin{Bmatrix} t_{20} & t_{11} \\ t_{11} & t_{02} \end{Bmatrix},$$

the c. f. (29.5.7) reduces to the second factor of (29.6.3). The corresponding distribution is then the particular case $k=2$ of (29.5.1), (which has already been given in 29.5.6), with the variables x_{11}, x_{12} and x_{22} replaced by m_{20}, m_{11} and m_{02} respectively. Thus by 22.4 we have the following theorem:

The combined random variables $(\bar{x}, \bar{y})$ *and* (m_{20}, m_{11}, m_{02}) *are independent. The joint distribution of* $\bar{x}$ *and* $\bar{y}$ *is normal, with the same first order moments as the parent distribution, and the moment matrix* $n^{-1}\boldsymbol{M}$. *The joint distribution of* m_{20}, m_{11} *and* m_{02} *has the fr. f.* f_n *given by*

$$(29.6.4)\qquad f_n(m_{20}, m_{11}, m_{02}) = \\ = \frac{n^{n-1}}{4\,\pi\,\Gamma(n-2)}\cdot\frac{(m_{20}\,m_{02}-m_{11}^2)^{\frac{n-4}{2}}}{M^{\frac{n-1}{2}}}\,e^{-\frac{n}{2\,M}(\mu_{02}\,m_{20}-2\,\mu_{11}\,m_{11}+\mu_{20}\,m_{02})}$$

in the domain $m_{20}>0$, $m_{02}>0$, $m_{11}^2<m_{20}\,m_{02}$, *while* $f_n=0$ *outside this domain.*

The mean values and the moment matrix of the five sample moments may be calculated from the c. f. (29.6.3). We find, e. g., $\boldsymbol{E}(m_{20})=\frac{n-1}{n}\mu_{20}$, $\boldsymbol{E}(m_{11})=\frac{n-1}{n}\mu_{11}$, $\boldsymbol{E}(m_{02})=\frac{n-1}{n}\mu_{02}$, in accordance with 27.4 and 27.8.

29.7. The correlation coefficient. — In the joint distribution (29.6.4) of the variables m_{20}, m_{11} and m_{02}, we now introduce the new variable

[1]) If, more generally, we consider a parent distribution with arbitrary mean values, we obviously obtain here the same means as for the parent distribution.

r by the substitution $m_{11} = r\sqrt{m_{20}\, m_{02}}$, so that r is the correlation coefficient of the sample. By (22.2.3), we then obtain the following expression for the joint fr. f. of m_{20}, m_{02} and r:

$$\sqrt{m_{20}\, m_{02}}\; f_n\left(m_{20},\; r\sqrt{m_{20}\, m_{02}},\; m_{02}\right) =$$

$$= \frac{n^{n-1}}{4\pi\, \Gamma(n-2)\, M^{\frac{n-1}{2}}}\, m_{20}^{\frac{n-3}{2}}\, m_{02}^{\frac{n-3}{2}}\, (1-r^2)^{\frac{n-4}{2}}\, e^{-\frac{n}{2M}\left(\mu_{02} m_{20} - 2\mu_{11} r\sqrt{m_{20} m_{02}} + \mu_{20} m_{02}\right)},$$

where $m_{20} > 0$, $m_{02} > 0$, $r^2 < 1$. The marginal fr. f. of r is now obtained by integrating the joint fr. f. with respect to m_{20} and m_{02} from 0 to $+\infty$. If the factor $e^{\frac{n}{M}\mu_{11} r\sqrt{m_{20} m_{02}}}$ is developed in power series, the integration can be explicitly performed, and we thus obtain the *fr. f. of the sample correlation coefficient* r:

$$\text{(29.7.1)} \qquad f_n(r) = \frac{2^{n-3}}{\pi\,(n-3)!}(1-\varrho^2)^{\frac{n-1}{2}}\,(1-r^2)^{\frac{n-4}{2}} \sum_{\nu=0}^{\infty} \Gamma^2\left(\frac{n+\nu-1}{2}\right)\frac{(2\varrho r)^\nu}{\nu!}$$

for $-1 < r < 1$. The power series appearing in this expression may be transformed in various ways. We find, e. g., by simple calculations the expansion

$$\int_0^1 \frac{x^{n-2}}{(1-\varrho r x)^{n-1}} \cdot \frac{dx}{\sqrt{1-x^2}} = \frac{2^{n-3}}{(n-2)!} \sum_{\nu=0}^{\infty} \Gamma^2\left(\frac{n+\nu-1}{2}\right)\frac{(2\varrho r)^\nu}{\nu!},$$

and hence obtain the following expression for the fr. f. of r:

$$\text{(29.7.2)} \qquad f_n(r) = \frac{n-2}{\pi}(1-\varrho^2)^{\frac{n-1}{2}}\,(1-r^2)^{\frac{n-4}{2}} \int_0^1 \frac{x^{n-2}}{(1-\varrho r x)^{n-1}} \cdot \frac{dx}{\sqrt{1-x^2}}.$$

The distribution of r was discovered by R. A. Fisher (Ref. 88). We observe the remarkable property that the distribution of r only depends on the size n of the sample and on the correlation coefficient ϱ of the population.

For $n = 2$, the fr. f. $f_n(r)$ reduces to zero, in accordance with the fact that a correlation coefficient calculated from a sample of only two observations is necessarily equal to ± 1, so that in this case the distribution belongs to the discrete type. For $n = 3$ the frequency

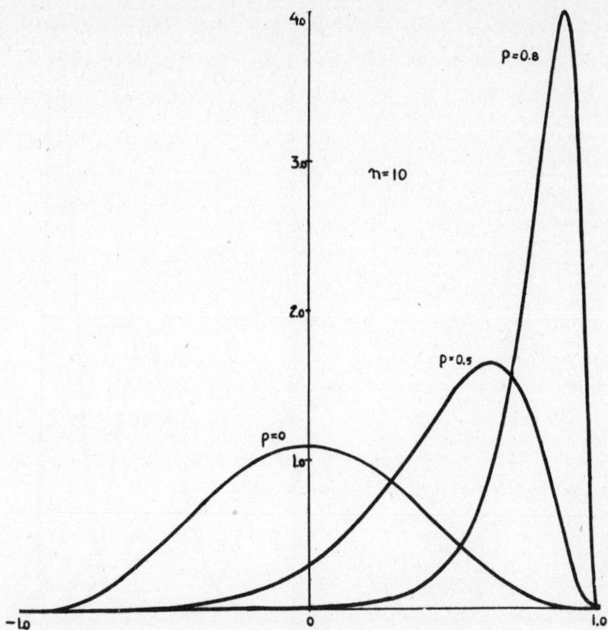

Fig. 29 a. Frequency curves for the correlation coefficient r in samples from a normal population. $n = 10$.

curve is U-shaped, with infinite ordinates in the points $r = \pm 1$. For $n = 4$ we have a rectangular distribution if $\varrho = 0$, and otherwise a J-shaped distribution. For $n > 4$, the distribution is unimodal, with the mode situated in the point $r = 0$ if $\varrho = 0$, and otherwise near the point $r = \varrho$. Some examples are shown in Figs 29 a—b.

The distribution of r has been studied in detail by several authors (cf e. g. Soper and others, Ref. 216, and Romanovsky, Ref. 208), and extensive tables have been published by David (Ref. 261). Various exact and approximate formulae for the characteristics of the distribution are known. Any moment of r can, of course, be directly calculated from (29.7.1), but we shall here content ourselves with the asymptotic formulae for $\boldsymbol{E}(r)$ and $\boldsymbol{D}^2(r)$ for large n that have already been given in (27.8.1) and (27.8.2).

For practical purposes, it is often preferable to use the transformation

$$z = \tfrac{1}{2} \log \frac{1 + r}{1 - r}, \quad \zeta = \tfrac{1}{2} \log \frac{1 + \varrho}{1 - \varrho}, \tag{29.7.3}$$

introduced by R. A. Fisher (Ref. 13, 90). Fisher has shown that the variable z is, already for moderate values of n, approximately nor-

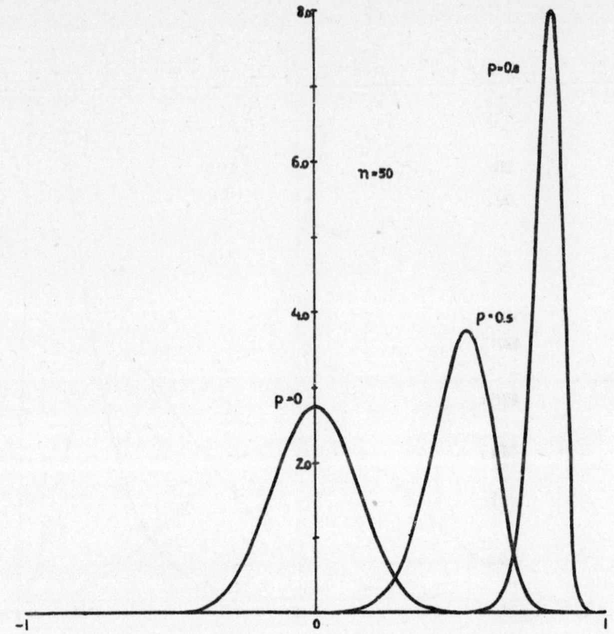

Fig. 29 b. Frequency curves for the correlation coefficient r in samples from a normal population. $n = 50$.

mally distributed with mean and variance given by the approximate expressions

$$(29.7.4) \qquad \boldsymbol{E}(z) = \zeta + \frac{\varrho}{2(n-1)}, \quad \boldsymbol{D}^2(z) = \frac{1}{n-3}.$$

Thus the form of the z-distribution is, in the first approximation, independent of the parameter ϱ, while the distribution of r changes its form considerably when ϱ varies. It is instructive to compare in this respect the illustrations of the r- and z-distributions given in Figs 29 and 30. Cf further 31.3, Ex. 6.

In the particular case $\varrho = 0$, the fr. f. (29.7.1) reduces by (12.4.4) to

$$(29.7.5) \qquad f_n(r) = \frac{1}{\sqrt{\pi}} \frac{\Gamma\left(\frac{n-1}{2}\right)}{\Gamma\left(\frac{n-2}{2}\right)} (1-r^2)^{\frac{n-4}{2}},$$

a form conjectured by Student (Ref. 222) in 1908. We have already encountered this fr. f. in other connections in (18.2.7) and (29.4.4). By 18.2, the transformed variable $t = \sqrt{n-2}\,\frac{r}{\sqrt{1-r^2}}$ is in this case

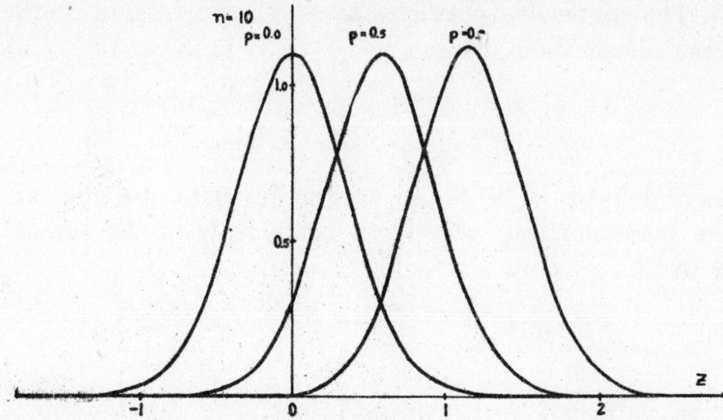

Fig. 30 a. **Frequency curves for** $z = \frac{1}{2}\log\frac{1+r}{1-r}$ **in samples from a normal population.** $n = 10$.

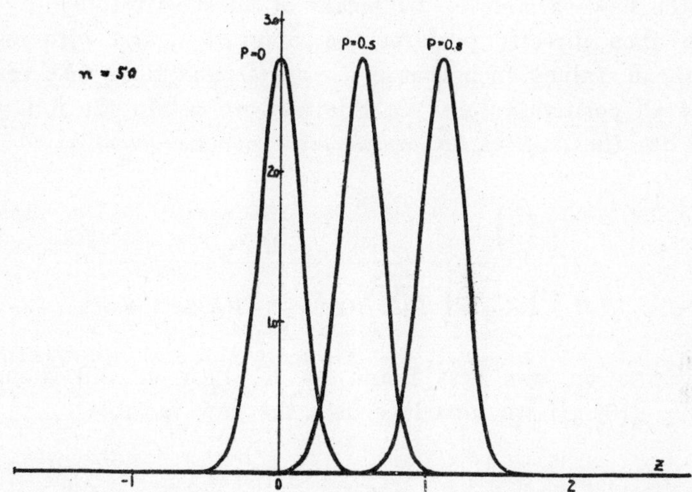

Fig. 30 b. Frequency curves for $z = \frac{1}{2}\log\frac{1+r}{1-r}$ in samples from a normal population. $n = 50$.

distributed in Student's distribution with $n - 2$ d. of fr. If t_p denotes the $p\,\%$ value of t for $n - 2$ d. of fr. (cf 18.2), we have the probability $p\,\%$ of obtaining a value of t such that $|t| > t_p$, and this inequality is equivalent with (cf 31.3, Ex. 7)

(29.7.6) $$|r| > \frac{t_p}{\sqrt{t_p^2 + n - 2}}.$$

29.8. The regression coefficients. — The regression coefficients of the parent distribution

$$\beta_{21} = \frac{\mu_{11}}{\mu_{20}} = \frac{\varrho\,\sigma_2}{\sigma_1}, \quad \beta_{12} = \frac{\mu_{11}}{\mu_{02}} = \frac{\varrho\,\sigma_1}{\sigma_2},$$

have been defined in 21.6. In accordance with the general rules of 27.1, the corresponding regression coefficients of the sample will be denoted by

$$b_{21} = \frac{m_{11}}{m_{20}} = \frac{r s_2}{s_1}, \quad b_{12} = \frac{m_{11}}{m_{02}} = \frac{r s_1}{s_2}. \tag{29.8.1}$$

It will be sufficient to consider the sampling distribution of one of these, say b_{21}. The distribution of b_{12} can then be obtained by permutation of indices.

In the joint distribution (29.6.4) of m_{20}, m_{11} and m_{02}, we replace m_{11} by the new variable b_{21} by means of the substitution $m_{11} = m_{20}\,b_{21}$. We can then directly perform the integration, first with respect to m_{02} over all values such that $m_{02} > m_{20}\,b_{21}^2$, and then with respect to m_{20} over all positive values. In this way we obtain the following expression for the *fr.f. of the sample regression coefficient* b_{21}:

$$\frac{\Gamma\left(\frac{n}{2}\right)}{\sqrt{\pi}\,\Gamma\left(\frac{n-1}{2}\right)} \cdot \frac{M^{\frac{n-1}{2}}}{\mu_{20}^{\frac{n-2}{2}}\left(\mu_{20}\,b_{21}^2 - 2\,\mu_{11}\,b_{21} + \mu_{02}\right)^{\frac{n}{2}}}. \tag{29.8.2}$$

This distribution was first found by K. Pearson and Romanovsky (Ref. 185, 210). If we introduce here the new variable

$$t = \frac{\mu_{20}\sqrt{n-1}}{\sqrt{M}}(b_{21} - \beta_{21}) = \frac{\sigma_1\sqrt{n-1}}{\sigma_2\sqrt{1-\varrho^2}}(b_{21} - \beta_{21}), \tag{29.8.3}$$

where $M = \mu_{20}\,\mu_{02} - \mu_{11}^2$, it is found that t *is distributed in Student's distribution with* $n-1$ *d. of fr.*

If we compare the distribution of b_{21} with the distribution of r, it is evident that the former has not the attractive property belonging to the latter, of containing only the population parameter directly corresponding to the variable. The fr. f. (29.8.2) contains, in fact, all three moments μ_{20}, μ_{11} and μ_{02}, and if we want to calculate the quantity t from (29.8.3) in order to test some hypothetical value of

β_{21}, we shall have to introduce hypothetical values of all these three moments. In order to remove this inconvenience, we consider the variable

$$t' = \frac{s_1 \sqrt{n-2}}{s_2 \sqrt{1-r^2}} (b_{21} - \beta_{21}), \tag{29.8.4}$$

where the population characteristics σ_1, σ_2 and ϱ occurring in (29.8.3) have been replaced by the corresponding sample characteristics s_1, s_2 and r, while the factor $\sqrt{n-1}$ has been replaced by $\sqrt{n-2}$. If this variable t' is introduced instead of m_{02} in the joint distribution (29.6.4), the integration with respect to m_{11} and m_{20} can be directly performed, and we obtain the interesting result that *t' is distributed in Student's distribution with $n-2$ d. of fr.* (Bartlett, Ref. 54.) The replacing of the population characteristics by sample characteristics has thus resulted in a loss of one d. of fr. — When it is required to test a hypothetical value of β_{21}, we can now calculate t' directly from an actual sample, and thus obtain a test of significance for the deviation of the observed value of b_{21} from the hypothetical β_{21}. (Cf 31.3, Ex. 6.)

29.9. Sampling from a k-dimensional normal distribution. — The results of 29.6 may be generalized to the case of a k-dimensional normal parent distribution. Consider a non-singular normal distribution in k dimensions (cf 24.2). Without loss of generality, we may assume the first order moments equal to zero, so that the fr. f. is (cf 24.2.1)

$$\frac{1}{(2\pi)^{k/2}\sqrt{\Lambda}} e^{-\frac{1}{2\Lambda}\sum_{i,j} \Lambda_{ij} x_i x_j} = \frac{1}{(2\pi)^{k/2}\sigma_1 \ldots \sigma_k \sqrt{P}} e^{-\frac{1}{2P}\sum_{i,j} P_{ij} \frac{x_i}{\sigma_i} \frac{x_j}{\sigma_j}}, \tag{29.9.1}$$

where $\Lambda = \{\lambda_{ij}\}$ is the moment matrix, and $\boldsymbol{P} = \{\varrho_{ij}\}$ the correlation matrix of the distribution (cf 22.3). Λ and P are the corresponding determinants. Throughout this paragraph, the subscripts i and j will always have to run from 1 to k.

Suppose now that we dispose of a sample of n observed points from this distribution. Let the ν:th point of the sample be denoted by $(x_{1\nu}, x_{2\nu}, \ldots, x_{k\nu})$, where $\nu = 1, 2, \ldots, n$, and suppose $n > k$. We then calculate the moment characteristics of the first and second order for the sample. According to the general rules of 27.1, and the notations for the corresponding population moments introduced in 22.3, these will be denoted by

$$\bar{x}_i = \frac{1}{n} \sum_{\nu=1}^{n} x_{i\nu},$$

$$(29.9.2) \qquad l_{ii} = s_i^2 = \frac{1}{n} \sum_{\nu=1}^{n} (x_{i\nu} - \bar{x}_i)^2,$$

$$l_{ij} = r_{ij} s_i s_j = \frac{1}{n} \sum_{\nu=1}^{n} (x_{i\nu} - \bar{x}_i)(x_{j\nu} - \bar{x}_j).$$

There are k sample means $\bar{x}_i$, and k variances $l_{ii} = s_i^2$. Further, since $l_{ji} = l_{ij}$, there are $\frac{1}{2} k(k-1)$ distinct covariances l_{ij} with $i \neq j$. The total number of distinct variables l_{ij} is thus $\frac{1}{2} k(k+1)$.

The matrices $\boldsymbol{L} = \{l_{ij}\}$ and $\boldsymbol{R} = \{r_{ij}\}$ are the moment matrix and the correlation matrix of the sample, while the corresponding determinants are $L = |l_{ij}|$ and $R = |r_{ij}|$.

The joint distribution of all the variables $\bar{x}_i$ and l_{ij} can now be found in the same way as the corresponding distribution in 29.6. In direct generalization of (29.6.2), we obtain for the joint c. f. of all these variables the expression

$$(29.9.3) \qquad \begin{gathered} \frac{1}{(2\pi)^{\frac{kn}{2}} \Lambda^{\frac{n}{2}}} \int e^{\Omega} \, dx_{11} \ldots dx_{kn}, \\ \Omega = \boldsymbol{i} \sum_i t_i \bar{x}_i + \boldsymbol{i} \sum_{i,j} \varepsilon_{ij} t_{ij} l_{ij} - \frac{1}{2\Lambda} \sum_{\nu=1}^{n} \sum_{i,j} \Lambda_{ij} x_{i\nu} x_{j\nu}, \end{gathered}$$

where the integral is extended over the kn-dimensional space of the variables $x_{i\nu}$ $(i = 1, \ldots, k,\ \nu = 1, \ldots, n)$, while as in 29.5 we write $\varepsilon_{ij} = 1$ for $i = j$, and $\varepsilon_{ij} = \frac{1}{2}$ for $i \neq j$.

For every i, we now replace the set of n variables $x_{i1}, \ldots, x_{in}$ by n new variables $\xi_{i1}, \ldots, \xi_{in}$, by means of an orthogonal transformation such that $\xi_{i1} = \sqrt{n}\, \bar{x}_i$, using the same transformation matrix for all values of i. We then have for all i and j

$$\sum_{\nu=1}^{n} x_{i\nu} x_{j\nu} = \sum_{\nu=1}^{n} \xi_{i\nu} \xi_{j\nu},$$

$$n\, l_{ij} = \sum_{\nu=1}^{n} x_{i\nu} x_{j\nu} - n \bar{x}_i \bar{x}_j = \sum_{\nu=2}^{n} \xi_{i\nu} \xi_{j\nu},$$

and hence

$$\Omega = \frac{i}{\sqrt{n}} \sum_i t_i \xi_{i1} - \frac{1}{2\Lambda} \sum_{i,j} \Lambda_{ij} \xi_{i1} \xi_{j1} -$$

(29.9.4)

$$- \frac{1}{n} \sum_{\nu=2}^{n} \sum_{i,j} \left(\frac{n \Lambda_{ij}}{2\Lambda} - i \varepsilon_{ij} t_{ij} \right) \xi_{i\nu} \xi_{j\nu}.$$

Introducing this expression of Ω in (29.9.3), the integral may be evaluated in the same way as the corresponding integral in (29.6.2), and the joint c. f. (29.9.3) assumes the form

$$e^{-\frac{1}{2n} \sum_{i,j} \lambda_{ij} t_i t_j} \cdot \left(\frac{A}{A^*} \right)^{\frac{n-1}{2}}, \tag{29.9.5}$$

where A and A^* denote the determinants of the matrices

$$\boldsymbol{A} = \left\{ \frac{n \Lambda_{ij}}{2\Lambda} \right\} = \frac{n}{2} \boldsymbol{\Lambda}^{-1},$$

and

$$\boldsymbol{A}^* = \left\{ \frac{n \Lambda_{ij}}{2\Lambda} - i \varepsilon_{ij} t_{ij} \right\}.$$

Thus in particular $A = (\frac{1}{2} n)^k \Lambda^{-1}$. In the same way as in 29.6, the joint c. f. is a product of two factors, the first of which is the c. f. of a normal distribution, while the second is of the form (29.5.7), and thus corresponds to a distribution of the form (29.5.1), with $\boldsymbol{A} = \frac{1}{2} n \boldsymbol{\Lambda}^{-1}$, and the matrix of variables $\mathbf{X} = \boldsymbol{L} = \{l_{ij}\}$. Denoting by S the set of all points in the $\frac{1}{2} k (k+1)$-dimensional space of the variables l_{ij} such that the symmetric matrix $\boldsymbol{L}$ is definite positive, we thus obtain the following generalization of the theorem of 29.6:

The combined random variables $(\bar{x}_1, \ldots, \bar{x}_k)$ *and* $(l_{11}, l_{12}, \ldots, l_{kk})$ *are independent. The joint distribution of* $\bar{x}_1, \ldots, \bar{x}_k$ *is normal, with the same first order moments as the parent distribution, and the moment matrix* $n^{-1} \boldsymbol{\Lambda}$. *The joint distribution of the* $\frac{1}{2} k (k+1)$ *distinct variables* l_{ij} *has the fr. f.* f_n *given by*

$$f_n(l_{11}, l_{12}, \ldots, l_{kk}) = C_{kn} \left(\frac{n^k}{2^k \Lambda} \right)^{\frac{n-1}{2}} L^{\frac{n-k-2}{2}} e^{-\frac{n}{2\Lambda} \sum_{i,j} \Lambda_{ij} l_{ij}} \tag{29.9.6}$$

for every point in the set S, *while* $f_n = 0$ *in the complementary set* S^*. *The constant* C_{kn} *is given by* (29.5.2).

This theorem was first proved by Wishart (Ref. 240) by an extension of the geometrical methods due to R. A. Fisher, and then by Wishart and Bartlett (Ref. 241) by the method of characteristic functions. We also refer to a paper by Simonsen (Ref. 213 a).

29.10. The generalized variance. — The determinant $L = |l_{ij}|$ represents the *generalized variance* of the sample (cf 22.7). Following Wilks (Ref. 232), we shall now indicate how the moments of L may be determined. For the explicit distribution of L, we refer to Kullback (Ref. 143).

The integral of the fr. f. f_n in (29.9.6) over the set S is obviously equal to 1. Now the set S is invariant under any transformation of the form $w_{ij} = a\, l_{ij}$, where $a > 0$. Taking $a = n$, and writing $W = |w_{ij}|$, we thus obtain

$$\int\limits_S W^{\frac{n-k-2}{2}} e^{-\frac{1}{2\Lambda}\sum\limits_{i,j} \Lambda_{ij} w_{ij}}\, dw_{11}\, dw_{12} \ldots dw_{kk} = \frac{(2^k \Lambda)^{\frac{n-1}{2}}}{C_{kn}}.$$

Since this relation holds for all values of $n > k$, we may replace n by $n + 2\nu$ and then obtain, after reintroducing the variables l_{ij},

$$\int\limits_S L^{\frac{n-k-2}{2}+\nu} e^{-\frac{n}{2\Lambda}\sum\limits_{i,j} \Lambda_{ij} l_{ij}}\, dl_{11}\, dl_{12} \ldots dl_{kk} = \left(\frac{2^k \Lambda}{n^k}\right)^{\frac{n-1}{2}+\nu} \frac{1}{C_{k,\,n+2\nu}}.$$

After multiplication with $C_{kn}\left(\frac{n^k}{2^k \Lambda}\right)^{\frac{n-1}{2}}$ this gives, taking account of (29.9.6) and (29.5.2),

$$\mathbf{E}(L^\nu) = \left(\frac{2^k \Lambda}{n^k}\right)^\nu \frac{C_{kn}}{C_{k,\,n+2\nu}} = \left(\frac{2^k \Lambda}{n^k}\right)^\nu \prod_{i=1}^{k} \frac{\Gamma\left(\frac{n-i}{2}+\nu\right)}{\Gamma\left(\frac{n-i}{2}\right)}$$

for $n + 2\nu > k$, i. e. for any $\nu > -\frac{1}{2}(n-k)$. In particular we have

$$\mathbf{E}(L) = \frac{(n-1)(n-2)\ldots(n-k)}{n^k}\Lambda,$$

$$\mathbf{D}^2(L) = \frac{k(2n+1-k)}{(n-k)(n-k+1)} \cdot \frac{(n-1)^2 \ldots (n-k)^2}{n^{2k}} \Lambda^2.$$

For a one-dimensional distribution ($k = 1$) we have $L = l_{11} = m_2$ and

$\Lambda = \sigma^2$, and the above expression for $\boldsymbol{E}(L^\nu)$ then reduces to the formula (29.3.2).

29.11. The generalized Student ratio. — Consider now a sample from a k-dimensional normal distribution with arbitrary mean values $m_1, m_2, \ldots, m_k$, and denote by l'_{ij} the product moments *about the population mean:*

$$(29.11.1) \qquad l'_{ij} = \frac{1}{n} \sum_{\nu=1}^{n} (x_{i\nu} - m_i)(x_{j\nu} - m_j) = l_{ij} + (\bar{x}_i - m_i)(\bar{x}_j - m_j),$$

where the $\bar{x}_i$ and the l_{ij} are given by (29.9.2).

There are $\frac{1}{2} k(k+1)$ distinct variables l'_{ij}. If we write $\xi_{i\nu} = x_{i\nu} - m_i$, the joint c. f. of the l'_{ij} becomes

$$\frac{1}{(2\pi)^{\frac{kn}{2}} \Lambda^{\frac{n}{2}}} \int e^{\Omega'} d\xi_{11} \ldots d\xi_{kn},$$

where

$$\Omega' = i \sum_{i,j} \varepsilon_{ij} t_{ij} l'_{ij} - \frac{1}{2\Lambda} \sum_{\nu=1}^{n} \sum_{i,j} \Lambda_{ij} \xi_{i\nu} \xi_{j\nu}$$

$$= -\frac{1}{n} \sum_{\nu=1}^{n} \sum_{i,j} \left(\frac{n \Lambda_{ij}}{2\Lambda} - i \varepsilon_{ij} t_{ij} \right) \xi_{i\nu} \xi_{j\nu}.$$

Comparing this with (29.9.3) — (29.9.5) we find that the c. f. of the l'_{ij} is $(A/A^*)^{n/2}$, where A and A^* denote the same determinants as in (29.9.5). It follows that the joint fr. f. of the l'_{ij} is obtained if, in (29.9.6), we replace n by $n+1$, except in the two factors $\frac{n^k}{2^k \Lambda}$ and $\frac{n}{2\Lambda}$, which arise from the matrix $\boldsymbol{A}$.

Writing $L' = |l'_{ij}|$, we then obtain by the same transformation as in the preceding paragraph

$$\boldsymbol{E}(L'^{\mu}) = \left(\frac{2^k \Lambda}{n^k} \right)^{\mu} \prod_{i=1}^{k} \frac{\Gamma\left(\frac{n+1-i}{2} + \mu \right)}{\Gamma\left(\frac{n+1-i}{2} \right)}$$

for any $\mu > -\frac{1}{2}(n+1-k)$. — On the other hand, according to (29.11.1) L' is a function of the random variables l_{ij} and $\xi_i = \bar{x}_i - m_i$, and the joint fr. f. of all these variables is by the theorem of 29.9

$$g(\xi, \boldsymbol{l}) = \frac{n^{\frac{k}{2}}}{(2\pi)^{\frac{k}{2}} \sqrt{\Lambda}} e^{-\frac{n}{2\Lambda} \sum_{i,j} \Lambda_{ij} \xi_i \xi_j} f_n(\boldsymbol{l}),$$

where $f_n(\boldsymbol{l}) = f_n(l_{11}, l_{12}, \ldots, l_{kk})$ is given by (29.9.6). Thus we may also write

$$\boldsymbol{E}(L'^{\mu}) = \int L'^{\mu} g(\xi, \boldsymbol{l})\, d\xi\, d\boldsymbol{l},$$

where the integral is extended over the set S (defined in 29.6) with respect to the l_{ij}, and over $(-\infty, \infty)$ with respect to every ξ_i. Here we may now apply once more the transformation of the preceding paragraph, writing $w_{ij} = n\, l_{ij}$ and $\eta_i = \sqrt{n}\, \xi_i$, and then replacing n by $n + 2\nu$. Equating the two expressions of $\boldsymbol{E}(L'^{\mu})$, we then obtain for any $\nu > 0$ and $\mu > -\nu - \frac{1}{2}(n + 1 - k)$

$$\boldsymbol{E}(L^{\nu} L'^{\mu}) = \left(\frac{2^k \Lambda}{n^k}\right)^{\mu+\nu} \prod_{i=1}^{k} \frac{\Gamma\left(\frac{n-i}{2} + \nu\right)}{\Gamma\left(\frac{n-i}{2}\right)} \cdot \frac{\Gamma\left(\frac{n+1-i}{2} + \mu + \nu\right)}{\Gamma\left(\frac{n+1-i}{2} + \nu\right)}.$$

Taking $\mu = -\nu$, this reduces to

$$\boldsymbol{E}\left(\frac{L}{L'}\right)^{\nu} = \frac{\Gamma\left(\frac{n-k}{2} + \nu\right)}{\Gamma\left(\frac{n-k}{2}\right)} \cdot \frac{\Gamma\left(\frac{n}{2}\right)}{\Gamma\left(\frac{n}{2} + \nu\right)}.$$

Thus by (18.4.4) the variable L/L' has the same moments as the Beta-distribution with the fr. f.

$$\text{(29.11.2)} \quad \beta\left(x; \frac{n-k}{2}, \frac{k}{2}\right) = \frac{\Gamma\left(\frac{n}{2}\right)}{\Gamma\left(\frac{n-k}{2}\right)\Gamma\left(\frac{k}{2}\right)} x^{\frac{n-k}{2}-1} (1-x)^{\frac{k}{2}-1},$$

$$(0 < x < 1).$$

Since a distribution with finite range is uniquely determined by its moments (cf 15.4), it follows that L/L' has the fr. f. (29.11.2). On the other hand, we obtain from (29.11.1)

$$L' = L + \sum_{i,j} L_{ij}(\bar{x}_i - m_i)(\bar{x}_j - m_j),$$

$$\frac{L}{L'} = \frac{1}{1 + \sum\limits_{i,j} \frac{L_{ij}}{L}(\bar{x}_i - m_i)(\bar{x}_j - m_j)},$$

where L_{ij} is the cofactor of l_{ij} in L. The quadratic form in the denominator is non-negative, since $\boldsymbol{L}$ is the moment matrix of a distribution, viz. the distribution of the sample. — If we now introduce a new variable T by writing

$$T^2 = (n-1) \sum_{i,j} \frac{L_{ij}}{L}(\bar{x}_i - m_i)(\bar{x}_j - m_j), \tag{29.11.3}$$

where $T \geqq 0$, we have

$$\frac{L}{L'} = \frac{1}{1 + \frac{T^2}{n-1}},$$

and by a simple transformation of (29.11.2) the fr. f. of T is found to be

$$\frac{2\,\Gamma\left(\frac{n}{2}\right)}{(n-1)^{k/2}\,\Gamma\left(\frac{n-k}{2}\right)\Gamma\left(\frac{k}{2}\right)} \cdot \frac{x^{k-1}}{\left(1 + \frac{x^2}{n-1}\right)^{n/2}}, \qquad (x > 0). \tag{29.11.4}$$

For $k = 1$, this reduces to the positive half of the ordinary Student distribution (18.2.4) with $n - 1$ degrees of freedom. The distribution of T has been found by Hotelling (Ref. 126), and the above proof is due to Wilks (Ref. 232).

Just as the ordinary Student ratio t may be used to test the significance of the deviation of an observed mean $\bar{x}$ from some hypothetical value m, the *generalized Student ratio* T provides a test of the joint deviation of the sample means $\bar{x}_1, \ldots, \bar{x}_k$ from some hypothetical system of values $m_1, \ldots, m_k$.

In 29.4, we have shown how the Student ratio may be modified so as to provide a test of the difference between two mean values. An analogous modification may be applied to the generalized ratio T.

Suppose that we are given two samples of n_1 and n_2 individuals respectively, drawn from the same k-dimensional normal population, and let $\bar{x}_{1i}$, l_{1ij} and $\bar{x}_{2i}$, l_{2ij} denote the means, variances and covariances of the two samples. Let further $\boldsymbol{H}$ denote the matrix

$$H = \{n_1 l_{1ij} + n_2 l_{2ij}\} = n_1 L_1 + n_2 L_2,$$

while H and H_{ij} are the corresponding determinant and its cofactors. Writing

$$U^2 = \frac{n_1 n_2 (n_1 + n_2 - 2)}{n_1 + n_2} \sum_{i,j} \frac{H_{ij}}{H} (\bar{x}_{1i} - \bar{x}_{2i})(\bar{x}_{1j} - \bar{x}_{2j}) \tag{29.11.5}$$

where $U \geqq 0$, it can be shown by the same methods as above that U has the fr. f. (29.11.4) with n replaced by $n_1 + n_2 - 1$. The expression (29.11.5) is entirely free from the parameters of the parent distribution, so that U can be directly calculated from a sample and used as a test of the joint divergence between the two systems $\bar{x}_{1i}$ and $\bar{x}_{2i}$ of sample means. For $k = 1$, it will be seen that U^2 is identical with u^2 as defined by (29.4.2).

29.12. Regression coefficients. — For a two-dimensional distribution we have seen that the variable (29.8.4), which is simply connected with a sample regression coefficient, has the t-distribution with $n-2$ d. of fr. This result has been generalized by Bartlett (Ref. 54) to distributions in any number of dimensions.

Replacing in (23.2.3) and (23.4.5) the population characteristics by sample characteristics, we obtain for the regression coefficient $b_{12 \cdot 34 \ldots k}$ the expressions

$$b_{12 \cdot 34 \ldots k} = -\frac{s_1}{s_2} \cdot \frac{R_{12}}{R_{11}} = r_{12 \cdot 34 \ldots k} \frac{s_{1 \cdot 34 \ldots k}}{s_{2 \cdot 34 \ldots k}},$$

where the residual variances s may be calculated from the sample correlation coefficients r as shown by the first relation (23.4.5).

If $\beta_{12 \cdot 34 \ldots k}$ denotes the population value of the regression coefficient, the variable

$$t = \sqrt{n-k} \frac{s_{2 \cdot 34 \ldots k}}{s_{1 \cdot 23 \ldots k}} (b_{12 \cdot 34 \ldots k} - \beta_{12 \cdot 34 \ldots k}) \tag{29.12.1}$$

has Student's distribution with $n - k$ d. of fr. In the same way as in the case of (29.8.4), we can thus obtain a test of significance for the deviation of the observed value b of a regression coefficient from any hypothetical value β. (Cf 31.3, Ex. 7.)

29.13. Partial and multiple correlation coefficients. — We now proceed to some further applications of the distribution (29.9.6), restricting ourselves to the particular case when *the k variables in the normal parent distribution are independent.* In this case λ_{ij}, ϱ_{ij} and Λ_{ij} all reduce to zero for $i \neq j$, so that the moment matrix Λ is a diagonal matrix, while the correlation matrix $\boldsymbol{P}$ is the unit matrix (cf 22.3).

In the joint distribution (29.9.6) of the l_{ij}, we replace the l_{ij} with $i \neq j$ by the sample correlation coefficients r_{ij}, by means of the substitution $l_{ij} = r_{ij} \sqrt{l_{ii} l_{jj}}$. We then have $L = l_{11} l_{22} \ldots l_{kk} R$, where $R = |r_{ij}|$ is the determinant of the correlation matrix $\boldsymbol{R}$ of the sample. The Jacobian of the transformation (cf the analogous transformation 29.5.3) is $(l_{11} \ldots l_{kk})^{(k-1)/2}$, and the joint fr. f. of the variables l_{ii} and r_{ij} becomes by (22.2.3), in the particular case considered here,

$$C_{kn} \left(\frac{n^k}{2^k \lambda_{11} \lambda_{22} \ldots \lambda_{kk}} \right)^{\frac{n-1}{2}} (l_{11} l_{22} \ldots l_{kk})^{\frac{n-3}{2}} R^{\frac{n-k-2}{2}} e^{-\frac{n}{2} \sum_i \frac{l_{ii}}{\lambda_{ii}}},$$

for $l_{ii} > 0$ and all values of the r_{ij} such that the matrix $\boldsymbol{R}$ is definite positive. For all other values of the variables, the fr. f. is zero.

We can now directly integrate over $(0, \infty)$ with respect to every l_{ii}. After introduction of the value (29.5.2) of C_{kn}, we obtain the *joint fr. f. of the sample correlation coefficients* r_{ij}:

$$\text{(29.13.1)} \qquad \frac{\left(\Gamma\left(\frac{n-1}{2}\right) \right)^{k-1}}{\pi^{\frac{k(k-1)}{4}} \Gamma\left(\frac{n-2}{2}\right) \ldots \Gamma\left(\frac{n-k}{2}\right)} R^{\frac{n-k-2}{2}}.$$

According to the terminology of Frisch (Ref. 113), the determinant R is the square of the *scatter coefficient* of the sample (cf. 22.7). The moments of R may be determined by the method of 29.10. Denoting by B_{kn} the factor of $R^{\frac{n-k-2}{2}}$ in (29.13.1), we find, e. g.,

$$\text{(29.13.2)} \qquad \begin{aligned} \boldsymbol{E}(R) &= \frac{B_{kn}}{B_{k,n+2}} = \frac{(n-2)(n-3) \ldots (n-k)}{(n-1)^{k-1}}, \\ \boldsymbol{D}^2(R) &= \frac{k(k-1)}{n^2} + O\left(\frac{1}{n^3}\right). \end{aligned}$$

The *partial correlation coefficient* between the sample values of the variables x_1 and x_2, after elimination of the remaining variables $x_3, x_4, \ldots, x_k$, is by (23.4.2)

$$\text{(29.13.3)} \qquad r_{12 \cdot 34 \ldots k} = -\frac{R_{12}}{\sqrt{R_{11} R_{22}}},$$

where the R_{ij} are the usual cofactors of R. In the particular case of an uncorrelated parent distribution considered here, the corresponding population value $\varrho_{12 \cdot 34 \ldots k}$ is, of course, equal to zero.

In order to find the distribution of $r_{12\cdot34\ldots k}$, we regard (29.13.3) as a substitution replacing r_{12} by a new variable $r_{12\cdot34\ldots k}$, while all the r_{ij} except r_{12} are retained as variables. R_{11} and R_{22} do not involve r_{12}, and thus (29.13.3) can be written, using notations analogous to those of 11.5,

$$r_{12\cdot34\ldots k} = \frac{R_{11\cdot22}}{\sqrt{R_{11}R_{22}}}\, r_{12} + Q,$$

where Q does not involve r_{12}. This shows that there is a one-to-one correspondence between the two sets of variables. The Jacobian of the transformation is

$$\frac{\partial r_{12}}{\partial r_{12\cdot34\ldots k}} = \frac{\sqrt{R_{11}R_{22}}}{R_{11\cdot22}}.$$

From (11.7.3) and (29.13.3) we further obtain

$$R = \frac{R_{11}R_{22}}{R_{11\cdot22}}(1 - r_{12\cdot34\ldots k}^2).$$

Introducing the substitution (29.13.3) in (29.13.1), we thus find that the joint fr. f. of $r_{12\cdot34\ldots k}$ and all r_{ij} other than r_{12} is

$$C\frac{(R_{11}R_{22})^{\frac{n-k-1}{2}}}{R_{11\cdot22}^{\frac{n-k}{2}}}(1 - r_{12\cdot34\ldots k}^2)^{\frac{n-k-2}{2}},$$

where C is a constant. This is the product of two factors, one of which depends only on $r_{12\cdot34\ldots k}$, while the other depends only on the r_{ij}. Since the variable $r_{12\cdot34\ldots k}$ obviously ranges over the whole interval $(-1, 1)$, the multiplicative constant in its fr. f. is easily determined, and we have by (22.1.2) the following theorem:

The partial correlation coefficient $r_{12\cdot34\ldots k}$ *is independent of all the* r_{ij} *other than* r_{12}, *and has the fr. f.*

$$\text{(29.13.4)} \qquad \frac{1}{\sqrt{\pi}}\cdot\frac{\Gamma\left(\frac{n-k+1}{2}\right)}{\Gamma\left(\frac{n-k}{2}\right)}(1 - x^2)^{\frac{n-k-2}{2}}, \quad (-1 < x < 1).$$

We observe that by (29.7.5) the total correlation coefficient r_{12} has in the present case the fr. f.

$$\frac{1}{\sqrt{\pi}} \cdot \frac{\Gamma\left(\frac{n-1}{2}\right)}{\Gamma\left(\frac{n-2}{2}\right)} (1-x^2)^{\frac{n-4}{2}}.$$

In order to pass from the distribution of r_{12} to the distribution of $r_{12 \cdot 34 \ldots k}$, we thus only have to replace n by $n-(k-2)$, i. e. to subtract from n the number of variables eliminated. R. A. Fisher (Ref. 93) has shown that this property subsists even in the general case when the variables in the parent distribution are not independent.

In the case of independence, it follows (cf 29.7) that the variable $t = \sqrt{n-k} \frac{r}{\sqrt{1-r^2}}$, where $r = r_{12 \cdot 34 \ldots k}$, has Student's distribution with $n-k$ d. of fr. Consequently the inequality

$$|r_{12 \cdot 34 \ldots k}| > \frac{t_p}{\sqrt{t_p^2 + n - k}}, \tag{29.13.5}$$

where t_p is the p % value of t for $n-k$ d. of fr., has the probability p %. (Cf 31.3, Ex. 7.)

The *multiple correlation coefficient* $\mathbf{r}_{1(2 \ldots k)}$ between the sample values of x_1 and $(x_2, \ldots, x_k)$ is, by (23.5.2), the non-negative square root

$$\mathbf{r}_{1(2 \ldots k)} = \sqrt{1 - \frac{R}{R_{11}}}. \tag{29.13.6}$$

The corresponding population value $\varrho_{1(2 \ldots k)}$ is, in the present case of an uncorrelated normal parent distribution, equal to zero. We now propose to find the distribution of $\mathbf{r}_{1(2 \ldots k)}$.

In the joint distribution (29.13.1) of the r_{ij}, we replace the $k-1$ variables $r_{12}, r_{13}, \ldots, r_{1k}$ by the k new variables $\mathbf{r} = \mathbf{r}_{1(2 \ldots k)}$ and $z_2, \ldots, z_k$, by means of the relations (29.13.6) and

$$r_{1i} = z_i \mathbf{r}, \qquad (i = 2, 3, \ldots, k).$$

Between the new variables, we then have by (11.5.3) the relation

$$\sum_{i,j=2}^{k} R_{11 \cdot ij} z_i z_j = R_{11},$$

by which one of the z_i, say z_2, may be expressed as a function of the other z_i and the r_{ij} with $i > 1$ and $j > 1$. The Jacobian of this transformation is

$$\begin{vmatrix} \frac{\partial r_{12}}{\partial r} & \frac{\partial r_{12}}{\partial z_3} & \cdots & \frac{\partial r_{12}}{\partial z_k} \\ \cdots & \cdots & \cdots & \cdots \\ \frac{\partial r_{1k}}{\partial r} & \frac{\partial r_{1k}}{\partial z_3} & \cdots & \frac{\partial r_{1k}}{\partial z_k} \end{vmatrix} = \begin{vmatrix} z_2 & r\frac{\partial z_2}{\partial z_3} & r\frac{\partial z_2}{\partial z_4} & \cdots & r\frac{\partial z_2}{\partial z_k} \\ z_3 & r & 0 & \cdots & 0 \\ z_4 & 0 & r & \cdots & 0 \\ \cdots & \cdots & \cdots & \cdots & \cdots \\ z_k & 0 & 0 & \cdots & r \end{vmatrix}$$

$$= r^{k-2} Q',$$

where Q' does not involve r. Further, we obtain from (29.13.6) $R = R_{11}(1 - r^2)$, and thus the introduction of the above substitution in (29.13.1) yields an expression of the form

$$r^{k-2}(1-r^2)^{\frac{n-k-2}{2}} Q'',$$

for the joint fr. f. of the new variables, where Q'' does not involve r.

Thus the multiple correlation coefficient $r_{1(2\ldots k)}$ *is independent of all the* r_{ij} *with* $i > 1$, $j > 1$, *and has the fr. f.*

$$(29.13.7) \qquad \frac{2\,\Gamma\left(\frac{n-1}{2}\right)}{\Gamma\left(\frac{k-1}{2}\right)\Gamma\left(\frac{n-k}{2}\right)} x^{k-2}(1-x^2)^{\frac{n-k-2}{2}}, \qquad (0 < x < 1).$$

The square r^2 has the Beta-distribution with the fr. f.

$$(29.13.8) \quad \beta\left(x; \frac{k-1}{2}, \frac{n-k}{2}\right) = \frac{\Gamma\left(\frac{n-1}{2}\right)}{\Gamma\left(\frac{k-1}{2}\right)\Gamma\left(\frac{n-k}{2}\right)} x^{\frac{k-3}{2}}(1-x)^{\frac{n-k-2}{2}}.$$

The distribution of r was found by R. A. Fisher (Ref. 94), who also (Ref. 98) solved the more general problem of finding this distribution in the case of an arbitrary normal parent distribution. In this general case, the fr. f. of r may be expressed as the product of the function (29.13.7) with a power series containing the population value $\varrho_{1(2\ldots k)}$, in a similar way as in the case of the ordinary correlation coefficient (cf 29.7.1).

Let us finally consider the behaviour of the distribution of r^2 for large values of n. The variable $n r^2$ has the fr. f.

$$\frac{\Gamma\left(\frac{n-1}{2}\right)}{\Gamma\left(\frac{k-1}{2}\right)\Gamma\left(\frac{n-k}{2}\right)}\cdot\frac{1}{n}\left(\frac{x}{n}\right)^{\frac{k-3}{2}}\left(1-\frac{x}{n}\right)^{\frac{n-k-2}{2}}.$$

When $n \to \infty$, this tends to the limit

$$\frac{1}{2^{\frac{k-1}{2}}\Gamma\left(\frac{k-1}{2}\right)}x^{\frac{k-3}{2}}e^{-\frac{x}{2}}, \tag{29.13.9}$$

which is the fr. f. of a χ^2-distribution with $k-1$ d. of fr. (cf 31.3, Ex. 7). Thus the distribution of $\boldsymbol{r}^2$ does not tend to normality as $n \to \infty$. Accordingly, we obtain from (29.13.8)

$$\boldsymbol{E}(\boldsymbol{r}^2) = \frac{k-1}{n-1}, \qquad \boldsymbol{D}^2(\boldsymbol{r}^2) = \frac{2(k-1)(n-k)}{(n-1)^2(n+1)} = O\left(\frac{1}{n^2}\right),$$

so that we have here an instance of the exceptional case mentioned at the end of 28.4, where the variance is of a smaller order than n^{-1}, and the theorem on the convergence to normality breaks down. This takes, however, only place in the case considered here, when the population value ϱ is equal to zero. When $\varrho \neq 0$, the variance of $\boldsymbol{r}^2$ is of order n^{-1}, and the distribution approaches normality as $n \to \infty$.

Chapters 30–31. Tests of Significance, I.

CHAPTER 30.

Tests of Goodness of Fit and Allied Tests.

30.1. The χ^2 test in the case of a completely specified hypothetical distribution. — We now proceed to study the problem of testing the agreement between probability theory and actual observations. In the present paragraph, we shall consider the situation indicated in 26.2, when a sample of n observed values of some variable (in any number of dimensions) is given, and we want to know if this variable can be reasonably regarded as a random variable having a given probability distribution.

Let us denote as *hypothesis* H the hypothesis that our data form a sample of n values of a random variable with the given pr. f. $P(S)$. We assume here that $P(S)$ is *completely specified*, so that no unknown parameter appears in its expression, and the probability $P(S)$ may be numerically calculated for any given set S. It is then required to work out a method for testing whether our data may be regarded as consistent with the hypothesis H.

If the hypothesis H is true, the distribution of the sample (cf 25.3), which is the simple discrete distribution obtained by placing the mass $1/n$ in each of the n observed points, may be regarded as a *statistical image* (cf 25.5) of the parent distribution specified by $P(S)$. Owing to random fluctuations, the two distributions will as a rule not coincide, but for large values of n the distribution of the sample may be expected to form an approximation to the parent distribution. As already indicated in 26.2, it then seems natural to introduce some *measure of the deviation* between the two distributions, and to base our test on the properties of the sampling distribution of this measure.

Such deviation measures may be constructed in various ways, the most generally used being that connected with the important χ^2 *test* introduced by K. Pearson (Ref. 183). Suppose that the space of the variable is divided into a finite number r of parts $S_1, \ldots, S_r$ without common points, and let the corresponding values of the given pr. f.

be $p_1, \ldots, p_r$, so that $p_i = P(S_i)$ and $\sum_1^r p_i = 1$. We assume that all the p_i are > 0. The r parts S_i may, e. g., be the r groups into which our sample values have been arranged for tabulation purposes. Let the corresponding group frequencies in the sample be $\nu_1, \ldots, \nu_r$, so that ν_i sample values belong to the set S_i, and we have $\sum_1^r \nu_i = n$.

Our first object is now to find a convenient measure of the deviation of the distribution of the sample from the hypothetical distribution. Any set S_i carries the mass ν_i/n in the former distribution, and the mass p_i in the latter. It will then be in conformity with the general principle of least squares (cf 15.6) to adopt as measure of deviation an expression of the form $\sum_1^r c_i(\nu_i/n - p_i)^2$ where the coefficients c_i may be chosen more or less arbitrarily. It was shown by K. Pearson that if we take $c_i = n/p_i$, we shall obtain a deviation measure with particularly simple properties. We obtain in this way the expression

$$\chi^2 = \sum_1^r \frac{(\nu_i - n p_i)^2}{n p_i} = \sum_1^r \frac{\nu_i^2}{n p_i} - n.$$

Thus χ^2 is simply expressed in terms of the *observed frequencies* ν_i and the *expected frequencies* $n p_i$ for all r groups.

We shall now investigate the sampling distribution of χ^2, *assuming throughout that the hypothesis H is true.* It will be shown that we have

$$\begin{aligned} &\boldsymbol{E}(\chi^2) = r - 1, \\ &\boldsymbol{D}^2(\chi^2) = 2(r-1) + \frac{1}{n}\left(\sum_1^r \frac{1}{p_i} - r^2 - 2r + 2\right). \end{aligned} \tag{30.1.1}$$

We shall further prove the following theorem due to K. Pearson (Ref. 183) which shows that, as the size of the sample increases, the sampling distribution of χ^2 tends to a limiting distribution completely independent of the hypothetical pr. f. $P(S)$.

As $n \to \infty$, the sampling distribution of χ^2 tends to the distribution defined by the fr. f.

$$k_{r-1}(x) = \frac{1}{2^{\frac{r-1}{2}}\,\Gamma\left(\frac{r-1}{2}\right)}\, x^{\frac{r-3}{2}} e^{-\frac{x}{2}}, \qquad (x > 0) \tag{30.1.2}$$

studied in 18.1. — *Using the terminology introduced in* 18.1 *and* 29.2, *we may thus say that, in the limit,* χ^2 *is distributed in a* χ^2*-distribution with* $r-1$ *degrees of freedom.*

At each of the n observations leading to the n observed points in our sample, we have the probability p_i to obtain a result belonging to the set S_i. For any set of non-negative integers $\nu_1, \ldots, \nu_n$ such that $\sum\limits_1^r \nu_i = n$, the probability that, in the course of n observations, we shall exactly ν_i times obtain a result belonging to S_i, for $i = 1, \ldots, r$, is then (cf Ex. 9, p. 318)

$$\frac{n!}{\nu_1! \ldots \nu_r!} p_1^{\nu_1} \ldots p_r^{\nu_r},$$

which is the general term of the expansion of $(p_1 + \cdots + p_r)^n$. Thus the joint distribution of the r group frequencies $\nu_1, \ldots, \nu_r$ is a simple generalization of the binomial distribution, which is known as the *multinomial distribution.* The joint c. f. of the variables $\nu_1, \ldots, \nu_r$ is

$$(p_1 e^{i t_1} + \cdots + p_r e^{i t_r})^n,$$

as may be directly shown by a straightforward generalization of the proof of the corresponding expression (16.2.3) in the binomial case. Writing

$$x_i = \frac{\nu_i - n p_i}{\sqrt{n p_i}}, \qquad (i = 1, 2, \ldots, r), \tag{30.1.3}$$

it is seen that the x_i satisfy the identity $\sum\limits_1^r x_i \sqrt{p_i} = 0$, and that we have

$$\chi^2 = \sum_1^r x_i^2.$$

Further, the joint c. f. of the variables $x_1, \ldots, x_r$ is

$$\varphi(t_1, \ldots, t_r) = e^{-i\sqrt{n}\sum\limits_1^r t_i \sqrt{p_i}} \left(p_1 e^{\frac{i t_1}{\sqrt{n p_1}}} + \cdots + p_r e^{\frac{i t_r}{\sqrt{n p_r}}}\right)^n.$$

From the MacLaurin expansion of this function, we deduce by some easy calculation the expressions (30.1.1). We further find for any fixed $t_1, \ldots, t_r$

$$\log \varphi(t_1, \ldots, t_r) = n \log \left[1 + \frac{i}{\sqrt{n}} \sum_1^r t_i \sqrt{p_i} - \frac{1}{2n} \sum_1^r t_i^2 + O(n^{-3/2})\right] - \\ - i\sqrt{n} \sum_1^r t_i \sqrt{p_i}$$

$$= -\tfrac{1}{2} \sum_1^r t_i^2 + \tfrac{1}{2}\left(\sum_1^r t_i \sqrt{p_i}\right)^2 + O(n^{-\frac{1}{2}}),$$

so that the c. f. tends to the limit

$$\lim_{n \to \infty} \varphi(t_1, \ldots, t_r) = e^{-\frac{1}{2}\left[\sum_1^r t_i^2 - \left(\sum_1^r t_i \sqrt{p_i}\right)^2\right]} = e^{-\frac{1}{2} Q(t_1, \ldots, t_r)}.$$

The quadratic form $Q(t_1, \ldots, t_r) = \sum_1^r t_i^2 - \left(\sum_1^r t_i \sqrt{p_i}\right)^2$ has the matrix $\boldsymbol{\Lambda} = \boldsymbol{I} - \boldsymbol{p}\boldsymbol{p}'$, where $\boldsymbol{I}$ denotes the unit matrix (cf. 11.1), while $\boldsymbol{p}$ denotes the column vector (cf 11.2) $\boldsymbol{p} = (\sqrt{p_1}, \ldots, \sqrt{p_r})$. Replacing $t_1, \ldots, t_r$ by new variables $u_1, \ldots, u_r$ by means of an orthogonal transformation such that $u_r = \sum_1^r t_i \sqrt{p_i}$, we obtain (cf 11.11)

$$Q(t_1, \ldots, t_r) = \sum_1^r t_i^2 - \left(\sum_1^r t_i \sqrt{p_i}\right)^2 = \sum_1^{r-1} u_i^2.$$

It follows that $Q(t_1, \ldots, t_r)$ is non-negative and of rank $r-1$ (cf 11.6), and that the matrix $\boldsymbol{\Lambda}$ has $r-1$ characteristic numbers (cf 11.9) equal to 1, while the r:th characteristic number is zero.

As $n \to \infty$, the joint c. f. of the variables $x_1, \ldots, x_r$ thus tends to the expression $e^{-\frac{1}{2} Q}$, which is the c. f. of a singular normal distribution (cf 24.3) of rank $r-1$, the total mass of which is situated in the hyperplane $\Sigma x_i \sqrt{p_i} = 0$. By the continuity theorem 10.7 it then follows that, in the limit, $x_1, \ldots, x_r$ are distributed in this singular normal distribution, with zero means and the moment matrix $\boldsymbol{\Lambda}$. It then follows from 24.5 that, in the limit, the variable $\chi^2 = \sum_1^r x_i^2$ is distributed in a χ^2-distribution with $r-1$ d. of fr. Thus the theorem is proved.

By means of this theorem, we can now introduce a test of the hypothesis H considered above. Let χ_p^2 denote the p % value of χ^2

for $r-1$ d. of fr. (cf 18.1 and Table 3). Then by the above theorem the probability $P = P(\chi^2 > \chi_p^2)$ will for large n be approximately equal to p %. Suppose now that we have fixed p so small that we agree to regard it as practically certain that an event of probability p % will not occur in one single trial (cf 26.2). Suppose further that n is so large that, for practical purposes, the probability P may be identified with its limiting value p %. *If the hypothesis H is true, it is then practically excluded that, in one single sample, we should encounter a value of χ^2 exceeding χ_p^2.*

If, in an actual sample, we find a value $\chi^2 > \chi_p^2$, we shall accordingly say that our sample shows a *significant deviation* from the hypothesis H, and we shall *reject* this hypothesis, at least until further data are available. The probability that this situation will occur in a case when H is actually true, so that H will be falsely rejected, is precisely the probability $P = P(\chi^2 > \chi_p^2)$, which is approximately equal to p %. We shall then say that we are working on a p % *level of significance.*

If, on the other hand, we find a value $\chi^2 \leqq \chi_p^2$, this will be regarded as *consistent* with the hypothesis H. Obviously one isolated result of this kind cannot be considered as sufficient evidence of the truth of the hypothesis. In order to produce such evidence, we shall have to apply the test repeatedly to new data of a similar character. Whenever possible, other tests should also be applied.

When the χ^2 test is applied in practice, and all the expected frequencies np_i are $\geqq 10$, the limiting χ^2-distribution tabulated in Table 3 gives as a rule the value χ_p^2 corresponding to a given $P = p/100$ with an approximation sufficient for ordinary purposes. If some of the np_i are < 10, it is usually advisable to pool the smaller groups, so that every group contains at least 10 expected observations, before the test is applied. When the observations are so few that this cannot be done, the χ^2 tables should not be used, but some information may still be drawn from the values of $\boldsymbol{E}(\chi^2)$ and $\boldsymbol{D}(\chi^2)$ calculated according to (30.1.1).

Table 3 is only applicable when the number of d. of fr. is $\leqq 30$. For more than 30 d. of fr., it is usually sufficient to use Fisher's proposition (cf 20.2) that $\sqrt{2\chi^2}$ for n d. of fr. is approximately normally distributed, with the mean $\sqrt{2n-1}$ and unit s. d.

30.2. Examples. — In practical applications of various tests of significance, the 5 %, 1 % and 0.1 % levels of significance are often used. Which level we should adopt in a given case will, of course, depend on the particular circumstances of the case. In the numerical examples that will be given in this book, we shall denote a value exceeding the 5 % limit but not the 1 % limit as *almost significant*, a value between the 1 % and 0.1 % limits as *significant*, and a value exceeding the 0.1 % limit as *highly significant*. This terminology is, of course, purely conventional.

Ex. 1. In a sequence of n independent trials, the event E has occurred ν times. Are these data consistent with the hypothesis that E has in every trial the given probability $p = 1 - q$?

The data may be regarded as a sample of n values of a variable which is equal to 1 or 0 according as E occurs or not. The hypothesis H consists in the assertion that the two alternatives have fixed probabilities p and q. Thus we have two groups with the observed frequencies ν and $n - \nu$, and the corresponding expected frequencies np and nq. Hence we obtain

$$\chi^2 = \frac{(\nu - np)^2}{np} + \frac{(n - \nu - nq)^2}{nq} = \frac{(\nu - np)^2}{npq}. \tag{30.2.1}$$

By the theorem of the preceding paragraph, this quantity is for large n approximately distributed in a χ^2-distribution with one d of fr. This agrees with the fact (cf 16.4 and 18.1) that the standardized variable $\frac{\nu - np}{\sqrt{npq}}$ is asymptotically normal (0, 1), so that its square has, in the limit, the fr. f. $k_1(x)$. Accordingly, the percentage values of χ^2 for one d. of fr. given in Table 3 are the squares of the corresponding values for the normal distribution given in Table 2.

In $n = 4040$ throws with a coin, Buffon obtained $\nu = 2048$ heads and $n - \nu = 1992$ tails. Is this consistent with the hypothesis that there is a constant probability $p = \frac{1}{2}$ of throwing heads? — We have here $\chi^2 = \frac{(\nu - np)^2}{npq} = 0.776$, and this falls well below the 5 % value of χ^2 for one d. of fr., which by Table 3 is 3.841, so that the data must be regarded as consistent with the hypothesis. The corresponding value of $P = P(\chi^2 \geqq 0.776)$ is about 0.38, which means that we have a probability of about 38 % of obtaining a deviation from the expected result at least as great as that actually observed.

Ex. 2. Suppose now that k independent sets of observations are available and let these contain $n_1, \ldots, n_k$ observations respectively, the corresponding numbers of occurrences of the event E being $\nu_1, \ldots, \nu_k$. The hypothesis of a constant probability equal to p may then be tested in various ways.

The totality of our data consist of $n = \Sigma n_i$ observations with $\nu = \Sigma \nu_i$ occurrences, so that we obtain a first test by calculating the quantity $\chi^2 = \frac{(\nu - np)^2}{npq}$. Further, the quantity $\chi_i^2 = \frac{(\nu_i - n_i p)^2}{n_i pq}$ provides a separate test for the i:th set of observations.

Then $\chi_1^2, \ldots, \chi_k^2$ are independent, and for large n_i all have asymptotically the same distribution, viz. the χ^2 distribution with one d. of fr. By the addition theorem (18.1.7) the sum $\Sigma \chi_i^2$ has, in the limit, a χ^2 distribution with k d. of fr., and this gives a joint test of all our χ_i^2-values.

Finally, when the n_i are large, $\chi_1^2, \ldots, \chi_k^2$ may be regarded as a sample of k observed values of a variable with the fr. f. $k_1(x)$, and we may apply the χ^2 test to judge the deviation of the sample from this hypothetical distribution.

In his classical experiments with peas, Mendel (Ref. 155) obtained from 10 plants the numbers of green and yellow peas given in Table 30.2.1. According to Mendelian theory, the probability ought to be $p = \frac{3}{4}$ for »yellow», and $q = \frac{1}{4}$ for »green» (the »3:1 hypothesis»). The ten values of χ_i^2, as well as the value $\chi^2 = 0.137$ for the totals, all fall below the 5 % value for one d. of fr. The sum of all ten χ_i^2 is 7.191, and this falls below the 5 % value for ten d. of fr., which by Table 3 is 18.307. Finally, the ten values of χ_i^2 may be regarded as a sample of ten values of a variable with the fr. f. $k_1(x)$. For this distribution, we obtain from Table 3 the following probabilities:

$$P(0 < \chi^2 < 0.148) = 0.3,$$
$$P(0.148 < \chi^2 < 1.074) = 0.4,$$
$$P(\chi^2 > 1.074) = 0.3,$$

while according to the last column of Table 30.2.1 the corresponding observed frequencies are respectively 2, 6 and 2. The calculation of χ^2 for this sample of $n = 10$ observations with $r = 3$ groups gives $\chi^2 = (2-3)^2/3 + (6-4)^2/4 + (2-3)^2/3 = 1.667$. In this case, the expected values are so small that the limiting distribution should not be used, but we may compare the observed value $\chi^2 = 1.667$ with the values $\boldsymbol{E}(\chi^2) = 2$ and $\boldsymbol{D}(\chi^2) = 1.902$ calculated from (30.1.1). Since the observed value only differs from the mean by about 18 % of the s. d., the agreement must be regarded as good.

TABLE 30.2.1.

Plant number i	Number of peas Yellow ν_i	Green $n_i - \nu_i$	Total n_i	χ_i^2
1	25	11	36	0.593
2	32	7	39	1.034
3	14	5	19	0.018
4	70	27	97	0.416
5	24	13	37	2.027
6	20	6	26	0.051
7	32	13	45	0.363
8	44	9	53	1.818
9	50	14	64	0.333
10	44	18	62	0.538
Total	355	123	478	7.191
χ^2 for the totals = 0.137				

Thus all our tests imply that the data of Table 30.2.1 are consistent with the 3:1 hypothesis. If either test had disclosed a significant deviation, we should have had to reject the hypothesis, at least until further experience had made it plausible that the deviation was due to random fluctuations.

Ex. 3. In another experiment, Mendel observed simultaneously the shape and the colour of his peas. Among $n = 556$ peas he obtained:

Round and yellow . . . . . 315, (expected 312.75),
Round and green . . . . . . 108, (» 104.25),
Angular and yellow . . . . . 101, (» 104.25),
Angular and green . . . . . 32, (» 34,75),

where the expected numbers are calculated on the hypothesis that the probabilities of the $r = 4$ groups are in the ratios $9:3:3:1$. From these numbers we find $\chi^2 = 0.470$. We have $r - 1 = 3$ d. of fr., and by Table 3 the probability of a χ^2 exceeding 0.470 lies between 90 and 95 %, so that the agreement is very good.

Ex. 4. We finally consider an example where the hypothetical distribution is of the continuous type. Aitken (Ref. 2, p. 49) gives the following distributions of times shown by two samples of 500 watches displayed in watchmakers' windows (hour 0 means 0 — 1, etc.):

TABLE 30.2.2.

Hour	0	1	2	3	4	5	6	7	8	9	10	11	Total
Sample 1. . . .	41	34	54	39	49	45	41	33	37	41	47	39	500
Sample 2. . . .	36	47	41	47	49	45	32	37	40	41	37	48	500

On the hypothesis that the times are uniformly distributed over the interval (0, 12), the expected number in each class would be $500/12 = = 41{,}67$, and hence we find $\chi_1^2 = 10.000$ for the first sample, and $\chi_2^2 = 8.032$ for the second, while for the combined sample of all 1 000 watches we have $\chi^2 = 9.464$. In each case we have $12 - 1 = 11$ d. of fr., and by Table 3 the agreement is good. We may also consider the sum $\chi_1^2 + \chi_2^2 = 18.032$, which has 22 d. of fr., and also shows a good agreement.

30.3. The χ^2 test when certain parameters are estimated from the sample. — The case of a completely specified hypothetical distribution is rather exceptional in the applications. More often we encounter cases where the hypothetical distribution contains a certain number of unknown parameters, about the values of which we only possess such information as may be derived from the sample itself. We are then given a pr. f. $P(S;\ \alpha_1, \ldots, \alpha_s)$ containing s unknown parameters $\alpha_1, \ldots, \alpha_s$, but otherwise of known mathematical form. The *hypothesis* H to be tested will now be the hypothesis that our sample has been drawn from a population having a distribution determined by the pr. f. P, with *some* values of the parameters α_j.

As in 30.1, we suppose that our sample is divided into r groups, corresponding to r mutually exclusive sets $S_1, \ldots, S_r$, and we denote the observed group frequencies by $\nu_1, \ldots, \nu_r$, while the corresponding probabilities are $p_i(\alpha_1, \ldots, \alpha_s) = P(S_i;\ \alpha_1, \ldots, \alpha_s)$ for $i = 1, 2, \ldots, r$.

If the »true values» of the α_j were known, we should merely have to calculate the quantity

$$\chi^2 = \sum_{i=1}^{r} \frac{[\nu_i - n\,p_i(\alpha_1, \ldots, \alpha_s)]^2}{n\,p_i(\alpha_1, \ldots, \alpha_s)}, \tag{30.3.1}$$

and apply the test described in 30.1, so that no further discussion would be required.

In the actual case, however, the values of the α_j are unknown and must be estimated from the sample. Now, if we replace in (30.3.1) the unknown constants α_j by estimates calculated from the sample, the p_i will no longer be constants, but functions of the sample values, and we are no longer entitled to apply the theorem of 30.1 on the limiting distribution of χ^2. As already pointed out in 26.4, there will generally be an infinite number of different possible *methods of estimation* of the α_j, and it must be expected that the properties of the sampling distribution of χ^2 will more or less depend on the method chosen.

The problem of finding the limiting distribution of χ^2 under these more complicated circumstances was first considered by R. A. Fisher (Ref. 91, 95), who showed that in this case it is necessary to modify the limiting distribution (30.1.2) due to K. Pearson. For an important class of methods of estimation, the modification indicated by Fisher is of a very simple kind. *It is, in fact, only necessary to reduce the number of d. of fr. of the limiting distribution* (30.1.2) *by one unit for each parameter estimated from the sample.*

We shall here choose one particularly important method of estimation, and give a detailed deduction of the corresponding limiting distribution of χ^2. It will be shown in 33.4 that there is a whole class of methods of estimation leading to the same limiting distribution.

It seems natural to attempt to determine the »best» values of the parameters α_j so as to render χ^2 defined by (30.3.1) as small as possible. This is the χ^2 *minimum method* of estimation. We then have to solve the equations

$$(30.3.2) \qquad -\frac{1}{2}\frac{\partial \chi^2}{\partial \alpha_j} = \sum_{i=1}^{r}\left(\frac{\nu_i - n p_i}{p_i} + \frac{(\nu_i - n p_i)^2}{2 n p_i^2}\right)\frac{\partial p_i}{\partial \alpha_j} = 0,$$

where $j = 1, 2, \ldots, s$, with respect to the unknowns $\alpha_1, \ldots, \alpha_s$, and insert the values thus found into (30.3.1). The limiting distribution of χ^2 for this method of estimation has been investigated by Neyman and E. S. Pearson (Ref. 170), who used methods of multi-dimensional geometry of the type introduced by R. A. Fisher. We also refer in this connection to a paper by Sheppard (Ref. 213).

Even in simple cases, the system (30.3.2) is often very difficult to solve. It can, however, be shown that for large n the influence of the second term within the brackets becomes negligible. If, when differentiating χ^2 with respect to the α_j, we simply *regard the denominators in the second member of* (30.3.1) *as constant*, (30.3.2) is replaced by the system

$$\sum_{i=1}^{r} \frac{\nu_i - n p_i}{p_i} \cdot \frac{\partial p_i}{\partial \alpha_j} = 0, \qquad (j = 1, \ldots, s), \tag{30.3.3}$$

and usually this will be much easier to deal with. The method of estimation which consists in determining the α_j from this system of equations will be called the *modified χ^2 minimum method.* Both methods give, under general conditions, the same limiting distribution of χ^2 for large n, but we shall here only consider the simpler method based on (30.3.3).

By means of the condition a) of the theorem given below, the equations (30.3.3) reduce to

$$\sum_{i=1}^{r} \frac{\nu_i}{p_i} \cdot \frac{\partial p_i}{\partial \alpha_j} = 0, \tag{30.3.3 a}$$

which may also be written $\frac{\partial L}{\partial \alpha_j} = 0$, where $L = p_1^{\nu_1} \ldots p_r^{\nu_r}$. The method of estimation which consists in determining the α_j such that L becomes as large as possible is the *maximum likelihood method* introduced by R. A. Fisher, which will be further discussed in Ch. 33. With respect to the problem treated in the present paragraph, the modified χ^2 minimum method is thus identical with the maximum likelihood method. The latter method is, however, applicable also to problems of a much more general character.

On account of the importance of the question, we shall now give a deduction of the limiting distribution of χ^2 under as general conditions as possible, assuming that the parameters α_j are estimated by the modified χ^2 minimum method. We first give a detailed statement of the theorem to be proved.

Suppose that we are given r functions $p_1(\alpha_1, \ldots, \alpha_s), \ldots, p_r(\alpha_1, \ldots, \alpha_s)$ of $s < r$ variables $\alpha_1, \ldots, \alpha_s$ such that, for all points of a non-degenerate interval A in the s-dimensional space of the α_j, the p_i satisfy the following conditions:

a) $\sum_{i=1}^{r} p_i(\alpha_1, \ldots, \alpha_s) = 1.$

b) $p_i(\alpha_1, \ldots, \alpha_s) > c^2 > 0$ for all i.

c) *Every* p_i *has continuous derivatives* $\frac{\partial p_i}{\partial \alpha_j}$ *and* $\frac{\partial^2 p_i}{\partial \alpha_j \partial \alpha_k}$.

d) *The matrix* $\mathbf{D} = \left\{\frac{\partial p_i}{\partial \alpha_j}\right\}$, *where* $i = 1, \ldots, r$ *and* $j = 1, \ldots, s$, *is of rank* s.

Let the possible results of a certain random experiment $\mathfrak{E}$ *be divided into* r *mutually exclusive groups, and suppose that the probability of obtaining a result belonging to the i:th group is* $p_i^0 = p_i(\alpha_1^0, \ldots, \alpha_s^0)$, *where* $\boldsymbol{\alpha}_0 = (\alpha_1^0, \ldots, \alpha_s^0)$ *is an inner point of the interval* A. *Let* ν_i *denote the number of results belonging to the i:th group, which occur in a sequence of* n *repetitions of* $\mathfrak{E}$, *so that* $\sum_1^r \nu_i = n$.

The equations (30.3.3) *of the modified* χ^2 *minimum method then have exactly one system of solutions* $\boldsymbol{\alpha} = (\alpha_1, \ldots, \alpha_s)$ *such that* $\boldsymbol{\alpha}$ *converges in probability to* $\boldsymbol{\alpha}_0$ *as* $n \to \infty$. *The value of* χ^2 *obtained by inserting these values of the* α_j *into* (30.3.1) *is, in the limit as* $n \to \infty$, *distributed in a* χ^2*-distribution with* $r - s - 1$ *degrees of freedom.*

The proof of this theorem is somewhat intricate, and will be divided into two parts. In the first part (p. 427—431) it will be shown that the equations (30.3.3) have exactly one solution $\boldsymbol{\alpha}$ such that $\boldsymbol{\alpha}$ converges in probability (cf 20.3) to $\boldsymbol{\alpha}_0$. In the second part (p. 431—434) we consider the variables

$$y_i = \frac{\nu_i - n\,p_i(\alpha_1, \ldots, \alpha_s)}{\sqrt{n\,p_i(\alpha_1, \ldots, \alpha_s)}}, \qquad (i = 1, \ldots, r), \tag{30.3.4}$$

where $\boldsymbol{\alpha} = (\alpha_1, \ldots, \alpha_s)$ is the solution of (30.3.3), the existence of which has just been established. It will be shown here that, as $n \to \infty$, the joint distribution of the y_i tends to a certain singular normal distribution of a type similar to the limiting distribution of the variables x_i defined by (30.1.3). As in the corresponding proof in 30.1, the limiting distribution of $\chi^2 = \sum_1^r y_i^2$ is then directly obtained from 24.5.

Throughout the proof, the subscript i will assume the values $1, 2, \ldots, r$, while j and k assume the values $1, 2, \ldots, s$.

We shall first introduce certain matrix notations, and transform the equations (30.3.3) into matrix form. Denoting by $\left(\frac{\partial p_i}{\partial \alpha_j}\right)_0$ the value assumed by $\frac{\partial p_i}{\partial \alpha_j}$ in the point $\boldsymbol{\alpha}_0$, (30.3.3) may be written

$$\sum_k (\alpha_k - \alpha_k^0) \sum_i \frac{1}{p_i^0} \left(\frac{\partial p_i}{\partial \alpha_j}\right)_0 \left(\frac{\partial p_i}{\partial \alpha_k}\right)_0 = \sum_i \frac{\nu_i - n p_i^0}{n p_i^0} \left(\frac{\partial p_i}{\partial \alpha_j}\right)_0 + \omega_j(\boldsymbol{\alpha}), \tag{30.3.5}$$

where

$$\begin{aligned} \omega_j(\boldsymbol{\alpha}) = \sum_i \frac{\nu_i - n p_i^0}{n} \left[\frac{1}{p_i}\frac{\partial p_i}{\partial \alpha_j} - \frac{1}{p_i^0}\left(\frac{\partial p_i}{\partial \alpha_j}\right)_0\right] - \\ - \sum_i (p_i - p_i^0) \left[\frac{1}{p_i}\frac{\partial p_i}{\partial \alpha_j} - \frac{1}{p_i^0}\left(\frac{\partial p_i}{\partial \alpha_j}\right)_0\right] - \\ - \sum_i \frac{1}{p_i^0}\left(\frac{\partial p_i}{\partial \alpha_j}\right)_0 \left[p_i - p_i^0 - \sum_k \left(\frac{\partial p_i}{\partial \alpha_k}\right)_0 (\alpha_k - \alpha_k^0)\right]. \end{aligned} \tag{30.3.6}$$

Let us denote by $\boldsymbol{B}$ the matrix of order $r \cdot s$

$$\boldsymbol{B} = \left\{\begin{matrix} \frac{1}{\sqrt{p_1^0}}\left(\frac{\partial p_1}{\partial \alpha_1}\right)_0 & \cdots & \frac{1}{\sqrt{p_1^0}}\left(\frac{\partial p_1}{\partial \alpha_s}\right)_0 \\ \cdot & \cdot\ \cdot\ \cdot & \cdot \\ \frac{1}{\sqrt{p_r^0}}\left(\frac{\partial p_r}{\partial \alpha_1}\right)_0 & \cdots & \frac{1}{\sqrt{p_r^0}}\left(\frac{\partial p_r}{\partial \alpha_s}\right)_0 \end{matrix}\right\}$$

By 11.1, we have $\boldsymbol{B} = \boldsymbol{P}_0 \boldsymbol{D}_0$, where $\boldsymbol{P}_0$ is the diagonal matrix formed by the diagonal elements $\frac{1}{\sqrt{p_1^0}}, \ldots, \frac{1}{\sqrt{p_r^0}}$, while $\boldsymbol{D}_0$ is the matrix obtained by taking $\alpha_j = \alpha_j^0$ in the matrix $\boldsymbol{D} = \left\{\frac{\partial p_i}{\partial \alpha_j}\right\}$. Hence by condition d) the matrix $\boldsymbol{B}$ is of rank s (cf 11.6). — We further write in analogy with (30.1.3)

$$x_i = \frac{\nu_i - n p_i^0}{\sqrt{n p_i^0}}, \tag{30.3.7}$$

and denote by $\boldsymbol{\alpha}$, $\boldsymbol{\alpha}_0$, $\boldsymbol{\omega}(\boldsymbol{\alpha})$ and $\boldsymbol{x}$ the column vectors (cf 11.2)

$$\begin{aligned} \boldsymbol{\alpha} &= (\alpha_1, \ldots, \alpha_s), \\ \boldsymbol{\alpha}_0 &= (\alpha_1^0, \ldots, \alpha_s^0), \\ \boldsymbol{\omega}(\boldsymbol{\alpha}) &= (\omega_1(\boldsymbol{\alpha}), \ldots, \omega_s(\boldsymbol{\alpha})), \\ \boldsymbol{x} &= (x_1, \ldots, x_r), \end{aligned}$$

the three first of which are, as matrices, of order $s \cdot 1$, while the fourth is of order $r \cdot 1$.

In matrix notation, the system of equations (30.3.5), where $j = 1, \ldots, s$, may now be written (cf 11.3)

$$\boldsymbol{B}'\boldsymbol{B}(\alpha - \alpha_0) = n^{-\frac{1}{2}}\boldsymbol{B}'\boldsymbol{x} + \boldsymbol{\omega}(\alpha).$$

$\boldsymbol{B}'\boldsymbol{B}$ is a symmetric matrix of order $s \cdot s$, which according to 11.9 is non-singular, so that the reciprocal $(\boldsymbol{B}'\boldsymbol{B})^{-1}$ exists (cf 11.7), and we obtain [1])

(30.3.8) $$\alpha = \alpha_0 + n^{-\frac{1}{2}}(\boldsymbol{B}'\boldsymbol{B})^{-1}\boldsymbol{B}'\boldsymbol{x} + (\boldsymbol{B}'\boldsymbol{B})^{-1}\boldsymbol{\omega}(\alpha).$$

This matrix equation is thus equivalent to the fundamental system of equations (30.3.3).

For every fixed i the random variable ν_i has the mean $n p_i^0$ and the s. d. $\sqrt{n p_i^0(1 - p_i^0)}$, so that by the Bienaymé-Tchebycheff inequality (15.7.2) the probability of the relation $|\nu_i - n p_i^0| \geqq \lambda\sqrt{n}$ is at most equal to $\frac{p_i^0(1 - p_i^0)}{\lambda^2} < \frac{p_i^0}{\lambda^2}$. Consequently the probability that we have $|\nu_i - n p_i^0| \geqq \lambda\sqrt{n}$ for *at least one* value of i is smaller than $\lambda^{-2}\sum_i p_i^0 = \lambda^{-2}$ and, conversely, with a probability greater than $1 - \lambda^{-2}$ we have

(30.3.9) $$|\nu_i - n p_i^0| < \lambda\sqrt{n} \qquad \text{for } all\ i = 1, \ldots, r.$$

Until further notice, we shall now assume that the ν_i satisfy the relations (30.3.9). We shall here allow λ to denote a function of n such that λ tends to infinity with n, while $\lambda^2/\sqrt{n}$ tends to zero. We may e. g. take $\lambda = n^q$, where $0 < q < \frac{1}{4}$. — *All results obtained under such assumptions will thus be true with a probability which is greater than* $1 - \lambda^{-2}$, *and which consequently tends to* 1 *as* $n \to \infty$.

From (30.3.7) we then obtain by condition b)

(30.3.10) $$|x_i| < \frac{\lambda}{c}.$$

Further, when $\alpha' = (\alpha_1', \ldots, \alpha_s')$ and $\alpha'' = (\alpha_1'', \ldots, \alpha_s'')$ are any points in

[1]) Note that we cannot write here $(\boldsymbol{B}'\boldsymbol{B})^{-1} = \boldsymbol{B}^{-1}(\boldsymbol{B}')^{-1}$, since by hypothesis $s < r$, so that $\boldsymbol{B}$ is not square, and the reciprocal $\boldsymbol{B}^{-1}$ is undefined. — If we take $s = r$, it will be seen that the conditions a) and d) of the theorem are incompatible. In this case, if we assume that a)—c) are satisfied, the matrices $\boldsymbol{D}$, $\boldsymbol{B}$ and $\boldsymbol{B}'\boldsymbol{B}$ are all singular, so that the reciprocal $(\boldsymbol{B}'\boldsymbol{B})^{-1}$ is undefined, and (30.3.8) has no sense.

the interval A, we obtain from (30.3.6) after some calculations, using the conditions b) and c), and expanding in Taylor's series,

$$(30.3.11)\quad |\omega_j(\alpha') - \omega_j(\alpha'')| \leqq K_1 |\alpha' - \alpha''| \cdot \left(|\alpha' - \alpha_0| + |\alpha'' - \alpha_0| + \frac{\lambda}{\sqrt{n}}\right).$$

In the second member, we use the notation $|\boldsymbol{a} - \boldsymbol{b}|$ for the distance (cf 3.1) between two points $\boldsymbol{a}$ and $\boldsymbol{b}$ in the s-dimensional space of the α_j, while K_1 is a constant independent of α', α'', j and n.

We now define a sequence of vectors $\boldsymbol{\alpha}_\nu = (\alpha_1^{(\nu)}, \ldots, \alpha_s^{(\nu)})$ by writing for $\nu = 1, 2, \ldots$

$$(30.3.12)\qquad \boldsymbol{\alpha}_\nu = \boldsymbol{\alpha}_0 + n^{-\frac{1}{2}} (\boldsymbol{B}' \boldsymbol{B})^{-1} \boldsymbol{B}' \boldsymbol{x} + (\boldsymbol{B}' \boldsymbol{B})^{-1} \omega(\boldsymbol{\alpha}_{\nu-1}),$$

and we propose to show that the sequence $\boldsymbol{\alpha}_1, \boldsymbol{\alpha}_2, \ldots$ converges to a definite limit $\boldsymbol{\alpha}$, which is then evidently a solution of (30.3.8). By (30.3.6) we have $\omega(\boldsymbol{\alpha}_0) = 0$, and thus

$$(30.3.13)\qquad \boldsymbol{\alpha}_1 - \boldsymbol{\alpha}_0 = n^{-\frac{1}{2}} (\boldsymbol{B}' \boldsymbol{B})^{-1} \boldsymbol{B}' \boldsymbol{x},$$

while for $\nu > 0$

$$(30.3.14)\qquad \boldsymbol{\alpha}_{\nu+1} - \boldsymbol{\alpha}_\nu = (\boldsymbol{B}' \boldsymbol{B})^{-1} [\omega(\boldsymbol{\alpha}_\nu) - \omega(\boldsymbol{\alpha}_{\nu-1})].$$

Now the matrices $(\boldsymbol{B}' \boldsymbol{B})^{-1} \boldsymbol{B}'$ and $(\boldsymbol{B}' \boldsymbol{B})^{-1}$ are both independent of n. Denoting by g an upper bound of the absolute values of the elements of these two matrices, it then in the first place follows from (30.3.13) and (30.3.10) that every element of the vector $\boldsymbol{\alpha}_1 - \boldsymbol{\alpha}_0$ satisfies the inequality

$$|\alpha_j^{(1)} - \alpha_j^0| < \frac{r g}{c} \cdot \frac{\lambda}{\sqrt{n}},$$

so that

$$|\boldsymbol{\alpha}_1 - \boldsymbol{\alpha}_0| < K_2 \frac{\lambda}{\sqrt{n}},$$

where K_2 is independent of n. In a similar way, it then follows from (30.3.14) and (30.3.11) that we have

$$|\boldsymbol{\alpha}_{\nu+1} - \boldsymbol{\alpha}_\nu| \leqq K_3 |\boldsymbol{\alpha}_\nu - \boldsymbol{\alpha}_{\nu-1}| \cdot \left(|\boldsymbol{\alpha}_\nu - \boldsymbol{\alpha}_0| + |\boldsymbol{\alpha}_{\nu-1} - \boldsymbol{\alpha}_0| + \frac{\lambda}{\sqrt{n}}\right)$$

for every $\nu > 0$, where K_3 is independent of ν and n. From the two last inequalities, it now follows by induction that we have for all sufficiently large n, and for all $\nu = 0, 1, 2, \ldots$

$$(30.3.15) \qquad |\boldsymbol{\alpha}_{\nu+1} - \boldsymbol{\alpha}_\nu| \leqq K_2 [(4 K_2 + 1) K_3]^\nu \left(\frac{\lambda}{\sqrt{n}}\right)^{\nu+1}$$

Since by hypothesis $\boldsymbol{\alpha}_0$ is an inner point of the interval A, it follows that for all sufficiently large n the vectors $\boldsymbol{\alpha}_1, \boldsymbol{\alpha}_2, \ldots$ (considered as points in the $\boldsymbol{\alpha}$-space) all belong to A, and that the sequence $\boldsymbol{\alpha}_1, \boldsymbol{\alpha}_2, \ldots$ converges to a definite limit

$$(30.3.16) \qquad \boldsymbol{\alpha} = \boldsymbol{\alpha}_0 + (\boldsymbol{\alpha}_1 - \boldsymbol{\alpha}_0) + (\boldsymbol{\alpha}_2 - \boldsymbol{\alpha}_1) + \cdots$$

which, as already observed, is a solution of (30.3.8), and thus also of the fundamental equations (30.3.3). It follows from (30.3.15) that $\boldsymbol{\alpha} \to \boldsymbol{\alpha}_0$ as $n \to \infty$. Moreover, $\boldsymbol{\alpha}$ is the only solution of (30.3.8) tending to $\boldsymbol{\alpha}_0$ as $n \to \infty$. In fact, if $\boldsymbol{\alpha}'$ is another solution tending to $\boldsymbol{\alpha}_0$, we have

$$\boldsymbol{\alpha}' - \boldsymbol{\alpha} = (\boldsymbol{B}' \boldsymbol{B})^{-1} (\boldsymbol{\omega}(\boldsymbol{\alpha}') - \boldsymbol{\omega}(\boldsymbol{\alpha})),$$

and by the same argument as above it follows that

$$|\boldsymbol{\alpha}' - \boldsymbol{\alpha}| \leqq K_3 |\boldsymbol{\alpha}' - \boldsymbol{\alpha}| \cdot \left(|\boldsymbol{\alpha}' - \boldsymbol{\alpha}_0| + |\boldsymbol{\alpha} - \boldsymbol{\alpha}_0| + \frac{\lambda}{\sqrt{n}}\right),$$

where the expression within the brackets tends to zero as $n \to \infty$, but this is evidently only possible if $\boldsymbol{\alpha}' = \boldsymbol{\alpha}$ for all sufficiently large n.

All this has been proved under the assumption that the relations (30.3.9) are satisfied, and thus holds with a probability which is greater than $1 - \lambda^{-2}$, and consequently tends to 1 as $n \to \infty$. We have thus established the existence of exactly one solution of (30.3.8), or (30.3.3), which converges in probability to $\boldsymbol{\alpha}_0$, and the first part of the proof is completed.

Still assuming that the relations (30.3.9) are satisfied, we obtain from (30.3.8), (30.3.13) and (30.3.16)

$$(\boldsymbol{B}' \boldsymbol{B})^{-1} \boldsymbol{\omega}(\boldsymbol{\alpha}) = \boldsymbol{\alpha} - \boldsymbol{\alpha}_1 = (\boldsymbol{\alpha}_2 - \boldsymbol{\alpha}_1) + (\boldsymbol{\alpha}_3 - \boldsymbol{\alpha}_2) + \cdots.$$

It then follows from (30.3.15) that every component of the vector $(\boldsymbol{B}' \boldsymbol{B})^{-1} \boldsymbol{\omega}(\boldsymbol{\alpha})$ is smaller than $K' \lambda^2/n$, where K' is independent of n, so that (30.3.8) may be written

$$(30.3.17) \qquad \boldsymbol{\alpha} - \boldsymbol{\alpha}_0 = n^{-\frac{1}{2}} (\boldsymbol{B}' \boldsymbol{B})^{-1} \boldsymbol{B}' \boldsymbol{x} + \frac{K' \lambda^2}{n} \boldsymbol{\theta}_1,$$

where $\boldsymbol{\theta}_1 = (\theta_1', \ldots, \theta_s')$ denotes a column vector such that $|\theta_j'| \leqq 1$ for $j = 1, \ldots, s$.

Consider now the variables y_i defined by (30.3.4). Still assuming that the relations (30.3.9) are satisfied, we obtain by means of (30.3.7), (30.3.10) and (30.3.17)

$$y_i = \frac{\nu_i - n p_i^0}{\sqrt{n p_i^0}} - \sqrt{n}\,\frac{p_i - p_i^0}{\sqrt{p_i^0}} + \frac{\nu_i - n p_i}{\sqrt{n}}\left(\frac{1}{\sqrt{p_i}} - \frac{1}{\sqrt{p_i^0}}\right)$$
$$= x_i - \sqrt{\frac{n}{p_i^0}} \sum_j \left(\frac{\partial p_i}{\partial \alpha_j}\right)_0 (\alpha_j - \alpha_j^0) + O\left(\frac{\lambda^2}{\sqrt{n}}\right).$$

Expressing this relation in matrix notation, we obtain

$$\boldsymbol{y} = \boldsymbol{x} - \sqrt{n}\,\boldsymbol{B}(\boldsymbol{\alpha} - \boldsymbol{\alpha}_0) + \frac{K'' \lambda^2}{\sqrt{n}}\,\boldsymbol{\theta}_2,$$

where $\boldsymbol{y} = (y_1, \ldots, y_r)$ and $\boldsymbol{\theta}_2 = (\theta_1'', \ldots, \theta_r'')$ with $|\theta_i''| \leq 1$, while K'' is independent of n. Substituting here the expression (30.3.17) for $\boldsymbol{\alpha} - \boldsymbol{\alpha}_0$, we obtain

$$\boldsymbol{y} = \boldsymbol{x} - \boldsymbol{B}(\boldsymbol{B}'\boldsymbol{B})^{-1}\boldsymbol{B}'\boldsymbol{x} + \frac{K\lambda^2}{\sqrt{n}}\,\boldsymbol{\theta}$$

(30.3.18)

$$= [\boldsymbol{I} - \boldsymbol{B}(\boldsymbol{B}'\boldsymbol{B})^{-1}\boldsymbol{B}']\,\boldsymbol{x} + \frac{K\lambda^2}{\sqrt{n}}\,\boldsymbol{\theta},$$

where $\boldsymbol{I}$ is the unit matrix of order $r \cdot r$, and $\boldsymbol{\theta} = (\theta_1, \ldots, \theta_r)$ with $|\theta_i| \leq 1$, while K is independent of n.

We now drop the assumption that the relations (30.3.9) are satisfied, and define a vector $\boldsymbol{z} = (z_1, \ldots, z_r)$ by writing

$$\boldsymbol{y} = \boldsymbol{A}\boldsymbol{x} + \boldsymbol{z},$$

where $\boldsymbol{A}$ denotes the symmetric matrix

$$\boldsymbol{A} = \boldsymbol{I} - \boldsymbol{B}(\boldsymbol{B}'\boldsymbol{B})^{-1}\boldsymbol{B}'.$$

It then follows from (30.3.18) that, with a probability greater than $1 - \lambda^{-2}$, we have $|z_i| \leq K\lambda^2/\sqrt{n}$ for all i, so that $\boldsymbol{z}$ converges in probability to zero. Further, it has been shown in 30.1 that the variables $x_1, \ldots, x_r$ are, in the limit as $n \to \infty$, normally distributed with zero means and the moment matrix $\boldsymbol{\Lambda} = \boldsymbol{I} - \boldsymbol{p}\boldsymbol{p}'$, where $\boldsymbol{p} = (\sqrt{p_1^0}, \ldots, \sqrt{p_r^0})$. By the last proposition of 22.6 it then follows that the limiting distribution of $\boldsymbol{y}$ is obtained by the linear transformation $\boldsymbol{y} = \boldsymbol{A}\boldsymbol{x}$, where $\boldsymbol{x} = (x_1, \ldots, x_r)$ has its normal limiting distribution, with the moment matrix $\boldsymbol{\Lambda}$ of rank $r - 1$.

By 24.4, the joint limiting distribution of $y_1, \ldots, y_r$ is thus normal, with zero means and the moment matrix

$$\boldsymbol{A}\boldsymbol{\Lambda}\boldsymbol{A}' = [\boldsymbol{I} - \boldsymbol{B}(\boldsymbol{B}'\boldsymbol{B})^{-1}\boldsymbol{B}'] \cdot [\boldsymbol{I} - \boldsymbol{p}\boldsymbol{p}'] \cdot [\boldsymbol{I} - \boldsymbol{B}(\boldsymbol{B}'\boldsymbol{B})^{-1}\boldsymbol{B}'].$$

Now by condition a) the j:th element of the vector $\boldsymbol{B}'\boldsymbol{p}$ is

$$\sum_i \left(\frac{\partial p_i}{\partial \alpha_j}\right)_0 = 0,$$

so that $\boldsymbol{B}'\boldsymbol{p}$ is identically zero. Hence we find on multiplication that the moment matrix of the limiting $\boldsymbol{y}$-distribution reduces to

$$\boldsymbol{A}\boldsymbol{\Lambda}\boldsymbol{A}' = \boldsymbol{I} - \boldsymbol{p}\boldsymbol{p}' - \boldsymbol{B}(\boldsymbol{B}'\boldsymbol{B})^{-1}\boldsymbol{B}'. \tag{30.3.19}$$

It now only remains to show that this symmetric matrix of order $r \cdot r$ has $r - s - 1$ characteristic numbers equal to 1, while the rest are 0, so that the effect of the last term is to reduce the rank of the matrix by s units. It then follows from 24.5 that the sum of squares

$$\chi^2 = \sum_i y_i^2$$

is, in the limit, distributed in a χ^2-distribution with $r - s - 1$ degrees of freedom, so that our theorem will be proved.

For this purpose we first observe that, by 11.9, the s characteristic numbers $\varkappa_j$ of the symmetric matrix $\boldsymbol{B}'\boldsymbol{B}$ are all positive. Writing $\varkappa_j = \mu_j^2$, where $\mu_j > 0$, and denoting by $\boldsymbol{M}$ the diagonal matrix formed by the diagonal elements $\mu_1, \ldots, \mu_s$, we may thus by 11.9 find an orthogonal matrix $\boldsymbol{C}$ of order $s \cdot s$ such that $\boldsymbol{C}'\boldsymbol{B}'\boldsymbol{B}\boldsymbol{C} = \boldsymbol{M}^2$, and hence $(\boldsymbol{B}'\boldsymbol{B})^{-1} = (\boldsymbol{C}\boldsymbol{M}^2\boldsymbol{C}')^{-1} = \boldsymbol{C}\boldsymbol{M}^{-1} \cdot \boldsymbol{M}^{-1}\boldsymbol{C}'$. It follows that

$$\boldsymbol{B}(\boldsymbol{B}'\boldsymbol{B})^{-1}\boldsymbol{B}' = \boldsymbol{B}\boldsymbol{C}\boldsymbol{M}^{-1} \cdot \boldsymbol{M}^{-1}\boldsymbol{C}'\boldsymbol{B}' = \boldsymbol{H}\boldsymbol{H}', \tag{30.3.20}$$

where $\boldsymbol{H} = \boldsymbol{B}\boldsymbol{C}\boldsymbol{M}^{-1}$ is a matrix of order $r \cdot s$ such that

$$\boldsymbol{H}'\boldsymbol{H} = \boldsymbol{M}^{-1}\boldsymbol{C}'\boldsymbol{B}'\,\boldsymbol{B}\boldsymbol{C}\boldsymbol{M}^{-1} = \boldsymbol{M}^{-1}\boldsymbol{M}^2\boldsymbol{M}^{-1} = \boldsymbol{I},$$

denoting here by $\boldsymbol{I}$ the unit matrix of order $s \cdot s$. The last relation signifies that the s columns of the matrix $\boldsymbol{H}$ satisfy the orthogonality relations (11.9.2). Further, we have shown above that $\boldsymbol{B}'\boldsymbol{p} = 0$, and hence $\boldsymbol{H}'\boldsymbol{p} = \boldsymbol{M}^{-1}\boldsymbol{C}'\boldsymbol{B}'\boldsymbol{p} = 0$. Thus if we complete the matrix $\boldsymbol{H}$ by an additional column with the elements $\sqrt{p_1^0}, \ldots, \sqrt{p_r^0}$, the $s + 1$ columns of the new matrix $\boldsymbol{H}_1$ will still satisfy the orthogonality relations. Since $s < r$, we may then by 11.9 find an orthogonal matrix $\boldsymbol{K}$ of order $r \cdot r$, the $s+1$ last columns of which are identical with the matrix $\boldsymbol{H}_1$.

Then $\boldsymbol{K}'\boldsymbol{p}$ is a matrix of order $r \cdot 1$, i. e. a column vector, and it follows from the multiplication rule that we have $\boldsymbol{K}'\boldsymbol{p} = (0, \ldots, 0, 1)$. Thus the product $\boldsymbol{K}'\boldsymbol{p}\boldsymbol{p}'\boldsymbol{K} = (0, \ldots, 0, 1) \cdot \{0, \ldots, 0, 1\}$ is a matrix of order $r \cdot r$, all elements of which are zero, except the last element of the main diagonal, which is equal to one. — In a similar way it is seen that the product $\boldsymbol{K}'\boldsymbol{H}\boldsymbol{H}'\boldsymbol{K}$ is a matrix of order $r \cdot r$, all elements of which are zero, except the s diagonal elements immediately preceding the last, which are all equal to one.

By (30.3.20), the moment matrix (30.3.19) now takes the form $\boldsymbol{I} - \boldsymbol{p}\boldsymbol{p}' - \boldsymbol{H}\boldsymbol{H}'$. It follows from the above that the transformed matrix $\boldsymbol{K}'(\boldsymbol{I} - \boldsymbol{p}\boldsymbol{p}' - \boldsymbol{H}\boldsymbol{H}')\boldsymbol{K}$ is a diagonal matrix, the $r - s - 1$ first diagonal elements of which are equal to 1, while the rest are 0. Thus we have proved our assertion about the characteristic numbers of the moment matrix (30.3.19). As observed above, this completes the proof of the theorem.

By means of this theorem, we can now introduce a test of the hypothesis H in exactly the same way as in the simpler case considered in 30.1. Some examples of the application of this test will be shown in the following paragraph.

30.4. Examples. — We shall here apply the χ^2 test to two particularly important cases, viz. the Poisson and the normal distribution. Other simple distributions may be treated in a similar way.

Ex. 1. *The Poisson distribution.* Suppose that it is required to test the hypothesis that a given sample of n values $x_1, \ldots, x_n$ is drawn from *some* Poisson distribution, with an unknown value of the parameter λ. Every x_μ is equal to some non-negative integer i, and we arrange the x_μ according to their values into r groups, pooling the data for the smallest and the largest values of i, where the observations are few. Suppose that we obtain in this way

ν_k observations with $x \leqq k$,
ν_i » » $x = i$, where $i = k+1, \ldots, k+r-2$,
ν_{k+r-1} » » $x \geqq k+r-1$.

If we write $\varpi_i = P(x = i) = \frac{\lambda^i}{i!} e^{-\lambda}$, the corresponding probabilities are

$$p_k = P(x \leqq k) = \sum_0^k \varpi_i,$$

$$p_i = P(x = i) = \varpi_i \quad \text{for} \quad i = k+1, \ldots, k+r-2,$$

$$p_{k+r-1} = P(x \geqq k+r-1) = \sum_{k+r-1}^{\infty} \varpi_i.$$

In order to estimate the unknown parameter λ by the modified χ^2 minimum method, we have to solve the system (30.3.3), or the equivalent system (30.3.3 a). Since there is only one unknown parameter, we have $s = 1$, so that each system reduces to one single equation, and (30.3.3 a) gives

$$\nu_k \frac{\sum_0^k \left(\frac{i}{\lambda} - 1\right) \varpi_i}{\sum_0^k \varpi_i} + \sum_{k+1}^{k+r-2} \left(\frac{i}{\lambda} - 1\right) \nu_i + \nu_{k+r-1} \frac{\sum_{k+r-1}^{\infty} \left(\frac{i}{\lambda} - 1\right) \varpi_i}{\sum_{k+r-1}^{\infty} \varpi_i} = 0.$$

This equation has a single root $\lambda = \lambda^*$, where

$$\lambda^* = \frac{1}{n} \left[\nu_k \frac{\sum_0^k i\, \varpi_i}{\sum_0^k \varpi_i} + \sum_{k+1}^{k+r-2} i\, \nu_i + \nu_{k+r-1} \frac{\sum_{k+r-1}^{\infty} i\, \varpi_i}{\sum_{k+r-1}^{\infty} \varpi_i} \right].$$

Here, the second term within the brackets is equal to the sum of all x_μ such that $k < x_\mu < k + r - 1$, while the first and the last term give approximately the sum of all x_μ which are $\leqq k$ or $\geqq k + r - 1$ respectively. The estimate λ^* to be used for λ is thus approximately equal to the arithmetic mean of the sample values:

$$\lambda^* = \frac{1}{n} \sum_1^n x_\mu = \bar{x}.$$

Taking $s = 1$ in the theorem of the preceding paragraph, we find that the limiting χ^2-distribution has in this case $r - 2$ d. of fr.

In Table 30.4.1, three numerical examples of the application of the test are shown. Ex. 1 a) gives the numbers of α-particles radiated from a disc in 2608 periods of 7.5 seconds according to Rutherford and Geiger (Ref. 2, p. 77). Ex. 1 b) gives the numbers of red blood

TABLE 30.4.1.

Application of the χ^2 test to the Poisson distribution.

i	Ex. 1 a)			Ex. 1 b)			Ex. 1 c)		
	No. of periods with i α particles ν_i	$n p_i$	$\frac{(\nu_i - n p_i)^2}{n p_i}$	No. of compartments with i blood-corpuscles ν_i	$n p_i$	$\frac{(\nu_i - n p_i)^2}{n p_i}$	No. of plants with i flowers ν_i	$n p_i$	$\frac{(\nu_i - n$ … $n p_i$
0	57	54.399	0.1244						
1	203	210.523	0.2688						
2	383	407.361	1.4568						
3	525	525.496	0.0005				5		
4	532	508.418	1.0938	1			2		
5	408	393.515	0.5332	3			10	25.0217	2.57
6	273	253.817	1.4498	5			19	19.1360	0.00
7	139	140.325	0.0125	8	15.7955	0.0919	20	24.1934	0.72
8	45	67.882	7.7132	13	11.4043	0.2233	42	26.7639	8.67
9	27	29.189	0.1642	14	15.0930	0.0792	27	26.3178	0.01
10	10	17.075	0.0677	15	17.9773	0.4931	25	23.2913	0.12
11	4			15	19.4661	1.0247	23	18.7389	0.96
12	2			21	19.3217	0.1458	11	13.8199	0.57
13				18	17.7032	0.0050	5	22.7171	1.98
14				17	15.0616	0.2495	6		
15				16	11.9599	1.3648	4		
16				9	8.9034	0.0010			
17				6	16.3140	0.3282			
18				3					
19				2					
20				2			1		
21				1					
Total	2608	2608 000	12.8849	169	169.0000	4.0065	200	200.0000	15.6
	$\bar{x} = 3.870$ $\chi^2 = 12.885$ (9 d. of fr.) $P = 0.17$			$\bar{x} = 11.911$ $\chi^2 = 4.006$ (9 d. of fr.) $P = 0.91$			$\bar{x} = 8.850$ $\chi^2 = 15.647$ (7 d. of fr.) $P = 0.03$		

corpuscles in the 169 compartments of a hæmacytometer observed by N. G. Holmberg. Ex. 1 c) gives the numbers of flowers of 200 plants of *Primula veris* counted by M.-L. Cramér at Utö in 1928. According to the rule given in 30.1, the tail groups of each sample have been pooled so that every group contains at least 10 expected observations. Thus e. g. in 1 b) the observed frequency in the groups $i = 7$ and $i = 17$ are respectively $1 + 3 + 5 + 8 = 17$ and $6 + 3 + + 2 + 2 + 1 = 14$. — The agreement is good in a), and even very good in b), while in c) we find an »almost significant» deviation from the hypothesis of a Poisson distribution, which is mainly due to the excessive number of plants with eight flowers.

The cases considered above are representative of classes of variables which often agree well with the Poisson distribution. — When the data show a significant deviation from the Poisson distribution, the agreement may sometimes be considerably improved by introducing the hypothesis that the parameter λ itself is a random variable, distributed in a Pearson type III distribution with the fr. f. $\frac{\alpha^{\varkappa}}{\Gamma(\varkappa)} x^{\varkappa-1} e^{-\alpha x}$, $(x > 0)$, where α and $\varkappa$ are positive parameters. In this way we obtain the *negative binomial distribution* (cf Ex. 21, p. 259), which has interesting applications e. g. to accident and sickness statistics (Greenwood and Yule, Ref. 119, Eggenberger, Ref. 81, Newbold, Ref. 159 a), and to problems connected with the number of individuals belonging to given species in samples from plant or animal populations (Eneroth, Ref. 81 a; Fisher, Corbet and Williams, Ref. 111). In the case of accident data, the introduction of a variable λ may be interpreted as a way of taking account of the *variation of risk* among the members of a given population. Analogous interpretations may be advanced in other cases. The subject may also be considered from the point of view of *random processes* (cf Lundberg, Ref. 152).

Ex. 2. *The normal distribution.* Let a sample of n values $x_1, \ldots, x_n$ be grouped into r classes, the i:th class containing ν_i observations situated in the interval $(\xi_i - \frac{1}{2}h,\ \xi_i + \frac{1}{2}h)$, where $\xi_i = \xi_1 + (i-1)h$. We want to test the hypothesis that the sample has been drawn from some normal population, with unknown values of the parameters m and σ. If the hypothesis is true, the probability p_i corresponding to the i:th class is

$$p_i = \frac{1}{\sigma\sqrt{2\pi}} \int e^{-\frac{(x-m)^2}{2\sigma^2}}\, dx,$$

where the integral is extended over the i:th class interval. For the two extreme classes ($i = 1$ and $i = r$), the intervals should be $(-\infty,\ \xi_1 + \frac{1}{2}h)$ and $(\xi_r - \frac{1}{2}h,\ +\infty)$ respectively. We then have, writing for brevity $g(x) = e^{-\frac{(x-m)^2}{2\sigma^2}}$,

$$\frac{\partial p_i}{\partial m} = \frac{1}{\sigma^3 \sqrt{2\pi}} \int (x - m)\, g(x)\, dx,$$

$$\frac{\partial p_i}{\partial \sigma} = \frac{1}{\sigma^4 \sqrt{2\pi}} \int (x - m)^2\, g(x)\, dx - \frac{p_i}{\sigma}.$$

The equations (30.3.3 a) then give after some simple reductions, all integrals being extended over the respective class intervals specified above,

$$m = \frac{1}{n} \sum_i \nu_i \frac{\int x\, g(x)\, dx}{\int g(x)\, dx},$$

$$\sigma^2 = \frac{1}{n} \sum_i \nu_i \frac{\int (x - m)^2\, g(x)\, dx}{\int g(x)\, dx}.$$

We first assume that the grouping has been arranged such that the two extreme classes do not contain any observed values. We then have $\nu_1 = \nu_r = 0$. For small values of h, an approximate solution may be obtained simply by replacing the functions under the integrals by their values in the mid-point ξ_i of the corresponding class interval. In this way we obtain estimates m^* and σ^* given by the expressions

$$m^* = \frac{1}{n} \sum_i \nu_i \xi_i, \qquad \sigma^{*2} = \frac{1}{n} \sum_i \nu_i (\xi_i - m^*)^2.$$

Thus m^* and σ^{*2} are identical with the mean $\bar{x}$ and the variance s^2 *of the grouped sample,* calculated according to the usual rule (cf 27.9) that all sample values in a certain class are placed in the mid-point of the class interval. — In order to obtain a closer approximation, we may develop the functions under the integrals in Taylor's series about the mid-point ξ_i. For small h, we then find by some calculation that the above formulae should be amended as follows:

$$m^* = \frac{1}{n} \sum_i \nu_i \xi_i + O(h^4), \qquad \sigma^{*2} = \frac{1}{n} \sum_i \nu_i (\xi_i - m^*)^2 - \frac{h^2}{12} + O(h^4).$$

Neglecting terms of order h^4, we may thus use the mean of the grouped sample as our estimate of m, while Sheppard's correction (cf 27.9) should be applied to the variance.

Even when h is not very small, and when the extreme classes are not actually empty, but contain only a small part of the total sample, the same procedure will lead to a reasonable approximation. — In practice, it is advisable to pool the extreme classes of a given sample according to the rule given in 30.1, so that every class contains at least 10 expected observations. Our estimates of m and σ^2 should then if possible be the values of $\bar{x}$ and s^2 calculated from the original grouping, before any pooling has taken place, and with Sheppard's correction applied to s^2. If r is the number of classes after the pooling, and actually used for the calculation of χ^2, the limiting distribution of χ^2 has $r-3$ d. of fr., since we have determined two parameters from the sample.

When the parent distribution is normal, asymptotic expressions for the means and variances of the sample characteristics g_1 and g_2 have been given in (27.7.9), while the corresponding exact expressions are found in (29.3.7). A further test of the normality of the distribution is obtained by comparing the values of g_1 and g_2 calculated from an actual sample with the corresponding means and variances.

TABLE 30.4.2.

Distribution of mean temperatures for June and July in Stockholm 1841—1940.

June			July		
Degrees Celsius	Observed	Expected	Degrees Celsius	Observed	Expected
—12.4	10	12 89	—14.9	11	10.41
12.5—12.9	12	7.89	15.0—15.4	7	6.72
13.0—13.4	9	10.20	15.5—15.9	8	9.00
13.5—13.9	10	11.93	16.0—16.4	13	10.95
14.0—14.4	19	12.62	16.5—16.9	14	12.12
14.5—14.9	10	12.08	17.0—17.4	13	12.20
15.0—15.4	9	10.46	17.5—17.9	6	11.16
15.5—15.9	6	8.19	18.0—18.4	9	9.28
16.0—16.4	7	5.81	18.5—18.9	7	7.02
16.5—	8	7.93	19.0—	12	11.14
Total	100	100.00	Total	100	100.00
$\bar{x} = 14.23$, $s = 1.574$, $g_1 = 0.098$, $g_2 = 0.062$, $\chi^2 = 7.86$ (7 d. of fr.) $P = 0.35$			$\bar{x} = 16.98$, $s = 1.615$, $g_1 = 0.382$, $g_2 = -0.044$, $\chi^2 = 3.34$ (7 d. of fr.) $P = 0.85$		

TABLE 30.4.3.

Breadth of beans. $\xi_1 = 6.825$ mm, $h = 0.25$ mm.

Class number i	Observed frequency ν_i	Expected frequency $n p_i$		
		Normal	First approx.	Second approx.
1	32	67.6	17.5	26.6
2	103	132.2	98.3	90.4
3	239	309.8	291.5	277.2
4	624	617.3	648.9	636.8
5	1 187	1 045.7	1 142.2	1 141.1
6	1 650	1 505.8	1 630.4	1 639.9
7	1 883	1 842.3	1 918.1	1 931.6
8	1 930	1 919.9	1 892.4	1 906.2
9	1 638	1 697.9	1 587.3	1 599.5
10	1 130	1 277.3	1 158.8	1 163.5
11	737	817.0	752.4	745.1
12	427	444.2	441.9	427.3
13	221	205.3	235.6	223.8
14	110	80.7	112.7	109.1
15	57	27.0	47.5	49.7
16	32	10.0	24.5	32.2
Total	12 000	12 000.0	12 000.0	12 000.0
$\bar{x} = 8.512$ $s = 0.6163$ $g_1 = -0.2878$ $g_2 = 0.1953$		$\chi^2 = 196.5$ (13 d. of fr.) $P < 0.001$	$\chi^2 = 34.3$ (12 d. of fr.) $P < 0.001$	$\chi^2 = 14.9$ (11 d. of fr.) $P = 0.19$

Table 30.4.2 shows the result of fitting normal curves to the distributions of mean temperatures for the months of June and July in Stockholm during the $n = 100$ years 1841—1940. In the original data, the figures are given to the nearest tenth of a grade, so that the exact class intervals are (12.45, 12.95) etc. We have here used somewhat smaller groups than is usually advisable. Both values of χ^2 indicate a satisfactory agreement with the hypothesis of a normal distribution. The values of g_1 and g_2 are also given in the table. On the normal hypothesis, the exact expressions (29.3.7) give in both cases $\boldsymbol{E}(g_1) = 0$, $\boldsymbol{D}(g_1) = 0.238$, and $\boldsymbol{E}(g_2) = -0.059$, $\boldsymbol{D}(g_2) = 0.455$, so that none of the observed values differs significantly from its mean.

A diagram of the sum polygon for the June distribution (drawn from the 100 individual sample values), together with the corresponding normal curve, has been given in Fig. 25, p. 328.

When g_1 or g_2 have significant values, the fit obtained by a normal curve may often be considerably improved by using the Charlier or Edgeworth expansions treated in 17.6—17.7. We must then bear in mind that, for every additional parameter determined from the sample, the number of d. of fr. should be reduced by one.

Table 30.4.3 shows the distribution of the breadths of $n = 12\,000$ beans of *Phaseolus vulgaris* (Johannsen's data, quoted from Charlier, Ref. 9, p. 73). On the hypothesis of a normal distribution, we have $\boldsymbol{E}(g_1) = 0$, $\boldsymbol{D}(g_1) = 0.0224$, and $\boldsymbol{E}(g_2) = -0.0005$, $\boldsymbol{D}(g_2) = 0.0447$, so that the actual values of g_1 and g_2 given in the table both differ significantly from the values expected on the normal hypothesis.

The table gives also the expected frequencies and the corresponding values of χ^2, calculated on the three hypotheses that the fr. f. of the standardized variable $\frac{x - \bar{x}}{s}$ is, in accordance with the expansion (17.7.3) or (17.7.5),[1])

a) »normal» . . . . . . $\varphi(x) = \frac{1}{\sqrt{2\pi}} e^{-\frac{x^2}{2}}$,

b) »first approx.» . . . . $\varphi(x) - \frac{g_1}{3!}\varphi^{(3)}(x)$,

c) »second approx.» . . . $\varphi(x) - \frac{g_1}{3!}\varphi^{(3)}(x) + \frac{g_2}{4!}\varphi^{(4)}(x) + \frac{10 g_1^2}{6!}\varphi^{(6)}(x)$.

In the first two cases, the deviations of the sample from the hypothetical distributions are highly significant, the values of P being < 0.001, while in the third case we have $P = 0.19$, so that the agreement is satisfactory. — In Fig. 26, p. 329, we have shown the histogram of this distribution, compared with the frequency curve for the »second approx.». More detailed comparisons for this and other examples are given by Cramér, Ref. 70.

30.5. Contingency tables. — Suppose that the n individuals of a sample are classified according to two variable arguments (quantitative or not) in a two-way table of the type shown in Table 30.5.1.

A table of this kind is known as a *contingency table*, and it is

[1]) By the same method as above, it is shown that the estimates to be used for the coefficients γ_1 and γ_2 are g_1 and g_2, as calculated from the grouped sample, using Sheppard's corrections.

often required to test the hypothesis that the two variable arguments are *independent.* Denote by p_{ij} the probability that a randomly chosen individual belongs to the i:th row and the j:th column of the table.

TABLE 30.5.1.

Arguments	1	2 . . . . . s	Total
1	ν_{11}	ν_{12} . . . . . ν_{1s}	$\nu_{1.}$
2	ν_{21}	ν_{22} . . . . . ν_{2s}	$\nu_{2.}$
.	—	— — — — — — —	—
.	—	— — — — — — —	—
.	—	— — — — — — —	—
r	ν_{r1}	ν_{r2} . . . . . ν_{rs}	$\nu_{r.}$
Total	$\nu_{.1}$	$\nu_{.2}$ . . . . . $\nu_{.s}$	n

The hypothesis of independence is then (cf 21.1.4) equivalent to the hypothesis that there exist $r+s$ constants $p_{i.}$ and $p_{.j}$ such that

$$p_{ij} = p_{i.}\, p_{.j},$$
$$\sum_i p_{i.} = \sum_j p_{.j} = 1.$$

According to this hypothesis, the joint distribution of the two arguments contains $r+s-2$ unknown parameters, since by means of the last relations two of the $r+s$ constants, say $p_{r.}$ and $p_{.s}$, may be expressed in terms of the remaining $r+s-2$.

In order to apply the χ^2 test to this problem, we have to calculate

$$\chi^2 = \sum_{i,j} \frac{(\nu_{ij} - n\, p_{i.}\, p_{.j})^2}{n\, p_{i.}\, p_{.j}},$$

where the sum is extended over all rs classes of the contingency table, and replace here the parameters $p_{i.}$ and $p_{.j}$ by their estimates derived from the equations (30.3.3) or (30.3.3 a), which in this case become

$$\sum_j \left(\frac{\nu_{ij}}{p_{i.}} - \frac{\nu_{rj}}{p_{r.}}\right) = 0, \qquad (i = 1, \ldots, r-1),$$

$$\sum_i \left(\frac{\nu_{ij}}{p_{.j}} - \frac{\nu_{is}}{p_{.s}}\right) = 0, \qquad (j = 1, \ldots, s-1$$

The solution of these equations is

$$p_{i.} = \frac{\nu_{i.}}{n}, \qquad p_{.j} = \frac{\nu_{.j}}{n},$$

so that the estimates to be used are simply the frequency ratios calculated from the marginal totals. Substituting these estimates for $p_{i.}$ and $p_{.j}$, the expression for χ^2 reduces to

$$\chi^2 = n \sum_{i,j} \frac{\left(\nu_{ij} - \frac{\nu_{i.}\,\nu_{.j}}{n}\right)^2}{\nu_{i.}\,\nu_{.j}} = n\left(\sum_{i,j} \frac{\nu_{ij}^2}{\nu_{i.}\,\nu_{.j}} - 1\right). \tag{30.5.1}$$

Since we have here rs groups and $r + s - 2$ parameters determined from the sample, the limiting distribution of χ^2 has $rs - (r + s - 2) - 1 = (r-1)(s-1)$ d. of fr. — Exact expressions for the mean and the variance of χ^2 as defined by (30.5.1) have been given by various authors (cf Haldane, Ref. 123, where further references are given). Assuming that the independence hypothesis is true, we have

$$\boldsymbol{E}(\chi^2) = \frac{n}{n-1}(r-1)(s-1). \tag{30.5.2}$$

The variance has a complicated expression that will not be given here.

A large value of χ^2 shows that the deviation from the hypothesis of independence is significant, but gives no direct information about the *degree of dependence* or *association* between the arguments. On the other hand, the quantity

$$f^2 = \frac{\chi^2}{n} = \sum_{i,j} \frac{\left(\frac{\nu_{ij}}{n} - \frac{\nu_{i.}}{n}\cdot\frac{\nu_{.j}}{n}\right)^2}{\frac{\nu_{i.}}{n}\cdot\frac{\nu_{.j}}{n}}$$

is the sample characteristic corresponding to the *mean square contingency* φ^2 defined by (21.9.6). If q is the smallest of the numbers r and s, it follows from 21.9 that

$$0 \leqq \frac{f^2}{q-1} = \frac{\chi^2}{n(q-1)} \leqq 1.$$

The upper limit 1 is attained when and only when each row (when $r \geqq s$) or each column (when $r \leqq s$) contains one single element different from zero. Thus $\frac{\chi^2}{n(q-1)}$ may be regarded as a measure of the degree of association indicated by the sample. The distribution of this measure is, of course, obtained by a simple change of variable in the distribution of χ^2. (For other measures of association, cf e. g. the text-book by Yule-Kendall, Ref. 43, chs 3—4.)

At the Swedish census of March 1936, a sample of 25 263 married couples was taken from the population of all married couples in country districts, who had been married for at most five years. Table 30.5.2 gives the distribution of the sample according to annual income and number of children. From (30.5.1) we obtain $\chi^2 = 568.5$ with $(5-1)(4-1) = 12$ d. of fr., so that the deviation from the hypothesis of independence is highly significant. On the other hand, the measure of association is $\frac{\chi^2}{n(q-1)} = 0.00750$, thus indicating only a slight degree of dependence.

Table 30.5.2.

Distribution of married couples according to annual income and number of children.

Children	Income (unit 1000 kr)				Total
	0—1	1—2	2—3	3—	
0	2 161	3 577	2 184	1 636	9 558
1	2 755	5 081	2 222	1 052	11 110
2	936	1 753	640	306	3 635
3	225	419	96	38	778
≧4	39	98	31	14	182
Total	6 116	10 928	5 173	3 046	25 263

In the particular case when $r = s = 2$, the contingency table 30.5.1 becomes a $2 \cdot 2$ table or a *fourfold table*, and the expression (30.5.1) reduces to

$$\chi^2 = n \frac{(\nu_{11}\nu_{22} - \nu_{12}\nu_{21})^2}{\nu_{1.}\,\nu_{2.}\,\nu_{.1}\,\nu_{.2}}, \tag{30.5.3}$$

so that $f^2 = \chi^2/n$ corresponds to the expression (21.9.7) for φ^2. When the arguments are quantitative, f^2 is identical with the square of the correlation coefficient of the sample (cf 21.9.7 and 21.7.3). — In the case of a fourfold table, there is only $(2-1)(2-1) = 1$ d. of fr. in the limiting distribution of χ^2, and we have $q - 1 = 1$.

In Table 30.5.3, we give the distribution of head hair and eyebrow colours of 46 542 Swedish conscripts according to Lundborg and Linders (Ref. 26). From (30.5.3) we obtain $\chi^2 = 19\,288$ and $f^2 = 0.414$, indicating a marked dependence between the arguments.

Table 30.5.3.

Hair colurs of Swedish conscripts.

Eyebrows	Head hair		Total
	Light or red	Dark or medium	
Light or red	30 472	3 238	33 710
Dark or medium . . .	3 364	9 468	12 832
Total	33 836	12 706	46 542

When the expected frequencies $\frac{\nu_{i.}\,\nu_{.j}}{n}$ in a fourfold table are small the approximation obtained by the usual χ^2 tables will be improved if we calculate χ^2 from the first expression (30.5.1), and reduce the absolute value of each difference $\nu_{ij} - \frac{\nu_{i.}\,\nu_{.j}}{n}$ by $\frac{1}{2}$ before squaring. This is known as *Yates' correction* (Ref. 250).

30.6. χ^2 as a test of homogeneity. — The contingency table 30.5.1 expresses the joint result of a sequence of n repetitions of a random experiment, each individual result being classified according to two variable arguments. In many cases, however, we encounter tables of the same formal appearance, where the situation is different.

Suppose that we have made s successive sequences of observations, consisting of $n_1, \ldots, n_s$ observations respectively, where the numbers n_j are not determined by chance, but are simply to be regarded as given numbers. At each observation we observe a certain variable argument, and the results of each sequence are classified according to this argument in r groups, the number of observations in the i:th group of the j:th sequence being denoted by ν_{ij}. Our data will then be expressed by a table which is formally identical with Table 30.5.1, the column totals $\nu_{.j}$ being here denoted by n_j. In the present case, however, the table does not express the result of one single sequence of observations, but of s independent sequences, each of which corresponds to one column of the table.

In such a case, it is often required to test the hypothesis that the s samples represented by the columns are *drawn from the same population*, so that the data are *homogeneous* in this respect. This is equivalent to the hypothesis that there are r constants $p_1, \ldots, p_r$ with

$\sum_i p_i = 1$, such that the propability of a result belonging to the i:th group is equal to p_i in all s sequences.

In order to test this hypothesis, we calculate χ^2 from the same formula (30.5.1) as in the previous case. A slight modification of the proof of 30.3 then shows that, if the hypothesis is true, χ^2 has the usual limiting distribution with the same number $(r-1)(s-1)$ of d. of fr. as before.

Unlike the corresponding proposition of the preceding paragraph, this is not a direct corollary of the general theorem of 30.3, but requires separate proof. The theorem of 30.3 may, in fact, be generalized to the case when we consider s independent samples of $n_1, \ldots, n_s$ individuals, all with the same r frequency groups, and determine a certain number, say t, of unknown parameters by applying the modified χ^2 minimum method to the expression $\chi^2 = \sum_{i,j} \frac{(\nu_{ij} - n_j p_i)^2}{n_j p_i}$. A straightforward generalization of the proof of 30.3 then shows that χ^2 has the usual limiting distribution with $(r-1)s - t$ d. of fr. In the case considered above, we are concerned with the hypothesis that the s samples are drawn from the same population, without further specification of the distribution, so that the parameters are the probabilities p_i themselves. Owing to the relation $\sum_i p_i = 1$ there are $t = r - 1$ parameters, and thus $(r-1)(s-1)$ d. of fr.

By means of the generalized theorem, we may also apply χ^2 to test the hypothesis that s given samples are drawn from the same population *of a specified type* such as the Poisson, the normal, etc. In such a case, the application of the modified χ^2 minimum method to the above expression for χ^2 shows that the parameters of the distribution should be determined in the same way as if we were concerned with one single sample with group frequencies equal to the row sums $\nu_{i.}$ of the given table. The proof of this statement will be left as an exercise for the reader.

In the particular case when $r = 2$, the table may be written:

ν_1	ν_2	$\ldots$	ν_s	$\sum_j \nu_j$
$n_1 - \nu_1$	$n_2 - \nu_2$	$\ldots$	$n_s - \nu_s$	$n - \sum_j \nu_j$
n_1	n_2	$\ldots$	n_s	n

We are here concerned with s sequences of observations, the number of occurrences of a certain event E being respectively $\nu_1, \ldots, \nu_s$, and we ask whether it is reasonable to assume that E has a constant, though unknown probability p throughout the observations. The estimate to be used for p will here be the frequency ratio of E in the totality of the data: $p^* = 1 - q^* = \frac{1}{n}\sum_j \nu_j$, and we obtain from the formula (30.5.1)[1])

$$\chi^2 = \sum_j \frac{(\nu_j - n_j p^*)^2}{n_j p^* q^*} = \frac{1}{p^* q^*}\sum_j \frac{\nu_j^2}{n_j} - n\frac{p^*}{q^*}, \tag{30.6.1}$$

with $s-1$ d. of fr. Writing $Q^2 = \frac{n-1}{n(s-1)}\chi^2$, the quantity Q is identical with the *divergence coefficient* introduced by Lexis. In accordance with (30.5.2), we have $\boldsymbol{E}(Q^2) = 1$. (Cf e. g. Tschuprow, Ref. 227 a, Cramér, Ref. 10, p. 105—123.)

Table 30.6.1 gives the number of children born in Sweden during the $s = 12$ months of the year 1935. The estimated probability of a male birth is $p^* = \frac{45\,682}{88\,273} = 0.517\,5082$. From (30.6.1) we find $\chi^2 = 14.986$ with 11 d. of fr., which corresponds to $P = 0.18$, so that the data are consistent with the hypothesis of a constant probability.

Table 30.6.1.

Sex distribution of children born in Sweden in 1935.

	Month												Total
	1	2	3	4	5	6	7	8	9	10	11	12	
Boys . . .	3743	3550	4017	4173	4117	3944	3964	3797	3712	3512	3392	3761	45682
Girls . . .	3537	3407	3866	3711	3775	3665	3621	3596	3491	3391	3160	3371	42591
Total	7280	6957	7883	7884	7892	7609	7585	7393	7203	6903	6552	7132	88273

We finally consider the case $s = 2$. In this case we are concerned with two independent samples, and we want to know whether these are drawn from the same population. The table may then be written

μ_1	ν_1	$\mu_1 + \nu_1$
μ_2	ν_2	$\mu_2 + \nu_2$
—	—	— —
—	—	— —
μ_r	ν_r	$\mu_r + \nu_r$
m	n	$m + n$

[1]) Cf also (30.2.1).

We have $r-1$ d. of fr., and (30.5.1) gives (cf. K. Pearson, Ref. 186, and R. A. Fisher, Ref. 91)

$$\chi^2 = m\,n \sum_i \frac{1}{\mu_i + \nu_i}\left(\frac{\mu_i}{m} - \frac{\nu_i}{n}\right)^2. \tag{30.6.2}$$

Writing $\varpi_i = \dfrac{\mu_i}{\mu_i + \nu_i}$ and $\varpi = \dfrac{m}{m+n}$, this reduces to the following expression due to Snedecor (Ref. 35, p. 173), which is often convenient for practical computation,

$$\begin{aligned}\chi^2 &= \frac{(m+n)^2}{m\,n}\left(\sum_i \frac{\mu_i^2}{\mu_i+\nu_i} - \frac{m^2}{m+n}\right)\\ &= \frac{1}{\varpi(1-\varpi)}\left(\sum_i \mu_i\varpi_i - m\,\varpi\right).\end{aligned} \tag{30.6.3}$$

Table 30.6.2 gives some income distributions from the Swedish census of 1930. When we compare the income distributions of the age groups 40—50 and 50—60 for all industrial workers and employees, (30.6.3) gives $\chi^2 = 840.62$ with 5 d. of fr., showing a highly significant difference between the distributions. It is evident that in this case

Table 30.6.2.

Income distributions from Swedish census of 1930.

Income (unit 1000 kr)	All workers and employees in industry			Foremen in industry		
	Age group		ϖ_i	Age group		ϖ_i
	40—50 μ_i	50—60 ν_i		40—50 μ_i	50—60 ν_i	
0—1	7 831	7 558	0.5088 6997	71	54	0.5680 0000
1—2	26 740	20 685	0.5638 3764	430	324	0.5702 9178
2—3	35 572	24 186	0.5952 6758	1 072	894	0.5452 6958
3—4	20 009	12 280	0.6196 8472	1 609	1 202	0.5723 9417
4—6	11 527	6 776	0.6297 8747	1 178	903	0.5660 7400
6—	6 919	4 222	0.6210 3940	158	112	0.5851 8519
Total	108 598	75 707	0.5892 2981	4 518	3 489	0.5642 5628
	$\chi^2 = 840.62$ (5 d. of fr.) $P < 0.001$			$\chi^2 = 4.27$ (5 d. of fr.) $P = 0.51$		

the numbers ϖ_i show a tendency to increase with increasing income. When we pass to the more homogeneous group of the foremen, however, this tendency disappears, and the comparison of the income distributions of the two age groups gives here $\chi^2 = 4.27$ and $P = 0.51$, so that we may consider these two samples as drawn from the same population.

30.7. Criterion of differential death rates. — Suppose that, in a mortality investigation, we have obtained the following data for two different classes (districts, occupations etc.) of persons:

Age group	Class A		Class B	
	Exposed to risk	Deaths	Exposed to risk	Deaths
1	n_1	d_1	n'_1	d'_1
2	n_2	d_2	n'_2	d'_2
.	.	.	.	.
.	.	.	.	.
r	n_r	d_r	n'_r	d'_r

It is required to test whether the sequences of death rates d_i/n_i and d'_i/n'_i obtained from these data are significantly different. For each age group, we may form a $2 \cdot 2$ table of the type

	Class A.	Class B.
Dead	d_i	d'_i
Surviving	$n_i - d_i$	$n'_i - d'_i$

and calculate from (30.6.2) the corresponding quantity

$$\chi_i^2 = \frac{n_i n'_i (n_i + n'_i)}{(d_i + d'_i)(n_i + n'_i - d_i - d'_i)} \left(\frac{d_i}{n_i} - \frac{d'_i}{n'_i}\right)^2,$$

which has one d. of fr. The successive χ_i^2 are independent. Thus if we assume that the two populations have identical death rates, the sum $\chi^2 = \sum_i \chi_i^2$ has the usual limiting distribution with r d. of fr., and this provides a test of the hypothesis (cf K. Pearson and Tocher, Ref. 187; R. A. Fisher, Ref. 91; Wahlund, Ref. 228).

Table 30.7.1 contains some data from a tuberculosis investigation by G. Berg (Ref. 61). It is required to test whether there are any significant differences in mortality between the two sexes during the first year after the finding of T.B. plus. The total χ^2 amounts to 22.2 with 10 d. of fr., which corresponds to $P = 0.014$, so that the deviation is »almost significant» according to our conventional terminology (cf 30.2). From the values of χ_i^2 given in the last column of the table, it is seen that the main contributions to χ^2 arise from the ages 30—50, where the women show a considerably higher mortality than the men.

TABLE 30.7.1.

Death rates for patients suffering from open pulmonary tuberculosis, during first year after finding T.B. plus.

Age group	Men			Women			χ_i^2
	Exposed to risk n_i	Deaths d_i	Death rate %	Exposed to risk n_i'	Deaths d_i'	Death rate %	
15–19	406	156	38.4	500	174	34.8	1.25
20–24	695	204	29.4	816	246	30.1	0.11
25–29	585	169	28.9	619	184	29.7	0.09
30–34	454	128	28.2	433	150	34.6	4.22
35–39	274	82	29.9	257	92	35.8	2.10
40–44	221	68	30.8	194	83	42.8	6.43
45–49	153	41	26.8	94	39	41.5	5.75
50–54	110	34	30.9	58	20	34.5	0.23
55–59	69	36	52.2	29	13	44.8	0.45
60–	89	43	48.3	47	28	59.6	1.57
Total	3 056	961		3 047	1 029		22.20

30.8. Further tests of goodness of fit. — As already observed in 30.1, it is always advisable to try to supplement the χ^2 test by other methods. In many cases, a simple inspection of the signs and magnitudes of the differences between observed and expected frequencies will reveal systematic deviations from the hypothesis tested, even though χ^2 may have a non-significant value.

When the χ^2 test is applied to a comparatively small sample, it is necessary to use a grouping with large class intervals, and thus sacrifice a good deal of the information conveyed by the sample. In such cases, it would be desirable to have recourse to a test based on the individual sample values. We shall now briefly mention a test of this type.

Let it be required to test the hypothesis that a sample of n observed values $x_1, \ldots, x_n$ has been drawn from a population with the given d. f. $F(x)$. The d. f. of the sample (cf 25.3) is $F^*(x) = \nu/n$, where ν is the number of sample values $\leqq x$. Since F^* converges in probability to F (cf 25.5) for any fixed x, we may consider the integral

$$\int_{-\infty}^{\infty} [F^*(x) - F(x)]^2 \, dK(x),$$

where $K(x)$ may be more or less arbitrarily chosen, as a measure of the deviation of our sample from the hypothesis. Tests based on measures of this type were first introduced by Cramér (Ref. 10 and 70) and von Mises (Ref. 27). Following Smirnoff (Ref. 215), we shall here take $K(x) = F(x)$, and thus obtain the integral

$$\omega^2 = \int_{-\infty}^{\infty} [F^*(x) - F(x)]^2 \, dF(x).$$

If the sample values $x_1, \ldots, x_n$ are arranged in increasing order, we have for any continuous $F(x)$

$$\omega^2 = \frac{1}{12 n^2} + \frac{1}{n} \sum_{1}^{n} \left[F(x_\nu) - \frac{2\nu - 1}{2n} \right]^2.$$

When the individual sample values are known, the exact value of ω^2 may thus be simply calculated. When only a grouped sample is available, an approximate value can be found, e. g. by the usual assumption that the x_ν are situated in the mid-points of the class intervals.

As observed in 25.5, $F^*(x)$ is the frequency ratio in n trials of an event of probability $F(x)$. Hence $\boldsymbol{E}(F^* - F)^2 = \frac{F(1-F)}{n}$. By means of this remark, it is possible to find the mean and the variance of ω^2. These are independent of $F(x)$, and we have

$$\boldsymbol{E}(\omega^2) = \frac{1}{6n}, \qquad \boldsymbol{D}^2(\omega^2) = \frac{4n - 3}{180 n^3}.$$

Comparing the value of ω^2 found in an actual sample with the mean and the variance calculated from these expressions, we obtain a test of our hypothesis. — The sampling distribution of ω^2, which is independent of $F(x)$, has been further investigated by Smirnoff (Ref. 215), who has shown that $n\omega^2$ has, as $n \to \infty$, a certain non-normal limiting distribution independent of n (cf the case of $n\,r^2$ in 29.13). It would be desirable to extend the theory to cases when the hypothetical $F(x)$ is not completely specified, but contains certain parameters that must be estimated from the sample.

Further important tests of goodness of fit have been proposed e. g. by Neyman (Ref. 164) and E. S. Pearson (Ref. 191).

CHAPTER 31.

Tests of Significance for Parameters.

31.1. Tests based on standard errors. — In the applications, it is often required to use a set of sample values for testing the hypothesis that a certain parameter of the corresponding population, such as a mean, a correlation coefficient, etc., has some value given in advance. In other cases, several independent samples are available, and we want to test whether the differences between the observed values of a certain sample characteristic are significant, i. e. indicative of a real difference between the corresponding population parameters.

Now we have seen in Ch. 28 that important classes of sample characteristics are, in large samples, asymptotically normal with means and variances determined by certain population parameters. Hence we may deduce tests of significance for hypotheses of the above type, following the general procedure indicated in 26.2 (cf also 35.1).

Thus if we draw a sample of n values $x_1, \ldots, x_n$ from any population (not necessarily normal) with the mean m and the s. d. σ, we know by 17.4 and 28.2 that the mean $\bar{x}$ of the sample values is asymptotically normal $(m, \sigma/\sqrt{n})$. Suppose for one moment that we know σ, and that we are testing the hypothesis that m has a specified value m_0. If the hypothesis is true, $\bar{x}$ is asymptotically normal $(m_0, \sigma/\sqrt{n})$. Denoting by λ_p the p % value of a normal deviate (cf 17.2), we thus have for large n a probability of approximately p % to encounter a deviation $|\bar{x} - m_0|$ exceeding $\lambda_p\,\sigma/\sqrt{n}$. Working on a p % level, we should thus reject the hypothesis if $|\bar{x} - m_0|$ exceeds this limit, whereas a smaller deviation should be regarded as consistent with the hypothesis.

Now in practice we usually do not know σ. By 27.3 we know, however, that the s. d. s of the sample converges in probability to σ as $n \to \infty$. Hence for large n there will only be a small probability that s differs from σ by more than a small amount. For the purposes of our test, we may thus simply replace σ by s, and act as if we had to test the hypothesis that $\bar{x}$ were normal $(m_0, s/\sqrt{n})$, where s is the known value calculated from our sample. An observed deviation $|\bar{x} - m_0|$ exceeding $\lambda_p s/\sqrt{n}$ will then lead us to reject the hypothesis $m = m_0$ on a p% level, while a smaller deviation will be regarded as consistent with the hypothesis.

The same method may be applied in more general cases. Consider any sample characteristic z, the distribution of which in large samples is asymptotically normal. In the expression for the variance of the asymptotic normal distribution of z, we replace any unknown population parameter by the corresponding known sample characteristic, retaining only the leading term of the expression for large n. The expression $\boldsymbol{d}(z)$ thus obtained will be denoted as the *standard error* of z in large samples. If it is required to test the hypothesis that the mean $\boldsymbol{E}(z)$ has some specified value z_0, we regard z as normally distributed with the known s. d. $\boldsymbol{d}(z)$. If the deviation $|z - z_0|$ exceeds $\lambda_p \boldsymbol{d}(z)$, the hypothesis will then be rejected on the p% level, and otherwise accepted.

In this way, all expressions deduced in Chs 27—28 for the s. d:s of sample characteristics and of their asymptotic normal distributions may be transformed to standard errors. Thus e. g. by (27.2.1), (27.4.2) and (27.7.2) the standard errors of the sample mean $\bar{x}$, the sample variance $s^2 = m_2$ and the sample s. d. $s = \sqrt{m_2}$ are

$$\boldsymbol{d}(\bar{x}) = \frac{s}{\sqrt{n}}, \quad \boldsymbol{d}(s^2) = \frac{\sqrt{m_4 - s^4}}{\sqrt{n}}, \quad \boldsymbol{d}(s) = \frac{\sqrt{m_4 - s^4}}{2 s \sqrt{n}}.$$

If it is assumed that the population is normal, the simpler expressions corresponding to this case may be applied. Thus e. g. by 28.5 the standard error of the median of a normal sample is

$$s \sqrt{\pi/(2\,n)} = 1.2533\, s/\sqrt{n}.$$

When a sample characteristic z has been computed, it is customary in practice to indicate its degree of reliability by writing the value z followed by $\pm\, \boldsymbol{d}(z)$. Thus e. g. the sample mean is written $\bar{x} \pm s/\sqrt{n}$, etc — For the frequency ratio in n trials of an event of constant probability p, we have by (16.2.2) $\boldsymbol{E}(\nu/n)=p$ and $\boldsymbol{D}(\nu/n)=\sqrt{p\,q/n}$, so that the standard error is $\sqrt{\frac{\nu(n-\nu)}{n^3}}$, and consequently the frequency ratio will be written $\frac{\nu}{n} \pm \sqrt{\frac{\nu(n-\nu)}{n^3}}$. The corresponding percentage $\varpi = 100\frac{\nu}{n}$ is accordingly written $\varpi \pm \sqrt{\frac{\varpi(100-\varpi)}{n}}$.

If two independent samples are given, the difference between their means or any other characteristics may be tested with the aid of the standard errors. If the means $\bar{x}$ and $\bar{y}$ are regarded as normal $(m_1, s_1/\sqrt{n_1})$ and $(m_2, s_2/\sqrt{n_2})$ respectively, the difference $\bar{x}-\bar{y}$ will be normal $\left(m_1-m_2, \sqrt{\frac{s_1^2}{n_1}+\frac{s_2^2}{n_2}}\right)$, and any hypothesis concerning the value of the difference m_1-m_2 can now be tested in the way shown above. In particular, the hypothesis $m_1=m_2$ will be rejected on the p % level, if $|\bar{x}-\bar{y}| > \lambda_p \sqrt{\frac{s_1^2}{n_1}+\frac{s_2^2}{n_2}}$, and otherwise accepted.

All the above methods are valid subject to the condition that our samples are »large». There are two kinds of approximations involved, as we have supposed a) that the sampling distributions of our characteristics are normal, and b) that certain population characteristics may be replaced by the corresponding values calculated from the sample. In practice, it is often difficult to know whether our samples are so large that these approximations are valid. However, some practical rules may be given. When we are dealing with means, the approximation is usually good already for $n > 30$. For variances, medians, coefficients of skewness and excess, correlation coefficients in the neighbourhood of $\varrho = 0$, etc., it is advisable to require that n should be at least about 100. For correlation coefficients considerably different from zero, even samples of 300 do not always give a satisfactory approximation.

Even in cases where n is smaller than required by these rules, or where the sampling distribution does not tend to normality, it is often possible to draw some information from the standard errors, though great caution is always to be recommended. — When the sampling distribution deviates considerably from the normal, the tables of the normal distribution do not give a satisfactory approximation to the probability of a deviation exceeding a given amount. We can then always use the inequality (15.7.2), which for any distribution gives the upper limit $1/k^2$ for the probability of a deviation from the mean exceeding k times the s. d. However, in most cases occurring in practice this limit is unnecessarily large. It follows, e. g., from (15.7.4) that for all unimodal and moderately skew distributions the limit may be substantially lowered. The same thing follows from the inequality given in Ex. 6, p. 256, if we assume that the coefficient γ_2 of the distribution is of moderate size. When there are reasons to assume that the sampling distribution belongs to one of these classes, a deviation exceeding four times the s. d. may as a rule be regarded as clearly significant. — When n is not large enough, it is advisable to use the complete expressions of the s. d:s, if these are available, and not only the leading terms. Further, we should then use the unbiased estimates (cf 27.6) of the population values, thus writing e. g. $s/\sqrt{n-1}$ instead of $s/\sqrt{n}$ for the standard error of the mean. — Whenever possible it is, however, preferable to use in such cases the tests based on exact distributions that will be treated in the next paragraph.

31.2. Tests based on exact distributions. — When the exact sampling distributions of the relevant characteristics are known, the approximate methods of the preceding paragraph may be replaced by exact methods. As observed in 29.1, this situation arises chiefly in cases where we are sampling from normal populations.

Suppose, e. g., that we are given a sample of n from a normal population, with unknown parameters m and σ, and that it is required to test the hypothesis that m has some value given in advance. If this hypothesis is true, the sample mean $\bar{x}$ is exactly normal $(m, \sigma/\sqrt{n})$, and the standardized variable $\sqrt{n}\,\frac{\bar{x}-m}{\sigma}$ is normal (0, 1). The approximate method of the preceding paragraph consists in replacing the unknown σ by an estimate calculated from the sample — for small n preferably $\sqrt{\frac{n}{n-1}}\,s$ — and regard the expression thus obtained, $t = \sqrt{n-1}\,\frac{\bar{x}-m}{s}$, as normal (0, 1). Now t is identical with the *Student ratio* of 29.4, and we have seen that the exact distribution of t is Student's distribution with $n-1$ d. of fr. If t_p denotes the p % value (cf 18.2) of t for $n-1$ d. of fr., the probability of a deviation such that $|t| > t_p$ is thus exactly equal to p %. The hypothetical value m will thus have to be rejected on a p % level if $|t| > t_p$, and otherwise accepted.

As $n \to \infty$, the t-distribution approaches the normal form (cf 20.2), and the figures for this limiting case are given in the last row of Table 4. It is seen from the table that the normal distribution gives a fairly good approximation to the t-distribution when $n \geqq 30$. For small n, however, the probability of a large deviation from the mean is substantially greater in the t-distribution (cf Fig. 20, p. 240).

When we wish to test whether the means $\bar{x}$ and $\bar{y}$ of two independent normal samples are significantly different, we may set up the »null hypothesis» that the two samples are *drawn from the same normal population.* It has been shown in 29.4 that, if this hypothesis is true, the variable

$$u = \sqrt{\frac{n_1 n_2 (n_1 + n_2 - 2)}{n_1 + n_2}} \cdot \frac{\bar{x} - \bar{y}}{\sqrt{n_1 s_1^2 + n_2 s_2^2}} \tag{31.2.1}$$

has the t-distribution with $n_1 + n_2 - 2$ d. of fr. When the means and variances of the samples are given, u can be directly calculated. If $|u|$ exceeds the p % value of t for $n_1 + n_2 - 2$ d. of fr., our data show a significant deviation from the null hypothesis on the p % level. If we have reason to assume that the populations are in fact normal, and that the s. d:s σ_1 and σ_2 are equal, the rejection of the null hypothesis implies that the means m_1 and m_2 are different (cf 35.5).

It is evident that we may proceed in the same way in respect of any function z of sample values, as soon as the exact distribution of z is known. We set up a probability hypothesis, according to which an observed value of z would with great probability lie in the neighbourhood of some known quantity z_0. If the hypothesis H is true, z has a certain known distribution, and from this distribution we may find the *p % value of the deviation* $|z - z_0|$, i. e. a quantity h_p such that the probability of a deviation $|z - z_0| > h_p$ is exactly p %. Working on a p % level, and always following the procedure of 26.2, we should then reject the hypothesis H if in an actual sample we find a deviation $|z - z_0|$ exceeding h_p, while a smaller deviation should be regarded as consistent with the hypothesis (cf 35.1).

When we are concerned with samples drawn from normal populations, tests of significance for various parameters may thus be founded on the exact sampling distributions deduced in Ch. 29. In practice, it is very often legitimate to assume that the variables encountered in different branches of statistical work are at least approximately normal (cf 17.8). In such cases, the tests deduced for the exactly normal case will usually give a reasonable approximation. It has, in fact, been shown that the sampling distributions of various important characteristics are not seriously affected even by considerable deviations from normality in the population. In this respect, the reader may be referred to some experimental investigations by E. S. Pearson (Ref. 190), and to the dissertation of Quensel (Ref. 200) on certain sampling distributions connected with a population of Charlier's type *A*. It seems desirable that investigations of these types should be further extended.

31.3. Examples. — We now proceed to show some applications of tests of the types discussed in the two preceding paragraphs. We shall first consider some cases where the samples are so large that it is perfectly legitimate to use the tests based on standard errors, and then proceed to various cases of samples of small or moderate size. With respect to the significance of the deviations etc. appearing in the examples, we shall use the conventional terminology introduced in 30.2.

Ex. 1. In Table 31.3.1 we give the distribution according to sex and ages of parents of 928 570 children born in Norway during the years 1871—1900. (From Wicksell, Ref. 231.) It is required to use these data to investigate the influence, if any, of the ages of the parents on the sex ratio of the offspring.

As a first approach to the problem, we calculate from the table the percentage of male births, and the corresponding standard error, for four large age groups, as shown by Table 31.3.2.

There are no significant differences between the numbers in this table. The largest difference occurs between the numbers 51.589 and 51.111, and this difference is 0.478 ± 0.222. The observed difference is here 2.15 times its standard error, and according to our conventional terminology this is only »almost significant». Nevertheless, the table might suggest a conjecture that the excess of boys would tend to increase when the age difference $x - y$ decreases.

In order to investigate the question more thoroughly, we consider the ages x and y of the parents of a child as an observed value of a two-dimensional random variable. Table 31.3.1 then gives the joint distributions of x and y for two samples of $n_1 = 477\,533$ and $n_2 = 451\,037$ values, for the boys and the girls respectively. If the

Table 31.3.1.
Live born children in Norway 1871—1900.

Age of father x	Age of mother y							Total
	—20	20—25	25—30	30—35	35—40	40—45	45—	
Boys								
—20	377	974	555	187	93	25	6	2 217
20—25	2 173	18 043	11 173	3 448	1 022	258	30	36 147
25—30	1 814	26 956	43 082	16 760	4 564	973	123	94 272
30—35	700	14 252	38 505	41 208	14 475	3 243	287	112 670
35—40	238	4 738	17 914	32 240	31 573	8 426	836	95 965
40—45	103	1 791	6 586	16 214	24 770	18 079	2 171	69 714
45—50	47	695	2 593	5 952	12 453	13 170	4 006	38 916
50—55	21	311	995	2 503	4 492	6 322	2 574	17 218
55—60	5	133	412	925	1 790	2 141	1 086	6 492
60—65	10	57	190	408	736	822	348	2 571
65—70	6	25	68	173	266	283	131	952
70—	2	12	46	59	119	113	48	399
Total	5 496	67 987	122 119	120 077	96 353	53 855	11 646	477 533
Girls								
—20	319	861	504	206	91	22	3	2 006
20—25	2 133	16 990	10 643	3 193	979	242	45	34 225
25—30	1 793	25 147	40 817	15 637	4 305	943	96	88 738
30—35	707	13 254	36 745	38 619	13 669	3 018	292	106 304
35—40	236	4 676	17 165	30 453	29 858	7 883	772	91 043
40—45	101	1 670	6 278	15 323	23 803	16 983	1 941	66 099
45—50	38	640	2 384	5 603	11 764	12 336	3 823	36 588
50—55	16	284	964	2 469	4 221	5 815	2 480	16 249
55—60	12	120	406	874	1 726	2 000	1 079	6 217
60—65	6	54	171	381	591	750	325	2 278
65—70	3	29	87	154	277	247	114	911
70—	1	18	30	67	108	115	40	379
Total	5 365	63 743	116 194	112 979	91 392	50 354	11 010	451 037

sex ratio among the newborn varies with the ages of the parents, the (x, y)-distribution must be different for the boys and the girls, so that the two samples are not drawn from the same population.

Table 31.3.2.

Percentage of male births.

Age of father x	Age of mother y	
	< 30	> 30
< 35	51.409 ± 0.090	51.589 ± 0.122
> 35	51.111 ± 0.186	51.430 ± 0.081

Table 31.3.3.

Sample moments for Table 31.3.1, in units of the classbreadth (5 years).

Central moments	Boys		Girls	
	Raw	Corrected	Raw	Corrected
m_{20}	2.9127	2.8294	2.9036	2.8203
m_{11}	1.4140	1.4140	1.4085	1.4085
m_{02}	1.7956	1.7123	1.7929	1.7096
m_{30}	3.0699	3.0699	3.0391	3.0391
m_{03}	0.4588	0.4588	0.4588	0.4588
m_{40}	28.6579	27.2307	28.4535	27.0309
m_{31}	10.3527	9.9992	10.2509	9.8988
m_{22}	7.7285	7.3431	7.6970	7.3126
m_{13}	5.8110	5.4575	5.8020	5.4499
m_{04}	7.5250	6.6564	7.5260	6.6587

Table 31.3.3 shows the uncorrected moments of the two samples, and the corrected moments calculated according to (27.9.4) and (27.9.6). We first observe that the distributions deviate significantly from normality. Consider, e. g., the marginal distribution of the father's age x for the boys. On the hypothesis that this distribution is normal, we find from the corrected moments $g_1 = 0.6450 \pm 0.0035$ and $g_2 = 0.4015 \pm 0.0071$, where the standard errors are calculated from (27.7.9). In both cases, the deviation from zero is highly significant, so that the hypothesis of normality is clearly disproved.[1])

[1]) According to Wicksell, l. c., the distribution is approximately *logarithmico-normal* (cf 17.5).

TABLE 31.3.4.

Sample characteristics for Table 31.3.1. Unit: one year.

Characteristics	Boys	Girls	$10^3 \cdot$ Diff.
$\bar{x}$	35.699 $\pm$ 0.0122	35.703 $\pm$ 0.0125	$+\ 4 \pm 17.5$
$\bar{y}$	32.128 $\pm$ 0.0095	32.116 $\pm$ 0.0097	-12 ± 13.6
$\bar{x} - \bar{y}$	3.571 $\pm$ 0.0095	3.587 $\pm$ 0.0097	$+16 \pm 13.6$
s_1	8.410 $\pm$ 0.0094	8.397 $\pm$ 0.0097	-13 ± 13.5
s_2	6.543 $\pm$ 0.0053	6.538 $\pm$ 0.0055	$-\ 5 \pm 7.6$
r	0.6424 $\pm$ 0.00097	0.6414 $\pm$ 0.00101	$-1.0 \pm\ 1.40$

Table 31.3.4 gives the values of some important sample characteristics for the boys and the girls, as well as the differences between corresponding characteristics for both sexes. The standard errors have been calculated according to the rules of 31.1 from the general formulae (27.2.1), (27.7.2) and (27.8.1); thus the simpler expressions (27.8.2) and (29.3.3) corresponding to the case of a normal population have not been applied here. For the difference $\bar{x} - \bar{y}$, we find

$$\boldsymbol{D}^2 (\bar{x} - \bar{y}) = (\sigma_1^2 - 2\,\varrho\,\sigma_1\,\sigma_2 + \sigma_2^2)/n,$$

and consequently the square of the standard error is

$$\boldsymbol{d}^2 (\bar{x} - \bar{y}) = (s_1^2 - 2\,r\,s_1\,s_2 + s_2^2)/n.$$

It is seen from the table that there are no significant differences between the characteristics. In particular we find that the mean of the age difference $x - y$ is not significantly greater for the girls than for the boys, so that the conjecture suggested by Table 31.3.2 is not supported by further analysis.

Finally, we may directly apply the χ^2 method to test whether the two samples in Table 31.3.1 may be regarded as drawn from the same population. In each of the two samples we have, in fact, $12 \cdot 7 = 84$ frequency groups, so that the whole table 31.3.1 may be rearranged as an $84 \cdot 2$ table of the type considered in 30.6, which may be tested for homogeneity by the χ^2 method, using (30.6.2) or (30.6.3) for the calculation of χ^2. Pooling all groups with fathers above 60, and with mothers above 40, we have a $60 \cdot 2$ table, and find $\chi^2 = 51.97$ with $(60 - 1)(2 - 1) = 59$ d. of fr. According to Fisher's approximation (cf 20.2), $\sqrt{2\chi^2} = 10.20$ would then be an observed value of a normal variable with the mean $\sqrt{117} = 10.82$ and unit s. d. By Table 1, the probability of obtaining a value of χ^2 at least as large as that actually observed is then approximately $1 - \Phi(10.20 - 10.82) = 0.73$, so that the agreement is very good, and the data are consistent with the hypothesis that the samples are drawn from the same population.

The analysis of the data in Table 31.3.1 has thus entirely failed to detect any significant influence of the ages of the parents on the sex of the children.

Ex. 2. In a racially homogeneous human population, the distributions of various body measurements usually agree well with the normal curve, and the small deviations are well represented by the first terms of a Charlier or Edgeworth series, as given e. g. by (17.7.5). We refer in this connection to a paper by Cramér (Ref. 70), where detailed examples are given.

In such cases, the standard errors of sample characteristics may be calculated from the simplified expressions which hold for the case of a normal parent distribution. Thus by (29.3.3) the standard error of s may be put equal to $s/\sqrt{2n}$, the standard error of the coefficient of variation V may be calculated from (27.7.11), etc.

For the stature of Swedish conscripts, measured in the years 1915—16 and 1924—1925 at an average age of 19 years 8 months, we find according to Hultkrantz (Ref. 128) the sample characteristics given in Table 31.3.5. The table shows a highly significant increase of the mean and the median during the interval of 9 years between the measurements. On the other hand, the s. d. and the coefficient

Table 31.3.5.

Sample characteristics for the stature of Swedish conscripts.

Characteristics	1915—16	1924—25	$10^2 \cdot$ Diff.
n	80 084	89 337	
Mean $\bar{x}$ . . . . cm	171.80 ± 0.022	172.58 ± 0.020	$+78 \pm 3.0$
Median . . . . »	171.81 ± 0.027	172.55 ± 0.025	$+74 \pm 3.7$
S. d. s . . . . »	6.15 ± 0.015	6.04 ± 0.014	-11 ± 2.1
Semi-interquartile range . »	4.05 ± 0.017	4.02 ± 0.016	-3 ± 2.8
$100\ V = 100\ s/\bar{x}$	3.58 ± 0.0090	3.50 ± 0.0083	-8 ± 1.2

of variation show a highly significant decrease, while the decrease of the semi-interquartile range is not significant.

These results agree well with further available data from Swedish conscription measurements. During the last 100 years, the mean stature of the conscripts has steadily increased, while the s. d. has decreased.

According to Table 31.3.5, the increase of the mean stature for the observed samples during the period of 9 years amounts to 0.78 ± 0.030 cm. What kind of conclusions can we draw from this fact with respect to the unknown increase Δm of the population mean m? — We have, in fact, observed the value 0.78 cm of a variable which is approximately normally distributed, with the unknown mean Δm, and a s. d. approximately equal to 0.030 cm. Let us, for the sake of the argument, assume that the word »approximately» may be omitted in both places, and let as usual λ_p denote the p % value of a normal deviate (cf 17.2). Consider the hypothesis that Δm is equal to a given quantity c. If we are working on a p % level, this hypothesis will evidently be regarded as consistent with the data if c is situated between the limits $0.78 \pm 0.030\, \lambda_p$, while otherwise it will be rejected. The quantities $0.78 \pm 0.030\, \lambda_p$ are called the *p % confidence limits* for Δm, and the interval between these limits is the *p % confidence interval.* — We shall return to these concepts in Ch. 34.

Ex. 3. The occurrence of exceptionally high or low water levels in lakes or rivers is often of great practical importance. For the average water levels of Lake Vänern in the month of June of the $n = 124$ years 1807—1930, we have (data from Lindquist, Ref. 149) the mean $\bar{x} = 4454.5$ cm above sea level, and the s. d. $s = 48.51$ cm. The distribution agrees well with the normal curve. Grouping the original data (which are not given here) into 9 groups with the class-breadth $h = 20$ cm, we find $\chi^2 = 3.728$. For $9 - 2 - 1 = 6$ d. of fr. this gives $P = 0.71$, so that the fit is very good.

If we denote by x_ν the ν:th value from the top in a normal sample of n values, while y_ν is the ν:th value from the bottom, the mean and the s. d. of x_ν are given by (28.6.16), while the corresponding expressions for y_ν are obtained by obvious modifications. Replacing in these expressions the population parameters m and σ by the sample values $\bar{x}$ and s given above, and neglecting the error terms, we obtain the means and standard errors given in Table 31.3.6, which also shows the extreme June levels actually observed during the period.

TABLE 31.3.6.

Extreme water levels of Lake Vänern, June 1807—1930.

ν	x_ν observed	$E(x_\nu)$ approx.	$d(x_\nu)$	Diff. in units of stand. error	y_ν observed	$E(y_\nu)$ approx.	$d(y_\nu)$	Diff. in units of stand. error
1	4566	4582.1	20.04	−0.80	4350	4326.9	20.04	+1.15
2	4548	4566.5	12.55	−1.47	4356	4342.6	12.55	+1.07
3	4546	4558.7	9.82	−1.29	4360	4350.4	9.82	+0.98
4	4535	4553.4	8.32	−2.21	4366	4355.6	8.32	+1.25
5	4535	4549.5	7.35	−1.97	4366	4359.5	7.35	+0.88

The absolute magnitude of the differences between the observed values and their means is in no case greater than might well be due to random fluctuations. We observe, however, that all the x_ν lie below their means, and conversely for the y_ν. This is partly due to the correlation between the x_ν (and the y_ν), and partly to the fact that the approximate mean values are affected with considerable errors, since we are dealing with the comparatively low value $n = 124$.

If we may assume that the distribution will remain unaltered for a period of, say, 500 years, we obtain in the same way as above the mean 4603.5 cm, and the standard error 17.6 cm, for the upper extreme level x_1 during this period. It would thus seem highly improbable that a level exceeding $4603.5 + 4 \cdot 17.6 = 4673.9$ cm will occur during this period.

Ex. 4. From Student's classical paper (Ref. 221) on the t-distribution, we quote the figures given in Table 31.3.7. It is required to test whether there is any significant difference between the effects of the drugs A and B. If we assume that the difference between the gains in sleep effected by the two drugs is normally distributed, the last column of the table constitutes a sample of $n = 10$ values from a normal population. On the usual null hypothesis that there is no difference between the effects, the mean m_3 of this population is zero. If this hypothesis is true, the Student ratio $t = \sqrt{9}\,\frac{\bar{z} - 0}{s_3}$ is distributed in the t-distribution with 9 d. of fr. (cf 31.2). From the observed values, we find $t = 4.06$, which by Table 4 corresponds to a value of P between 0.01 and 0.001. Thus the deviation from zero is significant, and the null hypothesis is disproved.

TABLE 31.3.7.

Additional hours of sleep gained by ten patients through the use of two soporific drugs A and B.

Patient	Drug A x	Drug B y	Difference $z = x - y$
1	1.9	0.7	1.2
2	0.8	−1.6	2.4
3	1.1	−0.2	1.3
4	0.1	−1.2	1.3
5	−0.1	−0.1	0.0
6	4.4	3.4	1.0
7	5.5	3.7	1.8
8	1.6	0.8	0.8
9	4.6	0.0	4.6
10	3.4	2.0	1.4
	$\bar{x} = 2.33$	$\bar{y} = 0.75$	$\bar{z} = 1.58$
	$s_1 = 1.899$	$s_2 = 1.697$	$s_3 = 1.167$

In this case, where we have the low value $n = 10$, it is to be expected that the approximate test based on the standard error of $\bar{z}$ will not give a very accurate result. If we apply this test, and use the estimate $s_3/\sqrt{10-1}$ for the standard error, we are led to regard the same value as above, $\sqrt{9}\,(\bar{z} - 0)/s_3 = 4.06$, as an observed value of a variable which, on the null hypothesis, is normal (0, 1). By Table 2, this corresponds to $P < 0.0001$. If we compare this with the value of P given by the exact test, it is seen that the error involved in applying the approximate test tends to exaggerate the significance of the deviation.

If, in the experiments recorded in Table 31.3.7, two different sets of ten patients had been used to test the two drugs, the data might also have been treated in another way (cf R. A. Fisher, Ref. 13, p. 123—125). Suppose that for each drug the gain in sleep is normally distributed, the s. d. having the same value in both cases. The samples headed x and y are then independent samples from normal populations with the same σ, and it is required to test the null hypothesis that the two population means m_1 and m_2 are equal. The variable u defined by (31.2.1), where we have to take $n_1 = n_2 = 10$, then has the

t-distribution with 18 d. of fr., and from Table 31.3.7 we find $u = 1.86$, which corresponds to $P = 0.08$, so that in this way we do not find any significant difference between the effects.

In cases where we may assume that the x and y columns are independent, both the above methods are available, and if either test shows a clearly significant difference, we must regard the null hypothesis as disproved, even if the other test fails to detect any significant difference. — In the case actually before us in Table 31.3.7 there is, however, an obvious correlation between the x and y columns due to the fact that corresponding figures refer to the same patient, so that it is not legitimate to apply the second method.

Ex. 5. For the July temperatures in Stockholm for the $n = 100$ years 1841—1940, we have (cf Table 30.4.2) the mean $\bar{x} = 16.982$ and the s. d. $s = 1.6145$. For the 30 first and the 30 last years of the period, the means are respectively 16.893 and 17.463. Are these group means significantly different from the general mean 16.982?

From the expression (29.4.5), we obtain $t = -0.36$ for the $k = 30$ first years, and $t = 1.97$ for the 30 last years, in both cases with

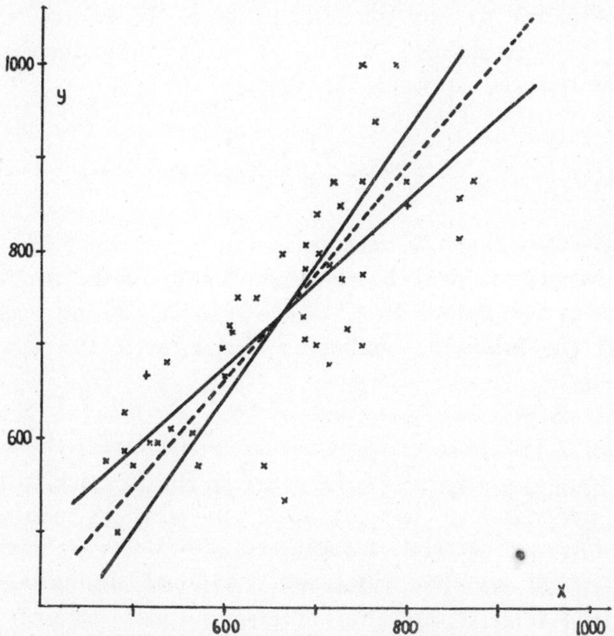

Fig. 31. Prices of potatoes at 46 places in Sweden, December 1936 (x), and December 1937 (y). Regression lines: ———. Orthogonal regression line: - - - - -.

$n - 2 = 98$ d. of fr. Both values lie below the 5 % limit, so that this test does not indicate any significant change in the summer temperature during the century.

Ex. 6. Fig. 31 shows the distribution of the prices of potatoes (öre per 100 kg) in December 1936 (x) and December 1937 (y), at $n = 46$ places in Sweden, according to official statistics. The ordinary characteristics of the sample are

$$\bar{x} = 660.57, \quad \bar{y} = 732.59, \quad s_1 = 106.86, \quad s_2 = 120.91,$$
$$r = 0.7928, \quad b_{12} = 0.7007, \quad b_{21} = 0.8971.$$

Let us assume that the (x, y)-values form a sample from a normal population, and that we wish to obtain information about the unknown values of the regression coefficient β_{21} and the correlation coefficient ϱ of this population.

According to (29.8.4), the variable $t = \frac{s_1 \sqrt{n-2}}{s_2 \sqrt{1-r^2}} (b_{21} - \beta_{21})$ has Student's distribution with $n - 2$ d. of fr. Introducing the values of the sample characteristics given above, we may thus test the hypothesis that β_{21} is equal to any given quantity c. If we are working on a p % level, this hypothesis will be regarded as consistent with the data if c is situated between the limits

$$b_{21} \pm \frac{s_2 \sqrt{1-r^2}}{s_1 \sqrt{n-2}} t$$

where t_p denotes the p % value of t for $n - 2$ d. of fr., while otherwise the hypothesis will be rejected. These limits are the p % confidence limits for β_{21} (cf Ex. 2 above). In the actual case we obtain in this way the following confidence limits for β_{21}:

$p = 5$ % . . . . 0.687 and 1.107,

$p = 1$ % . . . . 0.617 and 1.177,

$p = 0.1$ % . . . . 0.530 and 1.264.

For the sample correlation coefficient $r = 0.7928$, we have by (27.8.1) and (27.8.2) approximately the mean ϱ and the standard error

$$\boldsymbol{d}(r) = (1 - r^2)/\sqrt{n} = 0.0548.$$

If the sampling distribution of r shows a sufficiently close approach to normality, this may be used to test the hypothesis that ϱ is equal to any given quantity. However, the sampling distribution of r tends rather slowly to normality, when ϱ differs considerably from zero, and for $n = 46$ it must be expected that the results obtained by the use of the standard error are not very accurate. It is thus preferable to use the exact tables of the r-distribution (David, Ref. 261) or the logarithmic transformation (29.7.3)—(29.7.4) due to R. A. Fisher. In the latter case, we have to regard $z = \frac{1}{2}\log\frac{1+r}{1-r}$ as normally distributed, with the mean $\frac{1}{2}\log\frac{1+\varrho}{1-\varrho} + \frac{\varrho}{2(n-1)}$ and the s. d. $1/\sqrt{n-3}$, so that the variable

$$\lambda = \sqrt{n-3}\left(\frac{1}{2}\log\frac{1+r}{1-r} - \left(\frac{1}{2}\log\frac{1+\varrho}{1-\varrho} + \frac{\varrho}{2(n-1)}\right)\right)$$

is normal (0, 1). Working on a p % level, we are thus led to regard the data as consistent with any hypothetical value of ϱ, if

$$\frac{1}{2}\log\frac{1+\varrho}{1-\varrho} + \frac{\varrho}{2(n-1)}$$

falls between the limits

$$\frac{1}{2}\log\frac{1+r}{1-r} \pm \frac{\lambda_p}{\sqrt{n-3}},$$

where λ_p is the p % value of a normal deviate, while otherwise the hypothetical value will be rejected. When r is known, these limits may be calculated for any p, and the corresponding values of ϱ are then obtained by the numerical solution of an equation of the form $\frac{1}{2}\log\frac{1+\varrho}{1-\varrho} + \frac{\varrho}{2(n-1)} = k$. These values are the p % confidence limits for ϱ. In the actual case, we obtain the following confidence limits for ϱ:

$p = 5$ % . . . . 0.6486 and 0.8783,

$p = 1$ % . . . . 0.5913 and 0.8980,

$p = 0.1$ % . . . . 0.5164 and 0.9171.

Ex. 7. Table 31.3.8 gives the values (taken from official records) for the $n = 30$ years 1913—1942 of the following four variables:

x_1 = average yield of wheat (autumn sown) in kg per 10^4 m^2 for 20 rural parishes in the district of Kalmar (Sweden).

TABLE 31.3.8.

Wheat yield, temperature and rainfall in the Kalmar district.

Year	Wheat yield x_1	Winter temperature x_2	Summer temperature x_3	Rainfall x_4	Best linear estimate of x_1 x_1^*
1913	1990	2.7	12.8	230	2125
1914	1950	3.1	13.7	268	2295
1915	1630	1.9	12.0	188	1899
1916	1720	1.3	11.7	315	2058
1917	1560	1.0	12.7	180	1794
1918	1680	1.6	12.0	261	2004
1919	1980	2.3	12.2	216	2017
1920	2180	1.7	12.8	346	2223
1921	2370	3.1	13.1	131	1995
1922	1790	1.1	11.8	256	1918
1923	2400	1.6	11.2	327	2100
1924	1410	0.1	11.8	320	1913
1925	2570	3.7	13.2	382	2580
1926	2180	1.1	12.5	279	1996
1927	2150	2.5	12.2	351	2313
1928	2530	0.8	10.5	324	1956
1929	2100	0.8	10.9	196	1718
1930	2330	3.6	12.4	381	2529
1931	1850	1.6	10.7	273	1970
1932	2230	1.9	12.5	289	2123
1933	2510	2.2	11.9	338	2234
1934	2600	3.0	13.5	267	2271
1935	2480	3.2	12.3	372	2453
1936	1940	2.8	12.3	357	2370
1937	2770	2.1	13.5	358	2332
1938	2570	3.3	12.9	202	2154
1939	2510	3.8	13.4	311	2461
1940	1420	−1.1	11.3	172	1434
1941	810	−0.4	11.3	194	1572
1942	1990	−2.4	11.2	261	1434

x_2 = mean Celsius temperature of the air at Kalmar during the preceding winter (October—March).

x_3 = mean Celsius temperature of the air at Kalmar during the actual vegetation period (April—September).

x_4 = total rainfall in mm during the vegetation period, average for three meteorological stations in the district.

In this case it seems reasonable to regard the variables x_2, x_3 and x_4 as causes, each of which contributes more or less to the value of the yield x_1. It is required to investigate the nature of the causal relations between the variables. When the data are so few as in this example, we cannot hope to reach very precise results, but have to be satisfied with some general indications with respect to the significance or non-significance of the various possible influences.

We shall assume that the joint distribution of the four variables is normal. The correlation matrix $\boldsymbol{R} = \{r_{ij}\}$ of the sample is

$$\begin{Bmatrix} 1 & 0.59107 & 0.41082 & 0.46120 \\ 0.59107 & 1 & 0.67028 & 0.31838 \\ 0.41082 & 0.67028 & 1 & 0.10720 \\ 0.46120 & 0.31838 & 0.10720 & 1 \end{Bmatrix}$$

The determinant $R = |r_{ij}|$ is the square of the scatter coefficient (cf 22.7) of the sample. If the x_i are independent, we have by (29.13.2) $\boldsymbol{E}(R) = 0.806$ and $\boldsymbol{D}(R)$ approximately $= 0.115$. From the above matrix, we actually find $R = 0.273$, so that a dependence between the variables is clearly indicated.

The significance of the various r_{ij} may be judged by means of the distribution (29.7.5), which holds for r_{ij} if x_i and x_j are independent. According to (29.7.6), the hypothesis that x_i and x_j are independent will be disproved on the p % level, if $|r_{ij}|$ exceeds the limit $t_p/\sqrt{t_p^2 + \nu}$ where t_p is the p % value of t for $\nu = n - 2$ d. of fr. A table of this limit for various values of n and p is given by Fisher and Yates (Ref. 262). For the usual 5 %, 1 % and 0.1 % levels, the values of the limit are

D. of fr.	$p = 5$ %	$p = 1$ %	$p = 0.1$ %
$\nu = 26$	0.3740	0.4786	0.5880
$\nu = 27$	0.3673	0.4706	0.5790
$\nu = 28$	0.3609	0.4629	0.5703

For our r_{ij} we have $\nu = n - 2 = 28$ d. of fr., so that all r_{ij} except r_{24} and r_{34} exceed the 5 % limit. r_{13} lies between the 5 % and 1 % limits, and r_{14} is almost equal to the 1 % limit, while r_{12} and r_{23} even exceed the 0.1 % limit. It is interesting to note that r_{12} is considerably larger than r_{13}, which seems to indicate that the temperature of the last winter has a greater influence on the yield than the temperature of the summer.

The partial correlation coefficients $r_{ij.k}$ may be calculated from (23.4.3), and we find the following values:

$$r_{12.3} = 0.4666 \qquad r_{13.2} = 0.0244 \qquad r_{14.2} = 0.3570$$

$$r_{12.4} = 0.5281 \qquad r_{13.4} = 0.4096 \qquad r_{14.3} = 0.4602$$

For the significance limits of the $r_{ij.k}$, we have by (29.13.5) an expression of the same form as for the r_{ij}, with $\nu = n - 3 = 27$ d. of fr. Among the six coefficients given above, it is thus only $r_{12.4}$ that exceeds the 1 % limit, though both $r_{12.3}$ and $r_{14.3}$ lie very close to this value. If we compare e. g. $r_{13} = 0.41082$ with the values given for $r_{13.2}$ and $r_{13.4}$, we find that the elimination of the influence of the winter temperature x_2 has reduced the correlation between the yield x_1 and the summer temperature x_3 to the completely insignificant value $r_{13.2} = 0.0244$, while the elimination of the rainfall x_4 has practically no effect on the correlation. On the other hand, the comparison between $r_{12} = 0.59108$ and $r_{12.3}$ or $r_{12.4}$ shows that the correlation between yield and winter temperature is not substantially reduced by the elimination of summer temperature or rainfall. With respect to r_{14}, the situation is much the same as for r_{12}. — These comparisons seem to suggest the conjecture that the winter temperature x_2 and the rainfall x_4 are the really important factors, while the influence of the summer temperature x_3 is mainly due to the fact that x_3 is rather strongly correlated with x_2 ($r_{23} = 0.67028$).

The partial correlation coefficients with two secondary subscripts are calculated from (23.4.4). We find

$$r_{12.34} = 0.3739, \qquad r_{13.24} = 0.0848, \qquad r_{14.23} = 0.3650,$$

and these values seem to support the above conjecture, though none of them is strictly significant. We have here $\nu = n - 4 = 26$ d. of fr., and the 5 % significance limit for $r_{ij.kl}$ is 0.3740.

Consider now the multiple correlation coefficients. By means of (23.5.3) we find

$$\mathbf{r}_{1(23)} = 0.5914, \qquad \mathbf{r}_{1(24)} = 0.6575, \qquad \mathbf{r}_{1(34)} = 0.5872,$$

$$\mathbf{r}_{1(234)} = 0.6606.$$

The comparison between $r_{12} = 0.5911$ and $\mathbf{r}_{1(23)} = 0.5914$ confirms the results already obtained, since it shows that the knowledge of x_3 adds practically nothing to our information with respect to the yield x_1, when we already know x_2. Similarly, the multiple correlation coefficient $\mathbf{r}_{1(24)}$ is not appreciably smaller than $\mathbf{r}_{1(234)}$.

If the variables $x_1, \ldots, x_k$ are independent, the product $n\,\mathbf{r}^2_{1(2\ldots k)}$ is by (29.13.9) for large n approximately distributed in a χ^2-distribution with $k-1$ d. of fr. In the actual case, we find $n\,\mathbf{r}^2_{1(34)} = 10.344$ with 2 d. of fr., and $n\,\mathbf{r}^2_{1(234)} = 13.092$ with 3 d. of fr. Since $\mathbf{r}_{1(23)}$ and $\mathbf{r}_{1(24)}$ are both greater than $\mathbf{r}_{1(34)}$, it is thus seen that all four multiple correlation coefficients given above are significantly greater than zero.

Finally, we find the partial regression coefficients

$$b_{12.34} = 133.65, \text{ corresponding to } t = 2.055,$$

$$b_{13.24} = 44.87, \qquad » \qquad » \quad t = 0.434,$$

$$b_{14.23} = 1.9963, \qquad » \qquad » \quad t = 1.999,$$

where the t-values are calculated from (29.12.1), under the hypothesis that the corresponding population values $\beta_{1i.jk}$ are zero. We have

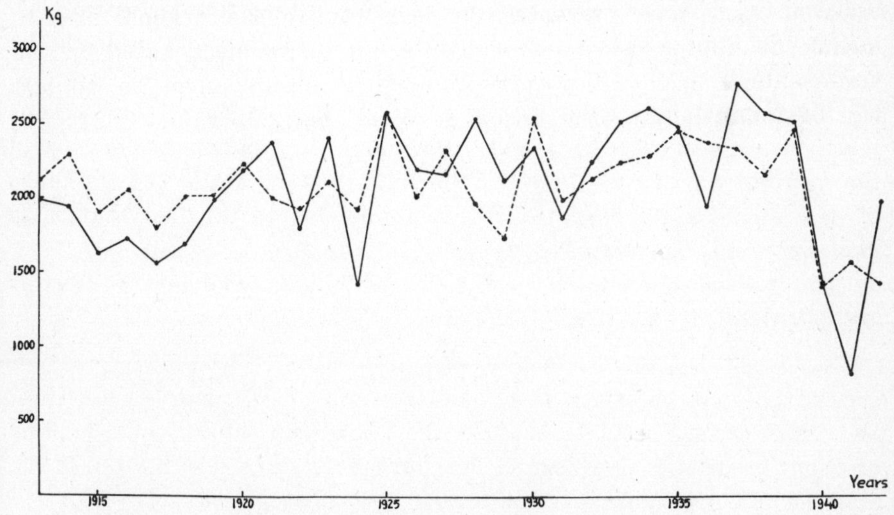

Fig. 32. Wheat yield x_1: ———. Best linear estimate x_1^*: ---------.

26 d. of fr. for t, and thus by Table 4 none of the three values is significant, though b_{12} and b_{14} are very near the 5 % limit. If we identify the observed b-values with the unknown population values, this would mean e. g. that an increase of one degree in the mean winter temperature would on the average produce an increase of about 134 kg in the yield per 10^4 m^2, summer temperature and rainfall being equal, whereas the corresponding figure for an increase of one degree in the summer temperature would only amount to 45 kg.

The equation of the sample regression plane for x_1 gives the best linear estimate of the observed values of x_1 in terms of x_2, x_3 and x_4:

$$x_1^* = 133.65\, x_2 + 44.87\, x_3 + 1.9963\, x_4 + 730.9.$$

The values of x_1^* calculated from this expression are given in the last column of Table 31.3.8. The values of x_1 and x_1^* are also shown in Fig. 32.

It should be borne in mind that, in all tests treated above, we have throughout assumed that we are concerned with samples obtained by *simple random sampling* (cf 25.2). This implies, i. a., that the sample values are supposed to be mutually *independent*. In many applications, however, situations arise where this assumption cannot be legitimately introduced. Cases of this character occur, e. g., often in connection with the analysis of statistical *time series*. Unfortunately, considerations of space have prevented the realization of the original plan to include in the present work a chapter on this subject, based on the mathematical theory of *random processes*. A discussion of the subject will be found in the dissertation of Wold (Ref. 246 a).

Chapters 32–34. Theory of Estimation.[1]

CHAPTER 32.

Classification of Estimates.

32.1. The problem. — In the preceding chapters, we have repeatedly encountered the problem of estimating certain population parameters by means of a set of sample values. We now proceed to a more systematic investigation of this subject.

The *theory of estimation* was founded by R. A. Fisher in a series of fundamental papers (Ref. 89, 96, 103, 104 and others). In Chs 32—33, we shall give an account of some of the main ideas introduced by Fisher, completing his results on certain points. In the present chapter, we shall be concerned with the classification and properties of various kinds of estimates. We shall then in Ch. 33 turn to consider some general methods of estimation, particularly the important *method of maximum likelihood* due to R. A. Fisher. Finally, Ch. 34 will be devoted to an investigation of the possibility of using the estimates for drawing valid inferences with respect to the parameter values.

Suppose that we are given a sample from a population, the distribution of which has a known mathematical form, but involves a certain number of unknown parameters. There will then always be an infinite number of functions of the sample values that might be proposed as estimates of the parameters. The following question then arises: *How should we best use the data to form estimates*? This question immediately raises another: *What do we mean by the »best» estimates?*

We might be tempted to answer that, evidently, the best estimate is the estimate falling nearest to the true value of the parameter to be estimated. However, it must be borne in mind that every estimate is a function of the sample values, and is thus to be regarded as an observed value of a certain random variable. Consequently we have

[1]) A considerable part of the topics treated in these chapters are highly controversial, and the relative merits of the various concepts and methods discussed here are subject to divided opinions in the literature.

no means of predicting the individual value assumed by the estimate in a given particular case, so that the goodness of an estimate cannot be judged from individual values, but only from the distribution of the values which it will assume in the long run, i. e. from its *sampling distribution.* When the great bulk of the mass in this distribution is concentrated in some small neighbourhood of the true value, there is a great probability that the estimate will only differ from the true value by a small quantity. From this point of view, an estimate will be »better» in the same measure as its sampling distribution shows a greater *concentration about the true value*, and the above question may be expressed in the following more precise form: *How should we use our data in order to obtain estimates of maximum concentration?* — We shall take this question as the starting-point of our investigation.

We have seen in Part II that the concentration (or the complementary property: the dispersion) of a distribution may be measured in various ways, and that the choice between various measures is to a great extent arbitrary. The same arbitrariness will, of course, appear in the choice between various estimates. Any measure of dispersion corresponds to a definition of the »best» estimate, viz. the estimate that renders the dispersion as expressed by this particular measure as small as possible.

In the sequel, we shall exclusively consider the measures of dispersion and concentration associated with the *variance* and its multidimensional generalizations. This choice is in the first place based on the general arguments in favour of the least-squares principle advanced in 15.6. Further, in the important case when the sampling distributions of our estimates are at least approximately normal, any reasonable measure of concentration will be determined by the second order moments, so that in this particular case the choice will be unique. — For a discussion of the theory from certain other points of view, the reader may be referred to papers by Pitman (Ref. 198, 199) and Geary (Ref. 116 a).

It will be convenient to consider first the case of samples from a population, the distribution of which contains a single unknown parameter. This case will be treated in 32.2—32.5, while 32.6—32.7 will be devoted to questions involving several unknown parameters. An important generalization of the theory will be indicated in 32.8.

32.2. Two lemmas. — We shall now prove two lemmas that will be required in the sequel. Each lemma is concerned with one of the two simple types of distributions, and there is a general proposition of which both lemmas are particular cases. The general proposition will, however, not be given here.

Lemma 1. *Suppose that, for every α belonging to a non-degenerate interval A, the function $g(x;\alpha)$ is a fr. f. in x, having the first moment $\psi(\alpha)$, and a finite second moment. Suppose further that, for almost all x, the partial derivative $\frac{\partial g}{\partial \alpha}$ exists for every α in A, and that $\left|\frac{\partial g}{\partial \alpha}\right| < G_0(x)$, where G_0 and $x\,G_0$ are integrable over $(-\infty, \infty)$. — Then the derivative $\frac{d\psi}{d\alpha}$ exists for every α in A, and we have*

$$(32.2.1) \qquad \int_{-\infty}^{\infty} (x-\alpha)^2 g(x;\alpha)\,dx \cdot \int_{-\infty}^{\infty} \left(\frac{\partial \log g}{\partial \alpha}\right)^2 g(x;\alpha)\,dx \geqq \left(\frac{d\psi}{d\alpha}\right)^2.$$

The sign of equality holds here, for a given value of α, when and only when there exists a quantity k, which is independent of x but may depend on α, such that

$$(32.2.2) \qquad \frac{\partial \log g}{\partial \alpha} = k(x-\alpha)$$

for almost all x satisfying $g(x;\alpha) > 0$.

By hypothesis we have for every α in A

$$(32.2.3) \qquad \int_{-\infty}^{\infty} g(x;\alpha)\,dx = 1, \quad \int_{-\infty}^{\infty} x\,g(x;\alpha)\,dx = \psi(\alpha),$$

and the conditions of 7.3 for differentiation under the integral sign are satisfied for both integrals, so that $\frac{d\psi}{d\alpha}$ exists and is given by the expression[1])

$$\frac{d\psi}{d\alpha} = \int_{-\infty}^{\infty} x\frac{\partial g}{\partial \alpha}\,dx = \int_{-\infty}^{\infty} (x-\alpha)\frac{\partial g}{\partial \alpha}\,dx$$

$$= \int_{-\infty}^{\infty} (x-\alpha)\sqrt{g}\;\frac{\partial \log g}{\partial \alpha}\sqrt{g}\,dx.$$

---

[1]) If $g(x;\alpha) = 0$ for all x in a certain interval, we must also have $\frac{\partial g}{\partial \alpha} = 0$, as otherwise g would assume negative values. The expression $\frac{\partial \log g}{\partial \alpha}\sqrt{g} = \frac{1}{\sqrt{g}}\frac{\partial g}{\partial \alpha}$ should then be given the value zero.

The relation (32.2.1) then immediately follows by an application of the Schwarz inequality (9.5.1).[1])

In (9.5.1) the sign of equality holds when and only when there are two constants u and v, not both equal to zero, such that $u g(x) + v h(x) = 0$ for almost all (P) values of x. Since $(x - \alpha)\sqrt{g}$ cannot vanish for almost all x it follows that, for a given value of α, the sign of equality holds in (32.2.1) when and only when

$$\frac{\partial \log g}{d\,\alpha}\sqrt{g} = k(x-\alpha)\sqrt{g}$$

for almost all x, where k is independent of x. This completes the proof of the lemma.

We give two examples of cases where the relation (32.2.2) is satisfied. Accordingly, it will be easily verified that in both these cases the sign of equality holds in (32.2.1).

Ex. 1. *The normal distribution with mean α and constant s. d.* Taking

$$g(x;\,\alpha) = \frac{1}{\sigma\sqrt{2\pi}}\,e^{-\frac{(x-\alpha)^2}{2\sigma^2}}$$

where σ is independent of x and α, we have $\psi(\alpha) = \alpha$ and $\frac{\partial \log g}{\partial \alpha} = \frac{x-\alpha}{\sigma^2}$ for all x and α.

Ex. 2. *The χ^2-distribution.* By (18.1.6), the fr. f. $k_n(x)$ of the χ^2-distribution has the first moment n. Thus the fr. f. $g(x;\,\alpha) = \frac{n}{\alpha}k_n\left(\frac{n\,x}{\alpha}\right)$, where $\alpha > 0$, has the first moment $\psi(\alpha) = \alpha$, and we obtain from (18.1.3) $\frac{\partial \log g}{\partial \alpha} = \frac{n}{2\alpha^2}(x-\alpha)$ for all $x > 0$ and $\alpha > 0$.

Lemma 2. *Suppose that, for every α belonging to a non-degenerate interval A, the finite or enumerable sequence of functions $p_1(\alpha), p_2(\alpha), \ldots$ are the probabilities of a distribution of the discrete type, the corresponding mass points $u_1, u_2, \ldots$ being independent of α. Suppose further that the distribution has the first moment $\psi(\alpha)$ and a finite second moment, and that the derivatives $p_i'(\alpha)$ exist for all i and for every α in A, and are such that the series $\Sigma\, u_i p_i'(\alpha)$ converges absolutely and uniformly in A. — Then the derivative $\frac{d\psi}{d\alpha}$ exists for every α in A, and we have*

$$\sum_i (u_i - \alpha)^2 p_i(\alpha) \cdot \sum_i \left(\frac{d \log p_i}{d\,\alpha}\right)^2 p_i(\alpha) \geqq \left(\frac{d\psi}{d\,\alpha}\right)^2. \tag{32.2.4}$$

---

[1]) I am indebted to professor L. Ahlfors for a remark leading to a simplification of my original proof of (32.2.1).

The sign of equality holds here, for a given value of α, when and only when there exists a quantity k, which is independent of i but may depend on α, such that

$$\frac{d \log p_i}{d\alpha} = k(u_i - \alpha), \tag{32.2.5}$$

for all i satisfying $p_i(\alpha) > 0$.

This is strictly analogous to Lemma 1, and is proved in the same way, by means of the following relations which correspond to (32.2.3):

$$\sum_i p_i(\alpha) = 1, \qquad \sum_i u_i p_i(\alpha) = \psi(\alpha).$$

As in the previous case, we give two examples of cases where the relation (32.2.5) is satisfied; in both cases it will be easily verified that the sign of equality holds in (32.2.4).

Ex. 3. For the *binomial distribution* with $p = \alpha/n$, we have $u_i = i$ and $p_i = \binom{n}{i}(\alpha/n)^i(1 - \alpha/n)^{n-i}$, where $i = 0, 1, \ldots, n$. Hence the mean is $\psi(\alpha) = np = \alpha$ and we have $\frac{d \log p_i}{d\alpha} = \frac{i}{\alpha} - \frac{n-i}{n-\alpha} = \frac{n}{\alpha(n-\alpha)}(u_i - \alpha)$.

Ex. 4. When $n \to \infty$ while α remains fixed, the binomial distribution tends to the *Poisson distribution* with $u_i = i$ and $p_i = \frac{\alpha^i}{i!}e^{-\alpha}$. Here we have $\psi(\alpha) = \alpha$ and $\frac{d \log p_i}{d\alpha} = \frac{u_i - \alpha}{\alpha}$.

32.3. Minimum variance of an estimate. Efficient estimates. — Suppose that, to every value of the parameter α belonging to a non-degenerate interval A, there corresponds a certain d. f. $F(x; \alpha)$. Let $x_1, \ldots, x_n$ be a sample of n values from a population with the d. f. $F(x; \alpha)$, where α may have any value in A, and let it be required to estimate the unknown »true value» of α. We shall use the general notation $\alpha^* = \alpha^*(x_1, \ldots, x_n)$ for any function of the sample values[1]) proposed as an estimate of α.

In the paragraphs 32.3—32.4, the size n of the sample will be considered as a *fixed* number $\geqq 1$. In 32.5, we proceed to consider

[1]) It is important to observe the different signification of the symbols α^* and α. By definition, α^* is a function of the sample values $x_1, \ldots, x_n$, which are conceived as random variables. Thus α^* is itself a *random variable*, possessing a certain sampling distribution. On the other hand, α is a *variable in the ordinary analytic sense* which, in the population corresponding to a given sample, may assume any constant, though possibly unknown, value in A.

questions related to the asymptotic behaviour of our estimates when n is large.

According to the terminology introduced in 27.6, α^* is called an *unbiased estimate* of α, if we have $\mathbf{E}(\alpha^*) = \alpha$. As shown by some simple examples in 27.6, it is often possible to remove the bias of an estimate by applying a simple correction, so that an unbiased estimate is obtained. In the general case, however, an estimate will have a certain *bias* $b(\alpha)$ depending on α, so that we have

$$\mathbf{E}(\alpha^*) = \alpha + b(\alpha).$$

It can be shown that, subject to certain general conditions of regularity, the mean square deviation $\mathbf{E}(\alpha^* - \alpha)^2$ *can never fall below a positive limit depending only on the d.f.* $F(x; \alpha)$, *the size* n *of the sample, and the bias* $b(\alpha)$. *In the particular case when* α^* *is unbiased whatever be the true value of* α *in* A, *the bias* $b(\alpha)$ *is identically zero, and it follows that the variance* $\mathbf{D}^2(\alpha^*)$ *can never fall below a certain limit depending only on* F *and* n.

We shall restrict ourselves to proving this theorem for the case when the d. f. $F(x; \alpha)$ belongs to one of the two simple types.

1. *The continuous type.* — Consider a distribution of the continuous type, with the fr. f. $f(x; \alpha)$, where α may have any value in A. The values $x_1, \ldots, x_n$ obtained in n independent drawings from this distribution are independent random variables, all of which have the same fr. f. $f(x; \alpha)$. Each particular sample will be represented by a definite point $\boldsymbol{x} = (x_1, \ldots, x_n)$ in the *sample space* $\boldsymbol{R}_n$ of the variables $x_1, \ldots, x_n$, and the probability element of the joint distribution is

$$L(x_1, \ldots, x_n; \alpha)\, dx_1 \ldots dx_n = f(x_1; \alpha) \ldots f(x_n; \alpha)\, dx_1 \ldots dx_n.$$

The joint fr. f. $L = f(x_1; \alpha) \ldots f(x_n; \alpha)$ is known as the *likelihood function* of the sample (cf 33.2).

Let now $\alpha^* = \alpha^*(x_1, \ldots, x_n)$ be a unique function of $x_1, \ldots, x_n$ not depending on α, which is continuous and has continuous partial derivatives $\frac{\partial \alpha^*}{\partial x_i}$ in all points $\boldsymbol{x}$, except possibly in certain points belonging to a finite number of hypersurfaces. We propose to use α^* as an estimate of α, and suppose that $\mathbf{E}(\alpha^*) = \alpha + b(\alpha)$, so that $b(\alpha)$ is the bias of α^*.

The equation $\alpha^* = c$ will, for various values of c, define a family of hypersurfaces in $\boldsymbol{R}_n$, and a point in $\boldsymbol{R}_n$ may be uniquely determined by the value of α^* corresponding to the particular hypersurface to which the point belongs, and by $n-1$ »local» coordinates $\xi_1, \ldots, \xi_{n-1}$ which determine the position of the point on the hypersurface. We may now consider the transformation by which the old variables $x_1, \ldots, x_n$ are replaced by the new variables α^* and $\xi_1, \ldots, \xi_{n-1}$. Choosing the »local» coordinates ξ_i such that the transformation satisfies the conditions A) and B) of 22.2, the joint fr. f. of the new variables will then be

$$f(x_1; \alpha) \ldots f(x_n; \alpha) \, |J|,$$

where J is the Jacobian of the transformation, and the x_i have to be replaced by their expressions in terms of the new variables.

The random variable α^* will have a certain distribution, in general dependent on the parameter α, and we denote the corresponding fr. f. by $g(\alpha^*; \alpha)$. Further, the joint conditional distribution of $\xi_1, \ldots, \xi_{n-1}$, corresponding to a given value of α^*, will have a fr. f. which we denote by $h(\xi_1, \ldots, \xi_{n-1} \,|\, \alpha^*; \alpha)$. By (22.1.1) we then have

$$(32.3.1) \qquad f(x_1; \alpha) \ldots f(x_n; \alpha) \, |J| = g(\alpha^*; \alpha) \, h(\xi_1, \ldots, \xi_{n-1} \,|\, \alpha^*; \alpha),$$

and the transformation of the probability element according to (22.2.3) may thus be written

$$(32.3.2) \qquad f(x_1; \alpha) \ldots f(x_n; \alpha) \, d x_1 \ldots d x_n = $$
$$= g(\alpha^*; \alpha) \, h(\xi_1, \ldots, \xi_{n-1} \,|\, \alpha^*; \alpha) \, d\alpha^* \, d\xi_1 \ldots d\xi_{n-1}$$

Suppose now that, for almost all values of x, α^*, $\xi_1, \ldots, \xi_{n-1}$, the partial derivatives $\frac{\partial f}{\partial \alpha}, \frac{\partial g}{\partial \alpha}$ and $\frac{\partial h}{\partial \alpha}$ exist for every α in A, and that

$$\left|\frac{\partial f}{\partial \alpha}\right| < F_0(x), \quad \left|\frac{\partial g}{\partial \alpha}\right| < G_0(\alpha^*), \quad \left|\frac{\partial h}{\partial \alpha}\right| < H_0(\xi_1, \ldots, \xi_{n-1}; \alpha^*),$$

where F_0, G_0, $\alpha^* G_0$ and H_0 are integrable over the whole space of the variables x, α^*, α^* and $\xi_1, \ldots, \xi_{n-1}$ respectively. We shall then say that we are concerned with a *regular estimation case of the continuous type*, and α^* will be called a *regular estimate* of α. — We now proceed to prove the following main theorem.

In any regular estimation case of the continuous type, the mean square deviation of the estimate α^* from the true value α satisfies the inequality

$$\text{(32.3.3)} \qquad \mathbf{E}(\alpha^* - \alpha)^2 \geqq \frac{\left(1 + \frac{d\,b}{d\,\alpha}\right)^2}{n \int\limits_{-\infty}^{\infty} \left(\frac{\partial \log f}{\partial \alpha}\right)^2 f(x;\,\alpha)\,d\,x}.$$

The sign of equality holds here, for every α *in* A, *when and only when the following two conditions are satisfied whenever* $g(\alpha^*;\,\alpha) > 0$:

A) *The fr.f.* $h(\xi_1, \ldots, \xi_{n-1} \mid \alpha^*;\,\alpha)$ *is independent of* α.

B) *We have* $\frac{\partial \log g}{\partial \alpha} = k(\alpha^* - \alpha)$, *where* k *is independent of* α^* *but may depend on* α.

In the particular case when α^* *is unbiased whatever be the value of* α *in* A, *we have* $b(\alpha) = 0$, *and* (32.3.3) *reduces to*

$$\text{(32.3.3 a)} \qquad \mathbf{D}^2(\alpha^*) \geqq \frac{1}{n \int\limits_{-\infty}^{\infty} \left(\frac{\partial \log f}{\partial \alpha}\right)^2 f\,d\,x}.$$

From our assumptions concerning the functions f and h, it follows according to 7.3 that the relations

$$\int\limits_{-\infty}^{\infty} f(x;\,\alpha)\,d\,x = \int\limits_{-\infty}^{\infty} \cdots \int\limits_{-\infty}^{\infty} h(\xi_1, \ldots, \xi_{n-1} \mid \alpha^*;\,\alpha)\,d\,\xi_1 \ldots d\,\xi_{n-1} = 1$$

may be differentiated with respect to α under the integrals. The resulting relations may be written

$$\text{(32.3.4)} \qquad \int\limits_{-\infty}^{\infty} \frac{\partial \log f}{\partial \alpha} f(x;\,\alpha)\,d\,x = \int\limits_{-\infty}^{\infty} \cdots \int\limits_{-\infty}^{\infty} \frac{\partial \log h}{\partial \alpha} h(\xi_1, \ldots, \xi_{n-1} \mid \alpha^*;\,\alpha)\,d\,\xi_1 \ldots d\,\xi_{n-1} = 0.$$

Taking the logarithmic derivatives with respect to α on both sides of (32.3.1) we obtain, the Jacobian J being independent of α,

$$\text{(32.3.5)} \qquad \sum_{1}^{n} \frac{\partial \log f(x_i;\,\alpha)}{\partial \alpha} = \frac{\partial \log g}{\partial \alpha} + \frac{\partial \log h}{\partial \alpha}.$$

We now square both members of this relation, multiply by (32.3.2), and integrate over the whole space. According to (32.3.4) all terms involving products of two different derivatives vanish, and we obtain

$$n\int_{-\infty}^{\infty}\left(\frac{\partial \log f}{\partial \alpha}\right)^2 f(x;\,\alpha)\,dx = \int_{-\infty}^{\infty}\left(\frac{\partial \log g}{\partial \alpha}\right)^2 g(\alpha^*;\,\alpha)\,d\alpha^* +$$

(32.3.6)

$$+\int_{-\infty}^{\infty} g\,d\alpha^* \int_{-\infty}^{\infty}\cdots\int_{-\infty}^{\infty}\left(\frac{\partial \log h}{\partial \alpha}\right)^2 h\,d\xi_1\ldots d\xi_{n-1} \geqq \int_{-\infty}^{\infty}\left(\frac{\partial \log g}{\partial \alpha}\right)^2 g(\alpha^*;\,\alpha)\,d\alpha^*.$$

The above proof of this inequality is due to Dugué (Ref. 76). The sign of equality holds here when and only when $\frac{\partial h}{\partial \alpha} = 0$ in almost all points such that $g > 0$, i. e. when the condition A) is satisfied.

Finally, the fr. f. $g(\alpha^*;\,\alpha)$ satisfies the conditions of Lemma 1 of the preceding paragraph, with $\psi(\alpha) = \alpha + b(\alpha)$, and an application of that lemma to the inequality (32.3.6) now immediately completes the proof of the theorem.

The integral occurring in the denominators of the second members of (32.3.3) and (32.3.3 a) may be expressed in any of the equivalent forms

$$\boldsymbol{E}\left(\frac{\partial \log f}{\partial \alpha}\right)^2 = \int_{-\infty}^{\infty}\left(\frac{\partial \log f}{\partial \alpha}\right)^2 f\,dx = \int_{-\infty}^{\infty}\frac{1}{f}\left(\frac{\partial f}{\partial \alpha}\right)^2 dx.$$

It will be readily seen that the above theorem remains true when we consider samples from a *multidimensional* population, specified by a fr. f. $f(x_1, \ldots, x_k;\,\alpha)$ containing the unknown parameter α.

Consider now the case when the estimate α^* is regular and unbiased. The second member of (32.3.3 a) then represents the smallest possible value of the variance $\boldsymbol{D}^2(\alpha^*)$. The ratio between this minimum value and the actual value of $\boldsymbol{D}^2(\alpha^*)$ will be called the *efficiency* of α^*, and will be denoted by $e(\alpha^*)$. We then always have $0 \leqq e(\alpha^*) \leqq 1$. When the sign of equality holds in (32.3.3 a), the variance $\boldsymbol{D}^2(\alpha^*)$ attains its smallest possible value, and we have $e(\alpha^*) = 1$. In this case we shall say that α^* is an *efficient estimate*[1]). These concepts are due to R. A. Fisher (Ref. 89, 96).

---

[1]) As a rule this term is used with reference to the behaviour of an estimate in large samples, i. e. for infinitely increasing values of n. However, we shall here find it convenient to distinguish between an *efficient estimate*, by which we mean an

It follows from the above theorem that a regular and unbiased estimate is efficient, when and only when the conditions A) and B) are satisfied. This becomes evident, if $e(\alpha^*)$ is written in the form

$$(32.3.7) \qquad e(\alpha^*) = \frac{\text{Min } \boldsymbol{D}^2(\alpha^*)}{\boldsymbol{D}^2(\alpha^*)} = \frac{1}{n\,\boldsymbol{E}\left(\frac{\partial \log f}{\partial \alpha}\right)^2 \boldsymbol{D}^2(\alpha^*)} =$$

$$= \frac{\boldsymbol{E}\left(\frac{\partial \log g}{\partial \alpha}\right)^2}{n\,\boldsymbol{E}\left(\frac{\partial \log f}{\partial \alpha}\right)^2} \cdot \frac{1}{\boldsymbol{E}\left(\frac{\partial \log g}{\partial \alpha}\right)^2 \boldsymbol{D}^2(\alpha^*)}.$$

Both factors in the last expression are $\leqq 1$, and the efficiency attains its maximum value 1 when and only when both factors are $= 1$. The first factor is $= 1$ when and only when the condition A) of the above theorem is satisfied, while the second factor has the same relation to condition B). — When an efficient estimate exists, it can always be found by the *method of maximum likehood* due to R. A. Fisher (cf. 33.2).

Let now α_1^* be an efficient estimate, while α_2^* is any regular unbiased estimate of efficiency $e > 0$. *We shall show that the correlation coefficient of* α_1^* *and* α_2^* *is* $\varrho(\alpha_1^*, \alpha_2^*) = \sqrt{e}$. In fact, the regular unbiased estimate $\alpha^* = (1 - k)\alpha_1^* + k\alpha_2^*$ has the variance

$$\boldsymbol{D}^2(\alpha^*) = \left((1-k)^2 + \frac{2\varrho k(1-k)}{\sqrt{e}} + \frac{k^2}{e}\right)\boldsymbol{D}^2(\alpha_1^*) =$$

$$= \left(1 + 2k\frac{\varrho - \sqrt{e}}{\sqrt{e}} + k^2\frac{e - 2\varrho\sqrt{e} + 1}{e}\right)\boldsymbol{D}^2(\alpha_1^*),$$

and if $\varrho \neq \sqrt{e}$, the coefficient of $\boldsymbol{D}^2(\alpha_1^*)$ can always be rendered < 1 by giving k a sufficiently small positive or negative value. Then it would follow that $\boldsymbol{D}^2(\alpha^*) < \boldsymbol{D}^2(\alpha_1^*)$, and the efficiency of α^* would be > 1, which is impossible.

In particular for $e = 1$ we have $\varrho = 1$. Thus two efficient estimates α_1^* and α_2^* have the same mean α, the same variance, and the correlation coefficient $\varrho = 1$. It then follows from 21.7 that the total

estimate of minimum variance for a given finite size n of the sample, and an *asymptotically efficient estimate* (cf 32.5), which has the analogous property for samples of infinitely increasing size. An *efficient estimate* exists only under rather restrictive conditions (cf 32.4), whereas the existence of an *asymptotically efficient estimate* can be proved as soon as certain general regularity conditions are satisfied (cf 33.3).

mass in the joint distribution of α_1^* and α_2^* is situated on the line $\alpha_1^* = \alpha_2^*$. *Thus two efficient estimates of the same parameter are »almost always» equal.*

We show in this paragraph several examples of efficient estimates (Ex. 1—2 for the continuous case, Ex. 5—6 for the discrete case). It will be left to the reader to verify that, in each case, the conditions A) and B) for efficient estimates are satisfied. In order to do this — we talk here of the continuous case, but in the discrete case everything is analogous — he will first have to find the fr. f. $g(\alpha^*; \alpha)$ of the estimate concerned, and then the examples given in 32.2 will directly provide the verification of condition B). Further, a convenient set of auxiliary variables $\xi_1, \ldots, \xi_{n-1}$ should be introduced, and the conditional fr. f. h should be calculated from (32.3.1); it then only remains to verify that h is independent of α. — In all examples, except in Ex. 4, we are dealing with regular estimates only. The reader should verify this in detail at least in some cases.

Ex. 1. *The mean of a normal population.* Writing

$$f(x; m) = \frac{1}{\sigma \sqrt{2\pi}} e^{-\frac{(x-m)^2}{2\sigma^2}},$$

where $\alpha = m$ is the parameter to be estimated, while σ is a known constant, we may choose for A any finite interval, and obtain

$$\boldsymbol{E}\left(\frac{\partial \log f}{\partial m}\right)^2 = \int_{-\infty}^{\infty} \left(\frac{x-m}{\sigma^2}\right)^2 f\,dx = \frac{1}{\sigma^2}\cdot$$

Consequently the variance of any regular unbiased estimate m^* satisfies the inequality $\boldsymbol{D}^2(m^*) \geqq \sigma^2/n$. For the particular estimate $m^* = \bar{x} = \sum x_i/n$ we have by 27.2 $\boldsymbol{E}(\bar{x}) = m$ and $\boldsymbol{D}^2(\bar{x}) = \sigma^2/n$, so that *the mean is an efficient estimate of m.*

Accordingly we have seen above that certain other possible estimates of m, such as the sample median (cf 28.5), and the mean of the ν:th values from the top and from the bottom of the sample (cf 28.6.17) have a larger variance than $\bar{x}$.

It is instructive to consider various other functions of the sample values that might be used as unbiased estimates of m; it will be found that the variance is always at least equal to σ^2/n. We give here a simple example of this kind. Consider a sample of $n = 3$ values from the normal distribution specified above, and let the sample values be arranged in order of magnitude: $x_1 \leqq x_2 \leqq x_3$. It might then be thought that the weighted mean

$$z = c x_1 + (1 - 2c) x_2 + c x_3$$

would, for some conveniently chosen value of c, be a »better» estimate of m than the simple arithmetic mean, which corresponds to $c = \frac{1}{3}$. We have, however, $\boldsymbol{E}(z) = m$ and

$$\boldsymbol{D}^2(z) = \frac{\sigma^2}{3} + \frac{3\sigma^2}{\pi}(2\pi - 3\sqrt{3})(c - \tfrac{1}{3})^2,$$

so that the variance of z attains its minimum precisely when $c = \frac{1}{3}$. — It will be left as an exercise for the reader to prove this formula, and to verify that the conditions for a regular estimate are satisfied in this case.

Ex. 2. *The variance of a normal population.* Writing

$$f(x;\, \sigma^2) = \frac{1}{\sqrt{2\pi\sigma^2}}\, e^{-\frac{(x-m)^2}{2\sigma^2}},$$

where $\alpha = \sigma^2$ is the parameter to be estimated, while m is a known constant, we may choose for A any finite interval $a < \sigma^2 < b$ with $a > 0$, and obtain

$$E\left(\frac{\partial \log f}{\partial \sigma^2}\right)^2 = \int_{-\infty}^{\infty} \left(\frac{(x-m)^2}{2\sigma^4} - \frac{1}{2\sigma^2}\right)^2 f\, dx = \frac{1}{2\sigma^4}.$$

Consequently the variance of any regular unbiased estimate of σ^2 is at least equal to $2\sigma^4/n$. Correcting the sample variance s^2 for bias (cf 27.6), we obtain the expression $\frac{n}{n-1} s^2 = \frac{1}{n-1} \sum (x_i - \bar{x})^2$, which by (27.4.5) is an unbiased estimate of σ^2 with the variance $2\sigma^4/(n-1)$. Obviously this is *not* an efficient estimate, but an estimate of efficiency $(n-1)/n < 1$. On the other hand, consider the estimate $s_0^2 = \frac{1}{n} \sum (x_i - m)^2$. This is legitimate, since m is now a known constant. It is easily seen that s_0^2 has the mean σ^2 and the variance $2\sigma^4/n$, and thus provides an efficient estimate of σ^2.

Ex. 3. *The s. d. of a normal population.* If, in the distribution of Ex. 2, we regard the s. d. σ instead of the variance σ^2 as the parameter to be estimated, we find

$$E\left(\frac{\partial \log f}{\partial \sigma}\right)^2 = \int_{-\infty}^{\infty} \left(\frac{(x-m)^2}{\sigma^3} - \frac{1}{\sigma}\right)^2 f\, dx = \frac{2}{\sigma^2}.$$

Consequently the variance of any regular unbiased estimate of σ is at least equal to $\sigma^2/(2n)$. Consider e. g. the expression

$$s' = \sqrt{\frac{n}{2}}\, \frac{\Gamma\left(\frac{n-1}{2}\right)}{\Gamma\left(\frac{n}{2}\right)}\, s,$$

where s is the s. d. of the sample. By (29.3.3) we have $E(s') = \sigma$, and

$$D^2(s') = \left(\frac{n-1}{2}\, \frac{\Gamma^2\left(\frac{n-1}{2}\right)}{\Gamma^2\left(\frac{n}{2}\right)} - 1\right) \sigma^2 = \frac{\sigma^2}{2n} + O\left(\frac{1}{n^2}\right),$$

so that the efficiency $e(s')$ tends to 1 as $n \to \infty$. For small n the efficiency is, however, considerably smaller than 1. Taking e. g. $n = 2$, we have $e(s') = \frac{1}{2(\pi - 2)} = 0.4380$, while for $n = 3$ we have $e(s') = \frac{\pi}{6(4-\pi)} = 0.6100$.

Similarly we find that the expression

$$s_0' = \sqrt{\frac{n}{2}}\,\frac{\Gamma\left(\frac{n}{2}\right)}{\Gamma\left(\frac{n+1}{2}\right)}\,s_0,$$

where s_0 is defined in Ex. 2, is an unbiased estimate of σ, with variance

$$\boldsymbol{D}^2(s_0') = \left(\frac{n}{2}\,\frac{\Gamma^2\left(\frac{n}{2}\right)}{\Gamma^2\left(\frac{n+1}{2}\right)} - 1\right)\sigma^2 = \frac{\sigma^2}{2n} + O\left(\frac{1}{n^2}\right).$$

The efficiency $e(s_0')$ tends to 1 as $n \to \infty$. For $n = 2$ we have $e(s_0') = \frac{\pi}{4(4-\pi)} = 0.9151$, while for $n = 3$ we have $e(s_0') = \frac{4}{3(3\pi - 8)} = 0.9358$, considerably above the corresponding figures for s'.

For the *mean deviation* $s_1 = \frac{1}{n}\sum |x_i - m|$, we find by easy calculations

$$\boldsymbol{E}\left(\sqrt{\frac{\pi}{2}}\,s_1\right) = \sigma, \quad \boldsymbol{D}^2\left(\sqrt{\frac{\pi}{2}}\,s_1\right) = (\pi - 2)\frac{\sigma^2}{2n},$$

so that $\sqrt{\pi/2}\,s_1$ is an unbiased estimate of σ, with the efficiency $\frac{1}{\pi - 2} = 0.8760$.

Ex. 4. *A non-regular case.* When the fr. f. has discontinuity points, the position of which depends on the parameter, the conditions for a regular case are usually not satisfied. In such cases, it is often possible to find unbiased estimates of »abnormally high» precision, i. e. such that the variance is smaller than the lower limit given by (32.3.3 a) for regular estimates.

Consider e. g. the fr. f. defined by $f(x;\alpha) = e^{\alpha - x}$ for $x \geqq \alpha$, and $f(x;\alpha) = 0$ for $x < \alpha$. In the point $x = \alpha$ the derivative $\frac{\partial f}{\partial \alpha}$ does not exist, so that this is a non-regular case. As we have seen in 7.3, the relation $\int f\,dx = 1$ cannot in this case be differentiated in the usual simple way; we have, in fact, $\int \frac{\partial f}{\partial \alpha}\,dx = 1$. When we pass from (32.3.5) to (32.3.6), all the n^2 terms in the first member will thus be equal to 1. Assuming that the functions g and h satisfy our conditions, we then obtain instead of $\boldsymbol{D}^2(\alpha^*) \geqq 1/n$, which would follow from (32.3.3 a), only the weaker inequality $\boldsymbol{D}^2(\alpha^*) \geqq 1/n^2$.

For the particular estimate $\alpha^* = \operatorname{Min} x_i - 1/n$, where $\operatorname{Min} x_i$ denotes the smallest of the sample values, we find the fr. f. $n f(n\alpha^*; n\alpha - 1)$, so that $\boldsymbol{E}(\alpha^*) = \alpha$, $\boldsymbol{D}^2(\alpha^*) = 1/n^2$. Thus α^* is an unbiased estimate, the variance of which is for all $n > 1$ smaller than the limit given by (32.3.3 a).

A further example of the same character is provided by the rectangular distribution, when we use the mean or the difference of the extreme values of the sample as estimates of the mean or the range of the population. According to (28.6.8) and (28.6.9), the variance is in both cases of the order n^{-2}, and thus certainly falls below the limit given by (32.3.3 a), when n is large.

2. *The discrete type.* — Consider a discrete distribution with the mass points $u_1, u_2, \ldots$, and the corresponding probabilities $p_1(\alpha)$, $p_2(\alpha), \ldots$, where α may have any value in A, and the u_i are independent of α. This case is largely analogous to the previous case, and will be treated somewhat briefly. As in the previous case, we consider an estimate $\alpha^* = \alpha^*(x_1, \ldots, x_n)$ with the mean $\boldsymbol{E}(\alpha^*) = \alpha + b(\alpha)$.

The probability that the *sample point* in $\boldsymbol{R}_n$ with the coordinates $x_1, \ldots, x_n$ assumes the particular position M determined by $x_1 = u_{i_1}, \ldots, x_n = u_{i_n}$ is equal to $p_{i_1}(\alpha) \ldots p_{i_n}(\alpha)$. The point M may, however, also be determined by another set of n coordinates, viz. by the value assumed by α^* in M, say α^*_ν, and by $n-1$ further coordinates $\nu_1, \ldots, \nu_{n-1}$ which determine the position of M on the hypersurface $\alpha^* = \alpha^*_\nu$. If $q_\nu(\alpha)$ denotes the probability that α^* takes the value α^*_ν, while $r_{\nu_1, \ldots, \nu_{n-1} \mid \nu}(\alpha)$ is the conditional probability of the set of values of $\nu_1, \ldots, \nu_{n-1}$ corresponding to M, for a given ν, we have the following relation which corresponds to (32.3.2):

$$p_{i_1}(\alpha) \ldots p_{i_n}(\alpha) = q_\nu(\alpha)\, r_{\nu_1, \ldots, \nu_{n-1} \mid \nu}(\alpha). \tag{32.3.8}$$

We now define a *regular estimation case of the discrete type* by the condition that, for every α in A, all derivatives $p_i'(\alpha)$, $q_\nu'(\alpha)$ and $r'_{\nu_1, \ldots, \nu_{n-1} \mid \nu}(\alpha)$ exist and are such that the series $\sum_i p_i'(\alpha)$ etc., which correspond to the analogous integrals considered in the continuous case, converge absolutely and uniformly in A. We shall then also call α^* a *regular estimate* of α.

In any regular estimation case of the discrete type, we have the inequality corresponding to (32.3.3):

$$\boldsymbol{E}(\alpha^* - \alpha)^2 \geqq \frac{\left(1 + \frac{d b}{d \alpha}\right)^2}{n \sum_i \left(\frac{d \log p_i}{d \alpha}\right)^2 p_i(\alpha)}. \tag{32.3.9}$$

The sign of equality holds here, for every α in A, when and only when the following two conditions are satisfied whenever $q_\nu(\alpha) > 0$:

A) *The conditional probability $r_{\nu_1 \ldots \nu_{n-1} \mid \nu}(\alpha)$ is independent of α.*

B) *We have $\frac{d \log q_\nu}{d \alpha} = k(\alpha^*_\nu - \alpha)$, where k is independent of ν but may depend on α.*

In the particular case when α^* is unbiased whatever be the value of α in A, we have $b(\alpha) = 0$, and (32.3.9) *reduces to*

(32.3.9 a)
$$D^2(\alpha^*) \geqq \frac{1}{n \sum_i' \left(\frac{d \log p_i}{d \alpha}\right)^2 p_i}.$$

The proof of this theorem follows the same lines as the corresponding proof in the continuous case. We take the logarithmic derivatives on both sides of (32.3.8), square, multiply by (32.3.8), and then sum over all possible sample points M. By means of Lemma 2 of the preceding paragraph, the truth of the theorem then follows.

As in the continuous case, an unbiased estimate will be called *efficient*, when the sign of equality holds in (32.3.9 a). The definition of the *efficiency* of an estimate, and the remarks concerning the correlation between various estimates, extend themselves with obvious modifications to the discrete case.

The expressions (32.3.3 a) and (32.3.9 a) are particular cases of the general inequality

$$D^2(\alpha^*) \geqq \frac{1}{n \int\limits_{-\infty}^{\infty} \frac{\left(d \frac{\partial F}{\partial \alpha}\right)^2}{d F}},$$

which holds, under certain conditions, even for a d. f. $F(x;\alpha)$ not belonging to one of the two simple types. The integral appearing here is of a type known as *Hellinger's integral* (cf e. g. Hobson, Ref. 17, I, p. 609). We shall not go into this matter here, but proceed to give some further examples of efficient estimates.

Ex. 5. For the *binomial distribution* we have $p_i = \binom{N}{i} p^i q^{N-i}$, where $\alpha = p$ is the parameter to be estimated, while N is a known integer, and $q = 1 - p$. Then

$$\sum_i \left(\frac{d \log p_i}{d p}\right)^2 p_i = \sum_0^N \left(\frac{i}{p} - \frac{N-i}{q}\right)^2 p_i = \frac{N}{p q}.$$

Thus the variance of any regular unbiased estimate p^* from a sample of n values is at least equal to $\frac{p q}{n N}$. For the particular estimate $p^* = \frac{\bar{x}}{N} = \frac{1}{n N} \sum x_i$ we find $E(p^*) = p$ and $D^2(p^*) = \frac{p q}{n N}$, so that this is an efficient estimate.

Ex. 6. For the *Poisson distribution* with the parameter λ we have $p_i = \frac{\lambda^i}{i!} e^{-\lambda}$, and

$$\sum_i \left(\frac{d \log p_i}{d \lambda}\right)^2 p_i = \sum_0^\infty \left(\frac{i}{\lambda} - 1\right)^2 p_i = \frac{1}{\lambda}.$$

Thus the variance of any regular unbiased estimate is at least equal to λ/n. For the particular estimate $\lambda^* = \bar{x} = \sum x_i/n$ we have $E(\lambda^*) = \lambda$ and $D^2(\lambda^*) = \lambda/n$, so that this is an efficient estimate.

32.4. Sufficient estimates. — In order that a regular unbiased estimate α^* should be *efficient*, i. e. of minimum variance, it is necessary and sufficient that the conditions A) and B) of the preceding paragraph are both satisfied. If we only require that condition A) should be satisfied, we obtain a wider class of estimates. We now proceed to consider this class, restricting ourselves to distributions of the continuous type, the discrete case being perfectly analogous.

For the continuous case, condition A) requires that the conditional fr. f. $h(\xi_1, \ldots, \xi_{n-1} | \alpha^*; \alpha)$ should be independent of α, whenever $g(\alpha^*; \alpha) > 0$. This means that the distribution of mass in the infinitesimal domain bounded by two adjacent hypersurfaces α^* and $\alpha^* + d\alpha^*$ is independent of α. In such a case, the estimate α^* may be said to summarize all the relevant information contained in the sample with respect to the parameter α. In fact, when we know the value of α^* corresponding to our sample, say α_0^*, the sample point M must lie on the hypersurface $\alpha^* = \alpha_0^*$, and the conditional distribution on this hypersurface is independent of α, so that the further specification of the position of M does not give any new information with respect to α. Using the terminology introduced by R. A. Fisher (Ref. 89, 96), we shall then call α^* a *sufficient estimate.* Since in (32.3.1) the Jacobian J is independent of α, it follows that α^* is sufficient if and only if

$$f(x_1; \alpha) \ldots f(x_n; \alpha) = g(\alpha^*; \alpha) H(x_1, \ldots, x_n), \tag{32.4.1}$$

where H is independent of α.

From the nature of the conditions A) and B), it is fairly evident that efficient or sufficient estimates can only be expected to exist for rather special classes of populations. There are important connections between these classes of estimates, when they exist, and the maximum likelihood method (cf 33.2).

For further information concerning the conditions of existence and other properties of efficient and sufficient estimates, the reader is referred to papers by R. A. Fisher (Ref. 89, 96. 103, 104 etc.), Neyman (Ref. 162), Neyman and E. S. Pearson (Ref. 173), Koopman (Ref. 141), Darmois (Ref. 74), Dugué (Ref. 76) and others.

In Ex. 1, 2, 5 and 6 of the preceding paragraph, we have considered various examples of efficient estimates. All these are, a fortiori, sufficient estimates. In each case, this can be directly shown by studying the transformation which replaces the original sample variables by the estimate α^* and $n-1$ further conveniently chosen new variables, and verifying that condition A) is satisfied. The reader is recommended to carry out these transformations in detail. (Cf also the analogous case in 32.6, Ex. 1.)

The estimate s_0' defined in 32.3, Ex. 3, is an example of a regular unbiased estimate satisfying condition A) but not condition B), i.e. a sufficient estimate which is not efficient. A further example of the same kind will be given in 33.3, Ex. 3. Thus the class of sufficient estimates is effectively more general than the class of efficient estimates.

The above definition of a sufficient estimate, which applies to the class of regular and unbiased estimates, may be directly extended to the class of all regular estimates, whether unbiased or not. After this extension, it follows immediately from the definition that the property of sufficiency is invariant under a change of variable in the parameter. Thus if α^* is a sufficient estimate of the parameter α, and if we replace α by a new parameter $\varphi(\alpha)$, then $\varphi(\alpha^*)$ will be a sufficient estimate of $\varphi(\alpha)$. For efficient estimates, there is no corresponding proposition.

32.5. Asymptotically efficient estimates. — In the preceding paragraphs, we have considered the size n of the sample as a fixed integer $\geqq 1$. Let us now suppose that the regular unbiased estimate $\alpha^* = \alpha^*(x_1, \ldots, x_n)$ is defined for all sufficiently large values of n, and let us consider the asymptotic behaviour of α^* as n tends to infinity.

If α^* converges in probability to α as n tends to infinity, α^* is a *consistent estimate* of α (cf 27.6). — In Chs 27—29, we have seen (cf e.g. 27.7 and 28.4) that in many important cases the s.d. of an estimate α^* is of order $n^{-\frac{1}{2}}$ for large n, so that we have $\boldsymbol{D}(\alpha^*) \sim c\, n^{-\frac{1}{2}}$, where c is a constant. If α^* is unbiased and has a s.d. of this form, it is obvious that α^* is consistent (cf 20.4). Further, in such a case the efficiency $e(\alpha^*)$ defined by (32.3.7) tends to a definite limit as n tends to infinity:

$$\lim_{n\to\infty} e(\alpha^*) = e_0(\alpha^*) = \frac{1}{c^2 \boldsymbol{E}\left(\dfrac{\partial \log f}{\partial \alpha}\right)^2}. \tag{32.5.1}$$

In the discrete case we obtain an analogous expression. This limit is called the *asymptotic efficiency* of α^*. Obviously $0 \leqq e_0(\alpha^*) \leqq 1$.

Consider further the important case of an estimate α^*, whether regular and unbiased or not, which for large n is asymptotically normal $(\alpha, c/\sqrt{n})$. We have seen in 28.4 that this situation may arise even in cases when $\boldsymbol{E}(\alpha^*)$ and $\boldsymbol{D}(\alpha^*)$ do not exist. However, when n is large, the distribution of α^* will then for practical purposes be equivalent to a normal distribution with the mean α and the s.d. $c/\sqrt{n}$, and accordingly we shall even in such cases denote the quantity

$e_0(\alpha^*)$ defined by the last member of (32.5.1) as the asymptotic efficiency of α^*.

When $e_0(\alpha^*) = 1$, we shall call α^* an *asymptotically efficient estimate* of α. Under fairly general conditions, an asymptotically efficient estimate can be found by the method of maximum likelihood (cf 33.3).

Ex. 1. For the *normal distribution,* the sample median may be used as an estimate of m, and by 28.5 this estimate has the asymptotic efficiency $2/\pi = 0.6366$. Thus if we estimate m by calculating the median from a sample of, say, $n = 10\,000$ observations, we obtain an estimate of the same precision as could be obtained by calculating the mean $\bar{x}$ from a sample of only $2n/\pi = 6366$ observations. Nevertheless, the median is sometimes preferable in practice, on account of the greater simplicity of its calculation.

We may also use the arithmetic mean of the ν:th values from the top and from the bottom of the sample as an estimate of m. By (28.6.17), this is an estimate of asymptotic efficiency zero.

When, in the normal distribution, m is known, and it is required to estimate the variance σ^2 or the s. d. σ, we may use various estimates connected with the sample variance s^2. In Ex. 2—3 of 32.3, we have already met with some examples of asymptotically efficient estimates of this kind. — We may also use the difference between the ν:th values from the top and from the bottom of the sample, multiplied by an appropriate constant, as an estimate of σ. According to (28.6.18), this is an estimate of asymptotic efficiency zero. The use of this estimate in large samples would thus involve a »loss of information» even greater than in the case of the sample median mentioned above. Nevertheless, the estimates of σ as well as of m based on the ν:th values may often be used in practice with great advantage, as their calculation is very simple, and the loss of information is not considerable for small values of n (cf the papers quoted in this connection in 28.6).

Ex. 2. For the *Cauchy distribution* with the fr. f. $f(x; \mu) = \pi^{-1}[1 + (x - \mu)^2]^{-1}$ we have

$$\mathbf{E}\left(\frac{\partial \log f}{\partial \mu}\right)^2 = \frac{4}{\pi}\int_{-\infty}^{\infty} \frac{(x-\mu)^2}{[1 + (x-\mu)^2]^3}\, dx = \tfrac{1}{2}.$$

Thus the variance of any regular unbiased estimate of μ is at least equal to $2/n$. By 19.2, the sample mean $\bar{x}$ has the same fr. f. $f(x; \mu)$, so that the mean is not a consistent estimate of μ. Neither is the arithmetic mean of the ν:th values from the top and from the bottom of the sample (cf 28.6.11). On the other hand, the sample median is by 28.5 asymptotically normal $(\mu, \frac{1}{2}\pi/\sqrt{n})$, and thus the median has the asymptotic efficiency $\dfrac{2}{n} : \dfrac{\pi^2}{4n} = \dfrac{8}{\pi^2} = 0.8106$.

32.6. The case of two unknown parameters. — We shall now briefly indicate how the concepts and propositions given in the preceding paragraphs may be generalized to cases involving several unknown parameters. It will be sufficient to give the explicit statements of the results for continuous distributions, as the corresponding results for the discrete case follow by analogy. In order to simplify the writing, we shall further restrict ourselves to the case of *unbiased* estimates.

In the present paragraph we shall consider a distribution with two unknown parameters α and β, specified by a fr. f. $f(x;\, \alpha, \beta)$. From a sample of n values $x_1, \ldots, x_n$ drawn from this distribution; we form two functions $\alpha^* = \alpha^*(x_1, \ldots, x_n)$ and $\beta^* = \beta^*(x_1, \ldots, x_n)$, which are assumed to be unbiased estimates of α and β respectively. We then consider a transformation in the sample space $\boldsymbol{R}_n$, replacing the old variables $x_1, \ldots, x_n$ by n new variables α^*, β^* and $\xi_1, \ldots, \xi_{n-2}$. For this transformation we have the following relations corresponding to (32.3.1) and (32.3.2):

$$J \prod_{i=1}^{n} f(x_i;\, \alpha, \beta) = g(\alpha^*, \beta^*;\, \alpha, \beta)\, h(\xi_1, \ldots, \xi_{n-2} \mid \alpha^*, \beta^*;\, \alpha, \beta),$$

$$\prod_{i=1}^{n} f(x_i;\, \alpha, \beta)\, d x_i =$$

$$= g(\alpha^*, \beta^*;\, \alpha, \beta)\, h(\xi_1, \ldots, \xi_{n-2} \mid \alpha^*, \beta^*;\, \alpha, \beta)\, d\alpha^*\, d\beta^*\, d\xi_1 \ldots d\xi_{n-2}.$$

Here g is the joint fr. f. of α^* and β^*, while h is the conditional fr. f. of $\xi_1, \ldots, \xi_{n-2}$ for given values of α^* and β^*. Finally J is a Jacobian independent of α and β.

A *regular estimation case* is now defined as a case where the fr. f:s f, g and h satisfy the regularity conditions stated in 32.3 with respect to *both* parameters α and β.

Operating in the same way as in 32.3, though dealing with total differentials with respect to α and β instead of partial derivatives with respect to α, we obtain (cf Dugué, Ref. 76)

$$(32.6.1) \qquad n \int_{-\infty}^{\infty} \left(\frac{\partial \log f}{\partial \alpha} d\alpha + \frac{\partial \log f}{\partial \beta} d\beta \right)^2 f\, dx \geqq$$

$$\geqq \int_{-\infty}^{\infty} \int_{-\infty}^{\infty} \left(\frac{\partial \log g}{\partial \alpha} d\alpha + \frac{\partial \log g}{\partial \beta} d\beta \right)^2 g\, d\alpha^*\, d\beta^*,$$

where the sign of equality holds when and only when the conditional fr. f. h is independent of α and β, whenever $g > 0$. In a case where this condition is satisfied, the estimates α^* and β^* may be said to summarize all relevant information contained in the sample with respect to α and β. In generalization of 32.4, we shall then say that α^* and β^* are *joint sufficient estimates* of α and β.

Both members of (32.6.1) are quadratic forms in $d\alpha$ and $d\beta$. Owing to the homogeneity, the same inequality between the forms holds true even if $d\alpha$ and $d\beta$ are replaced by any variables u and v, and thus (32.6.1) may be written

$$n\left[\boldsymbol{E}\left(\frac{\partial \log f}{\partial \alpha}\right)^2 u^2 + 2\boldsymbol{E}\left(\frac{\partial \log f}{\partial \alpha}\frac{\partial \log f}{\partial \beta}\right)uv + \boldsymbol{E}\left(\frac{\partial \log f}{\partial \beta}\right)^2 v^2\right] \geqq \tag{32.6.2}$$
$$\geqq \boldsymbol{E}\left(\frac{\partial \log g}{\partial \alpha}\right)^2 u^2 + 2\boldsymbol{E}\left(\frac{\partial \log g}{\partial \alpha}\frac{\partial \log g}{\partial \beta}\right)uv + \boldsymbol{E}\left(\frac{\partial \log g}{\partial \beta}\right)^2 v^2.$$

Consider now the inequality (32.2.1), which expresses the main result of Lemma 1 in 32.2, and suppose that $\psi(\alpha) = \alpha$. The inequality (32.2.1) may then be written as an inequality between two quadratic forms in one variable:

$$\boldsymbol{E}\left(\frac{\partial \log g}{\partial \alpha}\right)^2 u^2 \geqq \frac{u^2}{\boldsymbol{E}(\alpha^* - \alpha)^2},$$

where $g = g(\alpha^*; \alpha)$ is a fr. f. with the mean $\boldsymbol{E}(\alpha^*) = \alpha$, and the form in the second member is the reciprocal of the form $\boldsymbol{E}(\alpha^* - \alpha)^2 u^2$. When expressed in this way, the lemma may be generalized to fr. f:s involving several parameters (cf Cramér, Ref. 72; the detailed proof of this generalization will not be given here). In the case of two parameters, the generalized lemma asserts that the second member of (32.6.2) is at least equal to the reciprocal form of

$$\boldsymbol{E}(\alpha^* - \alpha)^2 u^2 + 2\boldsymbol{E}[(\alpha^* - \alpha)(\beta^* - \beta)]uv + \boldsymbol{E}(\beta^* - \beta)^2 v^2 =$$
$$= \sigma_1^2 u^2 + 2\varrho\sigma_1\sigma_2 uv + \sigma_2^2 v^2,$$

where σ_1, σ_2 and ϱ denote the s. d:s and the correlation coefficient of α^* and β^*, so that

$$\boldsymbol{E}\left(\frac{\partial \log g}{\partial \alpha}\right)^2 u^2 + 2\boldsymbol{E}\left(\frac{\partial \log g}{\partial \alpha}\frac{\partial \log g}{\partial \beta}\right)uv + \boldsymbol{E}\left(\frac{\partial \log g}{\partial \beta}\right)^2 v^2 \geqq \tag{32.6.3}$$
$$\geqq \frac{1}{1-\varrho^2}\left(\frac{u^2}{\sigma_1^2} - \frac{2\varrho uv}{\sigma_1\sigma_2} + \frac{v^2}{\sigma_2^2}\right).$$

Now the concentration ellipse of the joint distribution of α^* and β^* has the equation (cf 21.10.1)

$$(32.6.4) \qquad \frac{1}{1-\varrho^2}\left(\frac{(u-\alpha)^2}{\sigma_1^2} - \frac{2\varrho(u-\alpha)(v-\beta)}{\sigma_1\sigma_2} + \frac{(v-\beta)^2}{\sigma_2^2}\right) = 4.$$

The inequalities (32.6.2) and (32.6.3) thus imply that *the fixed ellipse*

$$(32.6.5) \quad n\left[\mathbf{E}\left(\frac{\partial \log f}{\partial \alpha}\right)^2 (u-\alpha)^2 + 2\mathbf{E}\left(\frac{\partial \log f}{\partial \alpha}\frac{\partial \log f}{\partial \beta}\right)(u-\alpha)(v-\beta) + \right.$$
$$\left. + \mathbf{E}\left(\frac{\partial \log f}{\partial \beta}\right)^2 (v-\beta)^2\right] = 4$$

lies wholly within the concentration ellipse of any pair of regular unbiased estimates α^*, β^*. — *This is the generalization to two parameters of the inequality* (32.3.3 a).

When the sign of equality holds in both relations (32.6.2) and (32.6.3), we shall say that α^* and β^* are *joint efficient estimates* of α and β. In this case the two ellipses (32.6.4) and (32.6.5) coincide, and the joint distribution of α^* and β^* has a *greater concentration* (cf 21.10) than the distribution of any non-efficient pair of estimates.

Consider now a pair of joint efficient estimates α_0^* and β_0^*. The variances of α_0^* and β_0^*, and the correlation coefficient between these two estimates, are obtained by forming the reciprocal of the quadratic form in the first member of (32.6.5):

$$\mathbf{D}^2(\alpha_0^*) = \frac{1}{n\Delta}\mathbf{E}\left(\frac{\partial \log f}{\partial \beta}\right)^2, \qquad \mathbf{D}^2(\beta_0^*) = \frac{1}{n\Delta}\mathbf{E}\left(\frac{\partial \log f}{\partial \alpha}\right)^2,$$

$$\varrho(\alpha_0^*, \beta_0^*) = -\frac{\mathbf{E}\left(\frac{\partial \log f}{\partial \alpha}\frac{\partial \log f}{\partial \beta}\right)}{\sqrt{\mathbf{E}\left(\frac{\partial \log f}{\partial \alpha}\right)^2 \mathbf{E}\left(\frac{\partial \log f}{\partial \beta}\right)^2}},$$

where

$$\Delta = \mathbf{E}\left(\frac{\partial \log f}{\partial \alpha}\right)^2 \mathbf{E}\left(\frac{\partial \log f}{\partial \beta}\right)^2 - \mathbf{E}^2\left(\frac{\partial \log f}{\partial \alpha}\frac{\partial \log f}{\partial \beta}\right).$$

Hence we obtain e. g.

$$\mathbf{D}^2(\alpha_0^*) = \frac{1}{1-\varrho^2(\alpha_0^*, \beta_0^*)} \cdot \frac{1}{n\,\mathbf{E}\left(\frac{\partial \log f}{\partial \alpha}\right)^2}.$$

As soon as $\mathbf{E}\left(\frac{\partial \log f}{\partial \alpha}\frac{\partial \log f}{\partial \beta}\right) \neq 0$, the variance of α_0^* is thus *greater* than the variance of an efficient estimate in the case when α is the only unknown parameter (cf 32.3.3 a). Now, in a case when there are two unknown parameters it often arrives that we are only interested in estimating one of the parameters, say α, and we may then ask if it would be possible to find some other pair of regular unbiased estimates α^*, β^*, yielding a variance $\boldsymbol{D}^2(\alpha^*) < \boldsymbol{D}^2(\alpha_0^*)$, no matter how large the corresponding $\boldsymbol{D}^2(\beta^*)$ becomes.

However, since the ellipse (32.6.5) lies wholly within the ellipse (32.6.4), the maximum value of the abscissa for all points of the former ellipse is at most equal to the corresponding maximum for the latter ellipse. Hence we obtain by some calculation the inequality

$$\boldsymbol{D}^2(\alpha^*) = \sigma_1^2 \geqq \frac{1}{n\Delta} \boldsymbol{E}\left(\frac{\partial \log f}{\partial \beta}\right)^2 = \boldsymbol{D}^2(\alpha_0^*),$$

which shows that *it is not possible to find a »better» estimate of α than α_0^*.*

The ratio between the two-dimensional variance (cf 22.7) of a pair of joint efficient estimates α_0^*, β_0^*, and the corresponding quantity for any pair of regular unbiased estimates α^*, β^*, will be called the *joint efficiency* of α^* and β^*, and denoted by $e(\alpha^*, \beta^*)$. This is identical with the square of the ratio between the areas of the ellipses (32.6.5) and (32.6.4), which by (11.12.3) is

$$e(\alpha^*, \beta^*) = \frac{1}{n^2 \Delta \sigma_1^2 \sigma_2^2 (1 - \varrho^2)}.$$

The concepts of *asymptotic efficiency* and *asymptotically efficient estimate* (cf 32.5) directly extend themselves to the present case.

As in 32.3, all the above results remain true in the case when we consider samples from a multidimensional population, specified by a fr. f. $f(x_1, \ldots, x_k; \alpha, \beta)$ containing two unknown parameters.

Ex. 1. When both parameters $\alpha = m$ and $\beta = \sigma^2$ of a normal distribution are unknown, we have (cf 32.3, Ex. 1—2)

$$\boldsymbol{E}\left(\frac{\partial \log f}{\partial m}\right)^2 = \frac{1}{\sigma^2}, \quad \boldsymbol{E}\left(\frac{\partial \log f}{\partial m}\frac{\partial \log f}{\partial \sigma^2}\right) = 0, \quad \boldsymbol{E}\left(\frac{\partial \log f}{\partial \sigma^2}\right)^2 = \frac{1}{2\sigma^4},$$

so that in this case the optimum ellipse (32.6.5) becomes

$$\frac{(u-m)^2}{\sigma^2} + \frac{(v-\sigma^2)^2}{2\sigma^4} = \frac{4}{n}.$$

Consequently this fixed ellipse lies within the concentration ellipse of the joint distribution of any pair of regular unbiased estimates of m and σ^2. For the particular pair of estimates $\alpha^* = \bar{x}$ and $\beta^* = \frac{n}{n-1} s^2$, the relation (29.3.6) shows the transformation which replaces the sample variables $x_1, \ldots, x_n$ by the new variables $\bar{x}$, s and $z_1, \ldots, z_{n-2}$. The last factor in the expression of the fr. f. of the new variables represents the conditional fr. f. of $z_1, \ldots, z_{n-2}$, and this is independent of the unknown parameters m and σ (and, in fact, also of $\bar{x}$ and s, but this is of no importance for our present purpose). Hence it follows that $\bar{x}$ and $\frac{n}{n-1} s^2$ are joint sufficient estimates of m and σ^2. Further, we have

$$\boldsymbol{D}^2(\bar{x}) = \frac{\sigma^2}{n}, \quad \boldsymbol{D}^2\left(\frac{n}{n-1} s^2\right) = \frac{2\sigma^4}{n-1}, \text{ and } \varrho\left(\bar{x}, \frac{n}{n-1} s^2\right) = 0.$$

Thus the concentration ellipse of $\bar{x}$ and $\frac{n}{n-1} s^2$ has the equation

$$\frac{(u-m)^2}{\sigma^2} + \frac{n-1}{n} \cdot \frac{(v-\sigma^2)^2}{2\sigma^4} = \frac{4}{n}.$$

The square of the ratio between the areas of the two ellipses gives the value $\frac{n-1}{n}$ for the joint efficiency of the estimates. When $n \to \infty$, the efficiency tends to unity, and thus $\bar{x}$ and $\frac{n}{n-1} s^2$ are asymptotically efficient estimates of m and σ^2. The same holds, of course, also for $\bar{x}$ and s^2, though s^2 is not unbiased.

Ex. 2. Consider a two-dimensional normal fr. f. (21.12.1) with known values of σ_1, σ_2 and ϱ, while $\alpha = m_1$ and $\beta = m_2$ are the two unknown parameters. From a sample of n pairs of values $(x_1, y_1), \ldots, (x_n, y_n)$, we form the estimates $\alpha^* = \bar{x}$ and $\beta^* = \bar{y}$. It is then easily shown that in this case the concentration ellipse of the estimates $\bar{x}$ and $\bar{y}$ coincides with the fixed ellipse (32.6.5), each having the equation

$$\frac{n}{1-\varrho^2}\left(\frac{(u-m_1)^2}{\sigma_1^2} - \frac{2\varrho(u-m_1)(v-m_2)}{\sigma_1\sigma_2} + \frac{(v-m_2)^2}{\sigma_2^2}\right) = 4.$$

Thus $\bar{x}$ and $\bar{y}$ are joint efficient estimates (and a fortiori joint sufficient estimates) of m_1 and m_2.

32.7. Several unknown parameters. — The results of the preceding paragraphs may be generalized to distributions involving any number of unknown parameters. If $\alpha_1^*, \ldots, \alpha_k^*$ are any regular unbiased estimates of the k unknown parameters $\alpha_1, \ldots, \alpha_k$, it is shown in a similar way as in the case $k = 2$ that the fixed k-dimensional ellipsoid

$$(32.7.1) \qquad n \sum_{i,j=1}^{k} \boldsymbol{E}\left(\frac{\partial \log f}{\partial \alpha_i} \frac{\partial \log f}{\partial \alpha_j}\right)(u_i - \alpha_i)(u_j - \alpha_j) = k + 2$$

lies wholly within the concentration ellipsoid (cf 22.7) of the joint distribution of $\alpha_1^*, \ldots, \alpha_k^*$. In the limiting case when the two ellipsoids coincide, we shall say that $\alpha_1^*, \ldots, \alpha_k^*$ are *joint efficient estimates* of $\alpha_1, \ldots, \alpha_k$. Thus the distribution of a set of joint efficient estimates has a *greater concentration* (cf 22.7) than the distribution of any set of non-efficient estimates. The moment matrix of a set of joint efficient estimates is the reciprocal of the matrix of the quadratic form in the first member of (32.7.1), as shown in the preceding paragraph for the case of two parameters. — The concepts of sufficiency, efficiency, etc. are introduced in the same way as in the case $k = 2$.

As an example, we consider a two-dimensional normal fr. f. with the five unknown parameters m_1, m_2, μ_{20}, μ_{11} and μ_{02}. From a sample of n pairs of values $(x_1, y_1), \ldots, (x_n, y_n)$, we obtain the unbiased estimates $\bar{x}$, $\bar{y}$, $\frac{n}{n-1} m_{20}$, $\frac{n}{n-1} m_{11}$ and $\frac{n}{n-1} m_{02}$ for the five parameters (cf 29.6). The moment matrix of the joint distribution of the five estimates can be calculated e. g. by means of the expression (29.6.3) of the joint c. f. of the estimates. Further, the coefficients in the equation (32.7.1) of the optimum ellipsoid may be found by introducing the expression of the fr. f. into (32.7.1) and performing the integrations. By simple, though somewhat tedious calculations, it will be found that the joint efficiency of the five estimates is $\left(\frac{n-1}{n}\right)^3$. When $n \to \infty$, this tends to unity, so that the estimates are asymptotically efficient.

32.8. Generalization. — Throughout the present chapter, we have been concerned with the problem of estimating certain parameters from a set of values, obtained by independent drawings from a fixed distribution. However, our methods are applicable under more general conditions. Consider e. g. the following problem:

The variables $x_1, \ldots, x_n$ have a joint distribution in $\boldsymbol{R}_n$, with the fr. f. $f(x_1, \ldots, x_n; \alpha)$ of known mathematical form, containing the unknown parameter α. An observed point $\boldsymbol{x} = (x_1, \ldots, x_n)$ is known, and it is required to find the »best possible» estimate $\alpha^* = \alpha^*(x_1, \ldots, x_n)$ of α by means of the observed coordinates x_i.

In the particular case when the joint fr. f. is of the form $f(x_1; \alpha) \ldots f(x_n; \alpha)$, this reduces to the problem treated in 32.3, where the x_i are independent variables having the same distribution. The general set-up covers e. g. also the cases when the x_i are correlated, or when they consist of several independent samples from different distributions. Even in the general case, we talk of the point $\boldsymbol{x} = (x_1, \ldots, x_n)$ as a *sample point*, which is represented in the *sample space* $\boldsymbol{R}_n$.

We now consider the same transformation of variables in the sample space as in (32.3.1) and (32.3.2). In the present case, however, we have to introduce the general form of the joint fr. f. into the formulae expressing the transformation, so that e. g. (32.3.2) becomes

$$f(x_1, \ldots, x_n; \alpha)\, dx_1 \ldots dx_n =$$
$$= g(\alpha^*; \alpha)\, h(\xi_1, \ldots, \xi_{n-1} \mid \alpha^*; \alpha)\, d\alpha^*\, d\xi_1 \ldots d\xi_{n-1}.$$

The whole argument of 32.3—32.5 (continuous case) now applies almost without modification, and in this way the concepts of unbiased, efficient and sufficient estimates etc. are extended to the present general case. Thus e. g. the generalized form of the inequality (32.3.3 a) for the variance of an unbiased estimate is

$$\boldsymbol{D}^2(\alpha^*) \geqq \left[\int \cdots \int \left(\frac{\partial \log f(x_1, \ldots, x_n; \alpha)}{\partial \alpha}\right)^2 f(x_1, \ldots, x_n; \alpha)\; dx_1 \ldots dx_n\right]^{-1} =$$
$$= \left[\boldsymbol{E}\left(\frac{\partial \log f}{\partial \alpha}\right)^2\right]^{-1}$$

and when the sign of equality holds here, we call α^* an *efficient* estimate. When the conditional fr. f. h is independent of α, we call α^* a *sufficient* estimate, etc.

The same generalization may evidently be applied to cases of discrete distributions, and to distributions containing several unknown parameters.

CHAPTER 33.

Methods of Estimation.

33.1. The method of moments. — We now proceed to discuss some general methods of forming estimates of the parameters of a distribution by means of a set of sample values.

The oldest general method proposed for this purpose is the *method of moments* introduced by K. Pearson (Ref. 180, 182, 184 and other works), and extensively used by him and his school. This method consists in equating a convenient number of the sample moments to the corresponding moments of the distribution, which are functions of the unknown parameters. By considering as many moments as there are parameters to be estimated, and solving the resulting equations with respect to the parameters, estimates of the latter are obtained. This method often leads to comparatively simple calculations in practice.

The estimates obtained in this way from a set of n sample values are functions of the sample moments, and certain properties of their sampling distributions may be inferred from Chs 27—28. Thus we have seen (cf in particular 27.7 and 28.4) that, under fairly general conditions, the distribution of an estimate of this kind will be asymptotically normal for large n, and that the mean of the estimate will differ from the true value of the parameter by a quantity of order n^{-1}, while the s. d. will be asymptotically of the form $c/\sqrt{n}$. By a simple correction, we may often remove the bias of such an estimate, and thus obtain an unbiased estimate (cf 27.6).

Under general conditions, the method of moments will thus yield estimates such that the asymptotic efficiency defined in 32.5 (or the corresponding quantity in the case of several parameters) exists. As pointed out by R. A. Fisher (Ref. 89), this quantity is, however, often considerably less than 1, which implies that the estimates given by the method of moments are not the »best» possible from the efficiency point of view, i. e. they do not have the smallest possible variance in large samples. Nevertheless, on account of its practical expediency the method will often render good service. Sometimes the estimates given by the method of moments may be used as first approximations, from which further estimates of higher efficiency may be determined by means of other methods.

In the particular case of the normal distribution, the method of moments gives the estimates $\bar{x}$ and s^2 for the unknown parameters m and σ^2. Correcting for bias, we obtain the unbiased and asymptotically efficient (cf 32.6, Ex. 1) estimates $\bar{x}$ and $\frac{n}{n-1} s^2$. It was shown by Fisher (Ref. 89) that, in this respect, the normal distribution is exceptional among the distributions belonging to the Pearson system (cf 19.4), the asymptotic efficiency in other cases being as a rule less than 1. Some examples will be given in 33.3.

33.2. The method of maximum likelihood. — From a theoretical point of view, the most important general method of estimation so far known is the *method of maximum likelihood.* In particular cases, this method was already used by Gauss (Ref. 16); as a general method of estimation it was first introduced by R. A. Fisher in a short paper (Ref. 87) of 1912, and has afterwards been further developed in a series of works (Ref. 89, 96, 103, 104 etc.) by the same author. Important contributions have also been made by others, and we refer in this connection particularly to Dugué (Ref. 76).

Using the notations of 32.3, we define the *likelihood function* L of a sample of n values from a population of the *continuous* type by the relation

(33.2.1 a) $$L(x_1, \ldots, x_n; \alpha) = f(x_1; \alpha) \ldots f(x_n; \alpha),$$

while in the *discrete* case we write

(33.2.1 b) $$L(x_1, \ldots, x_n; \alpha) = p_{i_1}(\alpha) \ldots p_{i_n}(\alpha).$$

When the sample values are given, the likelihood function L becomes a function of the single variable α. The method of maximum likelihood now consists in choosing, as an estimate of the unknown population value of α, the particular value that renders L as great as possible. Since $\log L$ attains its maximum for the same value of α as L, we thus have to solve the *likelihood equation*

(33.2.2) $$\frac{\partial \log L}{\partial \alpha} = 0$$

with respect to α. Let us agree to disregard any root of the form $\alpha = \text{const.}$, thus counting as a *solution* only a root which effectively depends on the sample values $x_1, \ldots, x_n$. Any solution of the likelihood equation will then be called a *maximum likelihood estimate* of α.

In the present paragraph, we shall consider some properties of the maximum likelihood method for samples of a fixed size n, while in the next paragraph the asymptotic behaviour of maximum likelihood estimates for large values of n will be investigated. — The importance of the method is clearly shown by the two following propositions:

If an efficient estimate α^* of α exists, the likelihood equation will have a unique solution equal to α^*.

If a sufficient estimate α^* of α exists, any solution of the likelihood equation will be a function of α^*.

It will be sufficient to prove these propositions for the continuous case, the modifications required for the discrete case being obvious. When an efficient estimate α^* exists, the conditions A) and B) stated in connection with (32.3.3 a) are satisfied, and thus by (32.3.5) we have

$$\frac{\partial \log L}{\partial \alpha} = \sum_1^n \frac{\partial \log f(x_i; \alpha)}{\partial \alpha} = \frac{\partial \log g}{\partial \alpha} = k(\alpha^* - \alpha),$$

where k is independent of the sample values, but may depend on α. According to our convention with respect to the solutions of the likelihood equation (33.2.2), this equation will thus have the unique solution $\alpha = \alpha^*$.

Further, when a sufficient estimate α^* exists, condition A) of 32.3 is satisfied, and by (32.3.5) the likelihood equation then reduces to

$$\frac{\partial \log L}{\partial \alpha} = \frac{\partial \log g(\alpha^*; \alpha)}{\partial \alpha} = 0.$$

The function g depends only on the two arguments α^* and α, and thus any solution will be a function of α^*.

The above definitions and propositions may be directly generalized to the case of several unknown parameters, and to samples from multidimensional distributions. Thus e. g. for a continuous distribution with two unknown parameters α and β the likelihood function is $L(x_1, \ldots, x_n; \alpha, \beta) = \prod f(x_i; \alpha, \beta)$, and the maximum likelihood estimates of α and β will be given by the solutions of the simultaneous equations $\frac{\partial \log L}{\partial \alpha} = 0$, $\frac{\partial \log L}{\partial \beta} = 0$, with respect to α and β. When a pair of joint efficient estimates α^* and β^* exists, the likelihood equations will have the unique solution $\alpha = \alpha^*$, $\beta = \beta^*$.

The maximum likelihood method may even be applied in the general situation considered in 32.8. In this case, the method consists in choosing as our estimate the value of α that renders the joint fr. f. $f(x_1, \ldots, x_n; \alpha)$ as large as possible for given values of the x_i.

Some examples will be given in the next paragraph.

33.3. Asymptotic properties of maximum likelihood estimates. — We now proceed to investigate the asymptotic behaviour of maximum likelihood estimates for large values of n. We first consider the case of a single unknown parameter α.

It will be shown that, under certain general conditions, the likelihood equation (33.2.2) *has a solution which converges in probability to the true value of* α, *as* $n \to \infty$. *This solution is an asymptotically normal and asymptotically efficient estimate of* α.

As before, it will be sufficient to give the proof for the case of a continuous distribution, specified by the fr. f. $f(x; \alpha)$. We shall use a method of proof indicated by Dugué (Ref. 76). — Suppose that the following conditions are satisfied:

1) For almost all x, the derivatives $\frac{\partial \log f}{\partial \alpha}$, $\frac{\partial^2 \log f}{\partial \alpha^2}$ and $\frac{\partial^3 \log f}{\partial \alpha^3}$ exist for every α belonging to a non-degenerate interval A.

2) For every α in A, we have $\left|\frac{\partial f}{\partial \alpha}\right| < F_1(x)$, $\left|\frac{\partial^2 f}{\partial \alpha^2}\right| < F_2(x)$ and $\left|\frac{\partial^3 \log f}{\partial \alpha^3}\right| < H(x)$, the functions F_1 and F_2 being integrable over $(-\infty, \infty)$, while $\int_{-\infty}^{\infty} H(x) f(x; \alpha)\, dx < M$, where M is independent of α.

3) For every α in A, the integral $\int_{-\infty}^{\infty} \left(\frac{\partial \log f}{\partial \alpha}\right)^2 f\, dx$ is finite and positive.

We now denote by α_0 the unknown true value of the parameter α in the distribution from which we are sampling, and we suppose that α_0 is an inner point of A. We shall then first show that the likelihood equation (33.2.2) has a solution which converges in probability to α_0. — For every α in A we have, indicating by the subscript 0 that α should be put equal to α_0,

$$\frac{\partial \log f}{\partial \alpha} = \left(\frac{\partial \log f}{\partial \alpha}\right)_0 + (\alpha - \alpha_0)\left(\frac{\partial^2 \log f}{\partial \alpha^2}\right)_0 + \tfrac{1}{2}\theta (\alpha - \alpha_0)^2 H(x),$$

where $|\theta| < 1$. Thus the likelihood equation (33.2.2) may, after multiplication by $1/n$, be written in the form

$$\text{(33.3.1)} \qquad \frac{1}{n}\frac{\partial \log L}{\partial \alpha} = B_0 + B_1(\alpha - \alpha_0) + \tfrac{1}{2}\theta B_2 (\alpha - \alpha_0)^2 = 0,$$

where, writing f_i in the place of $f(x_i; \alpha)$,

$$\text{(33.3.2)} \qquad \begin{aligned} B_0 &= \frac{1}{n}\sum_1^n \left(\frac{\partial \log f_i}{\partial \alpha}\right)_0, \quad B_1 = \frac{1}{n}\sum_1^n \left(\frac{\partial^2 \log f_i}{\partial \alpha^2}\right)_0, \\ B_2 &= \frac{1}{n}\sum_1^n H(x_i). \end{aligned}$$

The B_ν are functions of the random variables $x_1, \ldots, x_n$, and we now have to show that, with a probability tending to 1 as $n \to \infty$, the equation (33.3.1) has a root α between the limits $\alpha_0 \pm \delta$, however small the positive quantity δ is chosen.

Let us consider the behaviour of the B_ν for large values of n. From the conditions 1) and 2) it follows (cf 32.3.4) that

$$\int_{-\infty}^{\infty} \frac{\partial f}{\partial \alpha} dx = \int_{-\infty}^{\infty} \frac{\partial^2 f}{\partial \alpha^2} dx = 0$$

for every α in A, and hence we obtain

$$\boldsymbol{E}\left(\frac{\partial \log f}{\partial \alpha}\right)_0 = \int_{-\infty}^{\infty} \left(\frac{1}{f}\frac{\partial f}{\partial \alpha}\right)_0 f(x;\, \alpha_0)\, dx = 0$$

$$\boldsymbol{E}\left(\frac{\partial^2 \log f}{\partial \alpha^2}\right)_0 = \int_{-\infty}^{\infty} \left[\frac{1}{f}\frac{\partial^2 f}{\partial \alpha^2} - \left(\frac{1}{f}\frac{\partial f}{\partial \alpha}\right)^2\right]_0 f(x;\, \alpha_0)\, dx \tag{33.3.3}$$

$$= -\boldsymbol{E}\left(\frac{\partial \log f}{\partial \alpha}\right)_0^2 = -k^2$$

where by condition 3) we have $k > 0$. Thus by (33.3.2) B_0 is the arithmetic mean of n independent random variables, all having the same distribution with the mean value zero. By Khintchine's theorem 20.5, it follows that B_0 converges in probability to zero. In the same way we find that B_1 converges in probability to $-k^2$, while B_2 converges in probability to the non-negative value $\boldsymbol{E}\, H(x) < M$.

Let now δ and ε be given arbitrarily small positive numbers, and let $P(S)$ denote the joint pr. f. of the random variables $x_1, \ldots x_n$. For all sufficiently large n, say for all $n > n_0 = n_0(\delta, \varepsilon)$, we then have

$$P_1 = P(|B_0| \geqq \delta^2) < \tfrac{1}{3}\varepsilon,$$
$$P_2 = P(B_1 \geqq -\tfrac{1}{2}k^2) < \tfrac{1}{3}\varepsilon,$$
$$P_3 = P(|B_2| \geqq 2M) < \tfrac{1}{3}\varepsilon.$$

Let further S denote the set of all points $\boldsymbol{x} = (x_1, \ldots, x_n)$ such that all three inequalities

$$|B_0| < \delta^2, \quad B_1 < -\tfrac{1}{2}k^2, \quad |B_2| < 2M,$$

are satisfied. The complementary set S^* consists of all points $\boldsymbol{x}$ such that at least one of these three inequalities is *not* satisfied, and thus we have by (6.2.2)

$$P(S^*) \leqq P_1 + P_2 + P_3 < \varepsilon, \quad \text{and hence} \quad P(S) > 1 - \varepsilon.$$

Thus the probability that the point $\boldsymbol{x}$ belongs to the set S, which is identical with the P-measure of S, is $> 1 - \varepsilon$, as soon as $n > n_0(\delta, \varepsilon)$.

For $\alpha = \alpha_0 \pm \delta$, the second member of (33.3.1) assumes the values $B_0 \pm B_1 \delta + \frac{1}{2} \theta B_2 \delta^2$. In every point $\boldsymbol{x}$ belonging to S, the sum of the first and third terms of this expression is smaller in absolute value than $(M+1)\delta^2$, while we have $B_1 \delta < -\frac{1}{2} k^2 \delta$. If $\delta < \frac{1}{2} k^2/(M+1)$, the sign of the whole expression will thus for $\alpha = \alpha_0 \pm \delta$ be determined by the second term, so that we have $\dfrac{\partial \log L}{\partial \alpha} > 0$ for $\alpha = \alpha_0 - \delta$, and $\dfrac{\partial \log L}{\partial \alpha} < 0$ for $\alpha = \alpha_0 + \delta$. Further, by condition 1) the function $\dfrac{\partial \log L}{\partial \alpha}$ is for almost all $\boldsymbol{x} = (x_1, \ldots, x_n)$ a continuous function of α in A. Thus for arbitrarily small δ and ε the likelihood equation will, with a probability exceeding $1 - \varepsilon$, have a root between the limits $\alpha_0 \pm \delta$ as soon as $n > n_0(\delta, \varepsilon)$, and consequently the first part of the proof is completed.

Next, let $\alpha^* = \alpha^*(x_1, \ldots, x_n)$ be the solution of the likelihood equation, the existence of which has just been established. From (33.3.1) and (33.3.2) we obtain

$$(33.3.4) \qquad k\sqrt{n}\,(\alpha^* - \alpha_0) = \frac{\dfrac{1}{k\sqrt{n}} \displaystyle\sum_1^n \left(\frac{\partial \log f_i}{\partial \alpha}\right)_0}{-B_1/k^2 - \frac{1}{2}\theta B_2 (\alpha^* - \alpha_0)/k^2}.$$

It follows from the above that the denominator of the fraction in the second member converges in probability to 1. Further, by (33.3.3) $\left(\dfrac{\partial \log f}{\partial \alpha}\right)_0$ is a variable with the mean zero and the s. d. k. By the Lindeberg-Lévy theorem (cf 17.4), the sum $\displaystyle\sum_1^n \left(\frac{\partial \log f_i}{\partial \alpha}\right)_0$ is then asymptotically normal $(0, k\sqrt{n})$, and consequently the numerator in the second member of (33.3.4) is asymptotically normal $(0, 1)$.

Finally, it now follows from the convergence theorem of 20.6 that $k\sqrt{n}\,(\alpha^* - \alpha_0)$ is asymptotically normal $(0, 1)$, so that α^* is asymptotically normal $(\alpha_0, c/\sqrt{n})$, where $1/c^2 = k^2 = \boldsymbol{E}\left(\dfrac{\partial \log f}{\partial \alpha}\right)_0^2$. By (32.5.1) the asymptotic efficiency of α^* is then

$$e_0(\alpha^*) = \frac{1}{c^2 \boldsymbol{E}\left(\dfrac{\partial \log f}{\partial \alpha}\right)_0^2} = 1,$$

and thus our theorem is proved. The corresponding theorem for a discrete distribution is proved in the same way.

In the case of several unknown parameters, we have to introduce conditions which form a straightforward generalization of the conditions 1)—3). It is then proved in the same way as above, using the multi-dimensional form of the Lindeberg-Lévy theorem (cf 21.11 and 24.7), that the likelihood equations have a system of solutions which are asymptotically normal and joint asymptotically efficient estimates of the parameters.

Ex. 1. For a sample of n values from a normal distribution with the unknown parameters m and σ^2, the logarithm of the likelihood function is

$$\log L = -\frac{1}{2\sigma^2}\sum (x_i - m)^2 - \tfrac{1}{2} n \log \sigma^2 - \tfrac{1}{2} n \log 2\pi,$$

and the maximum likelihood method gives the equations

$$\frac{\partial \log L}{\partial m} = \frac{1}{\sigma^2}\sum (x_i - m) = 0,$$

$$\frac{\partial \log L}{\partial \sigma^2} = \frac{1}{2\sigma^4}\sum (x_i - m)^2 - \frac{n}{2\sigma^2} = 0.$$

Hence we obtain the maximum likelihood estimates

$$m^* = \frac{1}{n}\sum x_i = \bar{x}, \quad (\sigma^*)^2 = \frac{1}{n}\sum (x_i - \bar{x})^2 = s^2,$$

which coincide with the estimates given by the method of moments. We have already seen (cf 28.4 and 32.6, Ex. 1) that these estimates are asymptotically normal and asymptotically efficient.

Ex. 2. Consider the type III distribution (cf 19.4)

$$f(x;\lambda) = \frac{1}{\Gamma(\lambda)} x^{\lambda-1} e^{-x}, \quad (x > 0,\ \lambda > 0)$$

with the unknown parameter λ. For any finite interval $a < \lambda < b$ with $a > 0$ we may apply (32.3.3 a), and thus find that the lower limit of the variance of a regular unbiased estimate of λ from a sample of n values is (cf 12.3)

$$\frac{1}{n\,\mathbf{E}\left(\frac{\partial \log f}{\partial \lambda}\right)^2} = \frac{1}{n\,\mathbf{E}\left(\log x - \frac{d \log \Gamma(\lambda)}{d\lambda}\right)^2} = \frac{1}{n \frac{d^2 \log \Gamma(\lambda)}{d\lambda^2}}.$$

In order to estimate λ by the method of moments, we equate the sample mean $\bar{x}$ to the first moment λ of the distribution, and thus obtain the estimate $\lambda^* = \bar{x}$. We then easily find $\mathbf{E}(\lambda^*) = \lambda$, $\mathbf{D}^2(\lambda^*) = \lambda/n$. Hence it follows by (32.3.7) and (12.5.4) that the efficiency of λ^* is independent of n and has the value

$$e(\lambda^*) = \frac{1}{\lambda \frac{d^2 \log \Gamma(\lambda)}{d\lambda^2}} = \frac{1}{1 + \frac{1}{2\lambda} + 2\lambda \int\limits_0^\infty \frac{P_1(x)}{(\lambda+x)^3}\, dx}.$$

This is always less than 1, and tends to zero as $\lambda \to 0$. — On the other hand, the method of maximum likelihood leads to the equation

$$\frac{1}{n}\frac{\partial \log L}{\partial \lambda} = \frac{1}{n}\sum \log x_i - \frac{d \log \Gamma(\lambda)}{d\lambda} = 0,$$

and the maximum likelihood estimate is the unique positive root $\lambda = \lambda^{**}$ of this equation. According to the general theorem proved above, λ^{**} is asymptotically normal $\left[\lambda, \left(n \frac{d^2 \log \Gamma(\lambda)}{d\lambda^2}\right)^{-\frac{1}{2}}\right]$ and the asymptotic efficiency of λ^{**} is equal to 1. This can also without difficulty be seen directly, since the variable $\log x$ has the mean $\frac{d \log \Gamma(\lambda)}{d\lambda}$ and the variance $\frac{d^2 \log \Gamma(\lambda)}{d\lambda^2}$, and thus (cf 17.4) by the Lindeberg-Lévy theorem $\frac{1}{n}\sum \log x_i$ is asymptotically normal $\left[\frac{d \log \Gamma(\lambda)}{d\lambda}, \left(\frac{1}{n}\frac{d^2 \log \Gamma(\lambda)}{d\lambda^2}\right)^{\frac{1}{2}}\right]$.

Ex. 3. In the type III distribution

$$f(x; \alpha) = \frac{\alpha^\lambda}{\Gamma(\lambda)} x^{\lambda-1} e^{-\alpha x}, \quad (x > 0,\ \alpha > 0)$$

we now consider λ as a given positive constant, while α is the unknown parameter. We then have

$$\boldsymbol{E}\left(\frac{\partial \log f}{\partial \alpha}\right)^2 = \boldsymbol{E}\left(\frac{\lambda}{\alpha} - x\right)^2 = \frac{\lambda}{\alpha^2}.$$

In this case, the method of moments and the method of maximum likelihood give the same estimate $\lambda/\bar{x}$ for α. Correcting for bias, we obtain the unbiased estimate $\alpha^* = \frac{n\lambda - 1}{n\bar{x}}$, which has the fr. f.

$$g(\alpha^*; \alpha) = \frac{\alpha^{n\lambda}(n\lambda - 1)^{n\lambda}}{\Gamma(n\lambda)} \left(\frac{1}{\alpha^*}\right)^{n\lambda+1} e^{-\alpha(n\lambda-1)/\alpha^*},$$

as is found without difficulty, e. g. by means of the c. f. (12.3.4). Supposing $n\lambda > 2$, we then obtain $\boldsymbol{E}(\alpha^*) = \alpha$, $\boldsymbol{D}^2(\alpha^*) = \alpha^2/(n\lambda - 2)$, and

$$\boldsymbol{E}\left(\frac{\partial \log g}{\partial \alpha}\right)^2 = \boldsymbol{E}\left(\frac{n\lambda}{\alpha} - \frac{n\lambda - 1}{\alpha^*}\right)^2 = \boldsymbol{E}\left(\frac{n\lambda}{\alpha} - \sum x_i\right)^2 = \frac{n\lambda}{\alpha^2}.$$

Thus we have in this case $n\boldsymbol{E}\left(\frac{\partial \log f}{\partial \alpha}\right)^2 = \boldsymbol{E}\left(\frac{\partial \log g}{\partial \alpha}\right)^2$, so that the sign of equality holds in (32.3.6), which implies that condition A) of theorem (32.3.3) is satisfied. Hence it follows that α^* is a *sufficient* estimate of α, and this may also be directly verified by means of (32.4.1). On the other hand, condition B) is not satisfied, since $\frac{\partial \log g}{\partial \alpha}$ is not of the form $k(\alpha^* - \alpha)$. Accordingly the efficiency of α^* is

$$e(\alpha^*) = \frac{1}{n\,\mathbf{E}\left(\frac{\partial \log f}{\partial \alpha}\right)^2 \mathbf{D}^2(\alpha^*)} = \frac{n\lambda - 2}{n\lambda} < 1,$$

so that α^* is not *efficient* for any finite n (cf 32.3). Allowing n to tend to infinity we see, though, that α^* is *asymptotically efficient.*

33.4. The χ^2 minimum method. — The χ^2 *minimum method* discussed in 30.3 is only available in the case of a grouped continuous distribution, or a discrete distribution. For large n, the estimates obtained by this method are asymptotically equivalent to those given by the simpler *modified* χ^2 *minimum method* expressed by the equations (30.3.3) or (30.3.3 a), and we have already remarked in 30.3 that the latter method is, for the cases concerned, identical with the maximum likelihood method.

The main theorem on the limiting distribution of χ^2 when certain parameters are estimated from the sample has been proved in 30.3 under the hypothesis that the method of estimation is the modified χ^2 minimum method. However, we have stated in 30.3 that there is a whole class of methods of estimation leading to the same limiting distribution of χ^2. We shall now prove this statement.

Asymptotic expressions of the estimates obtained by the modified χ^2 minimum method have been given in an explicit form in (30.3.17), for the general case of s unknown parameters $\alpha_1, \ldots, \alpha_s$. Let us suppose that the conditions 1)—3) of the preceding paragraph — or the analogous conditions for a discrete distribution — are satisfied. It then follows from the preceding paragraph that the estimates (30.3.17) are asymptotically normal (this has, in fact, already been shown in 30.3) and asymptotically efficient.

Now in all sets of asymptotically normal and asymptotically efficient estimates of the parameters, the terms of order $n^{-\frac{1}{2}}$ must agree, and thus will be the same as in (30.3.17). An inspection of the deduction of the limiting distribution of χ^2 given in 30.3 shows, however, that this limiting distribution is entirely determined by the terms of order $n^{-\frac{1}{2}}$ in (30.3.17). In fact, by (30.3.1) and (30.3.4) we have $\chi^2 = \sum_1^r y_i^2$, and (30.3.18) shows that the limiting distribution of $\boldsymbol{y} = (y_1, \ldots, y_r)$ is determined by the terms in question.

It thus follows that the theorem of 30.3 *on the limiting distribution of* χ^2 *holds for any set of asymptotically normal and asymptotically efficient estimates of the parameters.*

CHAPTER 34.

Confidence Regions.

34.1. Introductory remarks. — Suppose that we are using a set of sample values to form estimates of a certain number of unknown parameters in a distribution of known mathematical form. Suppose further that the sampling distributions of our estimates are known, so that the respective means, variances etc. can be calculated.

Are we, in such a situation, entitled to make some kind of probability statements with respect to the unknown true values of the parameters? Will it, e. g., be possible to assign two limits to a certain parameter, and to assert that, with some specified probability, the true value of the parameter will be situated between these limits?

In the older literature of the subject, probability statements of this type were freely deduced by means of the famous *theorem of Bayes*, one of the typical problems treated in this way being the classical problem of *inverse probability* (cf 34.2, Ex. 2). However, these applications of Bayes' theorem have often been severely criticized, and there has appeared a growing tendency to avoid this kind of argument, and to reconsider the question from entirely new points of view. The attempts so far made in this direction have grouped themselves along two main lines of development, connected with the theory of *fiducial probabilities* due to R. A. Fisher (cf e. g. Ref. 14, 100, 102, 105—109) and the theory of *confidence intervals* due to J. Neyman (cf e. g. Ref. 30, 161, 163, 165—167). We shall here in the main have to restrict ourselves to a brief account of the latter theory.

In the next paragraph, we shall consider the case of a single unknown parameter, comparing the older treatment by means of Bayes' theorem with the modern theory. In 34.3, we then proceed to more general cases, and finally we discuss in 34.4 some examples.

34.2. A single unknown parameter. — Consider a sample of n values $x_1, \ldots, x_n$ from a distribution involving a single unknown parameter α. We shall first suppose that the distribution is of the continuous type, and has the fr. f. $f(x; \alpha)$. For simplicity we suppose that $f(x; \alpha)$ is defined for all values of α. Let $\alpha^* = \alpha^*(x_1, \ldots, x_n)$ be an estimate of α, with the fr. f. $g(\alpha^*; \alpha)$.

Having calculated the value of α^* from an actual sample, we now ask if it is possible to make some reasonable probability statement with respect to the unknown value of α in the distribution from which the sample is drawn. The question will be considered from two fundamentally different points of view.

1. *The classical method.* In some cases, it may be legitimate to assume that the actual value of the parameter α in the sampled population has been *determined by a random experiment.* Cases of this character occur e. g. in the statistics of mass production, when α denotes some unknown characteristic of a large batch of manufactured articles, which it is required to estimate from a small sample. The particular batch under consideration will then have to be regarded as an individual drawn from a population of similar batches, where the values of α are submitted to random fluctuations due to variations in the production process and the quality of raw materials. The drawing of one individual from this population of batches is the random experiment which determines the actual value of α. — Similar cases occur e. g. in certain genetical problems.

In such cases, α is itself a random variable, having a certain *a priori distribution.* Let us assume that this distribution is defined by a known fr. f. $\varpi(\alpha)$. In the joint distribution of α and α^*, the function $\varpi(\alpha)$ is then the marginal fr. f. of α, while $g(\alpha^*; \alpha)$ is the conditional fr. f. of α^* for a given value of α. Conversely, the conditional fr. f. of α, for a given value of α^*, is by (21.4.10)

$$h(\alpha \mid \alpha^*) = \frac{\varpi(\alpha)\, g(\alpha^*; \alpha)}{\int\limits_{-\infty}^{\infty} \varpi(\alpha)\, g(\alpha^*; \alpha)\, d\alpha}.$$

This relation expresses *Bayes' theorem* as applied to the present case. The quantity

$$P(k_1 < \alpha < k_2 \mid \alpha^*) = \int\limits_{k_1}^{k_2} h(\alpha \mid \alpha^*)\, d\alpha \tag{34.2.1}$$

then represents the conditional probability of the event $k_1 < \alpha < k_2$, relative to a given value of α^*. This probability is commonly known as the *a posteriori probability* of the event $k_1 < \alpha < k_2$, as distinct from the *a priori probability* of the same event, which is equal to $\int\limits_{k_1}^{k_2} \varpi(\alpha)\, d\alpha$.

By 14.3 and 21.4, the a posteriori probability (34.2.1) admits a frequency interpretation which runs as follows. Consider a sequence of a large number of independent trials, where each trial consists in drawing a batch from the population of batches, and then drawing a sample of n values from the batch (we use a terminology adapted to the example considered above, but the argument is evidently general). From the sample, we calculate the estimate α^*; we further assume that it is possible to examine all the articles in the total batch, so that the corresponding value of α may be directly determined. The result of each trial will thus be a pair of observed values of the variables α and α^*. From the sequence of all trials, we now select the sub-sequence formed by those cases where the observed value of α^* belongs to some small neighbourhood of a value α_0^* given in advance. The frequency ratio of the event $k_1 < \alpha < k_2$ in this sub-sequence will then, within the limits of random fluctuations, be given by the value of the a posteriori probability (34.2.1) for $\alpha^* = \alpha_0^*$.

The above is the direct frequency interpretation of the a posteriori probability. By a slight modification of the argument, we may obtain a result which shows a greater formal resemblance to the theory of confidence intervals as given below. Let ε be given such that $0 < \varepsilon < 1$. To every given α^* we can then determine the limits $k_1 = k_1(\alpha^*, \varepsilon)$ and $k_2 = k_2(\alpha^*, \varepsilon)$ in (34.2.1) such that the probability $P(k_1 < \alpha < k_2 \mid \alpha^*)$ takes the value $1 - \varepsilon$. (The reader may here consult Fig. 33, p. 511, replacing c_1 and c_2 by k_1 and k_2.) Consider now once more the above sequence of all trials, and let us calculate the limits $k_1 = k_1(\alpha^*, \varepsilon)$ and $k_2 = k_2(\alpha^*, \varepsilon)$ from the sample obtained in each trial. The interval (k_1, k_2) will then depend on α^*, so that in general the successive trials will yield different intervals. Let us in each trial count the occurrence of the event $k_1 < \alpha < k_2$ as a »success», and the occurrence of the opposite event as a »failure». The probability of a success is then constantly equal to $1 - \varepsilon$, and accordingly (cf 16.6) the frequency ratio of successes in a long series of trials should, within the limits of random fluctuations, be equal to $1 - \varepsilon$. The practical implications of this result, in a case where the method may be legitimately applied, are similar to those discussed below.

2. *The method of confidence intervals.* In a case where there are definite reasons to regard α as a random variable, with a known probability distribution, the application of the preceding method is perfectly legitimate, and leads to explicit probability statements about the value of α corresponding to a given sample. However, in the majority of cases occurring in practice, these conditions will not be satisfied. As a rule α is simply an unknown constant, and there is no evidence that the actual value of this constant has been determined by some procedure resembling a random experiment. Often there will even be evidence in the opposite direction, as e. g. in cases where the α-values of various populations are subject to systematic variation in time or space. Moreover, even when α may be legitimately regarded as a random variable, we usually lack sufficient information about its a priori distribution.

It would thus be highly desirable to be able to approach the question without making any hypothesis about the random or non-random nature of the parameter α. Certain methods designed to meet this desideratum have been developed by the authors quoted in the preceding paragraph, and we now proceed to show how the problem may be treated by the method of *confidence intervals* due to Neyman (l. c., cf also Wilks, Ref. 42, 234). In the present paragraph, we shall consider the question under certain simplifying assumptions, while more general cases will be dealt with in the next paragraph.

We shall now consider α as a variable in the ordinary analytic sense, which assumes a constant, though unknown value in the population from which an actual sample has been drawn. The results thus obtained will hold true whether the value of α has been determined by a random experiment or not, so that this method is actually of more general applicability than the preceding one.

As before, we consider a sample of n values from a distribution with the fr. f. $f(x; \alpha)$, and we denote by $g(\alpha^*; \alpha)$ the fr. f. of the estimate $\alpha^* = \alpha^*(x_1, \ldots, x_n)$. Denote further by $P(S; \alpha)$ the joint pr. f. of the sample variables $x_1, \ldots, x_n$, and let ε be given such that $0 < \varepsilon < 1$.

For every fixed α, the fr. f. $g(\alpha^*; \alpha)$ defines the probability distribution of α^*, which may be interpreted as a distribution of a unit of mass on the vertical through the point $(\alpha, 0)$ in the (α, α^*)-plane (cf Fig. 33). Suppose now that, for every value of α, two quantities $\gamma_1 = \gamma_1(\alpha, \varepsilon)$ and $\gamma_2 = \gamma_2(\alpha, \varepsilon)$ have been determined such that the quantity of mass belonging to the interval $\gamma_1 < \alpha^* < \gamma_2$ of the corresponding vertical — i. e. the probability of the event $\gamma_1 < \alpha^* < \gamma_2$ for the value α of the parameter — becomes

$$(34.2.2) \qquad P(\gamma_1 < \alpha^* < \gamma_2; \alpha) = \int_{\gamma_1}^{\gamma_2} g(\alpha^*; \alpha)\, d\alpha^* = 1 - \varepsilon.$$

Obviously this can always be done, and there are even an infinity of possible ways of choosing γ_1 and γ_2, since these quantities may be determined from the relations

$$\int_{-\infty}^{\gamma_1} g\, d\alpha^* = \varepsilon_1 \quad \text{and} \quad \int_{\gamma_2}^{\infty} g\, d\alpha^* = \varepsilon_2,$$

where ε_1 and ε_2 are any positive numbers such that $\varepsilon_1 + \varepsilon_2 = \varepsilon$.

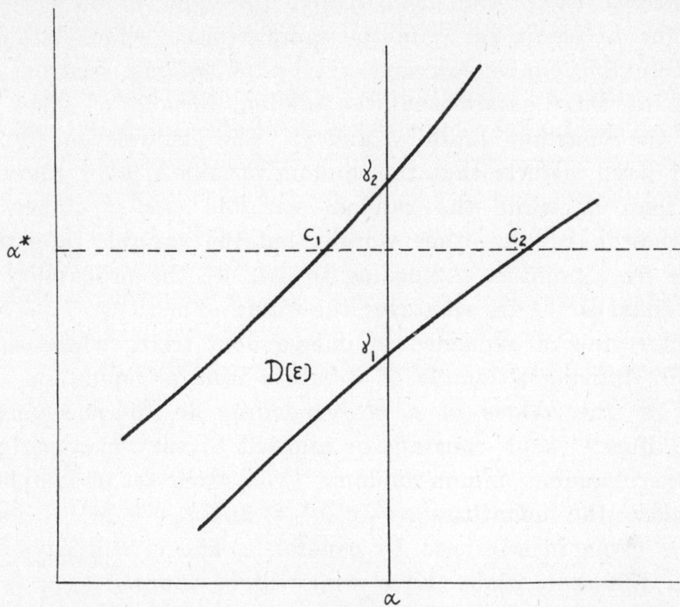

Fig. 33. Confidence intervals for a single unknown parameter.

If we draw a sample of n values from a distribution corresponding to any value of α, the event $\gamma_1 < \alpha^* < \gamma_2$ will thus always have a probability equal to $1 - \varepsilon$. The quantities γ_1 and γ_2 depend on α, and when α varies, the points (α, γ_1) and (α, γ_2) will describe two curves in the plane of (α, α^*), as indicated in Fig. 33. We shall assume that each curve is cut in one single point by a parallell to the axis of α. Let the abscissae of the two points where the curves are cut by the horizontal through the point $(0, \alpha^*)$ be $c_1 = c_1(\alpha^*, \varepsilon)$ and $c_2 = c_2(\alpha^*, \varepsilon)$, and let $D(\varepsilon)$ denote the domain situated between the curves. — Consider the three relations

$$(34.2.3) \quad (\alpha, \alpha^*) < D(\varepsilon), \quad \gamma_1(\alpha, \varepsilon) < \alpha^* < \gamma_2(\alpha, \varepsilon), \quad c_1(\alpha^*, \varepsilon) < \alpha < c_2(\alpha^*, \varepsilon).$$

For any fixed value of α, each of these relations is satisfied by a certain set of points $\boldsymbol{x} = (x_1, \ldots, x_n)$ in the sample space. However, the three relations are perfectly equivalent, since all three express the fact that the point (α, α^*) belongs to the domain $D(\varepsilon)$. Thus the three sets in the sample space are identical, and consequently we obtain from (34.2.2) for every value of α

$$(34.2.4) \qquad P(c_1 < \alpha < c_2; \alpha) = 1 - \varepsilon.$$

Both relations (34.2.2) and (34.2.4) give the value of the set function $P(S; \alpha)$ for a certain set S in the sample space, which is defined in two different but equivalent ways, viz. by the two last relations (34.2.3). The first of these asserts that the random variable α^* takes a value between the constant limits γ_1 and γ_2. The last relation (34.2.3), on the other hand, asserts that the random variable $c_1(\alpha^*, \varepsilon)$ takes a value smaller than α, while the random variable $c_2(\alpha^*, \varepsilon)$ takes a value greater than α or, in other words, that the variable interval (c_1, c_2) *covers* the fixed point α. According to (34.2.4), the probability of this event is equal to $1 - \varepsilon$, whatever the value of α.

Consider now a sequence of independent trials, where each trial consists in drawing a sample of n values from a population with the fr. f. $f(x; \alpha)$, the values of α corresponding to the successive trials being at liberty kept constant or allowed to vary in a perfectly arbitrary way, random or non-random. From each set of sample values, we calculate the quantities $c_1 = c_1(\alpha^*, \varepsilon)$ and $c_2 = c_2(\alpha^*, \varepsilon)$, using the value of ε given in advance. In general, c_1 and c_2 will have different values in different trials. Each trial will be counted as a »success», if the corresponding interval (c_1, c_2) covers the corresponding point α, and otherwise as a »failure». By (34.2.4), the probability of a success is then constantly equal to $1 - \varepsilon$, and accordingly (cf 16.6) the frequency ratio of successes in a long sequence of trials will, within the limits of random fluctuations, be equal to $1 - \varepsilon$.

Suppose now that we apply constantly the following rule of behaviour. We first choose once for all some small value of ε, say $\varepsilon = p/100$. Whenever a sample has been drawn, and the corresponding limits c_1 and c_2 have been calculated, we further state that the unknown value of α in the corresponding population is situated between c_1 and c_2. — According to the above, we shall then always have the probability $\varepsilon = p/100$ of giving a wrong statement. In the long run, our statements will thus be wrong in about p % of all cases, and otherwise correct.

The interval (c_1, c_2) will be called a *confidence interval* for the parameter α, corresponding to the *confidence coefficient* $1 - \varepsilon$, or the *confidence level* $\varepsilon = p/100$. The quantities c_1 and c_2 are the corresponding *confidence limits.*

Comparing this mode of treatment with the one based on Bayes' theorem, it will be seen that the method of confidence intervals is entirely free from any hypothesis with respect to the random or non-random nature of α. On the other hand, it follows from this very generality that the method does *not* lead to probability statements of the type: »The probability that α is situated between such and such fixed limits is equal to $1-\varepsilon$». In fact, such a statement has no sense except when α is a random variable. The statements provided by the method of confidence intervals are of the type of the relation (34.2.4), which expressed in words becomes: »The probability that such and such limits (which may vary from sample to sample) include between them the parameter value α corresponding to the actual sample, is equal to $1-\varepsilon$». As shown above, we may deduce from this statement a *rule of behaviour associated with a constant risk of error* ε, where ε may be arbitrarily fixed.

It must be observed that the system of confidence intervals corresponding to a given ε is not unique. Just as we may consider various different estimates of the same parameter α, we may also have various systems of confidence intervals, leading to different rules of behaviour, all associated with the same risk of error ε. This is by no means contradictory. As we have seen above, the confidence intervals obtained by applying a given rule will vary from sample to sample, and it is perfectly natural that, for a given sample, different rules may yield different intervals (cf Ex. 1 below).

Obviously it will be in our interest to find rules which, under given circumstances, yield as *short* confidence intervals as possible. Suppose e. g. that we are dealing with estimates α^* which are unbiased and approximately normally distributed. The strip $D(\varepsilon)$ in Fig. 33 will then be made as narrow as possible by choosing for α^* an estimate *of minimum variance*. Thus the classes of efficient and asymptotically efficient estimates studied in Ch. 32 will, under fairly general conditions, lead to the shortest or asymptotically shortest confidence intervals. We cannot go further into this subject here, but the reader is referred to papers by Neyman (Ref. 165) and Wilks (Ref. 233).

We finally observe that the above definitions and arguments apply even in the case of a *discrete* distribution involving a single unknown parameter α. However, there is one important modification to be made in this case. When the distribution on the vertical through the point $(\alpha, 0)$ in Fig. 33 has discrete mass points, the limits γ_1 and γ_2 cannot always be determined such that $P(\gamma_1 < \alpha^* < \gamma_2; \alpha) = 1-\varepsilon$ as required by (34.2.2). We shall have to be satisfied with choosing γ_1 and γ_2 such that $P(\gamma_1 < \alpha^* < \gamma_2; \alpha) \geqq 1-\varepsilon$, which is evidently always possible. The strip $D(\varepsilon)$ and the confidence interval (c_1, c_2) are then determined as in the continuous case. The risk of committing an error when stating that α belongs to (c_1, c_2) is in this case not exactly equal to ε, but *at most equal to* ε. With this exception, everything is perfectly similar to the continuous case.

Ex. 1. Let it be required to estimate the mean m of a normal population with a known s. d. σ. Replacing in Fig. 33 α and α^* by m and m^*, we first consider the efficient estimate $m^* = \bar{x} = \sum x_i/n$, which is normal $(m, \sigma/\sqrt{n})$. For the confidence level $\varepsilon = p/100$, the limits γ_1 and γ_2 in Fig. 33 may be put equal to $m \pm \lambda_p \sigma/\sqrt{n}$, where λ_p is the p % value of a normal deviate. The curves forming the boundary of the domain $D(\varepsilon)$ will then be the straight lines $\bar{x} = m \pm \lambda_p \sigma/\sqrt{n}$. The relations

$$m - \lambda_p \sigma/\sqrt{n} < \bar{x} < m + \lambda_p \sigma/\sqrt{n},$$

$$\bar{x} - \lambda_p \sigma/\sqrt{n} < m < \bar{x} + \lambda_p \sigma/\sqrt{n},$$

are evidently equivalent, so that the limits c_1 and c_2 are equal to $\bar{x} \pm \lambda_p \sigma/\sqrt{n}$. The rule which consists in asserting, whenever a sample has been drawn, that the unknown mean m is situated between the limits $\bar{x} \pm \lambda_p \sigma/\sqrt{n}$ is thus associated with a constant risk of error equal to p %.

We have, in fact, already encountered this interval in 31.3, Ex. 2. We have seen there that, working on a p % level of significance, the hypothesis that the mean of the distribution has a value c given in advance will be regarded as consistent with the data when c is situated between the confidence limits $\bar{x} \pm \lambda_p \sigma/\sqrt{n}$, while otherwise it will be rejected.

Suppose, on the other hand, that we consider the non-efficient estimate $m^* = z$, where z is the sample median. By 28.5, z is asymptotically normal $(m, k\,\sigma/\sqrt{n})$, where $k = \sqrt{\pi/2} = 1.2533$. Let us, for the sake of the argument, assume that the error of approximation can be neglected, so that the distribution is exactly normal. Each of the equivalent relations

$$m - k\,\lambda_p \sigma/\sqrt{n} < z < m + k\,\lambda_p \sigma/\sqrt{n} \quad \text{and} \quad z - k\,\lambda_p \sigma/\sqrt{n} < m < z + k\,\lambda_p \sigma/\sqrt{n}$$

then has a probability of p %, and consequently we obtain in this case the p % confidence limits $z \pm k\,\lambda_p \sigma/\sqrt{n}$. From a given sample, we thus obtain different confidence intervals for m, according as we apply the rule founded on $\bar{x}$ or on z. Nevertheless the risk of error is the same in both cases, if we are using the same value of ε. Obviously the former rule will always give a shorter interval than the latter.

Ex. 2. Suppose that we have made n repetitions of a random experiment, and that a certain event E has occurred ν times. It is required to estimate the unknown probability p of E. This is the classical problem of *inverse probability*, which is treated in the majority of text-books by means of Bayes' theorem.

We shall here apply the theory of confidence intervals to the problem, and consider the efficient estimate (cf 32.3, Ex. 5) $p^* = \nu/n$, which is asymptotically normal $(p, \sqrt{pq/n})$, where $q = 1 - p$. Taking the limits γ_1 and γ_2 equal to $p \pm \lambda \sqrt{pq/n}$ and assuming, as in the preceding example, that the distribution is exactly normal, Fig. 33 will take the form indicated in Fig. 34. The domain $D(\varepsilon)$ is here bounded by the curves $p^* = p \pm \lambda \sqrt{pq/n}$, which form the two halves of an ellipse, λ being the $100\,\varepsilon$ % value of a normal deviate. The fact that a point (p, p^*) is situated inside

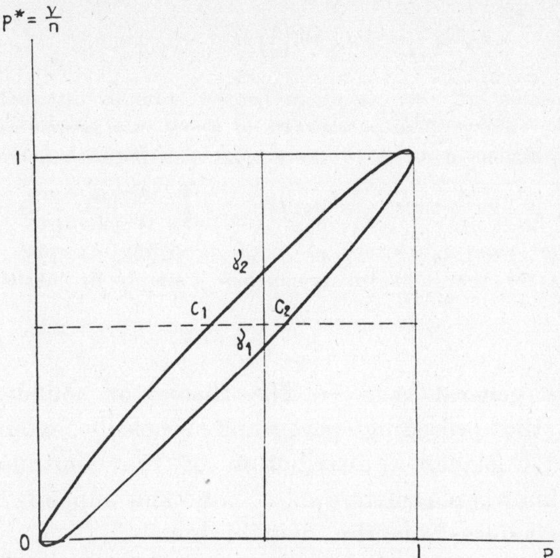

Fig. 34. Confidence intervals for an unknown probability. $n = 100$, $\varepsilon = 0.05$.

the ellipse may be expressed by saying that p^* lies between the limits $p \pm \lambda \sqrt{pq/n}$ or by the equivalent statement that p lies between the limits

(34.2.5) $$\frac{n}{n+\lambda^2}\left(p^* + \frac{\lambda^2}{2n} \pm \lambda \sqrt{\frac{p^* q^*}{n} + \frac{\lambda^2}{4n^2}}\right).$$

The latter limits determine a $100\,\varepsilon$ % confidence interval for p.

This result is, of course, only approximate, since in reality p^* has a discrete distribution which is only approximately normal. E. S. Pearson and Clopper (Ref. 195) have given graphs based on the exact distribution and permitting a determination of confidence intervals for the 5 % and 1 % levels. As Pearson and Clopper point out, their graphs may be used i. a. to determine the value of n which is necessary to provide a desired degree of accuracy in the estimation of p. Suppose, e. g., that p is about 50 %, and that we want a confidence interval of length at most equal to δ. From the approximate solution (34.2.5) we obtain, taking $p^* = \frac{1}{2}$,

$$\frac{\lambda}{\sqrt{n+\lambda^2}} \leqq \delta, \quad \text{or} \quad n \geqq \lambda^2 \frac{1-\delta^2}{\delta^2}.$$

Taking e. g. $\delta = \varepsilon = 0.01$, this gives $n > 66340$.

Ex. 3. Suppose that we have a population consisting of a finite number N of individuals, Np of which possess a certain attribute A, while the remaining $Nq = N - Np$ do not possess A. It is now required to estimate the unknown proportion p by the *representative method* (cf 25.7). Let us draw a random sample of n individuals *without replacement*, and observe the number ν of individuals in the sample possessing the attribute A. In current text-books on probability, it is shown that we have (cf e. g. Cramér, Ref. 10, p. 38)

$$E\left(\frac{\nu}{n}\right) = p, \quad D^2\left(\frac{\nu}{n}\right) = \frac{N-n}{N-1} \cdot \frac{p\,q}{n}.$$

Further, the variable $p^* = \nu/n$ is approximately normally distributed, when n and $N - n$ are large. Taking p^* as an estimate of p, we now assume as above that the error of approximation involved in the normal distribution can be neglected. The probability that p^* lies between the limits $p \pm \lambda \sqrt{\frac{N-n}{N-1} \cdot \frac{p\,q}{n}}$ is then equal to ε, where λ has the same significance as in the preceding example. Thus we obtain confidence limits for the unknown proportion p simply by substituting in (34.2.5) $\frac{N-1}{N-n} n$ for n.

34.3. The general case. — The theory of confidence intervals developed in the preceding paragraph is easily extended to more general cases. Consider a distribution of the continuous type containing k unknown parameters $\alpha_1, \ldots, \alpha_k$, and suppose that we draw a sample of n values from this distribution.

The sample variables will as usual be regarded as the coordinates of a point $\boldsymbol{x} = (x_1, \ldots, x_n)$ in the n-dimensional *sample space* $\boldsymbol{R}_n$, and similarly the set of parameters of an actual distribution will be represented by the point $\boldsymbol{\alpha} = (\alpha_1, \ldots, \alpha_k)$ in a k-dimensional *parametric space* $\boldsymbol{P}_k$. For simplicity we suppose that the distribution is defined for all points $\boldsymbol{\alpha}$ of $\boldsymbol{P}_k$, and we denote the joint pr. f. of the variables $x_1, \ldots, x_n$ by $P(S; \boldsymbol{\alpha})$, where S is a set in the sample space $\boldsymbol{R}_n$.

For the following developments, it is not necessary to suppose that the variables $x_1, \ldots, x_n$ are independent variables all having the same distribution. With a similar generalization as in 32.8 we may, in fact, allow $P(S; \boldsymbol{\alpha})$ to denote any n-dimensional pr. f. of the continuous type, which is defined for all parametric points $\boldsymbol{\alpha} = (\alpha_1, \ldots, \alpha_k)$.

To every parametric point $\boldsymbol{\alpha}$ in $\boldsymbol{P}_k$, we may determine a set $S(\boldsymbol{\alpha})$ of points $\boldsymbol{x}$ in $\boldsymbol{R}_n$ such that

$$P[\boldsymbol{x} < S(\boldsymbol{\alpha}); \boldsymbol{\alpha}] = 1 - \varepsilon, \tag{34.3.1}$$

where ε is given in advance. — The set $S(\boldsymbol{\alpha})$ corresponds to the interval $\gamma_1 < \alpha^* < \gamma_2$ in Fig. 33,[1]) and the relation (34.3.1) corresponds to (34.2.2). Further, the set D of all points $(\boldsymbol{\alpha}, \boldsymbol{x})$ in the product space $\boldsymbol{P}_k \cdot \boldsymbol{R}_n$ such that the relation $\boldsymbol{x} < S(\boldsymbol{\alpha})$ is satisfied, corresponds to the domain $D(\varepsilon)$ in Fig. 33. For every point $\boldsymbol{x}$ in $\boldsymbol{R}_n$, we now consider the set $\Sigma(\boldsymbol{x})$ of all points $\boldsymbol{\alpha}$ in $\boldsymbol{P}_k$ such that $(\boldsymbol{\alpha}, \boldsymbol{x}) < D$.

[1]) We may here regard Fig. 33 as concerned with a sample of one single observed value α^* from a distribution with the fr. f. $g(\alpha^*; \alpha)$.

Then $\Sigma(\boldsymbol{x})$ corresponds to the interval $c_1 < \alpha < c_2$ of Fig. 33, and the three relations

$$(\alpha, \boldsymbol{x}) < D, \qquad \boldsymbol{x} < S(\alpha), \qquad \alpha < \Sigma(\boldsymbol{x}),$$

are equivalent, for the same reasons as the corresponding relations (34.2.3). Hence we obtain the analogue of (34.2.4):

$$P[\alpha < \Sigma(\boldsymbol{x});\, \alpha] = 1 - \varepsilon. \tag{34.3.2}$$

The further development is exactly similar to the preceding particular case. If we draw repeatedly samples of n from distributions of the given type, the corresponding parametric points α being at liberty kept constant or allowed to vary in a perfectly arbitrary way, and if for every sample we state that the actual parametric point α belongs to the set $\Sigma(\boldsymbol{x})$ corresponding to the sample, we shall in each case have the probability $\varepsilon = p/100$ of being wrong. Consequently in the long run our statements will be wrong in about p % of all cases.

The set $\Sigma(\boldsymbol{x})$ will be called a *confidence region* for the parametric point α, corresponding to the confidence coefficient $1 - \varepsilon$, or the confidence level $\varepsilon = p/100$. If, in particular, the set $\Sigma(\boldsymbol{x})$ is an interval in $\boldsymbol{P}_k$ defined by one single relation of the form

$$c_1(\boldsymbol{x}, \varepsilon) < \alpha_r < c_2(\boldsymbol{x}, \varepsilon), \tag{34.3.3}$$

where r is one of the subscripts $1, \ldots, k$, while c_1 and c_2 are independent of $\alpha_1, \ldots, \alpha_k$, we shall call $\Sigma(\boldsymbol{x})$ a *confidence interval for the parameter* α_r. The last definition evidently includes the corresponding definition of the preceding paragraph as a particular case. More generally, if the set $\Sigma(\boldsymbol{x})$ is a cylinder set (cf 3.5), the base of which is a set in the subspace of the parameters $\alpha_1, \ldots, \alpha_r$, where $r < k$, we shall say that $\Sigma(\boldsymbol{x})$ is a confidence region for the parameters $\alpha_1, \ldots, \alpha_r$.

With respect to the generalization to distributions containing discrete mass points, the remarks of the preceding paragraph apply even in the present general case. Finally, the generalization to samples from multi-dimensional distributions is immediate.

34.4. Examples. — In 31.3, Ex. 6, we have already encountered some confidence intervals for coefficients of regression and correlation in the case of samples from a two-dimensional normal distribution. We shall now discuss some further examples, which will give rise to comments on certain points of general interest.

Ex. 1. *The mean of a normal distribution.* When $x_1, \ldots, x_n$ are a set of sample values from a normal distribution with unknown parameters m and σ, the ratio (cf 29.4)

$$t = \sqrt{n-1}\ \frac{\bar{x} - m}{s}$$

has Student's distribution with $n-1$ d. of fr., the corresponding fr. f. being $s_{n-1}(t)$. For any interval (t', t''), the relation

$$t' < \sqrt{n-1}\ \frac{\bar{x} - m}{s} < t'' \qquad (34.4.1)$$

has thus the probability $\int_{t'}^{t''} s_{n-1}(t)\,dt$, which is independent of the parameters m and σ, and by an appropriate choice of t' and t'' this can be made to assume any given value $1-\varepsilon$.

Suppose that t' and t'' are fixed. For every parametric point (m, σ), the relation (34.4.1) then defines a set of points $\boldsymbol{x}$ in the sample space which corresponds to the set $S(\alpha)$ of the preceding paragraph. However, (34.4.1) may also be written in the equivalent form

$$\bar{x} - t'' \frac{s}{\sqrt{n-1}} < m < \bar{x} - t' \frac{s}{\sqrt{n-1}}. \qquad (34.4.2)$$

For any fixed point $\boldsymbol{x} = (x_1, \ldots, x_n)$ in the sample space, this relation defines an interval in the parametric space, which is independent of σ, and is thus of the form (34.3.3), where α_r has been replaced by m. According to the definition of the preceding paragraph, (34.4.2) thus provides a *confidence interval for the mean* m, and we have the following relation corresponding to (34.3.2):

$$P\left(\bar{x} - t'' \frac{s}{\sqrt{n-1}} < m < \bar{x} - t' \frac{s}{\sqrt{n-1}};\ m, \sigma\right) = \int_{t'}^{t''} s_{n-1}(t)\,dt. \qquad (34.4.3)$$

Thus if we draw repeatedly samples of n from normal populations, the values of m and σ corresponding to the successive samples being at liberty kept constant or allowed to vary in an arbitrary way, and if for every sample we calculate the confidence limits $\bar{x} - t'' s/\sqrt{n-1}$ and $\bar{x} - t' s/\sqrt{n-1}$, the frequency of those cases where m is included between the limits will in the long run be approximately equal to $\int_{t'}^{t''} s_{n-1}(t)\,dt$.

Every choice of t' and t'' yields, according to (34.4.3), a rule for calculating confidence intervals for m, the corresponding confidence coefficient being $\int_{t'}^{t''} s_{n-1}(t)\,dt$. Taking e. g. $t' = -t_p$ and $t'' = t_p$, where t_p is the p % value of t for $n-1$ d. of fr., we obtain the confidence limits

$$\bar{x} \pm t_p \frac{s}{\sqrt{n-1}},$$

corresponding to the confidence coefficient $1 - p/100$, or the confidence level p %.

Consider the sample of $n = 10$ values from a supposedly normal population contained in the last column of Table 31.3.7. The mean and the s. d. of the sample are respectively 1.58 and 1.167. Hence we obtain according to the last rule the con fidence limits $1.58 \pm 0.389\, t_p$ for the unknown population mean m. For the confidence level $p = 5$ %, this gives the confidence interval $0.70 < m < 2.46$, while for $p = 1$ % the interval becomes $0.32 < m < 2.84$.

Choosing t' and t'' differently, we obtain other rules for calculating confidence intervals for m. Suppose, e. g., that an interval (a, b) is given in advance. We now draw a sample of n values from a normal population, and denote the observed sample point by $\boldsymbol{x}_0$, the sample mean by $\bar{x}_0$, and the s. d. by s_0. From these particular values $\bar{x}_0$ and s_0, we further determine t' and t'' such that

$$\bar{x}_0 - t'' \frac{s_0}{\sqrt{n-1}} = a, \qquad \bar{x}_0 - t' \frac{s_0}{\sqrt{n-1}} = b.$$

Like any other values of t' and t'', the values determined in this way correspond to a rule for calculating confidence intervals for m, and in the particular case of the sample $\boldsymbol{x}_0$, this rule leads precisely to the given interval (a, b). Solving the above equations for t' and t'', we find that the corresponding confidence coefficient is

$$\int_{\sqrt{n-1}\,(\bar{x}_0 - b)/s_0}^{\sqrt{n-1}\,(\bar{x}_0 - a)/s_0} s_{n-1}(t)\,dt. \tag{34.4.4}$$

When the sample $\boldsymbol{x}_0$ is known, this quantity can be numerically calculated for any interval (a, b). *Thus we may say that, with respect to the estimation of m by means of the sample characteristics $\bar{x}$ and s, the* *observed sample* $\boldsymbol{x}_0$ *assigns to any given interval* (a, b) *a confidence coefficient given by* (34.4.4).[1])

However, it is necessary to note carefully the concrete meaning of the last proposition. We are *not* saying that there is a probability given by (34.4.4) that m falls between the given limits a and b. As already pointed out in 34.2, such a statement would have no sense except when m is a random variable. *We do, in fact, only assert that there exists a rule for calculating confidence intervals for* m, *which in the particular case of the sample* $\boldsymbol{x}_0$ *would lead to the given interval* (a, b) *as confidence interval, and that this rule is associated with the confidence coefficient* (34.4.4).

In the case of the sample of $n = 10$ values from Table 31.3.7 considered above, we thus find by means of Table 4 that the interval $0.5 < m < 2.5$ has the confidence coefficient $\int_{-2.37}^{+2.78} s_9(t)\,dt = 0.97$.

As in 34.2, it should be observed that the above system of confidence intervals and confidence coefficients for the estimation of m is not unique. If, e.g., we replace $\bar{x}$ and s by the median and the mean deviation of the sample, we shall obtain a different system of rules.

Ex. 2. *The difference between the means of two normal distributions.* Let $x_1, \ldots, x_{n_1}$ and $y_1, \ldots, y_{n_2}$ be two independent samples with the means $\bar{x}$ and $\bar{y}$, and the s. d:s s_1 and s_2. Suppose that these are drawn from normal populations with the means m_1 and m_2, and the s. d:s σ_1 and σ_2 respectively. We suppose that all four parameters are unknown, and that it is required to estimate the difference $m_1 - m_2$ between the population means. This problem has been much discussed in the literature (cf e. g. Bartlett, Ref. 55, 56; Behrens, Ref. 60; Fisher, Ref. 105—109; Neyman, Ref. 167; Welch, Ref. 229).

In 31.2, we have considered the question whether $m_1 - m_2$ differs significantly from zero, under the simplifying assumption that σ_1 and σ_2 are equal. If, in the variable u defined by (31.2.1), we replace $\bar{x} - \bar{y}$ by $\bar{x} - \bar{y} - (m_1 - m_2)$, and if we assume that $\sigma_1 = \sigma_2$, the resulting variable will have Student's distribution with $n_1 + n_2 - 2$ d. of fr. Hence we obtain, in the same way as in the preceding example, the confidence limits

[1]) At this point, we possibly exceed the conceptual limits of the theory as given by Neyman (cf Ref. 167). The same remark applies to the corresponding part of Ex. 2.

$$(34.4.5)\qquad \bar{x}-\bar{y}\pm t_p\sqrt{\frac{(n_1+n_2)(n_1 s_1^2+n_2 s_2^2)}{n_1 n_2 (n_1+n_2-2)}}$$

for the unknown difference $m_1 - m_2$. Here we have to take t_p with $n_1 + n_2 - 2$ d. of fr. — We now proceed to make some remarks on the general case when σ_1 and σ_2 may have any values.

To any parametric point $(m_1, m_2, \sigma_1, \sigma_2)$ corresponds a joint distribution of the $n_1 + n_2$ variables x_i and y_j, which are represented in a space $\boldsymbol{R}$ of $n_1 + n_2$ dimensions. Let now four constants k_1, k_2, c_1 and c_2 be given, subject to the only condition that $k_1 < k_2$. For any parametric point, the relation

$$k_1 < c_1 \frac{\bar{x}-m_1}{s_1} + c_2 \frac{\bar{y}-m_2}{s_2} < k_2$$

defines a set S of points $(\boldsymbol{x}, \boldsymbol{y}) = (x_1, \ldots, x_{n_1}, y_1, \ldots, y_{n_2})$ in the space $\boldsymbol{R}$. Since the random variables

$$t = \sqrt{n_1 - 1}\,\frac{\bar{x}-m_1}{s_1} \quad \text{and} \quad u = \sqrt{n_2 - 1}\,\frac{\bar{y}-m_2}{s_2}$$

are independent and distributed in Student's distribution with n_1 and n_2 d. of fr. respectively, the probability that a sample point $(\boldsymbol{x}, \boldsymbol{y})$ belongs to the set S is

$$(34.4.6)\qquad J = \iint s_{n_1-1}(t)\, s_{n_2-1}(u)\, dt\, du,$$

where the integral is extended over the domain defined by the relation

$$k_1 < \frac{c_1 t}{\sqrt{n_1-1}} + \frac{c_2 u}{\sqrt{n_2-1}} < k_2.$$

The quantity J is independent of the parameters, and the set S corresponds to the set $S(\alpha)$ of 34.3. The relation which defines the set S may be written in the equivalent form

$$(34.4.7)\qquad \frac{c_1\bar{x}}{s_1} + \frac{c_2\bar{y}}{s_2} - k_2 < \frac{c_1 m_1}{s_1} + \frac{c_2 m_2}{s_2} < \frac{c_1\bar{x}}{s_1} + \frac{c_2\bar{y}}{s_2} - k_1.$$

For any fixed point $(\boldsymbol{x}, \boldsymbol{y})$, this relation defines a cylinder set $\Sigma(\boldsymbol{x}, \boldsymbol{y})$ in the four-dimensional $(m_1, m_2, \sigma_1, \sigma_2)$-space, the base of which is a strip bounded by two parallell lines in the (m_1, m_2)-subspace. Thus according to 34.3 the set $\Sigma(\boldsymbol{x}, \boldsymbol{y})$ is a confidence region for m_1 and m_2, with the confidence coefficient J given by (34.4.6).

Every choice of the constants k_1, k_2, c_1 and c_2 yields, according to (34.4.7), a confidence region for m_1 and m_2, the corresponding confidence coefficient being given by (34.4.6). By an appropriate choice of the constants, we may render the confidence coefficient equal to any given value $1-\varepsilon$.

As in the preceding example, we now suppose that an interval (a, b) is given in advance, and that two samples $\boldsymbol{x}_0$ and $\boldsymbol{y}_0$ have been drawn. From the particular values $\bar{x}_0$, $\bar{y}_0$, s_1^0 and s_2^0 observed in these samples, we determine k_1, k_2, c_1 and c_2 such that

$$c_1 = s_1^0, \qquad c_2 = -s_2^0, \qquad k_1 = \bar{x}_0 - \bar{y}_0 - b, \qquad k_2 = \bar{x}_0 - \bar{y}_0 - a.$$

Like any other values of the constants, the values obtained in this way correspond to a rule for determining confidence regions for m_1 and m_2. Inserting these values of the constants in (34.4.7), we find that in the particular case of the samples $\boldsymbol{x}_0$ and $\boldsymbol{y}_0$ this rule leads to the region

$$a < m_1 - m_2 < b,$$

while the domain of integration in the expression (34.4.6) of the confidence coefficient becomes

$$\bar{x}_0 - \bar{y}_0 - b < \frac{s_1^0 t}{\sqrt{n_1 - 1}} - \frac{s_2^0 u}{\sqrt{n_2 - 1}} < \bar{x}_0 - \bar{y}_0 - a. \tag{34.4.8}$$

Thus there exists a rule for determining confidence regions for m_1 *and* m_2, *which in the particular case of the samples* $\boldsymbol{x}_0$ *and* $\boldsymbol{y}_0$ *would lead to the region* $a < m_1 - m_2 < b$, *and this rule is associated with the confidence coefficient* J *given by* (34.4.6), *where the integral is extended over the domain* (34.4.8). — *In the sense explained by this statement, we may say that the samples* $\boldsymbol{x}_0$ *and* $\boldsymbol{y}_0$ *assign the confidence coefficient* J *to the region* $a < m_1 - m_2 < b$.

Hence we may deduce a test of significance due to Behrens and Fisher (l. c.). Let two samples with the means $\bar{x}$ and $\bar{y}$, and the s. d:s s_1 and s_2 be given, and let θ be an angle such that

$$\frac{s_1}{\sqrt{n_1 - 1}} = r \sin\theta, \qquad \frac{s_2}{\sqrt{n_2 - 1}} = r \cos\theta,$$

where

$$r = \sqrt{\frac{s_1^2}{n_1 - 1} + \frac{s_2^2}{n_2 - 1}}.$$

Consider the integral J in (34.4.6), extended over the domain

$$t \sin \theta - u \cos \theta > d,$$

and determine d such that $J = \delta$, where δ is a given number such that $0 < \delta < 1$. For fixed δ, the quantity d will be a function of n_1, n_2 and θ, which may be numerically calculated when these quantities are known. Now if $\bar{x} - \bar{y} > dr$, the region $m_1 \leqq m_2$ will according to the above have a confidence coefficient smaller than δ. Similarly, if $\bar{x} - \bar{y} < - dr$, the region $m_1 \geqq m_2$ will have a confidence coefficient smaller than δ. If δ is sufficiently small, the means $\bar{x}$ and $\bar{y}$ are accordingly regarded as significantly different, as soon as $|\bar{x} - \bar{y}| > dr$. Tables for the application of this test are available (cf Sukhatme, Ref. 223; Fisher-Yates, Ref. 262).

Ex. 3. *The mean of a finite population* (cf 34.2, Ex. 3). Suppose that we have a population consisting of a large, but finite number N of individuals, among which a certain character x is distributed. For the mean, the variance, and other characteristics of x in the total population, we use the ordinary notations: m, σ^2, μ_i etc. It is required to estimate the unknown mean m of the population by means of the *representative method* (cf 25.7). Let us draw a random sample of n individuals *without replacement*, and denote by $\bar{x} = \sum x_i / n$ and $s^2 = \sum (x_i - \bar{x})^2 / n$ the mean and the variance of the n observed sample values of x. We then have (cf e. g. Neyman, Ref. 160; Hagstroem, Ref. 121 a)

$$\boldsymbol{E}(\bar{x}) = m, \qquad \boldsymbol{D}^2(\bar{x}) = \frac{N-n}{N-1} \cdot \frac{\sigma^2}{n}, \qquad \boldsymbol{E}(s^2) = \frac{N}{N-1} \cdot \frac{n-1}{n} \sigma^2,$$

$$\boldsymbol{D}^2(s^2) = \frac{N(N-n)}{(N-1)^2 (N-2)(N-3)} \cdot \frac{(n-1)\sigma^4}{n^3} [2 n N^2 - 6(n+1)(N-1) + \\ + (nN - N - n - 1)(N-1)\gamma_2]$$

where $\gamma_2 = \mu_4/\sigma^4 - 3$ is the coefficient of excess (cf 15.8) of the population. When n and $N - n$ are both large, $\bar{x}$ is approximately normal, so that the variable $\sqrt{\frac{(N-1)n}{N-n}}(\bar{x} - m)$ is approximately normal $(0, \sigma)$. The formulae for the mean and the variance of s^2 may be written

$$\boldsymbol{E}\left(\frac{q^2}{\sigma^2}\right) = \frac{N(n-1)}{N-n}\left[1 + O\left(\frac{1}{N}\right)\right],$$

$$\boldsymbol{D}^2\left(\frac{q^2}{\sigma^2}\right) = \frac{2N(n-1)}{N-n}\left[1 + \frac{n-1}{2n}\gamma_2 + O\left(\frac{1}{N}\right)\right],$$

where $q^2 = N n s^2/(N-n)$. If we assume that the excess γ_2 of the population may be neglected, it now follows by means of (18.1.6) that for large N the variable q^2/σ^2 has approximately the same mean and the same variance as a χ^2-distribution with $N(n-1)/(N-n)$ d. of fr. Although in this case the exact distribution of s^2 or q^2 is not known, we may as a first approximation assume that the variable

$$t = \frac{\sqrt{\frac{(N-1)n}{N-n}}(\bar{x}-m)}{\sqrt{\frac{N-n}{N(n-1)}q^2}} = \sqrt{\frac{(N-1)(n-1)}{N-n}} \cdot \frac{\bar{x}-m}{s}$$

has Student's distribution (18.2.4), with n replaced by $N(n-1)/(N-n)$. For the unknown population mean m, we then obtain as in Ex. 1 the p % confidence limits

$$\bar{x} \pm t_p \, s \sqrt{\frac{N-n}{(N-1)(n-1)}}.$$

ADDITIONAL REMARK. The following important papers bearing on the subjects treated in Chs 32-34 (particularly 32.3-4 and 33.3) have unfortunately been omitted from the List of References:

Doob, J. L., Probability and Statistics, Trans. Amer. Math. Soc., 36 (1934), p. 759.

Doob, J. L., Statistical estimation, Trans. Amer. Math. Soc., 39 (1936), p. 410.

Fréchet, M., Sur l'extension de certaines évaluations statistiques au cas de petits échantillons, Rev. Inst. Intern. de Statistique, 1943, p. 182.

Chapters 35—37. Tests of Significance, II.

CHAPTER 35.

General Theory of Testing Statistical Hypotheses.[1]

35.1. The choice of a test of significance. — In the preliminary survey of problems of statistical inference given in Ch. 26, the introduction of a test of significance for a statistical hypothesis has been described (cf 26.2 and 26.4) in the following general terms: When it is required to test whether a set of sample values agree with a given hypothesis H, we consider the distribution of the sample, and calculate some convenient measure $D \geqq 0$ of the deviation of this distribution from the hypothetical distribution. By means of the sampling distribution of D, we then determine a critical value D_0 such that, if the hypothesis H is true, we have $P(D > D_0) = \varepsilon$, where ε is our level of significance chosen in advance. When, in an actual case, we find a deviation $D > D_0$, the hypothesis H is *rejected*, whereas the appearance of a value $D \leqq D_0$ is regarded as consistent with the hypothesis, which is then *accepted*.

By adopting this rule of behaviour, we have a probability equal to ε of committing the error of rejecting H in a case when, in fact, it is true. Since ε may be arbitrarily chosen, this probability may be reduced to any desired amount.

The general principle thus described, which lies behind all the particular tests discussed in Chs 30—31, has certainly a strong appeal to intuition. On the given hypothesis, the occurrence of a very large deviation D has a very small probability. If, in an actual case, such a deviation presents itself, we feel naturally inclined to consider the hypothesis as disproved by experience. The appearance of some deviation D of moderate size, on the other hand, seems to be exactly the kind of event that ought to be expected, if the hypothesis is true.

However, let us examine the principle a little more closely. Assume, e. g., that D has a continuous distribution, with a frequency curve of

[1]) Cf footnote p. 473.

a type similar to the χ^2-distribution for $n > 2$ (cf Fig. 19, p. 235). It is true that, on the hypothesis H, the probability of a large deviation, say $D > D_0$, is small. In fact, this probability is equal to the area of the tail of the frequency curve situated to the right of an ordinate through the point D_0, and we can always determine D_0 such that this becomes equal to any given $\varepsilon > 0$. But it is equally true that the appearance of a very *small* deviation, say $D < D_1$, also has a small probability, since we can determine D_1 such that the area of the tail to the *left* of an ordinate through D_1 is equal to ε. If we agree to reject H whenever $D < D_1$, and otherwise accept, we shall thus still have the same probability ε of rejecting H in a case when it is true. — More generally, we may in infinitely many ways choose a set of points S such that, if H is true, the probability that D takes a value in S is $P(D < S) = \varepsilon$. Consider, for any such S, the test which consists in rejecting H whenever D takes a value in S, and otherwise accepting. The probability of unjustly rejecting H in a case when it is true will then always be equal to ε, so that from this point of view the tests based on various possible sets S will all be equivalent. It is likely that our intuitive feeling will be in favour of the D_0 test, where the set S is the interval of large deviations $D > D_0$, and definitely opposed to the D_1 test, where we reject the hypothesis precisely in those cases where the deviations are small. However, can we advance any rational arguments in support of the view that some particular form of the set S should be preferred to other possible forms?

As an example, we may consider the χ^2 test. In Ch. 30, we have denoted an observed value of χ^2 as significant, when it exceeds the $p = 100\,\varepsilon\,\%$ value χ_p^2. This evidently corresponds to the D_0 test mentioned above, and the set S is here the interval $\chi^2 > \chi_p^2$. When the number n of d. of fr. is large, $\sqrt{2\chi^2}$ may be regarded as normal $(\sqrt{2n-1}, 1)$, and the same set S is then approximately represented by the interval $\sqrt{2\chi^2} > \sqrt{2n-1} + \lambda_{2p}$, or $\chi^2 > \frac{1}{2}(\sqrt{2n-1} + \lambda_{2p})^2$, where λ_{2p} is the $2p\,\%$ value of a normal deviate, thus making the area of the *right* tail of the approximating normal curve equal to $p/100 = \varepsilon$. — However, in the latter case it would also seem reasonable to take account of *both* tails of the normal curve, thus counting χ^2 as significant, when $|\sqrt{2\chi^2} - \sqrt{2n-1}| > \lambda$ In this case, the set S would be composed of the two intervals $\chi^2 < \frac{1}{2}(\sqrt{2n-1} - \lambda_p)^2$ and $\chi^2 > \frac{1}{2}(\sqrt{2n-1} + \lambda_p)^2$. In both cases, the probability of an unjust rejection of the hypothesis tested will be ε.

Further, the deviation measure D is by no means uniquely determined. We may, e. g., measure the goodness of fit of a hypothetical distribution to a sample by χ^2, by ω^2, etc. Similarly the deviation of a normal sample from the hypothesis that the population mean is equal to m may be measured e. g. by $|\bar{x} - m|$ or by $|z - m|$, where $\bar{x}$ and z are the mean and the median of the sample, etc. For any alternative deviation measure Δ, we may in infinitely many ways find a set of points Σ such that, if H is true, we have $P(\Delta < \Sigma) = \varepsilon$. The test which consists in rejecting H whenever Δ takes a value belonging to Σ, and otherwise accepting, will still correspond to the given probability ε of rejecting H when it is true.

Obviously it will be an important problem to find some rational method of discriminating between the various possible tests for a given hypothesis. Will it be possible to assign a reasonable meaning to the statement that, of two tests corresponding to the same value of ε, one is »better» or »more efficient» than the other?

During recent years, much work has been devoted to this problem by J. Neyman, E. S. Pearson and their followers. The reader is referred to a series of fundamental papers (Ref. 170—173) by Neyman and Pearson, and to a general exposition of the theory by Neyman (Ref. 168), where numerous references to the literature will be found.

The basic idea of the Neyman-Pearson theory may be briefly described in the following way. When a test of significance is applied in practice, there are in each case two possible alternatives: we may decide to *reject* or to *accept* the proposed hypothesis H, and then act according to our decision[1]). In either case our decision may be wrong, since we may reject H in a case when, in fact, it is true, and accept it in a case when it is false.[2]) It now seems a perfectly reasonable principle that, in choosing a test, we should try to *reduce the chances of committing both these kinds of errors as much as possible.*

In order that a test of the hypothesis H should be judged to be »good», we should accordingly require that the test has a small probability of rejecting H when this hypothesis is true, but a large probability of rejecting H when it is false. Of two tests corresponding to the same

---

[1]) There is, of course, also the third alternative that we may decide to remain in doubt and postpone action until further data have been collected. However, we consider here the case when such data are already available, and the course of action must be decided.

[2]) This double possibility of error distinguishes the present situation from the one arising in the theory of estimation When we assert, e. g., that the unknown value of a certain parameter belongs to such and such confidence interval, our statement may be right or wrong, but there is only one way of committing an error, viz. by indicating an interval which, in fact, does not contain the parameter.

probability ε *of rejecting H when it is true, we should thus prefer the one that gives the largest probability of rejecting H when it is false.*

We now proceed to show some applications of the general principle. It will be necessary to restrict ourselves to a very brief account of some of the most elementary features of this important theory, which is still in full development.

35.2. Simple and composite hypotheses. — Consider n random variables $x_1, \ldots, x_n$, with a joint distribution in $\boldsymbol{R}_n$ of the continuous type, defined by a pr. f. $P(S; \alpha) = P(S; \alpha_1, \ldots, \alpha_k)$ of known mathematical form, containing k unknown parameters $\alpha_1, \ldots, \alpha_k$, or by the corresponding fr. f. $f(\boldsymbol{x}; \alpha) = f(x_1, \ldots, x_n; \alpha_1, \ldots, \alpha_k)$.

When, in particular, the x_i are independent variables all having the same distribution, we have the ordinary case of a sample of n values from this distribution. However, as pointed out in the analogous case considered in 32.8 (cf also 34.3), the above definitions cover also more general cases, such as e. g. the case when the x_i consist of several independent samples from possibly unequal distributions. Even in the general case, we shall refer to the point $\boldsymbol{x} = (x_1, \ldots, x_n)$ and the space $\boldsymbol{R}_n$ as the sample point and the sample space respectively. — The parameters α_j will be represented by the parametric point $\alpha = (\alpha_1, \ldots, \alpha_k)$ in the parametric space $\boldsymbol{P}_k$.

Suppose now that a sample point $\boldsymbol{x}$ has been determined by a single performance of the random experiment corresponding to the combined variable $(x_1, \ldots, x_n)$. The hypothesis that, in the distribution of this variable, the unknown parametric point α belongs to a given set of points ω in the parametric space $\boldsymbol{P}_k$, will be briefly denoted as the *hypothesis H*. When ω consists of one single point α_0, we shall say that the hypothesis is *simple*, and otherwise that it is *composite*. Evidently a simple hypothesis specifies the distribution completely, while a composite hypothesis leaves it more or less undetermined.

Every parametric point α that is regarded as a priori possible will be called an *admissible point*, corresponding to an *admissible hypothesis*. The set Ω of all admissible points may coincide with the whole parametric space $\boldsymbol{P}_k$, but may also form only a part of $\boldsymbol{P}_k$.

If the x_i are a sample of independent values from a non-singular normal distribution, where no a priori information concerning the parameters m and σ is available, the set Ω of admissible hypotheses consists of the half-plane $\sigma > 0$. The hypothesis that $m = 0$ and $\sigma = 1$ is a simple hypothesis, while the hypothesis that $m = 0$, without specifying the value of σ, is a composite hypothesis.

35.3. Tests of simple hypotheses. Most powerful tests. — Suppose that it is required to test the simple hypothesis H_0 that the unknown parametric point $\boldsymbol{\alpha}$ coincides with the given point $\boldsymbol{\alpha}_0$. A test of this hypothesis will consist of a rule to reject H_0 whenever the observed point $\boldsymbol{x}$ belongs to a certain set S in $\boldsymbol{R}_n$, and otherwise to accept H_0. The set S will be called the *critical set* of the test, and the test based on the critical set S will often be briefly called the *test* S.

When the critical set S has been fixed, the probability of rejecting H_0 is identical with the probability $P(S; \boldsymbol{\alpha})$ that the sample point belongs to the set S. This is a function of the k variables $\alpha_1, \ldots, \alpha_k$, which will be called the *power function* of the test. According to the general desideratum expressed in 35.1, we should endeavour to arrange the test so as to render the power function *small when* H_0 *is true* (i. e. when $\boldsymbol{\alpha}$ coincides with $\boldsymbol{\alpha}_0$), and *large when* H_0 *is false* (i. e. when $\boldsymbol{\alpha}$ is any admissible point other than $\boldsymbol{\alpha}_0$).

Since the $\boldsymbol{x}$ distribution is continuous, there are always an infinity of different sets S such that $P(S; \boldsymbol{\alpha}_0) = \varepsilon$, where ε is our level of significance given in advance. If any of these sets is chosen as the critical set of a test, the probability of rejecting H_0 when it is true will be equal to ε, and we shall then briefly say that we are concerned with a test *of level* ε. It is now required to find, from among all tests of level ε, one that renders the probability of rejecting H_0 when it is false as large as possible, i. e. one that renders the power function $P(S; \boldsymbol{\alpha})$ as large as possible for any admissible $\boldsymbol{\alpha} \neq \boldsymbol{\alpha}_0$.

Let $\boldsymbol{\alpha}_1$ be a fixed admissible point $\neq \boldsymbol{\alpha}_0$. Since the values of a fr. f. may be arbitrarily changed over a set of measure zero, we may always suppose that $f(\boldsymbol{x}; \boldsymbol{\alpha}_0)$ and $f(\boldsymbol{x}; \boldsymbol{\alpha}_1)$ are finite and determined for every $\boldsymbol{x}$. For any $c \geqq 0$, the set X of all points $\boldsymbol{x}$ such that

$$f(\boldsymbol{x}; \boldsymbol{\alpha}_1) \geqq c f(\boldsymbol{x}; \boldsymbol{\alpha}_0) \tag{35.3.1}$$

is then well determined. When c increases from 0 to ∞, the function $\psi(c) = P(X; \boldsymbol{\alpha}_0)$ is never increasing. Further, $\psi(0) = 1$, and we easily find $0 \leqq \psi(c) \leqq 1/c$, so that $\psi(c) \to 0$ as $c \to \infty$. In order to avoid trivial complications, we shall assume[1] that there exists a value c such that $\psi(c) = \varepsilon$. For the corresponding set X we then have

[1] There always exists a value c such that $\psi(c-0) \geqq \varepsilon$, $\psi(c+0) \leqq \varepsilon$. The exceptional case when $\psi(c)$ does not actually assume the value ε is included in the argument by means of a slight modification of the definition of the set X. In fact, $\psi(c-0) - \psi(c+0)$ is the integral of $f(\boldsymbol{x}; \boldsymbol{\alpha}_0)$ over the set Z of all points $\boldsymbol{x}$ such that the sign of equality holds in (35.3.1). By excluding from the set X a conveniently

$$P(X;\, \alpha_0) = \int\limits_X f(\boldsymbol{x};\, \alpha_0)\, d\boldsymbol{x} = \varepsilon. \tag{35.3.2}$$

Let now S be the critical set of any test of level ε, so that

$$P(S;\, \alpha_0) = \int\limits_S f(\boldsymbol{x};\, \alpha_0)\, d\boldsymbol{x} = \varepsilon. \tag{35.3.3}$$

We shall then show that

$$P(X;\, \alpha_1) \geqq P(S;\, \alpha_1). \tag{35.3.4}$$

Thus, among all tests of level ε, the test X gives the largest possible value to the probability of rejecting H_0 when the alternative hypothesis H_1 that $\alpha = \alpha_1$ is true. Accordingly the test X will be called the most powerful test of H_0 with respect to H_1, among all tests of level ε.

From (35.3.2) and (35.3.3) we obtain

$$P(X - SX;\, \alpha_0) = \varepsilon - P(SX;\, \alpha_0) = P(S - SX;\, \alpha_0). \tag{35.3.5}$$

From the definition (35.3.1) of the set X, it follows that for any $\boldsymbol{x}$ not belonging to X, we have $c f(\boldsymbol{x};\, \alpha_0) > f(\boldsymbol{x};\, \alpha_1)$. Hence

$$\begin{aligned} P(X - SX;\, \alpha_1) &\geqq c\, P(X - SX;\, \alpha_0) = \\ &= c\, P(S - SX;\, \alpha_0) \geqq P(S - SX;\, \alpha_1). \end{aligned} \tag{35.3.6}$$

Adding $P(SX;\, \alpha_1)$ to the last inequality, we obtain (35.3.4).

It may occur that we obtain the same set X for all admissible points $\alpha_1 \neq \alpha_0$. In such a case we shall say that, among all tests of level ε, the test X is the *uniformly most powerful test* of H_0 with respect to the whole set Ω of admissible hypotheses. — When a uniformly most powerful test exists, it seems fairly clear that it should be regarded as superior to any alternative test of the same level ε. Unfortunately, this situation occurs but very rarely.

Consider the case when the x_i are n sample values from a distribution involving a single unknown parameter α, and suppose that there exists a sufficient estimate α^* of α. By 32.4, the joint fr. f. $f(x_1, \ldots, x_n;\, \alpha)$ can then be written in the form $g(\alpha^*;\, \alpha)\, H(x_1, \ldots, x_n)$, where H is independent of α. When $H > 0$, (35.3.1) then takes the form $g(\alpha^*;\, \alpha_1) \geqq c\, g(\alpha^*;\, \alpha_0)$. If certain general regularity conditions are satisfied, the set X will thus be a domain bounded by the hypersurface $g(\alpha^*;\, \alpha_1) =$

---

chosen subset of Z, we may always obtain a set satisfying (35.3.2). In all points of this modified set X, (35.3.1) is satisfied, while in all points of the complementary set we have $f(\boldsymbol{x};\, \alpha_1) \leqq c f(\boldsymbol{x};\, \alpha_0)$. This is obviously sufficient to permit the conclusion (35.3.6).

$c\,g(\alpha^*;\alpha_0)$, and this equation is equivalent to a certain number of equations of the form $\alpha^* = \text{const.}$ If, for different alternative hypotheses α_1, we always obtain the same individuals of the family $\alpha^* = \text{const.}$ as bounding hypersurfaces of the set X, it thus follows that a uniformly most powerful test exists. However, it can be shown by examples (cf Neyman and Pearson, Ref. 173) that this property does not always hold. Thus even in this simple case we cannot, without imposing further conditions, assert the existence of a uniformly most powerful test. Cf further Neyman, Ref. 165, where the question is brought into connection with the problem of the shortest confidence intervals mentioned in 34.2.

A still simpler case, where the above developments provide a complete solution of the problem, is the case when only two alternative hypotheses exist. The joint fr. f. of the x_i may then be written in the form $(1-\alpha)\,f_0(\boldsymbol{x}) + \alpha\,f_1(\boldsymbol{x})$, where f_0 and f_1 are given fr. f:s, and the admissible values of α are 0 and 1. The hypothesis H_0 to be tested is the hypothesis that $\alpha = 0$, i. e. the hypothesis that the observed sample values are drawn from a distribution with the fr. f. f_0, the only admissible alternative being f_1. We then have to find the set X of all points $\boldsymbol{x}$ such that $f_1 \geqq c\,f_0$, where c is determined by the condition $\int\limits_X f_0(\boldsymbol{x})\,d\boldsymbol{x} = \varepsilon$. The test which consists in rejecting H_0 whenever the observed sample point belongs to the set X, and otherwise accepting, is the most powerful test of level ε. — This test may be applied e. g. to problems of the following type (cf Quensel and Essen-Möller, Ref. 203): Suppose that we have measured certain characters x_i in two human individuals A and B, and that it is required to test the hypothesis that A is the father of B. If we know the distributions of the x_i among the children of persons having the characters shown by A, and among the general population, say with fr. f:s f_0 and f_1 respectively, the hypothesis implies that the sample values shown by B have been drawn from a distribution with the fr. f. f_0, the alternative being f_1. This hypothesis can be tested as shown above.

A further example will be given in the following paragraph.

35.4. Unbiased tests. — We now restrict ourselves to the case of a single unknown parameter α. Let the admissible values of α form an interval A, and suppose that, for almost all $\boldsymbol{x} = (x_1, \ldots, x_n)$, the fr. f. $f(\boldsymbol{x};\alpha)$ has for all inner points α of A a partial derivative $\dfrac{\partial f}{\partial \alpha} = f_1(\boldsymbol{x};\alpha)$ such that $|f_1(\boldsymbol{x};\alpha)| < F(\boldsymbol{x})$, where $F(\boldsymbol{x})$ is integrable over $\boldsymbol{R}_n$. Then by 7.3 the derivative

$$\frac{\partial P(S;\alpha)}{\partial \alpha} = \int\limits_S f_1(\boldsymbol{x};\alpha)\,d\boldsymbol{x} \tag{35.4.1}$$

exists for every set S in $\boldsymbol{R}_n$ and for every α in A.

Suppose that we are concerned with the simple hypothesis H_0 that $\alpha = \alpha_0$, where α_0 is an inner point of A, and let S denote the critical set of a test of level ε. The power function $P(S;\alpha)$ is then a function of α, such that $P(S; \alpha_0) = \varepsilon$. If, for some admissible $\alpha_1 \neq \alpha_0$, we have $P(S; \alpha_1) < \varepsilon$, this means that *we are less likely to reject H_0 when the alternative hypothesis H_1 that $\alpha = \alpha_1$ is true, than when H_0 itself is true.* Obviously this must be regarded as an unfavourable property of the test, which is then called a *biased* test.

When, on the other hand, $P(S; \alpha) \geqq \varepsilon$ for all admissible α, the test and the critical set S will be said to be *unbiased.* Since $P(S; \alpha_0) = \varepsilon$, and the derivative (35.4.1) exists for all α in A, it follows that we have

$$\left(\frac{\partial P(S; \alpha)}{\partial \alpha}\right)_0 = 0. \tag{35.4.2}$$

In generalization of (35.3.1), we now consider the set X of all points $\boldsymbol{x}$ such that

$$f(\boldsymbol{x}; \alpha_1) \geqq c f(\boldsymbol{x}; \alpha_0) + c_1 f_1(\boldsymbol{x}; \alpha_0), \tag{35.4.3}$$

where $\alpha_1 \neq \alpha_0$ is a point of A, and where the constants $c \geqq 0$ and c_1 are determined so as to satisfy the conditions[1])

$$\begin{aligned} P(X; \alpha_0) &= \int_X f(\boldsymbol{x}; \alpha_0)\, d\boldsymbol{x} = \varepsilon, \\ \left(\frac{\partial P(X; \alpha)}{\partial \alpha}\right)_0 &= \int_X f_1(\boldsymbol{x}; \alpha_0)\, d\boldsymbol{x} = 0. \end{aligned} \tag{35.4.4}$$

For the critical set S of any unbiased test of level ε, we then have the relation (35.3.5), and from (35.4.2) and (35.4.4) obtain the analogous relation

$$\left(\frac{\partial P(X - SX; \alpha)}{\partial \alpha}\right)_0 = -\left(\frac{\partial P(SX; \alpha)}{\partial \alpha}\right)_0 = \left(\frac{\partial P(S - SX; \alpha)}{\partial \alpha}\right)_0.$$

In a similar way as in 35.3 we then obtain

$$P(X; \alpha_1) \geqq P(S; \alpha_1).$$

It may occur that we obtain the same set X for all admissible points $\alpha_1 \neq \alpha_0$. In such a case it follows that the test X is unbiased

[1]) By a similar argument as in the case of (35.3.2), we can show that this is always possible, except in certain exceptional cases, where we have to modify the definition of the set X in the same way as indicated in the footnote p. 529, i. e. by excluding from X a certain subset of the set Z of all points $\boldsymbol{x}$ such that the sign of equality holds in (35.4.3).

and gives, among all unbiased tests, the largest possible value to the probability of rejecting H_0 when any alternative hypothesis $\alpha = \alpha_1$ is true[1]). The test X will then be called the *most powerful unbiased test of* H_0.

Consider the case of a sample of n values $x_1, \ldots, x_n$ from a normal distribution with a known s. d. σ, and an unknown mean m, and let it be required to test the hypothesis H_0 that $m = m_0$. We shall first try to find the conditions for the existence of a *uniformly most powerful test*, corresponding to a given level ε. For any $m_1 \neq m_0$ the relation (35.3.1) takes the form

$$\text{(35.4.5)} \qquad \frac{f(\boldsymbol{x}; m_1)}{f(\boldsymbol{x}; m_0)} = e^{-\frac{1}{2\sigma^2}\sum[(x_i - m_1)^2 - (x_i - m_0)^2]} = e^{M\lambda - \frac{1}{2}M^2} \geqq c,$$

where $M = \sqrt{n}\,(m_1 - m_0)/\sigma$, $\lambda = \sqrt{n}\,(\bar{x} - m_0)/\sigma$. Suppose first that $m_1 > m_0$. We then have $M > 0$, and if we take

$$c = e^{M\lambda_{2p} - \frac{1}{2}M^2},$$

where $p = 100\,\varepsilon$ and λ_{2p} is the $2p$ % value of a normal deviate, the inequality (35.4.5) will be satisfied in the set X of all points $\boldsymbol{x} = (x_1, \ldots, x_n)$ such that $\lambda \geqq \lambda_{2p}$, or $\bar{x} \geqq m_0 + \lambda_{2p}\,\sigma/\sqrt{n}$. Evidently this set is independent of m_1, and the probability that $\boldsymbol{x}$ belongs to the set X, on the hypothesis H_0, is equal to $p/100 = \varepsilon$, so that the condition (35.3.2) is satisfied. Thus the test based on the critical set X, which consists in rejecting H_0 whenever $\bar{x} \geqq m_0 + \lambda_{2p}\,\sigma/\sqrt{n}$, is a *uniformly most powerful test of H_0 with respect to the set of all alternative hypotheses such that* $m_1 > m_0$.

For all $m_1 < m_0$, we obtain in the same way the uniformly most powerful test based on the critical set X defined by $\bar{x} \leqq m_0 - \lambda_{2p}\,\sigma/\sqrt{n}$. However, as soon as the set of admissible alternatives includes values of m both to the right and to the left of the point m_0, we no longer obtain the same set X for all admissible m_1. *It follows that in this case no uniformly most powerful test exists.*

Consider the power function of the test based on the critical set $\bar{x} \geqq m_0 + \lambda_{2p}\,\sigma/\sqrt{n}$. The power function is equal to the probability that the sample point belongs to this set, when the true mean is m, which is $1 - \Phi(z)$, where $z = \lambda_{2p} + \sqrt{n}\,(m_0 - m)/\sigma$. This probability steadily increases with m, and for $m = m_0$ takes the value ε. For $m > m_0$ the power function is thus $> \varepsilon$, so that we have a probability $> \varepsilon$ of rejecting H_0 as soon as the true mean exceeds m_0. When $m < m_0$, on the other hand, the power function is $< \varepsilon$, which means that the test is biased. The corresponding properties hold, of course, for the test based on the set $\bar{x} \leqq m_0 - \lambda_{2p}\,\sigma/\sqrt{n}$.

We now proceed to consider the *best unbiased test*, using the same level $\varepsilon = p/100$ as before. The condition (35.4.3) takes here the form

$$e^{M\lambda - \frac{1}{2}M^2} \geqq c + c_1'\,\lambda,$$

---

[1]) This is a slight modification of a proposition due to Neyman and Pearson (Ref. 172).

where $c_1' = c_1 \sqrt{n}/\sigma$. We may always choose c and c_1 such that the sign of equality holds here when $\lambda = \pm \lambda_p$, and the set X will then consist of all points x such that $|\lambda| \geqq \lambda_p$, or $|\bar{x} - m_0| \geqq \lambda_p \sigma / \sqrt{n}$. This set evidently satisfies both conditions (35.4.4). *Thus the ordinary test which consists in rejecting H_0 whenever the absolute deviation $|\bar{x} - m_0|$ exceeds $\lambda_p \sigma / \sqrt{n}$ is the most powerful unbiased test of H_0.*

The power function of this test is equal to $\Phi(z') + 1 - \Phi(z'')$, where $z' = -\lambda_p + \sqrt{n}\,(m_0 - m)/\sigma$, $z'' = \lambda_p + \sqrt{n}\,(m_0 - m)/\sigma$, while m is the true mean. It is easily seen that this function attains its minimum for $m = m_0$, when it is equal to ε. For $m \neq m_0$, the power function always exceeds ε, and tends to 1 as $m \to \pm \infty$. According to the above, the graph of this power function lies entirely above the corresponding grap of any other unbia sed test. The power function of the preceding test based on $\bar{x} \geqq m_0 + \lambda_{2p} \sigma/\sqrt{n}$ is greater than the present power function for $m > m_0$, but falls below it for $m < m_0$, and even tends to zero as $m \to -\infty$.

In the ordinary tests based on the use of standard errors (cf 31.1), we assume that the variable z under investigation may, with a practically sufficient approximation, be regarded as normally distributed with a known s. d. $\boldsymbol{d}(z)$. If, on the basis of one observed value of z, we are testing the hypothesis that the mean $\boldsymbol{E}(z)$ has some specified value z_0, and if the circumstances of the problem permit us to restrict the set Ω of admissible alternatives e. g. to the domain $\boldsymbol{E}(z) \geqq z_0$, the above shows that we should certainly use the test which consists in rejecting the hypothesis (on the $100\,\varepsilon = p$ % level) when $z \geqq z_0 + \lambda_{2p}\, \boldsymbol{d}(z)$. This situation will sometimes occur in practice, e. g. when we are concerned with data relative to the effect of some method that will be very unlikely to impair, but may possibly improve, the quality of the thing produced. If, on the other hand, we are not prepared to introduce a priori a restriction of this »one-sided» type, we should use the ordinary test based on the absolute deviation $|z - z_0|$.

35.5. Tests of composite hypotheses. — As we proceed from simple to composite hypotheses, the theory becomes considerably more complicated, and we shall have to restrict ourselves to some brief remarks, referring for further information to the original papers quoted in 35.1.

Using the general notations introduced in 35.2, we consider the hypothesis H that the unknown parametric point α belongs to a given set ω which is a subset of the set Ω of all admissible points. As in the case of a simple hypothesis, a test of H will consist of a rule to reject H whenever the observed sample point x belongs to a certain critical set S, and otherwise to accept H. According to the general desideratum of 35.1, we should try to find S so as to render the power function $P(S;\, \alpha)$ small when α belongs to ω, and large when α belongs to the set $\Omega - \omega$ of admissible alternatives.

In some cases it is possible to find a set S — and even a family of sets — such that $P(S;\, \alpha)$ is constantly equal to any given level ε

for all α in ω. We shall then say that S is *similar to the sample space*[1]) with respect to the set ω. The test S, i. e. the test based on the critical set S, then always gives the probability ε for committing the error of rejecting H in a case when it is true, whatever be the value of α in ω, and we accordingly say that the test is of level ε.

Suppose now that it is possible to find a test X of level ε such that, for any α belonging to $\Omega - \omega$ and for any test S of level ε, we have $P(X; \alpha) \geqq P(S; \alpha)$. In analogy with 35.3 we shall then say that, among all tests of level ε, the test X is the *uniformly most powerful test* of H with respect to the set $\Omega - \omega$ of alternative hypotheses.

Similarly, if, for a test S of level ε, we have $P(S; \alpha) \geqq \varepsilon$ for all admissible α, the test will be called *unbiased.* A *most powerful unbiased test* is a test X of level ε, such that $P(X; \alpha) \geqq P(S; \alpha)$ for any α belonging to $\Omega - \omega$ and for any unbiased test S of level ε.

The general conditions under which these classes of tests exist, and the methods by which they may be found, are still very incompletely known. We shall only give some simple examples without proofs.

Consider n sample values $x_1, \ldots, x_n$ from a normal distribution with unknown parameters m and σ. Let it be required to test the hypothesis that $m = m_0$, without specifying the value of σ. In the (m, σ)-plane, the set Ω of all admissible hypotheses is (cf 35.2) the half-plane $\sigma > 0$, while the set ω consists of that part of the line $m = m_0$ that belongs to $\sigma > 0$.

Let T denote any set of real numbers such that $\int\limits_T s_{n-1}(t)\,dt = \varepsilon$, where $s_{n-1}(t)$ is the fr. f. of Student's ratio $t = \sqrt{n-1}\,(\bar{x} - m_0)/s$, and let S denote the set of all points $\boldsymbol{x}$ in $\boldsymbol{R}_n$ such that the corresponding ratio t belongs to the set T. Then for any σ we have $P(S; m_0, \sigma) = P(t \subset T) = \varepsilon$, and it follows that the set S is similar to the sample space with respect to the given set ω.

If the set $\Omega - \omega$ of admissible alternatives is restricted to cases with $m > m_0$, and if we choose for S the set of all $\boldsymbol{x}$ such that $t > t_{2p}$, where $p = 100\,\varepsilon$, it can be shown (cf the papers quoted in 35.1) that the test S is uniformly most powerful. Similarly, with respect to any alternatives $m < m_0$, the test based on the set $t < -t_{2p}$ is uniformly most powerful. If the admissible alternatives include values of m both to the right and to the left of the point m_0, no uniformly most powerful test exists, but the test which consists in rejecting H whenever $|t| > t_p$ is the most powerful unbiased test of level ε. All this is analogous to the results proved in 35.4 for the case when σ is known.

The case of the difference between the means of two normal distributions has been investigated from the power function standpoint by Welch and Hsu (Ref. 229, 127).

---

[1]) The introduction of this expression is due to the fact that the set $S = \boldsymbol{R}_n$ satisfies the condition with $\varepsilon = 1$.

It appears from their works that the test $|u| > t_p$ used in 31.2 and 31.3, Ex. 4, is only a satisfactory test of the hypothesis $m_1 = m_2$ on the condition that it is known that $\sigma_1 = \sigma_2$. If the admissible hypotheses include cases with $\sigma_1 \neq \sigma_2$, the test may be seriously biased.

CHAPTER 36.

Analysis of Variance.

36.1. Variability of mean values. — The *analysis of variance* is a statistical technique introduced by R. A. Fisher (Ref. 13, 14) in connection with certain experimental designs applied in various branches of biological research work, especially in agriculture. The domain of applicability of this technique is, however, much wider, and it has already been successfully applied in many branches of experimental work.

Suppose that an experiment has furnished the observed values $x_1, \ldots, x_n$ of certain variables, and that these can be regarded as independently drawn from normal distributions with a constant, though unknown s. d. σ. The means m_i of the distributions, on the other hand, may vary with certain factors entering into the experiment, such as different methods of treatment, different varieties of plants or animals, soil heterogeneity, etc. It is the purpose of the experiment to investigate this variability of the means, and it may thus be required to test various hypotheses bearing on these quantities, such as the null hypothesis (cf 26.4) that differences in treatment or variety have no influence on the means, etc. It may, of course, also be required to find estimates of certain means or functions of the means.

On the general null hypothesis that all the x_i have the same mean, we know that the sum $\Sigma (x_i - \bar{x})^2$ of squared deviations from the sample mean, divided by the appropriate number of degrees of freedom (viz. $n - 1$), provides an unbiased estimate of the unknown variance σ^2. The basic idea of the analysis of variance consists in dividing up this sum of squares into several components, each corresponding to a real or suspected source of variation in the means. These components are arranged so as to provide tests for various hypotheses concerning the behaviour of the means, and estimates of various functions of the means in which we may be interested.

In the next paragraph, we shall make a detailed study of the method in a simple particular case, and then proceed to more general cases.

36.2. Simple grouping of variables. — Consider the simple case when the observed variables are arranged in r groups, the i:th group containing n_i variables, all of which are assumed to be normal (m_i, σ), where σ isindependent of i. It is required to investigate the properties of the m_i, and in the first place to test the null hypothesis that all the m_i are equal, i. e. that there are no differences between the distributions of the groups. — In the particular case $r = 2$, this problem reduces to the problem of the difference between two mean values already discussed in 31.2 and 34.4.

Let x_{ij} denote the j:th variable in the i:th group, while $\bar{x}_{i.} = \frac{1}{n_i}\sum_{j=1}^{n_i} x_{ij}$ is the arithmetic mean of the variables in the i:th group, and $\bar{x} = \frac{1}{n}\sum_{i=1}^{r}\sum_{j=1}^{n_i} x_{ij} = \frac{1}{n}\sum_{i=1}^{r} n_i \bar{x}_{i.}$ is the arithmetic mean of all $n = \sum_1^r n_i$ variables. We then have the identity

$$\sum (x_{ij} - \bar{x})^2 = \sum (x_{ij} - \bar{x}_{i.})^2 + \sum (\bar{x}_{i.} - \bar{x})^2,$$

where the sum is in each case extended over all $n = \sum_1^r n_i$ variables. Thus the total sum of squared deviations from the general mean $\bar{x}$ is the sum of two components, viz. 1) the sum of squared deviations of each variable from the corresponding group mean (»sum of squares within groups»), and 2) the sum of squared deviations of group means from the general mean (»sum of squares between groups»). This identity bears an evident resemblance to the identity (21.9.1) used for the definition of the correlation ratio.

Rewriting the same identity in a more explicit notation, and at the same time changing the order of the terms in the second member, we obtain

$$(36.2.1)\qquad \sum_{i=1}^{r}\sum_{j=1}^{n_i} (x_{ij} - \bar{x})^2 = \sum_{i=1}^{r} n_i (\bar{x}_{i.} - \bar{x})^2 + \sum_{i=1}^{r}\sum_{j=1}^{n_i} (x_{ij} - \bar{x}_{i.})^2,$$

or briefly

$$Q = Q_1 + Q_2.$$

Then Q, Q_1 and Q_2 are quadratic forms in the x_{ij}, and we know (cf

11.11 and 29.3) that Q may be orthogonally transformed into the form $\sum_1^{n-1} y_i^2$, and consequently has the rank $n-1$. Further, Q_1 is the sum of the squares of r linear forms $L_i = \sqrt{n_i}(\bar{x}_{i.} - \bar{x})$ satisfying the identity $\sum_1^r \sqrt{n_i}\, L_i = 0$, so that by 11.6 the rank of Q_1 is $\leqq r-1$. Similarly Q_2 is the sum of the squares of n linear forms $L_{ij} = x_{ij} - \bar{x}_{i.}$ satisfying the r independent relations $\sum_{j=1}^{n_i} L_{ij} = 0$, $(i = 1, \ldots, r)$, so that the rank of Q_2 is $\leqq n - r$. Now by 11.6 the rank of Q is at most equal to the sum of the ranks of Q_1 and Q_2, and it thus follows that the latter are exactly $r-1$ and $n-r$ respectively, so that we have the following rank relation corresponding to (36.2.1):

$$n - 1 = r - 1 \quad + \quad n - r.$$

Hence we conclude by 11.11 that there exists an orthogonal transformation replacing the n variables x_{ij} by new variables $y_1, \ldots, y_n$, such that the three terms of (36.2.1) are transformed into the corresponding terms of the relation

$$\sum_1^{n-1} y_i^2 = \sum_1^{r-1} y_i^2 + \sum_r^{n-1} y_i^2.$$

By hypothesis, the x_{ij} are independent and normally distributed with a common s. d. σ, and consequently by 24.4 (cf also Ex. 16, p. 319) the same holds true for the y_i. *Thus Q_1 and Q_2 are independent.*

Let us now first assume that the null hypothesis is true, i. e. that $m_i = m$ for all i. Writing $x_{ij} = m + \xi_{ij}$, the ξ_{ij} are independent and normal $(0, \sigma)$. Introducing this transformation into Q, Q_1 and Q_2, and denoting by $\bar{\xi}_{i.}$ and $\bar{\xi}$ the arithmetic means corresponding to $\bar{x}_{i.}$ and $\bar{x}$, the three forms are transformed into the identical expressions with the letter x throughout replaced by ξ. The above orthogonal transformation replaces the ξ_{ij} by new variables $\eta_1, \ldots, \eta_n$, which are independent and normal $(0, \sigma)$. Q, Q_1 and Q_2 are hereby transformed into $\sum_1^{n-1} \eta_i^2$, $\sum_1^{r-1} \eta_i^2$ and $\sum_r^{n-1} \eta_i^2$ respectively. By 18.1 we then find that Q/σ^2, Q_1/σ^2 and Q_2/σ^2 are distributed in χ^2-distributions with $n-1$, $r-1$ and $n-r$ d. of fr. respectively. Writing

$$s^2 = \frac{1}{n-1}\,Q = \frac{1}{n-1}\sum_{i=1}^{r}\sum_{j=1}^{n_i}(x_{ij}-\bar{x})^2,$$

$$s_1^2 = \frac{1}{r-1}\,Q_1 = \frac{1}{r-1}\sum_{i=1}^{r} n_i(\bar{x}_{i.}-\bar{x})^2,$$

$$s_2^2 = \frac{1}{n-r}\,Q_2 = \frac{1}{n-r}\sum_{i=1}^{r}\sum_{j=1}^{n_i}(x_{ij}-\bar{x}_{i.})^2,$$

we thus have

$$\boldsymbol{E}(s^2) = \boldsymbol{E}(s_1^2) = \boldsymbol{E}(s_2^2) = \sigma^2.$$

The *variance ratio* $e^{2z} = s_1^2/s_2^2$ may be written

$$e^{2z} = \frac{s_1^2}{s_2^2} = \frac{\frac{1}{r-1}\,Q_1}{\frac{1}{n-r}\,Q_2} = \frac{\frac{1}{r-1}\sum_{1}^{r-1}\eta_i^2}{\frac{1}{n-r}\sum_{r}^{n-1}\eta_i^2}.$$

Since the η_i are independent and normal $(0, \sigma)$, the variable z has the distribution due to R. A. Fisher, defined by the fr. f. (18.3.5), where m and n have to be replaced by $r-1$ and $n-r$ respectively. In particular the mean and the s. d. of e^{2z} are given by (18.3.4). Tables of significance limits for e^{2z} and z, for various values of the significance level $\varepsilon = p/100$, are available (Fisher, Ref. 13; Fisher-Yates, Ref. 262; Snedecor, Ref. 35; Bonnier-Tedin, Ref. 8). The »z test» introduced by Fisher consists in rejecting the null hypothesis, on the p % level, whenever $|z| > z_p$, where z_p is determined so as to render $P(|z| > z_p) = \varepsilon = p/100$.

The null hypothesis is evidently a composite hypothesis (cf 35.2) concerning the parameters $m_1, \ldots, m_r$ and σ, viz. the hypothesis that the m_i are all equal to an unspecified value m. Whatever the values of m and σ, the probability of rejecting the null hypothesis when it is true is $P(|z| > z_p) = \varepsilon$. Thus the critical set corresponding to the z test is similar to the sample space, and the test is of level ε, according to the definition of 35.5.

It is customary to arrange the numerical values in a table of the following type:

Variation	Degrees of freedom	Sum of squares	Mean square
Between groups . .	$r-1$	$Q_1 = \sum_{i=1}^{r} n_i (\bar{x}_{i.} - \bar{x})^2$	$s_1^2 = Q_1/(r-1)$
Within groups . .	$n-r$	$Q_2 = \sum_{i=1}^{r} \sum_{j=1}^{n_i} (x_{ij} - \bar{x}_{i.})^2$	$s_2^2 = Q_2/(n-r)$
Total	$n-1$	$Q = \sum_{i=1}^{r} \sum_{j=1}^{n_i} (x_{ij} - \bar{x})^2$	$s^2 = Q/(n-1)$

Each of the three items under »Mean square» gives, on the null hypothesis, an unbiased estimate of the population variance σ^2, and the z test may be regarded as a test of the compatibility of the independent estimates given by s_1^2 and s_2^2.

We next proceed to consider the case when the null hypothesis is not true, i. e. when the group means m_i are not all equal. Writing $x_{ij} = m_i + \xi_{ij}$, the ξ_{ij} are independent and normal $(0, \sigma)$, and we have

$$(\bar{x}_{i.} - \bar{x})^2 = (\bar{\xi}_{i.} - \bar{\xi})^2 + 2(m_i - \bar{m})(\bar{\xi}_{i.} - \bar{\xi}) + (m_i - \bar{m})^2,$$

$$(x_{ij} - \bar{x}_{i.})^2 = (\xi_{ij} - \bar{\xi}_{i.})^2,$$

where $\bar{\xi}_{i.}$ and $\bar{\xi}$ are defined as above, while $\bar{m} = \frac{1}{n}\sum_1^r n_i m_i$. Introducing these expressions into Q_1 and Q_2, we find in the first place that Q_2 has the same distribution as in the case when the null hypothesis is true. We further obtain (cf Irwin, Ref. 133)

$$E(s_1^2) = E\left(\frac{1}{r-1} Q_1\right) = \sigma^2 + \frac{1}{r-1}\sum_1^r n_i (m_i - \bar{m})^2,$$

$$E(s_2^2) = E\left(\frac{1}{n-r} Q_2\right) = \sigma^2,$$

or

$$E\left(\frac{r-1}{n}(s_1^2 - s_2^2)\right) = \frac{1}{n}\sum_1^r n_i (m_i - \bar{m})^2.$$

The second member may be regarded as a measure of the variation among the unknown group means m_i. The quantity $(r-1)(s_1^2 - s_2^2)/n$, which may be calculated from our data, thus gives an unbiased estimate of this measure.

Finally, for any given $i \neq j$ the variable $\bar{x}_{i.} - \bar{x}_{j.}$ is normal

$$\left[m_i - m_j,\ \sigma \sqrt{(n_i + n_j)/(n_i n_j)}\right].$$

Writing

$$\bar{x}_{i.} - \bar{x}_{j.} = (\bar{x}_{i.} - \bar{x}) - (\bar{x}_{j.} - \bar{x}),$$

and observing that the above orthogonal substitution replacing the x_{ij} by the y_i changes every $\bar{x}_{i.} - \bar{x}$ into a linear combination of $y_1, \ldots, y_r$, we further see that $\bar{x}_{i.} - \bar{x}_{j.}$ is independent of Q_2. It follows that the variable

$$t = \sqrt{\frac{n_i n_j}{n_i + n_j}} \cdot \frac{\bar{x}_{i.} - \bar{x}_{j.} - (m_i - m_j)}{s_2}$$

has Student's distribution with $n - r$ d. of fr. Working on a p % level, we thus obtain (cf 34.4) the confidence limits

$$\bar{x}_{i.} - \bar{x}_{j.} \pm t_p s_2 \sqrt{\frac{n_i + n_j}{n_i n_j}} \tag{36.2.2}$$

for the difference $m_i - m_j$ between the two unknown group means. In the particular case when there are only two groups ($r = 2$), these limits are identical with the confidence limits given by (34.4.5). (Note the difference in notation with respect to s_2!) When $r > 2$ we may, of course, also apply (34.4.5) to obtain confidence limits for $m_i - m_j$ based only on the observations belonging to the groups i and j. However, t_p will then only have $n_i + n_j - 2$ d. of fr., so that (36.2.2) with its $n - r$ d. of fr. will generally yield a smaller value of t_p, i. e. a shorter confidence interval, for the same value of p.

When the null hypothesis is true, the power function (cf 35.3 and 35.5) of the z test assumes the value ε. The behaviour of the power function when the null hypothesis is not true has been investigated by Tang (Ref. 224), who has published tables for the numerical calculation of the function. These tables apply also to the more general cases considered in the following paragraphs.

The x_{ij} are n random variables, the joint distribution of which involves the $r + 1$ unknown parameters $m_1, \ldots, m_r$ and σ^2. The joint fr. f. of the n variables is

$$f = \frac{1}{(2\pi\sigma^2)^{n/2}} e^{-\frac{1}{2\sigma^2} \sum_{i=1}^{r} \sum_{j=1}^{n_i} (x_{ij} - m_i)^2}$$

The problem of estimating the parameters by means of a sample consisting of one observed value of each x_{ij} is a case of the generalized estimation problem considered in 32.8. The relations $\boldsymbol{E}(\bar{x}_{i.}) = m_i$ and $\boldsymbol{E}(s_2^2) = \sigma^2$ show that the quantities $\bar{x}_{1.}, \ldots, \bar{x}_{r.}$ and s_2^2 are *unbiased* estimates of the parameters. By means of the relation (32.4.1), duly generalized in the sense of 32.6—32.8, we find that these quantities are also *joint sufficient* estimates. Further, by some calculation it will be found that the *joint efficiency* of these estimates is $\frac{n-r}{n}$.

36.3. Generalization.[1] — The preceding developments may be generalized to cases when the observed variables are arranged in a more complicated system of groups and subgroups of various orders. Generally the variables will then be affected with two or even a greater number of subscripts, but for our present purpose it will be sufficient to retain the simple notation $x_1, \ldots, x_n$ of 36.1 for the variables. As before we suppose that the x_i are independent, and that x_i is normal (m_i, σ), where σ does not depend on i.

For any grouping system used in a particular problem, we may then consider sums of squared deviations more or less analogous to the sums Q_1 and Q_2 of the preceding paragraph, and it will often be possible to obtain in this way a relation of the same type as (36.2.1):

$$\sum_{1}^{n} (x_i - \bar{x})^2 = Q_1 + Q_2 + \cdots + Q_k, \tag{36.3.1}$$

where the Q_ν are sums of squares of certain linear forms in the x_i, such that we have the corresponding rank relation

$$n - 1 = r_1 + r_2 + \cdots + r_k,$$

r_ν being the rank of the quadratic form Q_ν. As in the preceding paragraph it then follows from 11.11 that there exists an orthogonal transformation changing $Q_1, \ldots, Q_k$ into sums of respectively $r_1, \ldots, r_k$ squares y_i^2, such that no two Q_ν contain a common variable y_i. The y_i being independent, it follows that $Q_1, \ldots, Q_k$ are independent.

Suppose now that it is required to test the hypothesis H that the unknown means m_i satisfy certain linear equations. It will then often be possible to arrange the decomposition (36.3.1) of the total sum of squares in such a way that, if the hypothesis H is true, then two of

[1]) I have here made use of an unpublished manuscript kindly placed at my disposal by fil. kand. H. Andersson. For a discussion of the theory from similar, but more general points of view, cf Kolodziejczyk, Ref. 140 a, and Tang, Ref. 224.

the forms Q_ν, say Q_1 and Q_2, will reduce to zero when all x_i are replaced by the corresponding m_i. Thus in the case considered in the preceding paragraph, the hypothesis tested is $m_1 = m_2 = \cdots = m_r$, where the m_i are the group means, and if this hypothesis is true, it is readily seen that Q_1 and Q_2 as defined by (36.2.1) both reduce to zero when the variables are replaced by their mean values.

Assuming that H is true, and that the decomposition has been arranged according to the above, we substitute $x_i = m_i + \xi_i$ into Q_1 and Q_2. When a non-negative quadratic form $q(x_1, \ldots, x_n)$ is equal to zero in a point $(m_1, \ldots, m_n)$, it is easily seen that all derivatives $\frac{\partial q}{\partial x_i}$ must also vanish in the same point. Thus we obtain identically $Q_\nu(x_1, \ldots, x_n) = Q_\nu(\xi_1, \ldots, \xi_n)$ for $\nu = 1$ and 2. The above orthogonal transformation will then change Q_1 into a sum of r_1 squares $\sum_1^{r_1} \eta_i^2$, where the η_i are independent and normal $(0, \sigma)$, and similarly for Q_2. Thus on the hypothesis H the variables Q_1 and Q_2 are independent and distributed in χ^2-distributions of r_1 and r_2 d. of fr. respectively. Introducing the mean squares

$$s_1^2 = Q_1/r_1, \qquad s_2^2 = Q_2/r_2,$$

and the variance ratio

$$e^{2z} = s_1^2/s_2^2,$$

it then follows that $\boldsymbol{E}(s_1^2) = \boldsymbol{E}(s_2^2) = \sigma^2$, while z has Fisher's distribution given in 18.3. Thus the z test may be used to test the hypothesis H.

When the hypothesis H is not true, we may deduce similar results as in the preceding paragraph.

36.4. Randomized blocks. — We now proceed to show the application of the above theory to some cases of great practical importance. We shall use a terminology referring to the agricultural applications, but the same experimental designs may be used in many branches of research work, in biology and elsewhere.

Consider an agricultural experiment where we want to compare the effects of r different fertilizing treatments on the crop yield of some cereal. We then lay out s blocks of equal size on a piece of land. Each block is divided into r equal plots, among which the r different treatments are randomly distributed. Thus each block contains one plot of each treatment, and for each particular treatment we have s different plots.

Let x_{ij} denote the weight of the crop from the plot receiving the i:th treatment and belonging to the j:th block. We assume that the x_{ij} are independent and normal (m_{ij}, σ), and write

$$\bar{x}_{i.} = \frac{1}{s}\sum_{j=1}^{s} x_{ij}, \qquad \bar{x}_{.j} = \frac{1}{r}\sum_{i=1}^{r} x_{ij}, \qquad \bar{x} = \frac{1}{rs}\sum_{i=1}^{r}\sum_{j=1}^{s} x_{ij}.$$

Thus $\bar{x}_{i.}$ and $\bar{x}_{.j}$ are the sample means for the i:th treatment and the j:th block respectively, while $\bar{x}$ is the general sample mean. — The identity

$$\begin{aligned}\sum_{i=1}^{r}\sum_{j=1}^{s}(x_{ij}-\bar{x})^2 &= s\sum_{i=1}^{r}(\bar{x}_{i.}-\bar{x})^2 + \\ &+ r\sum_{j=1}^{s}(\bar{x}_{.j}-\bar{x})^2 + \sum_{i=1}^{r}\sum_{j=1}^{s}(x_{ij}-\bar{x}_{i.}-\bar{x}_{.j}+\bar{x})^2 \\ &= Q_1 + Q_2 + Q_3,\end{aligned} \tag{36.4.1}$$

and the corresponding rank relation

$$rs - 1 = r - 1 \quad + \quad s - 1 \quad + \quad (r-1)(s-1)$$

are then easily verified. Hence we infer by the preceding paragraph that Q_1, Q_2 and Q_3 are independent.

Q_1 and Q_2 are known as the sums of squares due to variation »between treatments» and »between blocks» respectively, while for reasons that will appear below Q_3 is usually denoted as the »sum of squares due to error». The numerical values may be arranged in tabular form in the same way as shown in 36.2.

The variation in the mean values m_{ij} will be due to soil heterogeneity and to differences in treatment. Owing to the random arrangement of the treatments in each block, we may assume that the effects of soil heterogeneity *within each block* are included in the random part of the x_{ij}. Any difference between two m_{ij} belonging to the same block is then due to treatment, and we assume that $m_{ij} = f_i + b_j$, where f_i only depends on the fertilizing treatment, while b_j only depends on the block. We shall briefly call f_i the »treatment effect», and b_j the »block effect». — Under these assumptions, it will be seen that Q_3 reduces to zero when the x_{ij} are replaced by their means, so that Q_3/σ^2 has a χ^2-distribution with $(r-1)(s-1)$ d. of fr.

Consequently the mean square $s_3^2 = Q_3/(r-1)(s-1)$ gives an unbiased estimate of σ^2, which explains the above terminology.

We now want to test the hypothesis H that there are no differences between the fertilizing treatments. If H is true, we may take $f_i = 0$ for all i, so that $m_{ij} = b_j$ will only depend on the block number j. In this case, both Q_1 and Q_3 reduce to zero when the x_{ij} are replaced by their means. Introducing the mean square $s_1^2 = Q_1/(r-1)$, we may thus according to the preceding paragraph test H by applying the z test to the variance ratio $e^{2z} = s_1^2/s_3^2$.

When the hypothesis H is not true, it is shown as in 36.2 that the quantity $\frac{r-1}{rs}(s_1^2 - s_3^2)$ gives an unbiased estimate of the variance $\frac{1}{r}\sum_1^r (f_i - \bar{f})^2$ among the unknown treatment effects. Further, for any given $i \neq j$ we obtain the confidence limits

$$\bar{x}_{i.} - \bar{x}_{j.} \pm t_p s_3 \sqrt{\frac{2}{s}}$$

for the unknown difference $f_i - f_j$ between the effects of the i:th and j:th treatments. Here t_p is to be taken with $(r-1)(s-1)$ d. of fr.

In a case where we have had to reject the hypothesis H, we may be interested in testing the further hypothesis H_1 that the inequality between the treatments is wholly due to one particular treatment, say the one corresponding to $i = 1$, while there are no differences between the others. If H_1 is true, we may take $f_2 = \cdots = f_r = 0$, while f_1 is possibly different from zero.

Let $\bar{x}_{.(2 \ldots r)}$ denote the pooled sample mean for the treatments $2, \ldots, r$:

$$\bar{x}_{.(2 \ldots r)} = \frac{1}{(r-1)s} \sum_{i=2}^{r} \sum_{j=1}^{s} x_{ij}.$$

The sum of squares »between treatments» Q_1 appearing in (36.4.1) may then be further decomposed according to the identity

$$\begin{aligned} Q_1 &= \frac{(r-1)s}{r}(\bar{x}_{1.} - \bar{x}_{.(2 \ldots r)})^2 + s \sum_{i=2}^{r} (\bar{x}_{i.} - \bar{x}_{.(2 \ldots r)})^2 \\ &= Q_1' + Q_1'', \end{aligned}$$

which gives the rank relation

$$r - 1 = 1 \quad + \quad r - 2.$$

Q_1' and Q_1'' may be regarded as the sums of squares »between group 1 and the pooled groups $2, \ldots, r$», and »between groups $2, \ldots, r$» respectively. Introducing this expression into (36.4.1) we find that, if the hypothesis H_1 is true, both Q_1'' and Q_3 reduce to zero when the x_{ij} are replaced by their means. Introducing the mean square $s_1''^2 = Q_1''/(r-2)$, we may thus test H_1 by applying the z test to the variance ratio $e^{2z} = s_1''^2/s_3^2$. For the unknown treatment effect f_1, we obtain the confidence limits

$$\bar{x}_{1.} - \bar{x}_{.(2 \ldots r)} \pm t_p s_3 \sqrt{\frac{r}{(r-1)s}},$$

where as before t_p has $(r-1)(s-1)$ d. of fr.

Further hypotheses of a similar kind concerning the properties of the treatment effects may be tested by analogous methods. The requisite identities will as a rule be easily found.

36.5. Latin squares. — By the method of randomized blocks, we try to eliminate the effects of soil heterogeneity, so as to realize an unbiased comparison between the treatments (or varieties etc., as the case may be) dealt with in the experiment. An even more complete elimination is usually obtained by the method of *Latin squares.*

Consider r^2 plots arranged in a square, and let r different fertilizing treatments be applied to these plots in such a way that each treatment occurs once in each row, and also once in each column. Among the numerous possible arrangements satisfying these conditions, which are known as Latin squares[1]), we suppose that one has been chosen at random for the experiment. Denote by x_{ij} the weight of the crop from the plot in the i:th row and the j:th column, and let $\bar{x}_{i.}$ and $\bar{x}_{.j}$ be the row and column means, while $\bar{x}_h$ is the mean for the plots receiving the h:th treatment, and $\bar{x}$ is the general mean. In this case we have the identity

$$\begin{aligned} \sum_i \sum_j (x_{ij} - \bar{x})^2 &= r \sum_h (\bar{x}_h - \bar{x})^2 + r \sum_i (\bar{x}_{i.} - \bar{x})^2 + r \sum_j (\bar{x}_{.j} - \bar{x})^2 + \\ &\quad + \sum_i \sum_j (x_{ij} - \bar{x}_h - \bar{x}_{i.} - \bar{x}_{.j} + 2\bar{x})^2 \\ &= Q_1 + Q_2 + Q_3 + Q_4, \end{aligned}$$

where all sums are extended from 1 to r, while in each term of Q_4

1) Tables of such arrangements are given in Fisher-Yates, Ref. 262.

the subscript h should correspond to the treatment applied to the plot (i, j). The rank relation is here

$$r^2 - 1 = r - 1 \quad + \quad r - 1 \quad + \quad r - 1 \quad + \quad (r-1)(r-2).$$

We now assume that the mean value $\boldsymbol{E}(x_{ij}) = m_{ij}$ consists of one »treatment effect» f_h and another part due to soil heterogeneity, the latter being composed of a »row effect» r_i and a »column effect» c_j. We then have $m_{ij} = f_h + r_i + c_j$, and as before we find that Q_4 has a χ^2-distribution with $(r-1)(r-2)$ d. of fr., so that the mean square $s_4^2 = Q_4/(r-1)(r-2)$ gives an unbiased estimate of the common variance σ^2 of the x_{ij}. The tabular arrangement of the data here takes the following form:

Variation	Degrees of freedom	Sum of squares	Mean square
Between treatments	$r-1$	Q_1	$s_1^2 = Q_1/(r-1)$
Between rows	$r-1$	Q_2	$s_2^2 = Q_2/(r-1)$
Between columns	$r-1$	Q_3	$s_3^2 = Q_3/(r-1)$
Error	$(r-1)(r-2)$	Q_4	$s_4^2 = Q_4/(r-1)(r-2)$
Total	r^2-1	Q	

The hypothesis that there is no difference between the fertilizing treatments may be tested by applying the z test to the variance ratio $e^{2z} = s_1^2/s_4^2$. In a case where this hypothesis has been rejected, we may estimate the variance among the treatment effects, and the difference between any two treatment effects, by the same methods as in the preceding paragraph. Further hypotheses concerning the properties of the f_h may also be tested in the same way.

We have here only been concerned with the simplest cases of the analysis of variance. For further information on the theory of experimental designs, and for the generalization to the simultaneous analysis of several variables (»analysis of covariance»), we refer to books by R. A. Fisher (Ref. 13, 14), Snedecor (Ref. 35) and Bonnier-Tedin (Ref. 8).

CHAPTER 37.

Some Regression Problems.

37.1. Problems involving non-random variables. — In practical applications, we very often encounter problems where we are concerned with a random variable y, which depends on a certain number of *non-random* variables $x_1, \ldots, x_n$. In economic and social statistics, the values of the x_i will then as a rule simply occur as given non-random quantities in our statistical data. In experimental work, on the other hand, the values of the x_i may often be arbitrarily chosen by the experimenter. In both cases, the x_i will play the rôle of variable parameters entering into the distribution of y, and our statistical data will consist of a set of observed values of y, each corresponding to known values of the x_i. Besides the *known* parameters x_i, the y distribution may, of course, also contain certain *unknown* parameters.

Suppose, e. g., that we are investigating the relations between the quantity y of a commodity A consumed in a given market, and the prices $x_1, \ldots, x_n$ of A itself and a certain number of other commodities. It may possibly seem legitimate to regard y as a random variable with a distribution determined by the prices $x_1, \ldots, x_n$, while the procedure by which the latter are generated will perhaps not seem to resemble a random experiment. The x_i will then simply have to be taken as given quantities appearing in our data.

Suppose, on the other hand, that we are concerned with the influence upon the output y in a certain factory exerted by the quality of raw materials and the technical process employed, as characterized by the variables $x_1, \ldots, x_n$. We may then deliberately choose various systems of values of the x_i, and observe the corresponding values of y. As before, y will here be regarded as a random variable, the distribution of which contains the x_i as parameters.

The theory of mean square regression developed in Chs 21 and 23 holds, with due modifications, even in the present case. Further, in the case when the dependent variable y is normally distributed with a mean value which is a linear function of the variables x_i, it has been shown by Fisher (Ref. 92, 97) and Bartlett (Ref. 54) that certain regression coefficients have sampling distributions analogous to those deduced in 29.8 and 29.12, which may form the basis of tests of significance in a similar way as shown in 31.3, Ex. 6—7. — Some of the results due to these authors will be discussed in 37.2—37.3.

37.2. Simple regression. — A sample consisting of n observed pairs of values $(x_1, y_1), \ldots, (x_n, y_n)$ is given. For the sample moments, we use the ordinary notations $\bar{x}, \bar{y}, m_{20}$ etc. introduced by (27.1.6) and (27.1.7). However, we suppose now that x is a non-random variable while, for every fixed x, the random variable y is normally distributed, with the mean $\alpha + \beta(x - \bar{x})$ and the s. d. σ, where α, β and σ are unknown parameters not involving x. Thus the sample moments only involving the x_i, such as $\bar{x}$, $m_{20} = s_1^2$, etc., are not to be considered as random variables, but simply as given constants. On the other hand, all quantities depending on the y_i, such as $\bar{y}$, $m_{02} = s_2^2$, $m_{11} = r\,s_1\,s_2$, etc., are random variables. The y_i are supposed to be independent.

The maximum likelihood estimates (cf 33.2) of α, β and σ are found by minimizing the joint fr. f. of the y_i, which is

$$f = \frac{1}{(2\pi\sigma^2)^{n/2}}\, e^{-\frac{1}{2\sigma^2}\sum\limits_{1}^{n}[y_i - \alpha - \beta(x_i - \bar{x})]^2}$$

It will be found that the estimates of α and β are the values of these parameters that render the sum of squares occurring in the exponent as small as possible. Hence we obtain the estimates

$$\alpha^* = \bar{y}, \qquad \beta^* = \frac{\Sigma(x_i - \bar{x})(y_i - \bar{y})}{\Sigma(x_i - \bar{x})^2} = \frac{m_{11}}{s_1^2},$$

while the maximum likelihood estimate of σ is given by

$$\sigma^{*2} = \frac{1}{n}\sum_{1}^{n}[y_i - \alpha^* - \beta^*(x_i - \bar{x})]^2 = s_2^2(1 - r^2).$$

As linear functions of the y_i, the variables α^* and β^* are both normally distributed, and we obtain

$$\boldsymbol{E}(\alpha^*) = \alpha, \qquad \boldsymbol{D}^2(\alpha^*) = \sigma^2/n,$$
$$\boldsymbol{E}(\beta^*) = \beta, \qquad \boldsymbol{D}^2(\beta^*) = \sigma^2/(s_1^2\, n).$$

We further have the identity

$$\sum_{1}^{n}[y_i - \alpha^* - \beta^*(x_i - \bar{x})]^2 = \tag{37.2.1}$$
$$= \sum_{1}^{n}[y_i - \alpha - \beta(x_i - \bar{x})]^2 - n(\alpha^* - \alpha)^2 - s_1^2\, n(\beta^* - \beta)^2.$$

The variables $\eta_1, \ldots, \eta_n$, where

$$\eta_i = y_i - \alpha - \beta(x_i - \bar{x}),$$

are independent and normal $(0, \sigma)$, and the two linear forms

$$\zeta_1 = \sqrt{n}(\alpha^* - \alpha) = \frac{1}{\sqrt{n}} \sum_1^n \eta_i,$$

$$\zeta_2 = s_1 \sqrt{n}(\beta^* - \beta) = \frac{1}{s_1 \sqrt{n}} \sum_1^n (x_i - \bar{x}) \eta_i,$$

obviously satisfy the orthogonality conditions (11.9.1). Writing the identity (37.2.1) in the form

$$n \sigma^{*2} = \sum_1^n \eta_i^2 - \zeta_1^2 - \zeta_2^2,$$

we may thus apply Fisher's lemma (cf 29.2), and find that α^*, β^* and σ^* are independent, and that $n\sigma^{*2}/\sigma^2$ is distributed like χ^2 with $n-2$ d. of fr. Consequently by 18.2 the variables

$$\sqrt{n-2}\,\frac{\alpha^* - \alpha}{\sigma^*} \quad \text{and} \quad s_1 \sqrt{n-2}\,\frac{\beta^* - \beta}{\sigma^*}$$

have Student's distribution with $n-2$ d. of fr. With respect to the regression coefficient β^*, this result is formally identical with the result already obtained (cf 29.8.4) for the case when both variables are random, and the joint distribution is normal.

Since s_1, α^*, β^* and σ^* are all known, we may use this result to test any hypothetical values of α and β, and to deduce confidence limits for these parameters, in the same way as shown for the mean of an ordinary normal distribution in 31.2 and 34.4. In particular we find that the regression coefficient β differs significantly from zero on the p % level of significance, if $|\beta^*| > \dfrac{t_p \sigma^*}{s_1 \sqrt{n-2}}$, where t_p is taken with $n-2$ d. of fr.

We may finally be interested in estimating the unknown ordinate

$$Y = \alpha + \beta(X - \bar{x})$$

of the regression line in any given point X. It will be found that the variable

$$t = \frac{\sqrt{n-2}}{\sqrt{1 + \left(\frac{X-\bar{x}}{s_1}\right)^2}} \cdot \frac{\alpha^* + \beta^*(X-\bar{x}) - Y}{\sigma^*}$$

has Student's distribution with $n-2$ d. of fr., so that the p % confidence limits for Y are

$$\alpha^* + \beta^*(X-\bar{x}) \pm t_p \frac{\sigma^*}{\sqrt{n-2}} \sqrt{1 + \left(\frac{X-\bar{x}}{s_1}\right)^2}. \tag{37.2.2}$$

37.3. Multiple regression. — We now proceed to the case of a random variable y, the mean of which is a linear function of k non-random variables $x_1, \ldots, x_k$. Suppose that a sample of n independently observed points $(y_\nu, x_{1\nu}, \ldots, x_{k\nu})$ is given, where $\nu = 1, 2, \ldots, n$. For the sample moments, we use the notations introduced in 27.1 and 29.9, writing e. g. in accordance with (29.9.2)

$$l_{ij} = \frac{1}{n} \sum_{\nu=1}^{n} (x_{i\nu} - \bar{x}_i)(x_{j\nu} - \bar{x}_j), \qquad (i, j = 1, \ldots, k),$$

and further, regarding y as a variable x_0,

$$l_{0j} = \frac{1}{n} \sum_{\nu=1}^{n} (y_\nu - \bar{y})(x_{j\nu} - \bar{x}_j).$$

By L and L_{ij} we denote the determinant

$$L = \begin{vmatrix} l_{11} & \ldots & l_{1k} \\ \cdot & \cdot\ \cdot\ \cdot & \cdot \\ l_{k1} & \ldots & l_{kk} \end{vmatrix}$$

and its cofactors. We shall assume that $L \neq 0$.

Suppose now that, for any fixed values of $x_1, \ldots, x_k$, the random variable y is normally distributed, with the mean

$$\boldsymbol{E}(y) = \alpha + \beta_1(x_1 - \bar{x}_1) + \cdots + \beta_k(x_k - \bar{x}_k), \tag{37.3.1}$$

and the s. d. σ. The maximum likelihood estimates α^* and β_i^* $(i = 1, \ldots, k)$ are found to be the values of α and the β_i that render the sum

$$\sum_{\nu=1}^{n} [y_\nu - \alpha - \beta_1(x_{1\nu} - \bar{x}_1) - \cdots - \beta_k(x_{k\nu} - \bar{x}_k)]^2$$

as small as possible. Hence we obtain the estimates

$$\alpha^* = \bar{y}, \quad \beta_i^* = \frac{1}{L} \sum_{j=1}^{k} l_{0j} L_{ij}, \qquad (i = 1, \ldots, k), \tag{37.3.2}$$

while the maximum likelihood estimate of σ is given by

$$\sigma^{*2} = \frac{1}{n} \sum_{\nu=1}^{n} [y_\nu - \alpha^* - \beta_1^* (x_{1\nu} - \bar{x}_1) - \cdots - \beta_k^* (x_{k\nu} - \bar{x}_k)]^2 = s_{0.12\ldots k}^2 \tag{37.3.3}$$

where $s_{0.12\ldots k}^2$ is the sample value of the residual variance (cf 23.3 and 29.12) of y with respect to $x_1, \ldots, x_k$. We shall suppose that this is positive, which means that the observed values of y cannot be *exactly* represented by a linear function of the x_i.

As linear functions of the y_ν, the variables α^* and β_i^* are normally distributed. By some calculation, we find the following mean values and second order central moments:

$$\begin{aligned} &\boldsymbol{E}(\alpha^*) = \alpha, \qquad \boldsymbol{E}(\beta_i^*) = \beta_i, \\ &\boldsymbol{E}(\alpha^* - \alpha)^2 = \frac{\sigma^2}{n}, \qquad \boldsymbol{E}[(\alpha^* - \alpha)(\beta_i^* - \beta_i)] = 0, \\ &\boldsymbol{E}[(\beta_i^* - \beta_i)(\beta_j^* - \beta_j)] = \frac{\sigma^2}{n} \cdot \frac{L_{ij}}{L}, \end{aligned} \tag{37.3.4}$$

where $i, j = 1, \ldots, k$. Hence we obtain in particular by (23.3.4)

$$\boldsymbol{D}^2(\beta_1^*) = \boldsymbol{E}(\beta_1^* - \beta_1)^2 = \frac{\sigma^2}{n} \cdot \frac{L_{11}}{L} = \frac{\sigma^2}{n\, s_{1.23\ldots k}^2},$$

and analogous expressions for $\boldsymbol{D}^2(\beta_i^*)$, $i = 2, \ldots, k$.

Further, it can be shown that the variable σ^* is independent of the variables α^* and β_i^*, and that $n\sigma^{*2}/\sigma^2$ has a χ^2-distribution with $n - k - 1$ d. of fr. In the particular case when the matrix $\boldsymbol{L} = \begin{Bmatrix} l_{11} & \ldots & l_{1k} \\ \cdot & \cdot\ \cdot\ \cdot & \cdot \\ l_{k1} & \ldots & l_{kk} \end{Bmatrix}$ is a diagonal matrix, this can be proved by straightforward generalization of the method used in the preceding paragraph. In fact, the expressions $\sqrt{n}(\alpha^* - \alpha)$ and $s_i \sqrt{n}(\beta_i^* - \beta_i)$ are linear forms in the variables $\eta_\nu = y_\nu - \alpha - \beta_1(x_{1\nu} - \bar{x}_1) - \cdots - \beta_k(x_{k\nu} - \bar{x}_k)$, and when $\boldsymbol{L}$ is a diagonal matrix, these forms satisfy the orthogonality conditions for $i = 1, \ldots, k$, so that Fisher's lemma can be applied in the same way as before. — In the general case, we must first replace the variables x_i by new variables x_i' by means of an orthogonal transformation such that the moment matrix of the new variables is a diagonal matrix (cf 22.6). Applying the contragredient transformation (cf 11.7) to the β_i, the proof is then completed as in the particular case.

It now follows that the variables

$$\sqrt{n-k-1}\,\frac{\alpha^*-\alpha}{\sigma^*} = \sqrt{n-k-1}\,\frac{\alpha^*-\alpha}{s_{0.12\ldots k}},$$

$$s_{1.23\ldots k}\sqrt{n-k-1}\,\frac{\beta_1^*-\beta_1}{\sigma^*} = \sqrt{n-k-1}\,\frac{s_{1.23\ldots k}}{s_{0.12\ldots k}}(\beta_1^*-\beta_1),$$

and the analogous variables with $\beta_2^*, \ldots, \beta_k^*$, all have Student's distribution with $n-k-1$ d. of fr. With respect to the β_i^*, this result directly corresponds to (29.12.1). As before, we may now deduce tests of significance and confidence limits for the unknown parameters α and β_i.

We can also obtain a joint test for a set of hypothetical values of the regression coefficients $\beta_1, \ldots, \beta_k$. From the expressions (37.3.4) of the moments of the normally distributed variables β_i^*, it follows (cf Ex. 15, p. 319) that the variable

$$\frac{n}{\sigma^2}\sum_{i,j=1}^{k} l_{ij}(\beta_i^*-\beta_i)(\beta_j^*-\beta_j)$$

has a χ^2-distribution with k d. of fr. Consequently the variable

$$e^{2z} = \frac{n-k-1}{k\,\sigma^{*2}}\sum_{i,j=1}^{k} l_{ij}(\beta_i^*-\beta_i)(\beta_j^*-\beta_j)$$

is distributed like a variance ratio (cf 18.3 and 36.2) with k d. of fr. in the numerator, and $n-k-1$ d. of fr. in the denominator. When a set of hypothetical values $\beta_1, \ldots, \beta_k$ are given, the quantity e^{2z} can be calculated from our data, and we may thus use the tables of the z-distribution to test the proposed values of the β_i.

Suppose, in particular, that it is required to test the hypothesis that all regression coefficients are zero: $\beta_1 = \cdots = \beta_k = 0$. From (37.3.2) and (37.3.3) we obtain after some calculation, using (23.5.2), and (23.5.3),

$$\sum_{i,j=1}^{k} l_{ij}\beta_i^*\beta_j^* = l_{00}\,\boldsymbol{r}_{0(12\ldots k)}^2,$$

$$\sigma^{*2} = s_{0.12\ldots k}^2 = l_{00}(1-\boldsymbol{r}_{0(12\ldots k)}^2),$$

where $r_{0(12\ldots k)}$ is the multiple correlation coefficient between the sample values of y and $(x_1, \ldots, x_k)$. It then follows from 18.3 and 18.4 that $r^2_{0(12\ldots k)}$ has a Beta-distribution with the fr. f. $\beta\left(x; \frac{k}{2}, \frac{n-k-1}{2}\right)$. In this particular case, the above test is thus formally identical with the test based on the distribution (29.13.8) of the hypothesis that a multiple correlation coefficient differs significantly from zero.

For the ordinate $\alpha + \sum_1^k \beta_i (X_i - \bar{x}_i)$ of the regression line in any given point $(X_1, \ldots, X_k)$, we obtain in direct generalization of (37.2.2) the p % confidence limits

$$\alpha^* + \sum_1^k \beta_i^* (X_i - \bar{x}_i) \pm \\ \pm t_p \frac{\sigma^*}{\sqrt{n-k-1}} \sqrt{1 + \sum_{i,j=1}^k \frac{L_{ij}}{L} (X_i - \bar{x}_i)(X_j - \bar{x}_j)}, \tag{37.3.5}$$

where t_p is to be taken with $n-k-1$ d. of fr. — We finally add three remarks which are important in many applications:

1. Let us drop the assumption that y is normally distributed, and only suppose that, for any fixed values of the x_i, the mean value of y is given by the linear expression (37.3.1), while the s. d. is always equal to σ. Under these more general assumptions it can be shown that the estimates (37.3.2) of the parameters α and β_i are the best (i. e. those having the smallest variances) among all unbiased estimates that are *linear* functions of the observed y_ν. The variances and covariances of these estimates are still given by (37.3.4), while $n\sigma^{*2}/(n-k-1)$ gives an unbiased estimate of σ^2. Further, the best linear unbiased estimate of the ordinate of the regression line in any given point $(X_1, \ldots, X_k)$ is $\alpha^* + \sum_1^k \beta_i^* (X_i - \bar{x}_i)$, and the standard error of this estimate is equal to the coefficient of t_p in (37.3.5). — This is equivalent to a classical theorem on least squares due to Markoff and others. For a proof, we refer e. g. to Neyman and David (Ref. 169).

2. The variables x_i considered in the present paragraph may be any variables, dependent or independent, subject to the sole condition that $L \neq 0$, which implies that the n points $(x_{1\nu}, \ldots, x_{k\nu})$ do not all lie on the same hyperplane in the k-dimensional space of the x_i. In particular all the x_i may be functions of a single independent variable x. Suppose e. g. that x_i is a polynomial $p_i(x)$ of degree i in x. The above problem is then a problem in parabolic regression (cf 21.6). If the $p_i(x)$ satisfy the orthogonality conditions, which in this case take the form indicated in 12.6, Ex. 3, the matrix L considered above reduces to a diagonal matrix, and all calculations are considerably simplified, as we have seen in the analogous case considered in 21.6.

3. When the condition $L \neq 0$ is not satisfied, the variances and covariances of the β_i^* become infinite or undetermined, as shown by (37.3.4). When L is very small without being actually equal to zero, the points $(x_{1\nu}, \ldots, x_{k\nu})$ lie »almost» on the same hyperplane. In this case, very large coefficients, or coefficients which are the ratios between very small numbers, will appear in our formulae for confidence intervals etc. Small errors in the data or in the calculations, small deviations from normality etc. will then have a great influence, and particular caution must be recommended. This phenomenon will easily present itself when the x_i are strongly connected, as is often the case e.g. in economic data. The methods to be used for regression analysis with data of this kind have been much discussed, especially in connection with problems of the type considered in the next paragraph. We refer e.g. to the comprehensive work of Schultz (Ref. 34), and to papers by Frisch (Ref. 113, 114) and Wold (Ref. 247, 248).

37.4. Further regression problems. — In certain applications of the theory of regression, e.g. in psychology and economics, we are concerned with a set of random variables $x_1, \ldots, x_m$, which may be represented in the form

$$
\begin{aligned}
x_1 &= a_{11}\, u_1 + \cdots + a_{1n}\, u_n + v_1, \\
&\cdots\cdots\cdots\cdots\cdots \\
x_m &= a_{m1}\, u_1 + \cdots + a_{mn}\, u_n + v_m,
\end{aligned}
\tag{37.4.1}
$$

where $m > n$, while $u_1, \ldots, u_n, v_1, \ldots, v_m$ are $m + n$ *uncorrelated* random variables, and $\boldsymbol{A} = \boldsymbol{A}_{mn} = \{a_{ij}\}$ is a matrix of rank n.

In the psychological *factor analysis* of human ability, the variables $x_1, \ldots, x_m$ represent the measurements of m given different abilities of a person, while $u_1, \ldots, u_n$ are more or less »general» factors of intelligence, and $v_1, \ldots, v_m$ are »specific» factors, each associated with a particular ability. In these cases, the main problems are usually concerned with the possibility of representing a given set of variables x_i in the form (37.4.1), and with the existence and number of the »general» factors u_j.

In some economic problems, on the other hand, there are theoretical reasons to expect the variables concerned to satisfy certain linear (or approximately linear) relations. Often, however, these variables cannot be directly observed, owing to the appearance of »errors» or »disturbances». Instead of the »systematic parts» of the above variables x_i:

$$x_i' = a_{i1}\, u_1 + \cdots + a_{in}\, u_n,$$

between which there exist $m - n$ linear relations, we can then only observe the variables x_i themselves as given by (37.4.1) where, now, the v_i represent the »disturbances». Here, the main problems are connected with the estimation of the coefficients in the linear relations between the systematic parts of the x_i.

Problems of this kind are too intimately connected with particular fields of application to be fully discussed here. The psychological applications belonging to this order of ideas were first treated by Spearman. We refer in this connection e. g. to the surveys of the theory given by Spearman (Ref. 35 a) and by Thomson (Ref. 37 a). — The economic problems indicated above have given rise to the introduction of the *confluence analysis* of Frisch (Ref. 114), which has been further developed and brought into contact with sampling and estimation theory by Koopmans (Ref. 142), Reiersöl (Ref. 207) and others.

We shall here only deduce a simple property of the moment matrix Λ of a set of variables $x_1, \ldots, x_m$ that may be represented in the form (37.4.1). Without restricting the generality, we may suppose that all variables x_i, u_j and v_i are measured from their means, and that $\boldsymbol{E}(u_j^2) = 1$ for all j. We further write $\boldsymbol{E}(v_i^2) = \sigma_i^2$, and denote by $\boldsymbol{\Sigma}$ the diagonal matrix formed with $\sigma_1, \ldots, \sigma_m$ as its diagonal elements. We then have by 22.6

$$\Lambda = \boldsymbol{A}\boldsymbol{A}' + \boldsymbol{\Sigma}^2$$

If all the σ_i are positive, the moment matrix Λ is of rank m, so that the distribution of the variables $x_1, \ldots, x_m$ is non-singular (cf 22.5). On the other hand, the matrix $\boldsymbol{A}\boldsymbol{A}'$ is[1]) only of rank n. *It follows that any minor of order $\geqq n + 1$ of the moment matrix Λ, which does not contain any element of the main diagonal*[2]), *is equal to zero. It is immediately seen that the same property holds for the correlation matrix $\boldsymbol{P} = \{\varrho_{ij}\}$ of the variables $x_1, \ldots, x_m$.* — This theorem is due to Thurstone.

Consider e. g. the particular case $n = 1$. (In the psychological applications, this is the case when there is only one »general» factor.) The correlation coefficients ϱ corresponding to any four different subscripts h, i, j, k then satisfy the *tetrad relation*

$$\begin{vmatrix} \varrho_{hj} & \varrho_{hk} \\ \varrho_{ij} & \varrho_{ik} \end{vmatrix} = \varrho_{hj}\varrho_{ik} - \varrho_{hk}\varrho_{ij} = 0.$$

---

[1]) By 11.6, the rank is *at most* n, and it is easily seen that there is at least one non-zero minor of order n.

[2]) It will be noted that minors satisfying these conditions only exist when $2n + 2 \leqq m$.

TABLE 1.

THE NORMAL DISTRIBUTION (cf Ch. 17).

$$\Phi(x) = \frac{1}{\sqrt{2\pi}} \int_{-\infty}^{x} e^{-\frac{t^2}{2}} dt, \quad \varphi(x) = \Phi'(x) = \frac{1}{\sqrt{2\pi}} e^{-\frac{x^2}{2}},$$

$\varphi^{(\nu)}(x) = (-1)^\nu H_\nu(x)\, \varphi(x)$, where $H_\nu(x)$ is the Hermite polynomial of degree ν (cf 12.6). For negative values of x, the functions are calculated from the relations

$$\Phi(-x) = 1 - \Phi(x), \qquad \varphi(-x) = \varphi(x), \qquad \varphi^{(\nu)}(-x) = (-1)^\nu \varphi^{(\nu)}(x).$$

x	$\Phi(x)$	$\varphi(x)$	$\varphi'(x)$	$\varphi''(x)$	$\varphi^{(3)}(x)$	$\varphi^{(4)}(x)$	$\varphi^{(5)}(x)$	$\varphi^{(6)}(x)$
0.0	0.50000	0.39894	−0.00000	−0.39894	+0.00000	+1.19683	−0.00000	−5.98413
0.1	0.53983	0.39695	0.03970	0.39298	0.11869	1.16708	0.59146	5.77625
0.2	0.57926	0.39104	0.07821	0.37540	0.23150	1.07990	1.14197	5.17112
0.3	0.61791	0.38139	0.11442	0.34706	0.33295	0.94130	1.61420	4.22226
0.4	0.65542	0.36827	0.14731	0.30935	0.41835	0.76070	1.97770	3.01241
0.5	0.69146	0.35207	0.17603	0.26405	0.48409	0.55010	2.21141	1.64481
0.6	0.72575	0.33322	0.19993	0.21326	0.52783	0.32309	2.30517	−0.23237
0.7	0.75804	0.31225	0.21858	0.15925	0.54863	+0.09371	2.26012	+1.11354
0.8	0.78814	0.28969	0.23175	0.10429	0.54694	−0.12468	2.08800	2.29382
0.9	0.81594	0.26609	0.23948	−0.05056	0.52445	0.32034	1.80951	3.23026
1.0	0.84134	0.24197	0.24197	0.00000	0.48394	0 48394	1.45182	3.87153
1.1	0.86433	0.21785	0.23964	+0.04575	0.42895	0.60909	1.04580	4.19585
1.2	0.88493	0.19419	0.23302	0.08544	0.36352	0.69255	0.62301	4.21034
1.3	0.90320	0.17137	0.22278	0.11824	0.29184	0.73413	−0.21300	3.94753
1.4	0.91924	0.14973	0.20962	0.14374	0.21800	0.73642	+0.15897	3.45953
1.5	0.93319	0.12952	0.19428	0.16190	0.14571	0.70425	0.47355	2.81094
1.6	0.94520	0.11092	0.17747	0.17304	0.07809	0.64405	0.71813	2.07125
1.7	0.95543	0.09405	0.15988	0.17775	+0.01759	0.56316	0.88702	1.30785
1.8	0.96407	0.07895	0.14211	0.17685	−0.03411	0.46915	0.98090	+0.58014
1.9	0.97128	0.06562	0.12467	0.17126	0.07605	0.36928	1.00583	−0.06467
2.0	0.97725	0.05399	0.10798	0.16197	0.10798	0.26996	0.97184	0.59390
2.1	0.98214	0.04398	0.09237	0.14998	0.13024	0.17646	0.89150	0.98987
2.2	0.98610	0.03547	0.07804	0.13622	0.14360	0.09274	0.77844	1.24885
2.3	0.98928	0.02833	0.06515	0.12152	0.14920	−0.02141	0.64604	1.37883
2.4	0.99180	0.02239	0.05375	0.10660	0.14834	+0.03623	0.50642	1.39654
2.5	0.99379	0.01753	0.04382	0.09202	0.14242	0.07997	0.36974	1.32421
2.6	0.99534	0.01358	0.03532	0.07824	0.13279	0.11053	0.24376	1.18645
2.7	0.99653	0.01042	0.02814	0.06555	0.12071	0.12926	0.13381	1.00761
2.8	0.99744	0.00792	0.02216	0.05414	0.10727	0.13793	+0.04287	0.80970
2.9	0.99813	0.00595	0.01726	0.04411	0.09339	0.13850	−0.02810	0.61102
3.0	0.99865	0.00443	0.01330	0.03545	0.07977	0.13296	0.07977	0.42546
3.1	0.99903	0.00327	0.01013	0.02813	0.06694	0.12313	0.11395	0.26242
3.2	0.99931	0.00238	0.00763	0.02203	0.05523	0.11066	0.13319	0.12712
3.3	0.99952	0.00172	0.00568	0.01704	0.04485	0.09690	0.14036	−0.02130
3.4	0.99966	0.00123	0.00419	0.01301	0.03586	0.08290	0.13840	+0.05607
3.5	0.99977	0.00087	0.00305	0.00982	0.02825	0.06943	0.13000	0.10784
3.6	0.99984	0.00061	0.00220	0.00732	0.02194	0.05703	0.11755	0.13802
3.7	0.99989	0.00042	0.00157	0.00539	0.01680	0.04599	0.10297	0.15102
3.8	0.99993	0.00029	0.00111	0.00392	0.01269	0.03646	0.08777	0.15124
3.9	0.99995	0.00020	0.00077	0.00282	0.00946	0.02842	0.07302	0.14264
4.0	0.99997	0.00013	−0.00054	+0.00201	−0.00696	+0.02181	−0.05942	+0.12861

TABLE 2.

The Normal Distribution (cf 17.2).

The probability that an observed value of a normally distributed variable ξ differs from the mean m in either direction by more than λ times the standard deviation σ is

$$P = P(|\xi - m| > \lambda\sigma) = 2[1 - \Phi(\lambda)] = \frac{2}{\sqrt{2\pi}} \int_{\lambda}^{\infty} e^{-\frac{t^2}{2}}\, dt.$$

The value $\lambda = \lambda_p$ corresponding to $P = \frac{p}{100}$ is called the p percent value of a normal deviate.

λ_p as a function of p		p as a function of λ_p	
$p = 100\,P$	λ_p	λ_p	$p = 100\,P$
100	0.0000	0.0	100.000
95	0.0627	0.2	84.148
90	0.1257	0.4	68.916
85	0.1891	0.6	54.851
80	0.2533	0.8	42.371
75	0.3186	1.0	31.731
70	0.3853	1.2	23.014
65	0.4538	1.4	16.151
60	0.5244	1.6	10.960
55	0.5978	1.8	7.186
50	0.6745	2.0	4.550
45	0.7554	2.2	2.781
40	0.8416	2.4	1.640
35	0.9346	2.6	0.932
30	1.0364	2.8	0.511
25	1.1503	3.0	0.270
20	1.2816	3.2	0.137
15	1.4395	3.4	0.067
10	1.6449	3.6	0.032
5	1.9600	3.8	0.014
1	2.5758	4.0	0.006
0.1	3.2905		
0.01	3.8906		

TABLE 3.

THE χ^2-DISTRIBUTION (cf 18.1).

The fr. f. $k_n(x)$ of the χ^2-distribution with n degrees of freedom is defined by (18.1.3). The p percent value χ_p^2 of χ^2 for n d. of fr. is a value such that the probability that an observed value of χ^2 exceeds χ_p^2 is

$$P = \frac{p}{100} = P(\chi^2 > \chi_p^2) = \int_{\chi_p^2}^{\infty} k_n(x)\,dx.$$

By the kind permission of Prof. R. A. Fisher and Messrs Oliver and Boyd, the table is reprinted from R. A. Fisher, Ref. 13.

Degrees of freedom n	χ_p^2 as a function of n and $p = 100\,P$													
	p=99	98	95	90	80	70	50	30	20	10	5	2	1	0.1
1	0.000	0.001	0.004	0.016	0.064	0.148	0.455	1.074	1.642	2.706	3.841	5.412	6.635	10.827
2	0.020	0.040	0.103	0.211	0.446	0.713	1.386	2.408	3.219	4.605	5.991	7.824	9.210	13.815
3	0.115	0.185	0.352	0.584	1.005	1.424	2.366	3.665	4.642	6.251	7.815	9.837	11.341	16.268
4	0.297	0.429	0.711	1.064	1.649	2.195	3.357	4.878	5.989	7.779	9.488	11.668	13.277	18.465
5	0.554	0.752	1.145	1.610	2.343	3.000	4.351	6.064	7.289	9.236	11.070	13.388	15.086	20.517
6	0.872	1.134	1.635	2.204	3.070	3.828	5.348	7.231	8.558	10.645	12.592	15.033	16.812	22.457
7	1.239	1.564	2.167	2.833	3.822	4.671	6.346	8.383	9.803	12.017	14.067	16.622	18.475	24.322
8	1.646	2.032	2.733	3.490	4.594	5.527	7.344	9.524	11.030	13.362	15.507	18.168	20.090	26.125
9	2.088	2.532	3.325	4.168	5.380	6.393	8.343	10.656	12.242	14.684	16.919	19.679	21.666	27.877
10	2.558	3.059	3.940	4.865	6.179	7.267	9.342	11.781	13.442	15.987	18.307	21.161	23.209	29.588
11	3.053	3.609	4.575	5.578	6.989	8.148	10.341	12.899	14.631	17.275	19.675	22.618	24.725	31.264
12	3.571	4.178	5.226	6.304	7.807	9.034	11.340	14.011	15.812	18.549	21.026	24.054	26.217	32.909
13	4.107	4.765	5.892	7.042	8.634	9.926	12.340	15.119	16.985	19.812	22.362	25.472	27.688	34.528
14	4.660	5.368	6.571	7.790	9.467	10.821	13.339	16.222	18.151	21.064	23.685	26.873	29.141	36.123
15	5.229	5.985	7.261	8.547	10.307	11.721	14.339	17.322	19.311	22.307	24.996	28.259	30.578	37.697
16	5.812	6.614	7.962	9.312	11.152	12.624	15.338	18.418	20.465	23.542	26.296	29.633	32.000	39.252
17	6.408	7.255	8.672	10.085	12.002	13.531	16.338	19.511	21.615	24.769	27.587	30.995	33.409	40.790
18	7.015	7.906	9.390	10.865	12.857	14.440	17.338	20.601	22.760	25.989	28.869	32.346	34.805	42.312
19	7.633	8.567	10.117	11.651	13.716	15.352	18.338	21.689	23.900	27.204	30.144	33.687	36.191	43.820
20	8.260	9.237	10.851	12.443	14.578	16.266	19.337	22.775	25.038	28.412	31.410	35.020	37.566	45.315
21	8.897	9.915	11.591	13.240	15.445	17.182	20.337	23.858	26.171	29.615	32.671	36.343	38.932	46.797
22	9.542	10.600	12.338	14.041	16.314	18.101	21.337	24.939	27.301	30.813	33.924	37.659	40.289	48.268
23	10.196	11.293	13.091	14.848	17.187	19.021	22.337	26.018	28.429	32.007	35.172	38.968	41.638	49.728
24	10.856	11.992	13.848	15.659	18.062	19.943	23.337	27.096	29.553	33.196	36.415	40.270	42.980	51.179
25	11.524	12.697	14.611	16.473	18.940	20.867	24.337	28.172	30.675	34.382	37.652	41.566	44.314	52.620
26	12.198	13.409	15.379	17.292	19.820	21.792	25.336	29.246	31.795	35.563	38.885	42.856	45.642	54.052
27	12.879	14.125	16.151	18.114	20.703	22.719	26.336	30.319	32.912	36.741	40.113	44.140	46.963	55.476
28	13.565	14.847	16.928	18.939	21.588	23.647	27.336	31.391	34.027	37.916	41.337	45.419	48.278	56.893
29	14.256	15.574	17.708	19.768	22.475	24.577	28.336	32.461	35.139	39.087	42.557	46.693	49.588	58.302
30	14.953	16.306	18.493	20.599	23.364	25.508	29.336	33.530	36.250	40.256	43.773	47.962	50.892	59.703

TABLE 4.

THE t-DISTRIBUTION (cf 18.2).

The fr. f. $s_n(x)$ of the t-distribution with n degrees of freedom is defined by (18.2.4). The p percent value t_p of t for n d. of fr. is a value such that the probability P that an observed value of t differs from zero in either direction by more than t_p is

$$P = \frac{p}{100} = P(|t| > t_p) = 2 \int_{t_p}^{\infty} s_n(x)\, dx.$$

By the kind permission of Prof. R. A. Fisher and Messrs Oliver and Boyd, the table is reprinted from R. A. Fisher, Ref. 13.

Degrees of freedom n	t_p as a function of n and $p = 100\,P$												
	p=90	80	70	60	50	40	30	20	10	5	2	1	0.1
1	0.158	0.325	0.510	0.727	1.000	1.376	1.963	3.078	6.814	12.706	31.821	63.657	636.619
2	0.142	0.289	0.445	0.617	0.816	1.061	1.386	1.886	2.920	4.303	6.965	9.925	31.598
3	0.137	0.277	0.424	0.584	0.765	0.978	1.250	1.638	2.353	3.182	4.541	5.841	12.941
4	0.134	0.271	0.414	0.569	0.741	0.941	1.190	1.533	2.132	2.776	3.747	4.604	8.610
5	0.132	0.267	0.408	0.559	0.727	0.920	1.156	1.476	2.015	2.571	3.365	4.032	6.859
6	0.131	0.265	0.404	0.553	0.718	0.906	1.134	1.440	1.943	2.447	3.143	3.707	5.959
7	0.130	0.263	0.402	0.549	0.711	0.896	1.119	1.415	1.895	2.365	2.998	3.499	5.405
8	0.130	0.262	0.399	0.546	0.706	0.889	1.108	1.397	1.860	2.306	2.896	3.355	5.041
9	0.129	0.261	0.398	0.543	0.703	0.883	1.100	1.383	1.833	2.262	2.821	3.250	4.781
10	0.129	0.260	0.397	0.542	0.700	0.879	1.093	1.372	1.812	2.228	2.764	3.169	4.587
11	0.129	0.260	0.396	0.540	0.697	0.876	1.088	1.363	1.796	2.201	2.718	3.106	4.437
12	0.128	0.259	0.395	0.539	0.695	0.873	1.083	1.356	1.782	2.179	2.681	3.055	4.318
13	0.128	0.259	0.394	0.538	0.694	0.870	1.079	1.350	1.771	2.160	2.650	3.012	4.221
14	0.128	0.258	0.393	0.537	0.692	0.868	1.076	1.345	1.761	2.145	2.624	2.977	4.140
15	0.128	0.258	0.393	0.536	0.691	0.866	1.074	1.341	1.753	2.131	2.602	2.947	4.073
16	0.128	0.258	0.392	0.535	0.690	0.865	1.071	1.337	1.746	2.120	2.583	2.921	4.015
17	0.128	0.257	0.392	0.534	0.689	0.863	1.069	1.333	1.740	2.110	2.567	2.898	3.965
18	0.127	0.257	0.392	0.534	0.688	0.862	1.067	1.330	1.734	2.101	2.552	2.878	3.922
19	0.127	0.257	0.391	0.533	0.688	0.861	1.066	1.328	1.729	2.093	2.539	2.861	3.883
20	0.127	0.257	0.391	0.533	0.687	0.860	1.064	1.325	1.725	2.086	2.528	2.845	3.850
21	0.127	0.257	0.391	0.532	0.686	0.859	1.063	1.323	1.721	2.080	2.518	2.831	3.819
22	0.127	0.256	0.390	0.532	0.686	0.858	1.061	1.321	1.717	2.074	2.508	2.819	3.792
23	0.127	0.256	0.390	0.532	0.685	0.858	1.060	1.319	1.714	2.069	2.500	2.807	3.767
24	0.127	0.256	0.390	0.531	0.685	0.857	1.059	1.318	1.711	2.064	2.492	2.797	3.745
25	0.127	0.256	0.390	0.531	0.684	0.856	1.058	1.316	1.708	2.060	2.485	2.787	3.725
26	0.127	0.256	0.390	0.531	0.684	0.856	1.058	1.315	1.706	2.056	2.479	2.779	3.707
27	0.127	0.256	0.389	0.531	0.684	0.855	1.057	1.314	1.703	2.052	2.473	2.771	3.690
28	0.127	0.256	0.389	0.530	0.683	0.855	1.056	1.313	1.701	2.048	2.467	2.763	3.674
29	0.127	0.256	0.389	0.530	0.683	0.854	1.055	1.311	1.699	2.045	2.462	2.756	3.659
30	0.127	0.256	0.389	0.530	0.683	0.854	1.055	1.310	1.697	2.042	2.457	2.750	3.646
40	0.126	0.255	0.388	0.529	0.681	0.851	1.050	1.303	1.684	2.021	2.423	2.704	3.551
60	0.126	0.254	0.387	0.527	0.679	0.848	1.046	1.296	1.671	2.000	2.390	2.660	3.460
120	0.126	0.254	0.386	0.526	0.677	0.845	1.041	1.289	1.658	1.980	2.358	2.617	3.373
∞	0.126	0.253	0.385	0.524	0.674	0.842	1.036	1.282	1.645	1.960	2.326	2.576	3.291

List of References.

I. Books.

1. Aitken, A. C. Determinants and Matrices. University Mathematical Texts, 1. Third ed., Edinburgh and London 1944.
2. —— Statistical Mathematics. University Mathematical Texts, 2. Third ed., Edinburgh and London 1944.
3. Bôcher, M. Introduction to higher Algebra. New York 1908 (German ed. Leipzig 1910).
4. Bochner, S. Vorlesungen über Fouriersche Integrale. Leipzig 1932.
5. Bohr, H., and Mollerup, J. Lærebog i matematisk Analyse, I—IV. Second ed., København 1938—1942.
6. Borel, É. Leçons sur la théorie des fonctions. Second ed., Paris 1914.
7. Borel, É., and others. Traité du calcul des probabilités et de ses applications. Paris, from 1924.
8. Bonnier, G., and Tedin, O. Biologisk variationsanalys. Stockholm 1940.
9. Charlier, C. V. L. Vorlesungen über die Grundzüge der mathematischen Statistik. Lund 1931.

9a. —— Application de la théorie des probabilités à l'astronomie. Forms Vol. II, Part IV of Ref. 7. Paris 1931.

10. Cramér, H. Sannolikhetskalkylen och några av dess användningar. Stockholm 1927.
11. —— Random Variables and Probability Distributions. Cambridge Tracts in Mathematics, No. 36. Cambridge 1937.
12. Elderton, W. P. Frequency Curves and Correlation. Third ed., Cambridge 1938.
13. Fisher, R. A. Statistical Methods for Research Workers. Eighth ed., Edinburgh and London 1941.
14. —— The Design of Experiments. Second ed., Edinburgh and London 1937.
15. Fréchet, M. Recherches théoriques modernes sur la théorie des probabilités. Forms Vol. I, Part III of Ref. 7. Paris 1937—1938.
16. Gauss, C. F. Werke, Vol. 4, Göttingen 1880.
17. Hobson, E. W. The Theory of Functions of a Real Variable, I—II. Cambridge 1926—1927.
18. Jeffreys, H. Theory of Probability. Oxford 1939.
19. Kendall, M. G. The Advanced Theory of Statistics, I. London 1943.

—— See Yule, G. U.

20. Keynes, J. M. A Treatise on Probability. London 1921.
21. Kolmogoroff, A. Grundbegriffe der Wahrscheinlichkeitsrechnung. Berlin 1933.
22. Laplace, P. S. Théorie analytique des probabilités. Paris, first ed. 1812, second ed. 1814, third ed. 1820.
23. Lebesgue, H. Leçons sur l'intégration et la recherche des fonctions primitives. Second ed., Paris 1928.

24. Lévy, P. Calcul des probabilités. Paris 1925.
25. —— Théorie de l'addition des variables aléatoires. Paris 1937.
26. Lundborg, H., and Linders, F. J. The Racial Characters of the Swedish Nation. Uppsala 1926.
27. Mises, R. v. Wahrscheinlichkeitsrechnung und ihre Anwendung in der Statistik und theoretischen Physik. Leipzig—Wien 1931.
28. —— Wahrscheinlichkeit, Statistik und Wahrheit. Second ed., Wien 1936.
29. Moivre, A. de. Miscellanea Analytica. Second suppl. 1733.
Mollerup, J., see Bohr, H.
30. Neyman, J. Lectures and Conferences on Mathematical Statistics. Washington 1938.
31. Poincaré, H. Calcul des probabilités. Second ed., Paris 1912.
32. Poisson, S. D. Recherches sur la probabilité des jugements etc. Paris 1837.
33. Saks, S. Theory of the Integral. Second ed., Warszawa 1937.
34. Schultz, H. The Theory and Measurement of Demand. Chicago 1938.
35. Snedecor, G. W. Statistical Methods. Ames, Iowa, 1940.
35a. Spearman, C. The Abilities of Man. London 1927.
36. Szegö, G. Orthogonal Polynomials. New York 1939.
Tedin, O., see Bonnier, G.
37. Thiele, T. N. Theory of Observations. London 1903.
37a. Thomson, G. H. The Factorial Analysis of Human Ability. London 1939.
38. Titchmarsh, E. C. Introduction to the Theory of Fourier Integrals. Oxford 1937.
39. Uspensky, J. V. Introduction to Mathematical Probability. New York 1937.
40. Vallée Poussin, C. de la. Intégrales de Lebesgue, fonctions d'ensembles, classes de Baire. Second ed., Paris 1934.
41. Wiener, N. The Fourier Integral and certain of its Applications. Cambridge 1933.
42. Wilks, S. S. The Theory of Statistical Inference. Ann Arbor 1937.
43. Yule, G. U., and Kendall, M. G. An Introduction to the Theory of Statistics. Twelfth ed., London 1940.

II. Papers.

Abbreviations.

AE	= Annals of Eugenics.
AMS	Annals of Mathematical Statistics.
B	Biometrika.
CR	Comptes Rendus de l'Academie des Sciences, Paris.
JRS	Journal of the Royal Statistical Society.
MA	Mathematische Annalen.
M	Metron
PCPS	Proceedings of the Cambridge Philosophical Society.
PRS	Proceedings of the Royal Society, London, A.
PTRS	Philosophical Transactions of the Royal Society, London, A.
SA	Skandinavisk Aktuarietidskrift.
TAMS	Transactions of the American Mathematical Society.

50. AITKEN, A. C. On the graduation of data by the orthogonal polynomials of least squares. Proc. R. Soc. Edinburgh, 53 (1933), p. 54.
53. ARLEY, N. On the distribution of relative errors from a normal population of errors. K. Danske Vid. Selsk. Mat.-fys. Medd. 18 no. 3 (1940).
BABINGTON SMITH, B., see KENDALL, M. G.
54. BARTLETT, M. S. On the theory of statistical regression. Proc. R. Soc. Edinburgh, 53 (1933) p. 260.
55. —— The information available in small samples. PCPS 32 (1936) p. 560.
56. —— Complete simultaneous fiducial distributions. AMS 10 (1939) p. 129.
—— see WISHART, J.
60. BEHRENS, W. U. Ein Beitrag zur Fehlerberechnung bei wenigen Beobachtungen. Landwirtsch. Jahrbücher, 68 (1929) p. 807.
61. BERG, G. The prognosis of open pulmonary tuberculosis. Acta Tuberculosea Scand., Suppl. IV (1939).
62. BERGSTRÖM, H. On the central limit theorem. SA 1944, p. 139, and 1945, p. 106.
63. BERNSTEIN, S. Sur l'extension du théorème limite du calcul des probabilités aux sommes de quantités dépendantes. MA 97 (1927) p. 1.
63a. BORTKIEWICZ, L. v. Das Gesetz der kleinen Zahlen. Leipzig 1898.
64. CANTELLI, F. P. La tendenza ad un limite nel senzo del calcolo delle probabilità. Rend. Circ. Mat. Palermo, 16 (1916) p. 191.
65. CHARLIER, C. V. L. Researches into the theory of probability. K. Fysiogr. Sällsk. Handl. B 16 (1906).
CLOPPER, C. J., see PEARSON, E. S.
66. COCHRAN, W. G. The distribution of quadratic forms in a normal system, with applications to the analysis of covariance. PCPS 30 (1933—34) p. 178.
CORBET, A. S., see FISHER, R. A.
67. CRAIG, C. C. An application of Thiele's semi-invariants to the sampling problem. M 7 no. 4 (1928) p. 3.
68. CRAMÉR, H. Sur quelques points du calcul des probabilités. Proc. London Math. Soc., 23 (1925) p. LVIII.
69. —— On some classes of series used in mathematical statistics. Sixth Scandinavian Congr. of Math., København 1925.
70. —— On the composition of elementary errors. SA 1928, p. 13 and p. 141.
71. —— On the representation of a function by certain Fourier integrals. TAMS 46 (1939) p. 191.
72. —— Contributions to the theory of statistical estimation. SA 1946.
74. DARMOIS, G. Sur les lois de probabilités à estimation exhaustive. CR 200 (1935) p. 1265.
DAVID, F. N., see NEYMAN, J.
DAVIES, O. L., see PEARSON, E. S.
75. DOOB, J. L. Probability as measure. AMS, 12 (1941) p. 206.
76. DUGUÉ, D. Application des propriétés de la limite au sens du calcul des probabilités à l'étude de diverses questions d'estimation. Journ. de l'Éc. Polytechn. 1937, p. 305.
80. EDGEWORTH, F. Y. The law of error. PCPS 20 (1905) p. 36.

81. Eggenberger, F. Die Wahrscheinlichkeitsansteckung. Mitt. d. Ver. schweizerischer Vers.-Math., 1924, p. 31.
81a. Eneroth, O. Om frömängden vid fläcksådd samt om sambandet mellan plantantal och slutenhetsgrad vid självsådd. Norrl. Skogsv.-förb. Tidskr. 1945, p. 161.
82. Esscher, F. On graduation according to the method of least squares by means of certain polynomials. Försäkr.-A.-B. Skandias Festskr. 1930, II, p. 107.
83. Esseen, C. G. Fourier analysis of distribution functions. A mathematical study of the Laplace-Gaussian law. Acta Math. 77 (1944) p. 1.
Essen-Möller, E., see Quensel, C. E.
84. Feller, W. Sur les axiomatiques du calcul des probabilités et leurs relations avec les expériences. Actualités scientifiques et industrielles, no. 735 (1938) p. 7.
85. —— Über den zentralen Grenzwertsatz der Wahrscheinlichkeitsrechnung. Math. Zeitschr. 40 (1935) p. 521.
86. —— Über den zentralen Grenzwertsatz der Wahrscheinlichkeitsrechnung, II. Math. Zeitschr. 42 (1937) p. 301.
87. Fisher, R. A. On an absolute criterion for fitting frequency curves. Mess. of Math., 41 (1912) p. 155.
88. —— Frequency distribution of the values of the correlation coefficient in samples from an indefinitely large population. B, 10 (1915) p. 507.
89. —— On the mathematical foundations of theoretical statistics. PTRS, 222 (1921) p. 309.
90. —— On the »probable error» of a coefficient of correlation deduced from a small sample. M, 1 no. 4 (1921) p. 1.
91. —— On the interpretation of χ^2 from contingency tables, and the calculation of P. JRS, 85 (1922) p. 87.
92. —— The goodness of fit of regression formulae, and the distribution of regression coefficients. JRS, 85 (1922) p. 597.
93. —— The distribution of the partial correlation coefficient. M, 3 (1924) p. 329.
94. —— On a distribution yielding the error functions of several well-known statistics. Proc. Intern. Math. Congr. Toronto 1924, p. 805.
95. —— The conditions under which χ^2 measures the discrepancy between observation and hypothesis. JRS, 87 (1924) p. 442.
96. —— Theory of statistical estimation. PCPS, 22 (1925) p. 700.
97. —— Applications of Student's distribution. M, 5 no. 3 (1925) p. 90.
98. —— The general sampling distribution of the multiple correlation coefficient. PRS, 121 (1928) p. 654.
99. —— Moments and product moments of sampling distributions. Proc. London Math. Soc., 30 (1929) p. 199.
100. —— Inverse probability. PCPS, 26 (1930) p. 528.
101. —— The moments of the distribution for normal samples of measures of departure from normality. PRS, 130 (1930) p. 16.
102. Fisher, R. A. The concepts of inverse probability and fiducial probability referring to unknown parameters. PRS, 139 (1933) p. 343.

103. FISHER, R. A. Two new properties of mathematical likelihood. PRS, 144 (1934) p. 285.
104. —— The logic of inductive inference. JRS, 98 (1935) p. 39.
105. —— The fiducial argument in statistical inference. AE, 6 (1935) p. 391.
106. —— On a point raised by M. S. Bartlett on fiducial probability. AE, 7 (1937) p. 370.
107. —— The comparison of samples with possibly unequal variances. AE, 9 (1939) p. 174.
108. —— A note on fiducial inference. AMS, 10 (1940) p. 383.
109. —— The asymptotic approach to Behrens' integral with further tables for the d test of significance. AE, 11 (1941).
110. FISHER, R. A., and TIPPETT, L. H. C. Limiting forms of the frequency distribution of the largest or smallest member of a sample. PCPS, 24 (1928) p. 180.
111. FISHER, R. A., CORBET, A. S., and WILLIAMS, C. B. The relation between the number of species and the number of individuals in a random sample of an animal population. J. of Animal Ecology, 12 (1943) p. 42.
112. FRÉCHET, M. Sur la convergence »en probabilité». M, 8 no. 4 (1930) p. 3.
113. FRISCH, R. Correlation and scatter in statistical variables. Nord. Statist. Tidskr., 8 (1929) p. 36.
114. —— Statistical confluence analysis by means of complete regression systems. Oslo 1934.
115. GEARY, R. C. Distribution of Student's ratio for non-normal samples. JRS, Suppl. 3 (1936).
116. —— A general expression for the moments of certain symmetrical functions of normal samples. B, 25 (1933) p. 184.
116a. —— Comparison of the concepts of efficiency and closeness for consistent estimates of a parameter. B, 33 (1944) p. 123.
117. GNEDENKO, B. Sur les fonctions caractéristiques. Bull. Univ. Moscou, A 1, no. 5 (1937).
118. GRAM, J. P. Om Rækkeudviklinger bestemte ved Hjælp av de mindste Kvadraters Methode. København 1879.
119. GREENWOOD, M., and YULE, G. U. An inquiry into the nature of frequency distributions representative of multiple happenings with particular reference to the occurrence of multiple attacks of disease or of repeated accidents. JRS, 83 (1920) p. 255.
120. GUMBEL, E. J. Les valeurs extrêmes des distributions statistiques. Ann. Inst. Henri Poincaré, 5 (1936) p. 115.
121. HAGSTROEM, K. G. La loi de Pareto et la réassurance. SA, 1925 p. 65.
121a. —— Alcune formule appartenenti alla statistica rappresentativa. Giorn. Ist. Italiano d. Attuari, 3 (1932) p. 147.
122. —— Inkomstutjämningen i Sverige. Skand. Bankens Kvart.-skr., April 1944.
HALD, A., see RASCH, G.
123. HALDANE, J. B. S. The mean and variance of χ^2, when used as a test of homogeneity, when expectations are small. B, 31 (1940) p. 346.
124. HARTLEY, H. O. The range in normal samples. B, 32 (1942) p. 334.
—— see PEARSON, E. S.

125. Helmert, F. R. Über die Wahrscheinlichkeit von Potenzsummen der Beobachtungsfehler etc. Z. f. Math. u. Phys. 21 (1876).
126. Hotelling, H. The generalization of Student's ratio. AMS, 2 (1931) p. 360.
127. Hsu, P. L. Contribution to the theory of Student's t-test as applied to the problem of two samples. Statist. Research Mem., 2 (1938) p. 1.
128. Hultkrantz, J. V. Über die Zunahme der Körpergrösse in Schweden in den Jahren 1840—1926. Uppsala 1927.
130. Ingham, A. E. An integral which occurs in statistics. PCPS, 29 (1932) p. 271.
131. Irwin, J. O. The further theory of Francis Galton's individual difference problem. B, 17 (1925) p. 100.
132. —— On the frequency distribution of the means of samples from populations of certain of Pearson's types. M, 8 no. 4 (1930) p. 51.
133. —— Mathematical theorems involved in the analysis of variance. JRS, 94 (1931) p. 284.
134. Jordan, C. Approximation and graduation according to the principle of least squares by orthogonal polynomials. AMS, 3 (1932) p. 257.
135. Kapteyn, J. C. Skew frequency curves in biology and statistics. Groningen 1903 and 1916.
136. Kendall, M. G. The conditions under which Sheppard's corrections are valid. JRS, 101 (1938) p. 592.
137. —— and Babington Smith, B. Randomness and random sampling numbers. JRS, 101 (1938) p. 147, and JRS Suppl., 6 (1939) p. 51.
139. Khintchine, A. Sur la loi des grands nombres. CR, 188 (1929) p. 477.
140. —— Sul dominio di attrazione della legge di Gauss. Giorn. Ist. Italiano d. Attuari, 6 (1935) p. 378.
140a. Kolodziejczyk, S. On an important class of statistical hypotheses. B, 27 (1935) p. 161.
141. Koopman, B. O. On distributions admitting a sufficient statistic. TAMS, 39 (1936) p. 399.
142. Koopmans, T. Linear regression analysis of economic time series. Netherlands Econ. Inst., Haarlem 1937.
143. Kullback, S. An application of characteristic functions to the distribution problem of statistics. AMS, 5 (1934) p. 263.
144. Langdon, W. H., and Ore, Ø. Semi-invariants and Sheppard's correction. Annals of Math., 31 (1930) p. 230.
145. Lévy, P. Propriétés asymptotiques des sommes de variables aléatoires indépendantes ou enchainées. Journ. Math. pures appl., 14 (1935) p. 347.
146. Liapounoff, A. Sur une proposition de la théorie des probabilités. Bull. Acad. Sc. St-Pétersbourg, 13 (1900) p. 359.
147. —— Nouvelle forme du théorème sur la limite de probabilité. Mém. Acad. Sc. St-Pétersbourg, 12 (1901) no. 5.
148. Lindeberg, J. W. Eine neue Herleitung des Exponentialgesetzes in der Wahrscheinlichkeitsrechnung. Math. Zeitschr., 15 (1922) p. 211.
149. Lindquist, R. A treatise on reliable predictions of water conditions. Stockholm 1932.
150. Lukacs, E. A characterization of the normal distribution. AMS, 13 (1942) p. 91.

151. LUKOMSKI, J. On some properties of multidimensional distributions. AMS, 10 (1939) p. 236.

152. LUNDBERG, O. On random processes and their application to sickness and accident statistics. Dissert. Stockholm, Uppsala 1940.

154. MADOW, W. G. Limiting distributions of quadratic and bilinear forms. AMS, 11 (1940) p. 125.

155. MENDEL, G. Versuche mit Pflanzenhybriden. Verhandl. naturforsch. Ver. Brünn, 4 (1865).

156. MISES, R. v. Grundlagen der Wahrscheinlichkeitsrechnung. Math. Zeitschr., 4 (1919) p. 1.

157. —— Deux nouveaux théorèmes de limite dans le calcul des probabilités. Revue Fac. Sc. Istanbul, 1 (1935) p. 61.

158. —— Les lois de probabilité pour les fonctions statistiques. Ann. Inst. Henri Poincaré, 6 (1936) p. 185.

159. —— On the foundations of probability and statistics. AMS, 12 (1941) p. 191.

159a. NEWBOLD, E. Practical applications of the statistics of repeated events, particularly to industrial accidents. JRS, 90 (1927) p. 487.

160. NEYMAN, J. Contributions to the theory of small samples drawn from a finite population. B, 17 (1925) p. 472.

161. —— On the two different aspects of the representative method: the method of stratified sampling and the method of purposive selection. JRS, 97 (1934) p. 558.

162. —— Su un teorema concernente le cosiddette statistiche sufficienti. Giorn. Ist. Italiano d. Attuari, 6 (1935) p. 320.

163. —— On the problem of confidence intervals. AMS, 6 (1935) p. 111.

164. —— »Smooth test» for goodness of fit. SA, 1937, p. 149.

165. —— Outline of a theory of statistical estimation based on the classical theory of probability. PTRS, 236 (1937) p. 333.

166. —— L'estimation statistique traitée comme un problème classique de probabilité. Actualités scientifiques et industrielles, no. 739 (1938) p. 25.

167. —— Fiducial argument and the theory of confidence intervals. B, 32 (1941) p. 128.

168. —— Basic ideas and some recent results of the theory of testing statistical hypotheses. JRS, 105 (1942) p. 292.

169. NEYMAN, J., and DAVID, F. N. Extension of the Markoff theorem on least squares. Statist. Research. Mem., 2 (1938) p. 105.

170. NEYMAN, J., and PEARSON, E. S. On the use and interpretation of certain test criteria for purposes of statistical inference. B, 20 A (1928) p. 175 and p. 263.

171. NEYMAN, J., and PEARSON, E. S. On the problem of the most efficient tests of statistical hypotheses. PTRS, 231 (1933) p. 289.

172. —— Contributions to the theory of testing statistical hypotheses. Statist. Research Mem., 1 (1936) p. 1, and 2 (1938) p. 25.

173. —— Sufficient statistics and uniformly most powerful tests of statistical hypotheses. Statist. Research Mem., 1 (1936) p. 113.

ORE, Ø., see LANGDON, W. H.

180. Pearson, K. Contributions to the mathematical theory of evolution. PTRS, 185 (1894) p. 71.
181. —— Contributions etc., II: Skew variation in homogeneous material. PTRS, 186 (1895) p. 343.
182. —— Contributions etc., IV: On the probable errors of frequency constants and on the influence of random selection on variation and correlation. PTRS, 191 (1898) p. 229.
183. —— On the criterion that a given system of deviations from the probable in the case of a correlated system of variables is such that it can be reasonably supposed to have arisen from random sampling. Phil. Mag., V, 50 (1900) p. 157.
183a. —— On lines and planes of closest fit to systems of points in space. Phil. Mag. VI, 2 (1901) p. 559.
184. —— On the systematic fitting of curves to observations and measurements. B, 1 (1902) p. 265, and 2 (1902) p. 1.
185. —— Researches on the mode of distribution of the constants of samples taken at random from a bivariate normal population. PRS, 112 (1926) p. 1.
186. —— On the probability that two independent distributions of frequency are really samples from the same population. B, 8 (1911) p. 250.
187. Pearson, K., and Tocher, J. F. On criteria for the existence of differential death-rates. B, 11 (1916) p. 159.
190. Pearson, E. S. The distribution of frequency constants in small samples from non-normal symmetrical and skew populations. B, 20 A (1928) p. 356.
191. —— The probability integral transformation for testing goodness of fit and combining independent tests of significance. B, 30 (1938) p. 134.
—— See also Neyman, J.
195. Pearson, E. S., and Clopper, C. J. The use of confidence or fiducial limits illustrated in the case of the binomial. B, 26 (1934) p. 404.
196. Pearson, E. S., and Davies, O. L. Methods of estimating from samples the population standard deviation. JRS Suppl., 1 (1934) p. 76.
197. Pearson, E. S., and Hartley, H. O. The probability integral of the range in samples of n observations from a normal population. B, 32 (1942) p. 301.
198. Pitman, E. J. G. The »closest» estimates of statistical parameters. PCPS, 33 (1937) p. 212.
199. —— The estimation of the location and scale parameters of a continuous population of any given form. B, 30 (1939) p. 391.
200. Quensel, C. E. The distributions of the second moment and of the correlation coefficient in samples from populations of type A. Kungl. Fysiogr. Sällsk. Handl., 49 (1938) no. 4.
201. —— Inkomstfördelning och skattetryck. Publ. by Sveriges Industriförbund, Stockholm 1944.
202. —— On the logarithmico-normal distribution. SA, 1945, p. 141.
203. Quensel, C. E., and Essen-Möller, E. Zur Theorie des Vaterschaftsnachweises auf Grund von Ähnlichkeitsbefunden. Zeitschr. f. gerichtl. Medizin, 31 (1939) p. 70.

205. RADON, J. Theorie und Anwendung der absolut additiven Mengenfunktionen. Sitzungsber. Akad. Wien, 122 (1913) p. 1295.

206. RASCH, G., and HALD, A. Nogle Anvendelser af Transformationsmetoden i den normale Fordelings Teori. Festskrift til Prof. J. F. Steffensen, København 1943, p. 52.

207. REIERSÖL, O. Confluence analysis by means of instrumental sets of variables. Arkiv för matematik etc., 32 A (1945) no. 4.

208. ROMANOVSKY, V. Sur certaines espérances mathématiques et sur l'erreur moyenne du coefficient de corrélation. CR, 180 (1925) p. 1897.

209. —— On the moments of standard deviations and of correlation coefficient in samples from normal population. M, 5 no. 4 (1925) p. 3.

210. —— On the distribution of the regression coefficient in samples from normal population. Bull. Acad. Sc. Leningrad, 20 (1926) p. 643.

211. SHEPPARD, W. F. On the application of the theory of error to cases of normal distribution and normal correlation. PTRS, 192 (1898) p. 101.

212. —— On the calculation of the most probable values of frequency-constants for data arranged according to equidistant divisions of a scale. Proc. London Math. Soc., 29 (1898) p. 353.

213. —— The fit of a formula for discrepant observations. PTRS, 228 (1929).

213a. SIMONSEN, W. On distributions of functions of samples from a normally distributed infinite population. SA, 1944, p. 235, 1945, p. 20.

214. SLUTSKY, E. Über stochastische Asymptoten und Grenzwerte. M, 5 no. 3 (1925) p. 3.

215. SMIRNOFF, N. Sur la distribution de ω^2. CR, 202 (1936) p. 449.

216. SOPER, H. E., and others. On the distribution of the correlation coefficient in small samples. B, 11 (1917) p. 328.

217. STEFFENSEN, J. F. Factorial moments and discontinuous frequency-functions. SA, 1923, p. 73.

218. —— Free functions and the Student-Fisher theorem. SA, 1936 p. 108.

220. STIELTJES, T. J. Extrait d'une lettre adressée à M. Hermite. Bull. Sc. Math., 2:e série, 13 (1889) p. 170.

221. »STUDENT.» The probable error of a mean. B, 6 (1908) p. 1.

222. —— Probable error of a correlation coefficient. B, 6 (1908) p. 302.

223. SUKHATME, P. V. On Fisher and Behrens' test of significance for the difference in means of two normal samples. Sankhyā, 4 (1938) p. 39.

224. TANG, P. C. The power function of the analysis of variance tests with tables and illustrations of their use. Statist. Research Mem., 2 (1938) p. 126.

225. THOMPSON, W. R. On a criterion for the rejection of observations and the distribution of the ratio of deviation to sample standard deviation. AMS, 6 (1935) p. 214.

226. TIPPETT, L. H. C. On the extreme individuals and the range of samples taken from a normal population. B, 17 (1925) p. 364.

—— see FISHER, R. A.,

TOCHER, J. F., see PEARSON, K.

227. TSCHUPROW, A. A. On the mathematical expectation of the moments of frequency distributions. B, 12 (1919) p. 140 and 185, and B, 13 (1921) p. 283.

227a. —— Zur Theorie der Stabilität statistischer Reihen. SA, 1918 and 1919.

228. Wahlund, S. Demographic studies in the nomadic and the settled population of northern Lapland. Uppsala 1932.

229. Welch, B. L. The significance of the difference between two means when the population variances are unequal. B, 29 (1938) p. 350.

230. Wicksell, S. D. On the genetic theory of frequency. Arkiv för matematik etc., 12 (1917) no. 20.

231. —— Sex proportion and parental age. Kungl. Fysiogr. Sällsk. Handl., 37 (1926) no. 6.

232. Wilks, S. S. Certain generalizations in the analysis of variance. B, 24 (1932) p. 471.

233. —— Shortest average confidence intervals from large samples. AMS, 9 (1938) p. 166.

234. —— Fiducial distributions in fiducial inference. AMS, 9, (1938) p. 272.

Williams, C. B., see Fisher, R. A.

240. Wishart, J. The generalized product moment distribution in samples from a normal multivariate population. B, 20 A (1928) p. 32.

241. Wishart, J., and Bartlett, M. S. The generalized product moment distribution in a normal system. PCPS, 29 (1932) p. 260.

245. Wold, H. Sulla correzione di Sheppard. Giorn. Ist. Italiano d. Attuari, 5 (1934) p. 304.

246. —— Sheppard's correction formulae in several variables. SA, 1934, p. 248.

246a. —— A study in the analysis of stationary time series. Diss. Stockholm, Uppsala 1938.

247. —— Efterfrågan på jordbruksprodukter och dess känslighet för pris- och inkomstförändringar. Statens Off. Utr., 1940 no. 16.

248. —— A theorem on regression coefficients obtained from successively extended sets of variables. SA, 1945, p. 181.

250. Yates, F. Contingency tables involving small numbers and the χ^2 test. JRS, Suppl. 1 (1934) p. 217.

251. Yule, G. U. On the theory of correlation for any number of variables treated by a new system of notation. PRS 79 (1907) p. 182.

—— see also Greenwood, M.

III. Tables.

260. British Association, Mathematical Tables, Vol. 7: Tables of the Probability integral by W. F. Sheppard (1939).

261. David, F. N. Tables of the Correlation Coefficient. London 1938.

262. Fisher, R. A., and Yates, F. Statistical Tables. Second ed., Edinburgh and London 1943.

263. Kendall, M. G., and Babington Smith, B. Tables of Random Sampling Numbers. Tracts for computers, no. 24, 1940.

264. Pearson, K. Tables for Statisticians and Biometricians. I, second ed., 1924. II, 1931.

265. —— Tables of the Incomplete Γ-function. 1922.

266. —— Tables of the Incomplete B-function.

267. Tippett, L. H. C. Random Sampling Numbers. Tracts for computers, no. 15, 1927.

Index.